Krause - Minkus

STANDARD CATALOG OF
CANADIAN
& UNITED NATIONS STAMPS

Includes Canadian Provincials and UN Offices in Geneva and Vienna

MW00561517

Maurice D. Wozniak – Editor

Wayne Youngblood
Publisher, Philatelics Division, Krause Publications

Special Contributors
Denis J. Norrington • Marios Theodossiou

A fully illustrated catalog for the postage stamps of Canada and the United Nations.

Published by

 **krause
publications**

700 E. State Street • Iola, WI 54990-0001
Telephone: 715/445-2214

Please call or write for our free catalog.
Our toll-free number to place an order or obtain a free catalog is 800-258-0929
or please use our regular business telephone 715-445-2214
for editorial comment and further information.

Library of Congress Catalog Number: 99-63754
ISBN: 0-87341-964-2

Printed in the United States of America

Contents

Catalog Introduction

While such factors as age, quantity issued, scarcity and especially demand all have a bearing on the value of a given stamp or cover, the fundamental determinants of value for any given stamp are its grade and its condition. In general, the scarcer and more valuable the basic stamp, the greater the importance of grade or centering in determining its market value.

Grade is a rough measure of the relationship between the printed design of the stamp and its edges or margins, a characteristic that also is often referred to as a stamp's *centering*.

Generally speaking, the more nearly equal in width all margins of a stamp are and the farther those equal margins are from the printed design, the more desirable the stamp will be to collectors. A stamp with unusually broad margins of identical width on all sides may sell for as much as 100 times the price of an otherwise identical stamp with unbalanced margins and perforations or, in the case of imperforate stamps, a copy with a straight edge cutting the printed design.

Condition refers to the overall appearance and quality of the stamp — the state of its health, so to speak — which can enhance or detract from the desirability (and hence the demand and value) of a stamp.

Stamp Grade

Values shown in this catalog reflect the prices that you may expect to pay for a listed stamp in a grade between **fine** (visibly off-center on two sides, with margins or perforations either just touching or barely clear of the printed design on one side) and **very fine** (barely off-center on one side, with all margins or perforations almost equally distinct and well clear of the printed stamp design.)

This intermediate grade, which has been the predominant grade in which stamps have been collected for more than a century, is referred to as **fine-to-very-fine**, often abbreviated as "**f-vf**." To define the term more explicitly, fine-to-very-fine stamps may be perceptibly off-center to one side, or very slightly off-center on two sides, with the stamp design printed clear of all sides and untouched by any of the margins. (Imperforate stamps graded f-vf will have at least two and usually three margins clear of the printed design.)

Stamps of grades lower than fine-to-very-fine (such as **very good** and **fine**) will usually sell for less than the f-vf copies that are priced here, whereas stamps of grades higher than fine-to-very fine (including very fine and the elusive **extremely fine** or **superb**) will sell for more than the stamps that are priced here.

Unused Canadian and Provincial stamps in a grade of fine

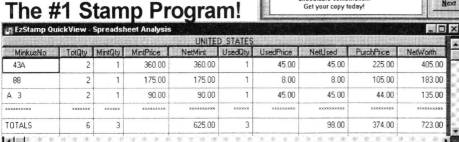

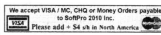

Stamp Condition

Values shown in this catalog reflect the prices that you may expect to pay for a listed stamp in fault-free condition, clear of any detectable defects.

Defects of condition on stamps include (but are not necessarily limited to) tears, scrapes, thins (places where some of the paper is missing from the back of a stamp, often due to inept removal of a hinge), stains, foxing and so-called tropical toning (brown spots on the gum or perforation tips), absence of original gum, the presence of substantial hinge remnants, inclusions (pieces of foreign matter accidentally embedded in the stamp paper during manufacture), heavy, smeared or otherwise disfiguring cancellations or postal markings, pulled, torn or clipped perforations, creases, pinholes, missing corners, and faded, bleached or oxidated pigments and other color changelings (wherein the color of the stamp has changed after it was produced.) Extremely defective stamps, with pieces missing, the design unrecognizable due to stains or postmarks and other serious shortcomings, may be virtually uncollectible and unsalable at any price, even if sound, well-centered examples of the same stamp have a high catalog value. The actual, nominal value of stamps in such poor condition has no relationship whatsoever to the values listed in this or any other catalog.

Stamps that have been repaired or altered (with filled thins, regumming, reperforation, repaired tears, bleaching to remove soiling or lighten a cancel, handprinted notes on the back of the stamp) also are generally regarded as defective and valued accordingly. Repaired stamps may be quite presentable and collectible, but they will generally have only a fraction of the value of a comparable, sound example of the same stamp. Knowingly attempting to represent and sell a repaired copy of a damaged stamp as a sound copy in original condition is fraud.

Just as defects and other undesirable traits detract from a stamp's condition, thereby diminishing its value, exceptionally desirable aspects of a stamp's condition can enhance that value substantially.

Positive attributes to a stamp's condition can include unusually wide margins on all sides, exceptionally fresh-looking paper and ink color and sharpness of the printing, unusually crisp, sharp and regular perforations (especially on older stamps), the presence of margin salvage (especially with a plate number or other marginal printing of significance) and, on 19th-century stamps, most or all of the original gum.

Minkus Catalog Values

Values in the price columns reflect either unused, original-gum fine-very fine stamps (UnFVF) or canceled fine-very fine stamps (UseFVF). For stamps issued since 1940, the price grades reflect mint never-hinged very fine (MNHVF) and canceled very fine (UseVF) stamps. Most unused stamps since 1940 are collected in mint, never-hinged condition, with full, undisturbed and unblemished original gum on the back.

Where a stamp or other catalog-listed item is seldom sold publicly, values appear in italics. Where adequate pricing information for a specific item has proven to be currently unobtainable (as in the case of a recently discovered error or, more prosaically, a common plate black in used condition) in the place of a value a line appears (-).

Every reasonable effort has been made to make the values in this catalog as accurate, realistic and up-to-date as possible. Sources for pricing information may include (but are not necessarily limited to) dealers' published retail price lists and advertisements, auction catalogs with published prices realized, and prices solicited from selected dealers, individuals and collector organizations. This information may have been reviewed for accuracy and consistency by individual specialists-collectors and specialist-dealers.

The minimum stamp value in this catalog (20¢) represents the cost to a retail stamp dealer to maintain in inventory and supply to a collector on demand a single copy of even the most common stamp in fault-free condition and a grade of fine-to-very-fine. The comparable minimum for a first day cover is $1. These figures more accurately reflect a dealer's cost of doing business than the scarcity of a given stamp or FDC.

Values in this catalog do not reflect the generally much lower cost of stamps acquired in mixtures, collections, bulk lots or other large-quantity purchases, nor stamps sold at unusually advantageous prices to attract additional business or offered as approvals, premiums, and so forth. In addition, some stamps can be acquired at lower prices through public auctions and mail-bid sales in which the collector may sometimes secure a lot at a minimum bid or reserve price.

The publishers of this catalog neither buy or sell stamps.

Minkus Catalog Listings

Shown here is a typical listing from the catalog, displaying the kinds of information that this catalog can provide.

1979. INTERNATIONAL YEAR OF CHILD ISSUE Offset by Ashton-Potter; perforated 13.

936 *Girl nurturing Tree of Life.*

936		MNHVF	UseVF
17¢	**multicolored**, FDD (Oct. 24, 1979) tagged	.26	.20

A. Year of Issue

B. Title of Issue often as assigned by the Postal Service of country of issue.

C. Description of Issue a brief synopsis of the person, place or thing depicted on or commemorated by the issue, with information on any special characteristics or significance and any series of which it is a part.

D. Printing details of the type of printing, printer(s) and gauge of the perforations or rouletting.

E. Minkus Catalog Number appears adjacent to the image of the stamp and also at the beginning of the corresponding price listing. Collectors can use the Minkus catalog numbers to organize their collections, and to identify stamps when buying, selling or exchanging stamps for their collections. Minkus catalog numbers also are used in Minkus stamp albums and supplements.

Each Minkus catalog number refers to a specific stamp. Varieties of that stamp are identified by suffixes appended to the basic catalog number (see item M.) Where stamps that are similar in appearance are regarded as distinct issues, collectors are referred to the other issue or issues in a footnote (see item N.)

With but few exceptions, and unlike other catalogs, Minkus catalog numbers are assigned in strict chronological sequence. Definitive series that extend over many years are identified by series name, but

are also in the order and at the intervals at which they were released by the respective Postal Service. This avoids the confusing situation of clumps of stamps from an ongoing series being listed at random and arbitrary intervals throughout the catalog, and the necessity of introducing additional subnumbers (e.g., 123B, 123C, 123D) due to a miscalculation of the number of stamps in a given set or series.

Minkus catalog numbers consist of numerals only for regular definitive issues, commemoratives and air mails. Later Canadian revenue stamps listed in this catalog are indicated by a suffix. "O" indicates official stamps, "PC" indicates postal cards, and "E" indicates envelopes.

F. Description of Image sometimes but not invariably the same as item B, this is intended to represent the design title by which collectors refer to the individual stamp. In practice, many stamps are readily recognized both ways.

G. Denomination is the numeric value of the stamp (or in the case of a lettered-value issue or an unvalued issue, the equated value at time of issue.

H. Color(s) when a single color or up to three distinct colors are used they are listed, else the term multicolor is used.

I. Tagging where relevant, on selected stamps beginning in the 1960s, refers to the presence of a special ink on the face of the stamp visible only under ultraviolet light, used to position the envelope on which the stamp is affixed correctly so that the cancellation will be applied in automated facing-canceling equipment.

J. Quantity Printed is recorded, where available. For definitives, which may go back to press many times in the course of their working life, accurate figures are rarely available. Quantities include accurate counts and approximate estimates made by the Postal Service, counts of quantities shipped but not including stamps returned, unused or destroyed when the issue was taken off sale and, in some cases, accurate counts of copies sold.

K. Catalog Values are expressed in U.S. dollars for unused stamps (UnFVF) and used stamps (UseFVF) in **fine-to-very-fine** condition for issues prior to 1940, and for mint never-hinged (MNH) and used (Use F-VF) for post 1940 releases. Unused stamps refer to those that have not been canceled with most of their original gum (for 19th century issues) or full original gum, lightly hinged (for early 20th century stamps.) Stamps issued without gum are identified in the listings. Used stamps refer to those that have been canceled correctly in the course of performing their intended function.

L. Date of Issue is displayed, in most cases on the same line as that used for the basic first day cover listing.

M. Additional Varieties includes (where relevant) plate blocks, se-tenant configurations, paper type, gum type, tagging presence and type, perforation varieties, major errors, plate flaws and varieties.

N. Footnotes convey additional important information about the stamp and related varieties or issues.

Introduction to Stamps

The ability to accurately identify a stamp is indispensable to your full enjoyment of and participation in the stamp hobby. Differences in printing, gum, paper, watermark, ink, perforation, luminescence and design — variations that may be slight, but which are readily apparent to the trained eye — can be the key to getting the most out of the time you spend with your collection. They also can be the difference between a common stamp that is worth a handful of pennies and a rarity that is valued at thousands of dollars.

There is no substitute for the knowledge that you can gain from the experience of closely examining and working with stamps, not only those in your own collection, but also those that you can read about in philatelic literature, and see on display at stamp shows and, if you are fortunate, in the albums of friends at the local stamp club.

The following text is intended to familiarize you with the basic considerations of collecting stamps and the terminology and jargon of the stamp hobby. Inquiries, suggestions and requests for additional clarifications may be addressed to Editor, Krause-Minkus Stamp Catalog, Krause Publications, 700 East State Street, Iola, WI 54990-0001. (www.krause.com)

Stamp Printing

All stamps may be characterized by the technique or techniques by which they are printed. Although others exist, five primary printing technologies have been used, alone or in combination, on postal paper: intaglio; lithography; gravure; letterpress; and emobssing.

Intaglio (also known as Line-Engraving, Engraving, Etching)

The first step in the intaglio process is creating a **master die**, a small, flat block of soft steel upon which the stamp design is recessed engraved in reverse. The original art intended for use on the stamp is photographically reduced to the appropriate size to serve as a tracing guide for the initial outline of the design on steel.

The highly skilled and detailed work of crating the master die is done by an engraver, who lightly traces the design on the steel, then slowly develops the fully detailed engraving, using gravers, burins and other small chisel-like tools to carve a fine pattern of precisely positioned grooves that collectively form the finished image.

At various points during the engraving process, the engraver handinks the dies and makes an impression to check his progress, thereby creating incomplete images of what will become the finished design, known as **progressive die proofs**.

After the engraving is complete, the soft steel of the master die is hardened greatly through various processes so that it will be able to withstand the stress and pressure of the subsequent operations that are needed to convert it into an intaglio printing plate.

Next, a **transfer roll** is prepared, consisting of a roll of soft steel mounted on a mandrel which, as the name implies, is used to transfer the engraved subject from the master die to the intaglio printing plate, a blank roll of soft steel, mounted at the center of a mandrel, which is a metal axle of lesser diameter. The mandrel is placed in a transfer press, in which it rotates freely, and the highly polished soft steel of the transfer roll is brought into contact with the hardened master die in the bed of the press.

The bed of the transfer press is slowly rocked back and forth under increasing pressure, forcing or "rocking in" the soft steel of the transfer roll in every finely engraved line of the hard master die, and eventually transferring the complete engraved image. The resulting design on the transfer roll, now positive in appearance (with its design components as they are intended to appear on the printed stamp), is referred to as a **relief transfer**, because the lines of engraving that were carved into the master die stand out on the completed roll. The soft steel of the transfer roll is hardened, as was the master die before it, after the number of relief transfers required have been created.

Because the relief is used to create the intaglio printing plate, any imperfections during the creation of the relief transfer may result in flaws that will appear on the finished stamps. A small fleck of foreign material present during the rocking-in process may leave a mark on the relief transfer. Similarly, imperfections in the steel of the transfer roll may cause the loss of part of the design from the master die. These flaws are known as **relief breaks**, which appear as small, uninked areas on the finished stamp. Reliefs also may be deliberately modified to minimize or rectify such flaws, resulting in what is referred to as an **altered relief**, the characteristics of which again will be expressed on the finished stamp.

When the transfer roll has been completed and hardened, it is used to rock in the design to a large plate of polished, soft steel, where it again appears in reversed form as on the original master die. Layout lines or position dots are placed to precisely locate the transfer roll over the plate, and may sometimes later appear on stamps if they are not burnished away during final plate preparation.

It is during this process that double transfers, shifted transfers and dropped transfers occur.

A **shifted transfer** on a plate is one that shows doubling of part or all the design (typically one edge or corner of the design), usually because the relief transfer shifted slightly while the design was being rocked into the printing plate.

A similar effect also can be achieved on the plate when a defective transfer is incompletely removed, and a second transfer is rocked in over it. Any place where the engraving of the original transfer remains and is not covered by the second transfer is likely to appear on the printed stamp as a **double transfer** (or, in cases where traces of two previous transfers exist, a **triple transfer**.) Sometimes the printers need to delete the original transfer from a plate and enter it from scratch again. Should this completed transfer show some traces of the original impression, it is referred to as a **partial double transfer**.

A **dropped transfer** is one that is made normally but is mis-aligned with respect to the other designs on the plate. A stamp printed from such a dropped transfer will be noticeably out of alignment with the stamps around it in the final sheet.

Failure to center the transfer roll correctly on the plate will result in the failure of the relief transfer to completely record all portions of the master die, resulting in the loss of the edge of the engraved design on the finished stamp. This is known as a **short transfer**.

The impressions of the transfer roll on the plate often are referred to as **subjects**, and as many of these subjects are transferred as are required for the final plate (typically 200 or 400 subjects on most plates up to the 1950s and 1960s.)

When all the subjects have been put in place, all position dots, layout lines and any other minor scratches, burrs or imperfections are removed from the printing surface. With the addition of marginal and other sheet markings including guide lines, arrows and plate numbers, a **plate proof** is printed to confirm that the plate is ready to produce stamps. (**Trial color proofs** may also be printed in a variety of colors other than those eventually selected for the finished stamps, to test the clarity and appearance of the finished print in different hues.) When these impressions are approved, the **printing plate** is machined for fitting onto a press, hardened and sent off to the plate vault, ready to be used.

On the press, the intaglio plate is inked, and its smooth surface is wiped clean, leaving ink only in the lines created by the relief transfer. Paper is then forced under pressure into the engraved recessed lines, the ink of which is transferred to the surface of the stamp paper. When dry, the lines of raised ink on the intaglio stamp are slightly raised, giving such stamps their characteristic crisply ridged feel, and slight depressions (known as debossing) on the back of the stamp show where these inked lines appear on the front.

For the first century or so of intaglio stamp production, prior to the advent of modern, high-speed presses, paper used in intaglio stamp production often was moistened to facilitate the transfer of the ink, known as a **wet printing**. However, this sometimes led to uneven shrinkage by the time the stamps were perforated, resulting in improp-erly perforated stamps, or misperfs. More modern presses do not require the use of moistened paper, thus giving rise to stamps that exist in both **wet print** and **dry print** versions.

At first, only **flat press plates** were used to print engraved stamps. **Rotary press** printing was introduced early in the 1900s and slowly spread to account for larger share of stamp production. Older **rotary press plates** require additional machining, and are curved under pressure to fit the press cylinder. The stretching of the plate during the curving process distorts the subjects on it, with the result that stamps printed from rotary press plates usually are longer or wider than the same stamps printed from flat plate presses.

In the early days of intaglio flat-plate printing, heavily worn plates were sometimes spruced up to give additional service by re-entering their designs, reapplying the transfer roll to the old plate to sharpen worn-down designs. However, if the registration between the transfer roll and the engraving on the worn plate is not exact, or if the original transfer is not completely burnished flat before the design is rocked in again, the result is often a **re-entry**. In a **re-entry**, another sort of **double transfer** can be created, which will appear on stamps printed from such a subject as a design with portions of the previous worn design still visible.

If the alignment is exact and the placement of the transfer roll is true, a skillful re-entry may be all but undetectable.

Other, slightly less radical techniques of rendering a worn plate fit for continued use usually require that the plate be softened by having its temper drawn (generally by the precise application of heat and cooling) for retooling by hand. Among the techniques involved are **retouching** (the deepening or modification of lines by etching), and **recutting** (the deepening or alteration of lines with an engraving tool.) If the resulting inked impression varies slightly from the original, it is referred to as a **re-engraved** stamp.

The intricate line patterns of intaglio printing are an excellent safeguard against would-be counterfeiters, but additional techniques also have been used to make intaglio stamps even more difficult to forge. One of these that was especially popular in the early days of stamp production was the incorporation of **lathework** and other **engine-turned designs** into the backgrounds and frames of various issues — complicated and precisely repeated designs produced on a mechanical device called an engraving engine.

Bicolored engraved stamps are created by passing the printing sheet through a flat-bed press two times, once with a plate to print the frame and a then with a second plate, inked in a different color, to print the vignette at the center of the design. Performing either of these operations with the sheet incorrectly oriented would result in one part of the stamp being printed upside-down in relation to the rest of the design, creating the category of major error referred to as inverted-center (or inverted-frame) errors, or **inverts**, in common parlance.

Lithography (also Photolithography, Offset Lithography, Stone Lithography, Dilitho, Planography, Collotype)

Lithography uses the principle that oil and water do not mix to produce a printed design. The design is produced from original artwork and transferred in an oily or greasy ink onto the printing surface, originally a prepared surface of stone (from which lithography takes its name) but now more frequently a metal surface. This greasy design can attract and hold the ink for transfer onto the surface to be printed, while the rest of the plate is moistened with an acidic fluid that repels such ink, corresponding to the uninked portions of the design. To create a plate, special transfer paper is used to make duplicates of the desired design from the original lithographic stone or plate, which are in turn assembled to create the final lithographic printing plate.

In a well-crafted lithographic stamp, the design may have fine and sharply printed lines as in an intaglio stamp, but its design also will have distinct, solidly inked areas that are not to be seen either on intaglio or on gravure issues. Also, unlike either intaglio printing (where lines of ink are raised on the surface of the stamp) or letterpress printing (where the inked areas are impressed into the paper, leaving a debossed surface on the back of the stamp), both sides of a stamp printed by lithography are completely flat.

Offset Lithography, also known as offset printing, refers to a refinement of the basic lithographic technique, whereby a greasy ink impression on a rubber blanket transfers the lithographic image from the printing surface to the paper, when the technique was introduced due to manpower and material restrictions on intaglio printing caused by World War I. Offset lithography and intaglio may be used together.

Because of its greater ease of use and range of applications, offset lithography has largely replaced lithography today, and is frequently referred to simply as "offset."

Gravure (including such variants as Photogravure, Rotogravure, Heliogravure)

The preparation of stamps for printing by gravure begins with the photographing of the intended design through a fine mesh, referred to as a dot-matrix screen, which renders it onto a metal plate as a pattern of tiny dots. A chemical process etches this fine dot or halftone pattern onto the plate, where it is converted into a multitude of shallow pits or depressions, known as cells, which hold the ink during the printing process.

In the gravure printing process, the paper pressed against the gravure plate lifts the ink out of the cells to produce the intended design. Deeper, larger cells produce the more heavily inked and frequently darker portions of the printed designs. Shallow, small cells produce more lightly inked and often lightly colored areas on the stamp.

The chief use of gravure is in producing multi-colored stamps. Using only the primary colors red, yellow and cyan (blue), along with black, gravure's dot pattern can be combined and recombined to furnish almost any color that might be required. These overlapping patterns of dots, clearly visible under magnification, are the key characteristic by which gravure stamps may be easily identified.

Letterpress (also known as Typography, Surface Printing, Flexography, Dry Offset, High Etch)

Essentially the opposite of intaglio printing, in letterpress printing it is the raised rather than the incised areas of the printing plate that are inked to print the finished design. In fact, the process of creating the printing plate is an inversion of the intaglio process as well, with an additional step in which the design is transferred to another surface before the creation of the transfer roll. This results in the transfer roll having a recessed rather than a relief design, which means that the final plate will have the areas that are to be inked raised above rather than carved into the surface, similar to a rubber handstamp.

Reproducing a letterpress transfer electromechanically is referred to as **electrotype** or **stereotype** production, and these are then gathered together in the desired configuration to form the plate from which stamps are produced. A plate for letterpress printing made using the assembled electrotypes is referred to as an **electroplate**.

As with a piece of paper printed using a handstamp or a typewriter, paper printed by letterpress will show a slight depression (debossing) in the printed portion of the printed side of the paper, and a slight elevation (embossing) on the reverse side of the paper. This is characteristic of this printing method.

Embossing (also Colorless Embossing, Blind Embossing, Relief Printing)

Not truly a printing technique (since, technically, ink need not be involved), embossing is, however, an important security technique used on postal paper (chiefly stamped envelopes.) In embossing, a design is carved into a die, which is reproduced to yield a shallow, three-dimensional sculpture from which additional embossing dies are made. A similar back plate, or platen, mirroring the design is created, and the two sides are pressed together to create the embossed image (often with ink on the inside of the die in front, producing the inscribed, denominated printed collar around the embossed portrait or image.)

Stamp Components and Characteristics

If a stamp's image is derived in large measure from its printing (and the techniques used), the rest of the characteristics that define it have to do with the materials used in the stamp's creation — ink, gum, paper and separation technique — and some of the key observable characteristics of these materials, including the watermark, the method of stamp separation and the gauge of its perforations or rouletting, as well as the presence or absence of luminescence.

Examples may be found of otherwise identical stamps that differ in only one or two subtle respects, creating, at the least, two interesting varieties to seek out for your album and, at the most, an opportunity for the observant stamp collector to pick out a gem amid a pile of perfectly common postage. Few of us may ever have such an experience, to be sure, but fortune favors those who have prepared. Contrarily, collectors who are unaware that a rarity exists will never find it.

Ink and Color

Ink is the basic stuff of printing, typically consisting of a finely powered admixture or suspension of mineral, natural organic or synthetic organic pigment in a liquid solvent or base.

Ink is directly related to color. Many of the inks used in printing 19th-century stamps were mixed by hand to the closely guarded specifications of the private printing firms that did the work, and often varied perceptibly from batch to batch. This gave rise to at least some of the many collectible shades and hues found on a number of classic Canadian issues.

In the early 20th century, inks became considerably more standardized, and the number and variety of color varieties diminished.

One consequence of the arrival of single-press-run multicolor printing in the 1950s and 1960s was that minor variations in the individual colors on a stamp became harder to clearly discern, and in time came to be largely ignored, except on monochrome engraved stamps where such varieties remained easy to see. At the same time, however, there slowly developed a considerable increase in the number of color-omitted errors-errors that could never have taken place on monochrome intaglio stamps.

An important transition in inks took place in the 1970s when solvent-based inks were screened for potential toxicity and adverse health and environmental effects, and replaced with new, safer water-based inks of similar color.

In fact, ink is not the only variable that determines the color of a stamp. The quantity of ink, the pressure with which it is applied, the type of paper and its moisture content at the time that the printing takes place and the type of base that carries the pigment in the ink all can affect the apparent color.

Of special concern to collectors are stamps printed in **fugitive ink**, which is soluble and tends to run or dissolve when the stamp is immersed in such otherwise innocuous liquids as water or watermark fluid. Fugitive inks include synthetic organic pigments produced as derivatives of nitrobenzene (aniline inks) and some photogravure stamps as well.

Stamps that have had their color altered after they were printed, intentionally or accidentally, are referred to as **color changelings**.

Generally such changelings occur as the result of a photochemical reaction (such as prolonged exposure to sunlight or artificial light) or chemical activity (such as the use of a cleaning agent or solvent to remove soiling or lighten a heavy cancel.)

One especially notorious kind of accidental color changeling is often seen on 19th-century and early 20th-century yellow, orange and red stamps in which the oxidation of sulfur compounds in the pigment turns the image a deep brown shade, occasionally approaching black. The immersion of one of these affected stamps in a mild solution of hydrogen peroxide frequently will reverse the effects of such oxidation, though it may not return the stamp precisely to its original color.

While many collectors retain color changelings as curios, they are in fact nothing more than stamps in which the ink has been irreversibly damaged (much as the paper or perforations might be damaged.) Color changelings have no place in an authentic collection of the production varieties of stamps.

Gum

Stamp gum is known in a wide range of textures, shades and degrees of reflectivity. Most stamp gums today use dextrine or polyvinyl alcohol as a base.

Shiny and matt gum varieties are cataloged separately in those instances where both are known to be found on the same stamp, even though such stamps may not be distinguishable in used condition or used on cover.

The gum on unused stamps encountered by collectors exists in a variety of conditions, which are listed, abbreviated and defined here in decreasing order of desirability:

Mint Never Hinged (MNH) stamps have pristine gum just as originally acquired from the post office, without a blemish, fingerprint or mark of any kind. Mint prices in this catalog for stamps issued since 1945 refer to stamps in this condition.

Lightly Hinged (LH) stamps have 50 percent to 100 percent of their original gum, but show a minor disturbance on the back, such as traces where a stamp hinge was previously located, so-called disturbed gum or a fingerprint. Mint prices in this catalog for stamps issued prior to 1945 are for stamps in this condition, although in practice many earlier 19th-century stamps are less likely to have much of their original gum still intact.

Heavily Hinged (HH) stamps have less than 50 percent of their original gum and/or remnants of older non-peelable paper hinges still affixed to the back of the stamp.

All Three of the preceding types of unused stamps are sometimes referred to as **original gum** stamps, their desirability and value increasing according to the quantity and quality of the gum. However, not all unused stamps have original gum.

No Gum (NG) stamps are stamps from which the original gum has been removed. For purposes of saving the stamp, it may sometimes be advisable to soak off an especially heavy hinge remnant, which may cause a stamp to warp, buckle or even tear internally.

Regummed (R, RG or RE) stamps are stamps from which the original gum has been removed and other gum has been added later. When it is clearly identified as such, there is nothing objectionable about a regummed stamp, and auction catalog realizations often seem to suggest that collectors are willing to pay a bit more for an expertly regummed stamp than for its NG counterpart.

However, it is fraud to knowingly represent and sell regummed stamps as original-gum copies, which is often attempted to obtain the considerably higher price that such OG stamps typically command. Similarly, it is fraudulent to chemically or otherwise remove a light cancellation from a stamp and offer it as unused. Both regumming and removal of cancellations have some skilled practiners, which is why expertization is recommended for valuable mint stamps.

Paper

Paper, the medium for all printing, consists of dried sheets of processed vegetable fiber laid down on a fine screen from a water suspension. The two basic broad classifications of paper are **laid paper** in which the lines left by the screen during the papermaking process are still visible in transmitted light, and **wove paper**, which has no such visible grain or lines. Papers also may be categorized as thin or thick, soft or hard, and according to its naturally occurring color.

India paper, refers both to a soft, thin translucent paper used for pulling intaglio die and plate proofs and to a tougher, opaque thin paper.

In addition, **colored paper** has been deliberately selected for use in specific issues.

Double paper has two very different meanings. It refers to a security paper patented by Charles F. Steel, in which a thin, weak surface paper and a thicker, stronger backing paper were bonded before printing. This produced a two-layer stamp, the printed design of which would be ruined if any attempt were made to clean a cancel after the stamp had been used.

The second meaning of double paper is in reference to rotary press printing. Rotary presses print stamps on a continuous roll of paper, and when one roll of paper ends, the beginning of a new roll is spliced to the end of it so that production will not be interrupted. Stamps printed on the splice, where paper of the old and new rolls overlaps, is typically marked, cut out and discarded when the stamps are separated into sheets and panes. However, stamps printed across the splice do occasionally escape detection and survive to reach collectors, and these are known as **rotary press double paper** varieties.

Paper with silk fibers also was used in printing some issues. As the name implies, this paper has one or several long colored silk threads embedded in it.

Watermarks

A watermark is a pattern laid down on paper during manufacturing. Shallow designs in metal, called bits, are woven into the screen on which the pulp is formed and drained. When the paper is dry and light is transmitted through it, the impression of the designs of these bits shows as a bright pattern in the paper, which is slightly thinner where the bits were positioned.

On most stamps, watermarks also may best be seen by immersing them in **watermark fluid**, a non-aqueous fluid that will not moisten gum on mint stamps. The fluid increases the transparency of the paper, to make watermarks show more clearly as dark patterns when the stamp is placed face-down in the fluid against a black background.

Perforation Errors

In addition to plate manufacturing errors, which include double impressions in the engraving, and printing errors, which include missing or inverted colors, and folding of the paper in the press, the widest variety of errors occur in the perforation process

CANADA

Europeans first reached Canada in 1497 when a British expedition under Italian-born John Cabot landed in Newfoundland. After Cabot's voyage, the English lost interest in the New World and the next explorers to visit Canada were French, beginning with  Jacques Cartier in 1537 who discovered the Gulf of St. Lawrence. Following the later explorations of Samuel de Champlain, the first permanent settlers, who were also French, arrived in what is now Quebec. Champlain's company, which had been granted a fur monopoly by the French crown, controlled all French interests in Canada until 1632 when the area became a royal province of France. During the 17th century French explorers Marquette, Joliet and LaSalle moved west and south, penetrating the Mississippi River valley down to Louisiana.

However, Canada became involved in the great European dynastic wars of the 18th century, which pitted the France of Louis XIV against England and her allies. During these conflicts the English, who had shown little interest in Canada up until that time, extracted parts of the giant French domain for the English crown. During the first two of these struggles, the French lost New Brunswick, Nova Scotia and Newfoundland. In the third and final round, the famed French and Indian Wars, which ended in 1763, the French lost all the rest of Canada to the British. However, in 1774 the Quebec Act allowed the French inhabitants to retain their own language, religion and laws.

English settlement was given a large boost by the arrival of large numbers of English loyalists from the United States following the end of the American Revolution. In the War of 1812, 35 years later, U.S. attempts again to invade Canada sparked the first embers of Canadian nationalism.

In the first half of the 19th century Canada consisted of Newfoundland, New Brunswick, Nova Scotia, Prince Edward Island, Canada (what is now modern day Quebec and Ontario) and British Columbia and Vancouver Island. All issued their own postage stamps in the 1850s. After  the British crown granted internal self-government to the Canadian colonies in 1849, New Brunswick, Nova Scotia and Canada proper joined together to form the Dominion of Canada on July 1, 1867. British Columbia and Prince Edward Island joined in 1871 and 1873 respectively. Canada was the first federal union in the history of the British Empire.

Following the British North American Act which created the Dominion of Canada, a slow but steady movement of settlement westward began. Aided by Canada's purchase of the area controlled by the private Hudson's Bay Company in 1869 out of which grew the provinces of Manitoba (1870) and Alberta and Saskatchewan (1905), vast new areas of the Canadian prairie were opened up to farming and cattle ranching. The process was accelerated by the successful construction of two Canadian transcontinental railroads, the Canadian Pacific and the Canadian National.

A sense of joint French-British Canadian nationalism slowly evolved, symbolized by Canada's first French Canadian Prime Minister, Sir Wilfred Laurier, who served from 1896-1911, longer than any other Canadian Prime Minister. During the First World War, Canadian units served with the Allies on the Western Front, suffering heavy casualties and performing with great valor. In 1931 Canada was proclaimed a self governing dominion within the British Empire. Its status continued when the British Empire became the British Commonwealth after World War II, during which once again Canadian military units took part.

Following World War II, Canada's economic growth continued, fueled by the discovery of extensive oil and uranium deposits in the West and Far North and the influx of new immigrants, many from Eastern Europe. After Canada's first paved transcontinental highway was completed in 1962, a movement began to create a sense of nationalism totally separate from its connection to Britain. The Canadian flag was changed from the old Union Jack with provincial shields to the current Maple Leaf banner in 1965, and the old national anthem of "God Save the Queen" was replaced by "Oh Canada."

The latest changes in the Canadian Constitution in 1982 by which Canada severed its last formal link with the British Parliament, allows amendment of the Constitution by 7 provinces constituting 50% of the Canadian population. The province of Newfoundland joined Canada in 1949, up until which time it issued its own postage stamps. Canadian troops have taken part in almost all of the United Nations peacekeeping operations since that organization's inception in 1945.

Denis J. Norrington

Province of Canada

1851. 1st Pence Issue *Intaglio by Rawdon, Wright, Hatch & Edson, New York. Prices are for no-gum examples. Laid paper, imperforate.*

1, 5, 10 *Beaver, a symbol of Canada. Pelts were popular in the fur trade.*

		UNF	UseF
1			
3p	**red,** shades, FDD *(April 23, 1851)*	9,375.00	600.00

2, 6, 11 *Prince Albert (1819-61) was royal consort of Queen Victoria*

		UNF	UseF
2			
6p	**slate violet,** FDD *(May 15, 1851)*	9,000.00	750.00
	y. bisect on cover		26,250.00

3 Queen *Victoria (1819-1901), queen of England (1837-1901), was married to her cousin, Prince Albert of Saxe-Coburg. Her reign was the longest in English history, and she personified the era.*

		UNF	UseF
3			
12p	**black,** FDD *(June 14, 1851)*	45,000.00	37,500.00

1852-57. 2nd Pence Issue *Intaglio, wove paper, imperforate.*

4, 9 *Queen Victoria*

		UNF	UseF
4			
1/2p	**deep rose,** FDD *(Aug.1,1857)*	450.00	340.00
	p. horizontal ribbed paper	3,750.00	1,125.00
	p1. vertical ribbed paper	4,500.00	2,065.00
5		UNF	UseF
3p	**red,** FDD *(April 1852)*	950.00	110.00
	brown red	975.00	130.00
	p. thin paper	750.00	115.00
	p1. ribbed paper (softwove)	1,875.00	300.00
	y. bisect on cover		26,250.00
6		UNF	UseF
6p	**greenish gray,** FDD *(March 1855)*	5,625.00	750.00
	p. gray violet, thick hard paper	6,750.00	1,125.00
	p1. reddish purple, very thick soft paper 1857	9,000.00	2,250.00
	y. bisect on cover		16,500.00

7 Queen *Victoria*

		UNF	UseF
7			
7 1/2p	**pale yellow green,** FDD *(June 2, 1857)*	4,350.00	1,690.00

8 *Jacques Cartier (1491-1557), French explorer, discovered the St. Lawarence River and sailed as far as the present city of Quebec. (Riss painting)*

		UNF	UseF
8			
10p	**bright blue,** FDD *(Jan. 1855)*	3,750.00	750.00
	p. thick paper	4,500.00	950.00

Width of No. 7, 8 varies from 17mm to 18 1/2mm due to shrinkage of paper, moistened before printing.

1858-59. 3rd Pence Issue *Intaglio, perforated 11 1/4.*

		UNF	UseF
9			
1/2p	**deep rose,** FDD *(Dec. 1858)*	1,500.00	675.00
10		UNF	UseF
3p	**red,** FDD *(Jan. 1859)*	3,000.00	375.00

No. 10 exists unofficially perforated 14 or serrate rouletted 13.

11 *Prince Albert*

		UNF	UseF
11			
6p	**slate violet,** FDD *(Jan. 1859)*	5,625.00	2,825.00
	y. bisect on cover		

Re-entries of No. 1-11 exist. Major re-entry of 3p has a line through EE PEN. No.1.

1859. Regular Issue *Designs as No. 1-8 with values in cents. Intaglio, by American Bank Note Co., New York; paper of varying thickness, shades, perforated 12.*

12, 13 *Victoria*

		UNF	UseF
12			
1¢	**rose,** T4	150.00	25.00
	v. Pair, imperforate	3,750.00	
13		UNF	UseF
2¢	**rose red,** FDD *(Aug. 1, 1864)*	250.00	130.00
	v. Pair, imperforate	2,250.00	

14 *Beaver*

14		**UNF**	**UseF**
5¢	**orange red,** T1	169.00	11.25
	v. Pair, imperforate	13,100.00	

Major re-entry of No. 14 has oval frame line above CANADA and entire left side double.

15 *Prince Albert*

15		**UNF**	**UseF**
10¢	**bright red lilac**	375.00	45.00
	Black brown	4,875.00	2,250.00
	v. Pair, imperforate (lilac)	9,000.00	

16 *Victoria*

16		**UNF**	**UseF**
12 1/2¢	**yellow green** T7	245.00	45.00
	Blue green	340.00	53.00
	v. Pair, imperforate (blue green)	3,375.00	

17 *Cartier*

17		**UNF**	**UseF**
17¢	**blue,** T8	450.00	75.00
	Slate blue	525.00	90.00
	Prussian blue	675.00	105.00
	v. Pair, imperforate (blue)	4,500.00	

Dominion of Canada

1868-97. LARGE QUEEN ISSUE Queen Victoria in various frames; 1/2¢: 17 x 21mm, 1¢-15¢: 20 x 24mm. *Intaglio by British American Bank Note Co. at Montreal or Ottawa on medium to thick wove paper. Perforated 12.*
   No. 18-25: First printings, March 1868, on rather transparent paper with lines of background less clearly impressed than in later printings. No. 18 - 25 (1868) with parts of papermaker's watermark, double-line L & G BOTHWELL/CLUTHA MILLS. No. 25: see note after No. 28.

18, 26, 19, 20 *Victoria*

18		**MLHF**	**UseF**
1/2¢	**black**	55.00	30.00
	p1. thin paper	62.00	37.50
	p2. w/watermark (Bothwell paper)	19,000.00	6,750.00
19		**MLHF**	**UseF**
1¢	**brown red**	400.00	50.00
	p. thin paper	450.00	50.00
	p1. laid paper	17,000.00	2,250.00
	p2. w/watermark (Bothwell paper)	1,980.00	190.00
20		**MLHF**	**UseF**
1¢	**orange yellow,** FDD *(1869)*	800.00	75.00
	deep orange	845.00	95.00

21, 22, 23 *Victoria*

21		**MLHF**	**UseF**
2¢	**green (shades)**	420.00	30.00
	p. thin paper (deep green)	750,000.00	
	p1. laid paper		18,750.00
	p2. w/watermark (Bothwell paper)	1,980.00	169.00
	y. bisect on cover		3,375.00
22		**MLHF**	**UseF**
3¢	**pale red**	800.00	15.00
	p. thin paper	845.00	18.75
	p1. laid paper (bright red)	11,900.00	800.00
	p2. w/watermark	2,815.00	150.00
23		**MLHF**	**UseF**
6¢	**dark brown**	800.00	45.00
	yellow brown, FDD *(1870)*	730.00	45.00
	p. thin paper	1,125.00	55.00
	p1. w/watermark (Bothwell paper)	7,300.00	750.00
	y. bisect diagonal half on cover		1,875.00

24, 25 *Victoria*

24		**MLHF**	**UseF**
12 1/2¢	**blue**	450.00	40.00
	p. thin paper, deep blue	525.00	55.00
	p1. w/watermark	1,700.00	150.00
25		**MLHF**	**UseF**
15¢	**violet gray**	55.00	18.75
	gray, (many shades)	45.00	18.75
	blue gray, FDD *(1875)*	87.00	26.00
	p. very thick paper, deep violet	3,375.00	600.00
	v. Pair, imperforate, brown purple	1,125.00	
	p1. thin paper, red lilac	510.00	68.00
	p2. w/watermark (watermarked "Bothwell")	3,375.00	375.00

1873-77. 2ND LARGE QUEEN ISSUE *Intaglio, perforated 11 1/2 x 12.*

  27, 28 *Victoria*

 32, 33 Victoria

26		MLHF	UseF
1/2¢	**black**	55.00	30.00
27		MLHF	UseF
5¢	**gray olive green,** FDD *(Oct. 1, 1875)*	845.00	95.00
28		MLHF	UseF
15¢	**grayish purple,** FDD *(March 1877)*	845.00	95.00
	p. w/script watermark, FDD *(1876)*	7,320.00	1,700.00
	greenish gray (1873)	675.00	95.00

No. 28p: parts of papermaker's watermark Alexr. Pirie & Sons in script letters.

1870-97. SMALL QUEEN ISSUE Various frames; No. 29, 15 x 18 1/4mm, Nos. 30-40, 17 x 21mm; M: Montreal printings on thin white (1870-72), medium to thick (1870-80) or thinnish and poor quality (1878-97) papers. O: Ottawa printings of 1883-97 on thinnish, poor quality, sometimes grayish or yellowish paper. *Intaglio, perforated 12.*

 29 *Victoria*

29		MLHF	UseF
1/2¢	**black,** (M,O), FDD *(July 1882)*	5.70	4.70
	v. Pair imperforate	560.00	
	v1. Pair, imperforate horizonally between	750.00	

 30 *Victoria*

30 *v*

30		MLHF	UseF
1¢	**yellow,** (O)	26.00	.70
	orange, (M)	53.00	4.90
	yellow, (M)	22.50	.95
	v. Pair, imperforate	265.00	
	y. bisect on cover		2,625.00

 31 *Victoria*

31		MLHF	UseF
2¢	**green,** (M,O), FDD *((1872)*	45.00	15.00
	blue green, (O), FDD *(1889)*	37.50	.55
	v. Pair, imperforate	450.00	
	y. bisect on cover		1,875.00

32		MLHF	UseF
3¢	**dull red,** FDD *(1872)*	40.00	.95
	rose red, (M) (1871)	225.00	5.70
	orange red, FDD *(1873)*	40.00	.95
	copper red, FDD (1870)	675.00	30.00
	v. perforated 12 1/2, copper red FDD (1870)	3,750.00	450.00
33		MLHF	UseF
3¢	**bright vermilion,** (O), FDD *(1889)*	15.00	.25
	v. Pair, imperforate	340.00	
	rose carmine, FDD *(1888)*	225.00	3.75

 34, 35 *Victoria*

		MLHF	UseF
34			
5¢	**slate green,** (M), FDD *(1876)*	206.00	9.50
	deep olive green		
35		MLHF	UseF
5¢	**gray,** (O), FDD *(1888)*	37.50	2.50
	v. Pair, imperforate	560.00	

 36, 37 *Victoria*

38 *Victoria*

		MLHF	UseF
36			
6¢	**yellow brown,** (M), FDD *(1872)*	190.00	9.50
	y. bisect on cover		375.00
37		MLHF	UseF
6¢	**red brown**	37.50	6.00
	chocolate, *(1891)*	110.00	15.00
	chestnut, (O) FDD *(1890)*	55.00	7.50
	v. Pair, imperforate, (red brown)	490.00	
38		MLHF	UseF
8¢	**gray,** (O), FDD *(Aug. 1, 1893)*	45.00	2.25
	violet black	45.00	2.25
	blue gray	55.00	2.25
	slate	53.00	2.25
	v. Pair, imperforate, (blue gray)	490.00	

 39, 40 *Victoria*

		MLHF	UseF
39			
10¢	**dull rose lilac** (M), FDD *(1877)*	450.00	75.00
	magenta, FDD *(1880)*	225.00	32.00
40		MLHF	UseF
10¢	**brown red,** (O), FDD *(1897)*	200.00	10.00
	pink, FDD *(1891)*	130.00	28.50
	v. Pair, imperforate	375.00	

41, 42 *Victoria*

41		MLHF	UseF
20¢	**vermilion,** (O), FDD *(Feb. 17, 1893)*	400.00	100.00
	v. Pair, imperforate	375.00	
42		MLHF	UseF
50¢	**blue,** (O), FDD *(Feb. 17, 1893)*	600.00	90.00
	v. Pair, imperforate	1,125.00	

1873-79. SMALL QUEEN ISSUE *Intaglio by Montreal printing. Perforated 11 1/2x12.*

43		MLHF	UseF
1¢	**orange**	110.00	7.50
44		MLHF	UseF
2¢	**deep green**	130.00	10.50
45		MLHF	UseF
3¢	**orange red**	92.50	5.70
46		MLHF	UseF
5¢	**slate green,** FDD *(1876)*	300.00	18.75
47		MLHF	UseF
6¢	**yellow brown,** FDD *(1876)*	300.00	18.75
48		MLHF	UseF
10¢	**pale milky rose lilac,** FDD *(1874)*	640.00	190.00
	magenta	450.00	110.00

Nos. 29-48 come in numerous shades and our color designations are for groups of shades.

1875-88. REGISTRATION ISSUE *Intaglio, perforated 12.*

49-51 *Registration*

49		MLHF	UseF
2¢	**orange**	55.00	2.25
	vermilion	75.50	6.75
	rose carmine, FDD *(1888)*	165.00	72.50
	v. Pair, imperforate, (one pair known)		1,875.00
50		MLHF	UseF
5¢	**dark green**	75.00	2.25
	yellow green	75.00	2.25
	blue green, FDD *(1888)*	120.00	3.75
	v. Pair, imperforate	750.00	
51		MLHF	UseF
8¢	**blue**	190.00	150.00

Commemoratives Issues

1897. 60TH JUBILEE ISSUE *Anniversary of Victoria's reign. Intaglio, perforated 12.*

52-65 *Queen Victoria in 1837 and 1897*

52		MLHF	UseF
1/2¢	**black**	55.00	55.00
53		MLHF	UseF
1¢	**orange**	7.50	3.00

54		MLHF	UseF
2¢	**green**	9.00	7.20
55		MLHF	UseF
3¢	**bright rose**	6.00	1.30
56		MLHF	UseF
5¢	**deep blue**	22.50	14.25

57 *Victoria*

57		MLHF	UseF
6¢	**yellow brown**	110.00	95.00
58		MLHF	UseF
8¢	**dark violet**	28.50	16.90

59 *Victoria*

59		MLHF	UseF
10¢	**brown violet**	53.00	45.00

60, 61 *Victoria*

60		MLHF	UseF
15¢	**steel blue**	95.00	90.00
61		MLHF	UseF
20¢	**vermilion**	95.00	86.25

62, 63 *Victoria*

62		MLHF	UseF
50¢	**ultramarine**	97.50	86.00
63		MLHF	UseF
$1	**lake**	450.00	450.00

64, 65 *Victoria*

64		MLHF	UseF
$2	**dark purple**	750.00	340.00

65		MLHF	UseF
$3	yellow bistre	850.00	525.00

66, 67 *Victoria*

66		MLHF	UseF
$4	purple	850.00	525.00

67		MLHF	UseF
$5	olive green	850.00	525.00

Regular Issues

1897-98. VICTORIA ISSUE *Intaglio, perforated 12.*

68-75 *Queen Victoria and maple leaves in four corners*

68		MLHF	UseF
1/2¢	**black,** FDD *(Nov. 6, 1897)*	3.75	3.75
	v. Pair, imperforate	340.00	

69		MLHF	UseF
1¢	**blue green,** FDD *(Dec. 1897)*	9.50	.55

70		MLHF	UseF
2¢	**purple,** FDD *(Dec. 1897)*	9.50	.95
	v. Pair, imperforate	340.00	

71		MLHF	UseF
3¢	**carmine,** FDD *(Jan. 1898)*	15.00	.20
	v. Pair, imperforate	750.00	

72		MLHF	UseF
5¢	**deep blue** on bluish paper, FDD *(Dec. 1897)*	45.00	3.75
	v. Pair, imperforate	375.00	

73		MLHF	UseF
6¢	**brown,** FDD *(Dec. 1, 1897)*	37.50	15.00
	v. Pair, imperforate	750.00	

74		MLHF	UseF
8¢	**orange,** FDD *(Dec. 1897)*	75.00	5.70
	v. Pair, imperforate	560.00	

75		MLHF	UseF
10¢	**brown violet,** FDD *(Jan. 1898)*	110.00	45.00
	v. Pair, imperforate	490.00	

1898-1902. VICTORIA ISSUE numerals in lower corners; TI 4 thin frame lines; TII: 1 thick line between 2 thin lines. *Intaglio, perforated 12.*

76-86 *Queen Victoria, denominations in lower corners*

76		MLHF	UseF
1/2¢	**black,** FDD *(Sept. 1898)*	1.50	.95
	v. Pair, imperforate	375.00	

77		MLHF	UseF
1¢	**gray green,** FDD *(June 1898)*	7.50	.20
	v. Pair, imperforate	900.00	

78		MLHF	UseF
2¢	**purple,** TI, FDD *(Sept. 1898)*	9.00	.20

79		MLHF	UseF
2¢	**carmine red,** TI, FDD *(Aug. 20, 1899)*	10.50	.20
	TII	11.25	.25
	v. Pair, imperforate	375.00	
	n. Booklet pane of 6	750.00	

80		MLHF	UseF
3¢	**carmine,** FDD *(June 1898)*	15.00	.35

81		MLHF	UseF
5¢	**blue** on bluish paper FDD *(July 3, 1898)*	55.00	.70
	v. Pair, imperforate	950.00	

82		MLHF	UseF
6¢	**brown,** FDD *(Sept. 14, 1899)*	60.00	26.00
	v. Pair, imperforate	950.00	

83		MLHF	UseF
7¢	**olive yellow,** FDD *(Dec. 23, 1902)*	50.00	11.25
	v. Pair, imperforate	950.00	

84		MLHF	UseF
8¢	**orange,** FDD *(Oct. 1898)*	101.00	11.25
	v. Pair, imperforate	950.00	

85		MLHF	UseF
10¢	**brown violet,** FDD *(Nov. 1898)*	120.00	11.25
	v. Pair, imperforate	950.00	

86		MLHF	UseF
20¢	**olive green,** FDD *(Dec. 29, 1900)*	225.00	55.00
	v. Pair, imperforate	2,625.00	

Special Delivery

1898. CITY LIMITS ISSUE *Intaglio, perforated 12.*

87 *"Special Delivery within City Limits"*

87		MLHF	UseF
10¢	**blue green**	37.50	5.70
	yellow green	68.00	11.25
	deep green, FDD *(Aug. 1898)*	75.00	15.00

Commemorative Issue

1898. IMPERIAL PENNY ISSUE Postage (effective on Christmas Day 1898); black design, empire in scarlet; inscription from Sir Lewis Morris poem *The Song of Empire. Intaglio, perforated 12.*

88 *Map of world (The stamp is often referred to as the first Christmas stamp.)*

88		MLHF	UseF
2¢	**oceans in pale gray**	15.00	4.70
	oceans in lavender	18.75	4.70
	oceans in blue	15.00	4.70
	v. Pair, imperforate	375.00	

Regular Issues

1899. ISSUE No. 80 divided vertical and overprinted with a greenish blue 1 on 1/3 of stamp and a violet 2 on 2/3 of stamp was prepared and used by a junior assistant to the Postmaster at Port Hood during the latter's absence. *Intaglio.*

89 *Queen Victoria and maple leaves in four corners and overprint "2 CENTS"*

90 *Queen Victoria and overprint "2 CENTS"*

	MLHF	UseF
89		
2¢ on 3¢ No. 71, FDD *(July 28, 1899)*	5.70	3.40
90	**MLHF**	**UseF**
2¢ on 3¢ No. 80, FDD *(Aug. 8, 1899)*	9.50	2.85

1903-1912. EDWARD VII ISSUE *Intaglio, perforated 12.*

91-97 *King Edward VII (1841-1910) eldest son of Queen Victoria, ruled 1901-10*

	MLHF	UseF
91		
1¢ green	7.50	.20
v. Pair, imperforate	600.00	
92	**MLHF**	**UseF**
2¢ carmine	7.50	.20
v. Pair, imperforate	30.00	30.00
n. Booklet pane of 6	750.00	1,125.00
93	**MLHF**	**UseF**
5¢ blue on bluish paper	50.00	2.10
v. Pair, imperforate	950.00	
94	**MLHF**	**UseF**
7¢ olive bistre, FDD *(June 1903)*	33.75	2.25
v. Pair, imperforate	600.00	
95	**MLHF**	**UseF**
10¢ brown lilac	75.00	4.50
v. Pair, imperforate	950.00	
96	**MLHF**	**UseF**
20¢ olive green, FDD *(Sept. 27, 1904)*	190.00	18.75
97	**MLHF**	**UseF**
50¢ purple, FDD *(Nov, 19, 1908)*	300.00	45.00

Postage Due Stamps

1906-28. ISSUE *Intaglio, perforated 12.*

98-102 *Postage Due Stamp*

	MLHF	UseF
98		
1¢ violet	5.70	2.65
p. thin paper	10.50	4.90
v. Pair, imperforate	375.00	
99	**MLHF**	**UseF**
2¢ violet	5.70	.55
p. thin paper, FDD *(1924)*	10.50	5.70
v. Pair, imperforate		375.00
100	**MLHF**	**UseF**
4¢ violet	26.00	9.50
101	**MLHF**	**UseF**
5¢ violet	5.70	1.15
p. thin paper, FDD *(1924)*, (red violet)	4.70	4.70
v. Pair, imperforate		375.00

	MLHF	UseF
102		
10¢ violet, FDD *(1928)*	18.75	7.20

Commemorative Issues

1908. QUEBEC TERCENTENARY ISSUE *Intaglio, perforated 12.*

103 *Princess and Prince of Wales (George V)*

	MLHF	UseF
103		
1/2¢ brown black	15.00	20.00
v. Pair, imperforate	475.00	

104 *Jacques Cartier, first explorer of Canada; and Samuel de Champlain, whose founding of Quebec in 1608 marked the real beginning of Canadian settlement*

	MLHF	UseF
104		
1¢ green	2.25	2.25
v. Pair, imperforate	450.00	

105 *Queen Alexandra and King Edward VII*

	MLHF	UseF
105		
2¢ carmine	7.50	.55
v. Pair, imperforate	450.00	

106 *Champlain's home in Quebec*

	MLHF	UseF
106		
5¢ blue	22.50	22.50
v. Pair, imperforate	450.00	

107 *Marquis Louis Joseph de Montcalm de Saint-Véran, French field marshal, and British Maj. Gen. James Wolfe, who defeated him at Quebec (1759), securing Canada for the British. Both gallant young commanders were killed in the battle.*

	MLHF	UseF
107		
7¢ olive green	55.00	30.00
v. Pair, imperforate, (with gum)	450.00	

108 *Quebec in 1700*

108		MLHF	UseF
10¢	violet	55.00	45.00
	v. Pair imperforate, (with gum)	450.00	

109 *Champlain's departure to explore the west*

109		MLHF	UseF
15¢	orange	75.00	55.00
	v. Pair, imperforate, (with gum)	450.00	

110 *Cartier's arrival at the site of Quebec, where he spent the winter of 1535 (after painting by J.L. David).*

110		MLHF	UseF
20¢	brown	95.00	95.00
	v. Pair, imperforate, (with gum)	450.00	

Regular Issues

1911-31. GEORGE V ISSUE in uniform of Admiral of fleet. *Intaglio, perforated 12; No. 117: perforated 12 x 8.*

111-129 *King George V*

111		MLHF	UseF
1¢	dark green, FDD *(Dec. 22, 1911)*	4.50	.20
	fine horizontal lines across stamp	18.75	5.70
	n. Booklet pane of 6	11.25	11.25
112		MLHF	UseF
1¢	yellow, FDD *(June 7, 1922)*	3.75	.20
	n. Booklet pane of 4	26.00	26.00
	n1. Booklet pane of 6	26.00	30.00
113		MLHF	UseF
2¢	carmine, FDD *(Dec. 22, 1911)*	3.75	.20
	(hair lines) fine horizontal lines across stamp	18.75	2.65
	n. Booklet pane of 6	18.75	22.50
114		MLHF	UseF
2¢	yellow green, FDD *(June 6, 1922)*	3.00	.20
	p. thin paper, FDD *(1924)*	3.00	1.50
	n. Booklet pane of 4	37.50	37.50
	n1. Booklet pane of 6	190.00	190.00
115		MLHF	UseF
3¢	brown, FDD *(Aug. 6, 1918)*	6.00	.20
	n. Booklet pane of 4	45.00	55.00
116		MLHF	UseF
3¢	carmine, FDD *(Dec. 14, 1923)*	3.00	.20
	Carmine (Die I)	3.00	.20
	Carmine (Die II)	15.00	15.00
	n. Booklet pane of 4	30.00	45.00

117		MLHF	UseF
3¢	deep rose red, perforated 12 x 8, FDD *(June 24, 1931)*	2.25	1.90
118		MLHF	UseF
4¢	olive bistre, FDD *(July 3, 1922)*	15.00	1.15
	v. Pair, imperforate	1,320.00	
119		MLHF	UseF
5¢	dark blue, FDD *(Jan. 17, 1912)*	45.00	26.00
120		MLHF	UseF
5¢	violet, FDD *(Feb. 2, 1922)*	9.50	.26
	p. thin paper, FDD *(Oct. 19, 1924)*	8.25	3.75
	v. Pair, imperforate	1,320.00	
121		MLHF	UseF
7¢	yellow ochre, FDD *(1916)*	15.00	1.30
	olive bistre, FDD *(Dec. 27, 1911)*	15.00	1.30
122		MLHF	UseF
7¢	red brown, FDD *(Dec. 12, 1924)*	9.00	4.50
	v. Pair, imperforate	1,320.00	
123		MLHF	UseF
8¢	blue, FDD *(Sept. 1, 1925)*	13.20	4.50
	v. Pair, imperforate	1,320.00	
124		MLHF	UseF
10¢	plum, FDD *(Jan. 12, 1912)*	75.00	.55
125		MLHF	UseF
10¢	blue, FDD *(Feb. 20, 1922)*	18.75	.75
126		MLHF	UseF
10¢	bistre brown, FDD *(Aug. 1, 1925)*	40.00	1.90
	v. Pair, imperforate	1,320.00	
127		MLHF	UseF
20¢	olive green, FDD *(Jan. 23, 1912)*	33.75	.55
	v. Pair, imperforate	1,320.00	
128		MLHF	UseF
50¢	brown black, FDD *(Jan. 26, 1912)*	37.50	1.30
	black	68.00	3.75
	v. Pair, imperforate	1,500.00	
129		MLHF	UseF
$1	orange, FDD *(July 2, 1923)*	55.00	5.25
	v. Pair, imperforate	1,500.00	

1912. VERTICAL COIL ISSUE *Intaglio, perforated 8, horizontal.*

130		MLHF	UseF
1¢	dark green	45.00	30.00
131		MLHF	UseF
2¢	carmine	45.00	30.00

1912-24. HORIZONTAL COIL ISSUE Thick paper varieties show no embossed effect on their backs. *Intaglio, perforated 8, vertically.*

132		MLHF	UseF
1¢	green, FDD *(Sept. 1912)*	9.00	.55
133		MLHF	UseF
1¢	orange, FDD *(1923)*	5.70	3.75
	y. Block of 4, "2nd dry printing"	30.00	30.00
134		MLHF	UseF
2¢	carmine	11.25	.45
135		MLHF	UseF
2¢	green, FDD *(Aug. 1922)*	7.50	.35
	y. Block of 4, "2nd dry printing"	30.00	30.00
136		MLHF	UseF
3¢	brown, FDD *(Nov. 1918)*	5.70	.35
137		MLHF	UseF
3¢	carmine, FDD *(1924)*	37.50	.45
	y. Block of 4, "1st wet printing"	490.00	

1915-1924. COIL ISSUE *Intaglio, vertical, perforated 12, horizontal.*

138		MLHF	UseF
1¢	dark green	3.75	3.00
139		MLHF	UseF
2¢	carmine	11.25	4.50
140		MLHF	UseF
2¢	yellow green, FDD *(1924)*	45.00	37.50

141
3¢   **brown,** FDD *(Jan. 1921)*

	MLHF	UseF
	4.50	3.00

1924. ISSUE *Imperforate, (double price for pairs).*

142
1¢   **yellow**

	MLHF	UseF
	26.00	26.00

143
2¢   **green**

	MLHF	UseF
	26.00	26.00

144
3¢   **carmine red**

	MLHF	UseF
	13.20	13.20

War Tax Revenue Stamps

1915. WAR TAX ISSUE *Intaglio, perforated 12.*

145, 146 *1915 War tax*

145
1¢ (+1¢) **green,** FDD *(April 1915)*

	MLHF	UseF
	6.00	.20

146
2¢ (+1¢) **carmine,** FDD *(March 1915)*

	MLHF	UseF
	6.00	.20

1916. WAR TAX ISSUE *Intaglio, perforated 12, No. 149 perforated 12 x 8.*

147, 148, 149 *1916 War tax*

147
2¢ (+1¢) **carmine,** TI FDD *(Jan. 1)*
     a. TII, *(Sept. 1916)*

	MLHF	UseF
	7.50	.20
	150.00	2.65

148
2¢ (+1¢) **brown,** TII
     a. brown, TI, FDD *(Sept. 1916)*
     v. Pair, imperforate, TII yellow brown
     b. TII, yellow brown

	MLHF	UseF
	6.00	.20
	188.00	6.00
	1,125.00	
	6.00	.20

149
2¢ (+1¢) **carmine,** No. 1

	MLHF	UseF
	22.50	18.75

1916. WAR TAX ISSUE *Intaglio, perforated 8, vertical.*

150
2¢ (+1¢) **carmine,** FDD *(Aug. 2, 1916)*

	MLHF	UseF
	55.00	3.75

151
2¢ (+1¢) **brown,** TII, FDD *(Dec.)*
     TI, yellow brown

	MLHF	UseF
	11.25	.55

Commemorative Issues

1917. 50TH ANNIVERSARY FEDERATION ISSUE *Intaglio, perforated 12.*

152 Fathers of the Confederation, *depicts Quebec Conference (1864) which led to the British North America Act: Harris painting.*

152
3¢   **brown**
     v. Pair, imperforate, ungummed

	MLHF	UseF
	15.00	37.50
	450.00	

Special Delivery

1922. SPECIAL DELIVER ISSUE *Intaglio, perforated 12.*

153 *Special Delivery*

153
20¢   **deep carmine red**

	MLHF	UseF
	37.50	5.10

Regular Issues

1926. KING GEORGE V REVALUED ISSUE No. 116 overprinted. *Intaglio.*

154, 155 *King George V with "2 CENTS" overprint at bottom*

154
2¢ on 3¢ **carmine,** FDD *(Oct. 26, 1926)*
     v. Double surcharge

	MLHF	UseF
	30.00	30.00
	150.00	

155
2¢ on 3¢ **carmine**
     v. Double overprint
     v1. Triple overprint

	MLHF	UseF
	15.00	15.00
	150.00	
	150.00	

Commemorative Issues

1927. 60TH ANNIVERSARY FEDERATION ISSUE *Intaglio, perforated 12.*

156 *Sir John A. MacDonald (1815-91), one of the framers of the British North America Act, is regarded as the organizer of the dominion and was its first prime minister;* 157 *Fathers of the Confederation*

156
1¢   **orange**
     v. Pair, imperforate
     v1. Pair, imperforate vertical or horizontal
          between

	MLHVF	USEV
	3.00	1.50
	120.00	
	120.00	

157
2¢   **green**
     v. Pair, imperforate
     v1. Pair, imperforate vertical or horizontal
          between

	MLHVF	USEV
	1.90	.20
	120.00	
	120.00	

158 *Parliament buildings at Ottawa;* 159 *Sir Wilfred Laurier (1841-1919), first French-Canadian elected prime minister, was life-long advocate of close cooperation with U.S.*

158		MLHVF	USEV
3¢	**red**	9.50	5.70
	v. Pair, imperforate	120.00	
	v1. Pair, imperforate vertical or horizontal between	120.00	

159		MLHVF	USEV
5¢	**purple**	4.90	2.65
	v. Pair, imperforate	120.00	
	v1. Pair, imperforate vertical or horizontal between	120.00	

160 *Map of Canada*

160		MLHVF	USEV
12¢	**blue**	22.50	5.70
	v. Pair, imperforate	120.00	
	v1. Pair, imperforate vertical or horizontal between	120.00	

Special Delivery

1927. ISSUE Mail transportation. *Intaglio.*

161 *Mail transportation*

161		MLHVF	USEVF
20¢	**orange**	15.00	12.00
	v. Pair, imperforate	190.00	
	v1. Pair, imperforate vertical or horizontal between	190.00	

Commemorative Issues

1927. HISTORICAL SERIES ISSUE Prepared in 1926 but issued with Confederation series; inscribed in English only. *Intaglio, perforated 12.*

162 *Thomas d'Arcy McGee (1825-68), poet, orator and statesman; former revolutionary leader in Ireland, he was scurrilously attacked by Irish extremists and assassinated by P.J. Whelan in 1868.*

162		MLHVF	USEV
5¢	**purple**	4.50	2.65
	v. Pair, imperforate	120.00	
	v1. Pair, imperforate vertical or horizontal between	120.00	

163 *Laurier & MacDonald*

163		MLHVF	USEVF
12¢	**green**	11.25	5.70
	v. Pair, imperforate	120.00	
	v1 Pair, imperforate vertical or horizontal between	120.00	

164 *Robert Baldwin (1804-58) and Sir Louis Hippolyte Lafontaine (1807-64) formed the first Liberal administration, freed the Provincial University from sectarian control and introduced the municipal system into Upper Canada (Ontario).*

164		MLHVF	USEVF
20¢	**red**	27.00	6.75
	v. Pair, imperforate	120.00	
	v1. Pair, imperforate vertical or horizontal between	120.00	

Regular Issues

1928-29. ISSUE *Intaglio, perforated 12.*

165-170, 176, 177 *King George V*

165		MLHVF	USEVF
1¢	**orange,** FDD *(Oct. 29, 1928)*	3.00	.35
	v. Pair, imperforate	95.00	
	v1. Pair, imperforate between	110.00	
	t. Tete-beche pair	281.25	
	n. Booklet pane of 6	20.00	20.00

166		MLHVF	USEVF
2¢	**green,** FDD *(Oct. 17, 1928)*	1.50	.20
	v. Pair, imperforate	95.00	
	v1. Pair, imperforate between	110.00	
	t. Tete-beche pair	281.25	
	n. Booklet pane of 6	20.00	20.00

167		MLHVF	USEVF
3¢	**dark carmine,** FDD *(Dec. 12, 1928)*	24.35	13.20
	v. Pair, imperforate	110.00	
	v1. Pair, imperforate between	150.00	

168		MLHVF	USEVF
4¢	**yellow bistre,** FDD *(1929)*	22.50	5.70
	v. Pair, imperforate	110.00	
	v1. Pair, imperforate between	110.00	

169		MLHVF	USEVF
5¢	**deep violet,** FDD *(Dec. 12, 1929)*	11.25	3.00
	v. Pair, imperforate	95.00	
	v1. Pair, imperforate between	110.00	
	t. Tete-beche pair	281.00	
	n. Booklet pane of 6	110.00	110.00

170		MLHVF	USEVF
8¢	**blue,** FDD *(Dec. 12, 1929)*	15.00	7.50

			MLHVF	USEVF
	v. Pair, imperforate		110.00	
	v1. Pair, imperforate between		110.00	

171 *Mount Hurd (9,275 ft.) in British Columbia: Bell-Smith painting,* The Ice-crowned Monarch of the Rockies. *Totem poles are Northwest Indian art.* **172** *Bridge across the St. Lawrence at Quebec. Completed in 1917, this 1,800 ft. structure is still the longest cantilever bridge in the world (1975).*

171			MLHVF	USEVF
10¢	**green,** FDD *(Nov. 5, 1928)*		15.00	1.50
	v. Pair, imperforate		190.00	
	v1. Pair, imperforate between		190.00	
172			MLHVF	USEVF
12¢	**slate black,** FDD *(Jan. 8, 1929)*		30.00	7.50
	v. Pair, imperforate		190.00	
	v1. Pair, imperforate between		190.00	

173 *Harvesting with horses in the wheat provinces: Manitoba, Saskatchewan and Alberta.*

173			MLHVF	USEVF
20¢	**red,** FDD *(Jan. 8, 1929)*		37.50	12.00
	v. Pair, imperforate		190.00	
	v1. Pair, imperforate between		190.00	

174 *Nova Scotian fishing smack* Bluenose *leading the U.S.* Columbia *in the International Fisherman's Race off Halifax in 1926.*

174			MLHVF	USEVF
50¢	**deep blue,** FDD *(Jan. 8, 1929)*		225.00	68.00
	v. Pair, imperforate		750.00	
	v1. Pair, imperforate between		750.00	

175 *Parliament buildings at Ottawa*

175			MLHVF	USEVF
$1	**olive green,** FDD *(Aug. 1, 1929)*		265.00	75.00
	v. Pair, imperforate		675.00	
	v1. Pair, imperforate between		675.00	

1929. ISSUE *Intaglio, horizontal, perforated 8 vertically.*

176		MLHVF	USEVF
1¢	**orange**	30.00	22.50

177		MLHVF	USEVF
2¢	**green**	22.50	3.75

Airmail Stamps

1928. ISSUE Plane over Canada. *Intaglio, perforated 12.*

178 *Plane over Canada*

178			MLHVF	USEVF
5¢	**brown olive,** FDD *(Sept. 21, 1928)*		12.00	3.75
	v. Pair, imperforate		225.00	
	v1. Pair, imperforate between		225.00	

Regular Issues

1930-32. ISSUE George V (Nos. 179-189) and pictorials with maple leaves in upper corners. *Intaglio, perforated 11.* Die I has 3 lines above postage, die II has 4 lines above postage.

179-189, 196-201 *King George V*

179			MLHVF	USEVF
1¢	**orange,** Die I, FDD *(July 17, 1930)*		1.15	.75
180			MLHVF	USEVF
1¢	**green,** Die II		1.90	.20
	Die I, FDD *(Dec. 6, 1930)*		1.90	.20
	v. Pair, imperforate		1,500.00	
	n. Booklet pane of 4		95.00	95.00
	n1. Booklet pane of 6		16.50	18.75
181			MLHVF	USEVF
2¢	**dull green,** Die I, FDD *(June 6, 1930)*		1.15	.20
	n. Booklet pane of 6, (flat press)		28.15	28.15
182			MLHVF	USEVF
2¢	**deep red,** Die II		1.90	.20
	Die I, FDD *(Nov. 17, 1930)*		1.50	.20
	n. Booklet pane of 6		20.65	22.50
183			MLHVF	USEVF
2¢	**brown,** Die II		1.90	.20
	Die I, FDD *(July 4, 1931)*		3.75	3.75
	n. Booklet pane of 4		105.00	120.00
	n1. Booklet pane of 6		30.00	30.00
184			MLHVF	USEVF
3¢	**deep red,** FDD *(July 13, 1931)*		2.65	.20
	n. Booklet pane of 4		30.00	30.00
185			MLHVF	USEVF
4¢	**yellow bistre,** FDD *(Nov. 5, 1930)*		11.25	6.00
186			MLHVF	USEVF
5¢	**dull violet,** FDD *(June 18, 1930)*		7.50	4.50
187			MLHVF	USEVF
5¢	**blue,** FDD *(Nov. 13, 1930)*		3.40	.20
188			MLHVF	USEVF
8¢	**deep blue,** FDD *(Aug. 13, 1930)*		15.00	11.25
189			MLHVF	USEVF
8¢	**red orange,** FDD *(Nov. 5, 1930)*		6.00	4.90

190 *Parliament library*

190		MLHVF	USEVF
10¢	**olive green,** FDD *(Sept. 15, 1930)*	11.25	1.30
	v. Pair, imperforate	1,500.00	

191, 192 *The Citadel at Quebec*

191		MLHVF	USEVF
12¢	**gray black,** FDD *(Dec. 4, 1930)*	18.75	6.35
	v. Pair, imperforate	400.00	

192		MLHVF	USEVF
13¢	**dull violet,** FDD *(Dec. 1, 1932)*	37.50	3.00
	v. Pair, imperforate	450.00	

193 *Harvesting wheat;* 194 *Acadian Memorial Church and statue of Evangeline at Grand Pré, Nova Scotia. Both commemorate the 6,500 French settlers, banished in 1755 when Britain expected war with France. The Acadians were immortalized in Longfellow's epic poem Evangeline.*

193		MLHVF	USEVF
20¢	**brown red,** FDD *(Dec. 4, 1930)*	30.00	.55
	v. Pair, imperforate	375.00	

194		MLHVF	USEVF
50¢	**blue,** FDD *(Dec. 4, 1930)*	187.50	22.50
	v. Pair, imperforate	900.00	

195 *Mt. Edith Cavell (11,026 ft.) British Columbia, named in honor of heroic WWI nurse.*

195		MLHVF	USEVF
$1	**olive green,** FDD *(Dec. 4, 1930)*	187.50	28.15
	v. Pair, imperforate	600.00	

1930-31. ISSUE Intaglio; horinzontal, perforated 8 1/2, vertically.

196		MLHVF	USEVF
1¢	**orange,** Die I	15.00	10.15

197		MLHVF	USEVF
1¢	**deep green,** Die I	6.00	5.70

198		MLHVF	USEVF
2¢	**dull green,** Die I	6.00	3.00

199		MLHVF	USEVF
2¢	**deep red,** Die I	26.00	2.65

200		MLHVF	USEVF
2¢	**dark brown,** Die I, FDD *(July 4, 1931)*	12.00	.75

201		MLHVF	USEVF
3¢	**deep red,** FDD *(July 13, 1931)*	18.75	.75

Airmail Stamps

1930. ISSUE Mercury and western hemisphere. *Intaglio, perforated 11.*

202 *Mercury and Western hemisphere*

202		MLHVF	USEVF
5¢	**olive brown**	50.00	32.50

Special Delivery

1930. ISSUE Inscribed TWENTY CENTS at bottom. *Intaglio.*

203 *"Canada Special Delivery Expres" - inscribed "TWENTY CENTS"*

203		MLHVF	USEVF
20¢	**henna brown**	60.00	15.00

Postage Due Stamps

1930-32. ISSUE *Intaglio, perforated 11.*

204 *"1 CENT" Postage Due*

204		MLHVF	USEVF
1¢	**dark violet,** FDD *(July 14, 1930)*	7.50	4.50

205		MLHVF	USEVF
2¢	**dark violet,** FDD *(Aug. 21, 1930)*	7.50	1.15

206		MLHVF	USEVF
4¢	**dark violet,** FDD *(Oct. 14, 1930)*	18.75	5.70

207		MLHVF	USEVF
5¢	**dark violet,** FDD *(Dec. 12, 1931)*	16.50	6.75

208		MLHVF	USEVF
10¢	**dark violet,** FDD *(Aug. 24, 1932)*	90.00	11.25
	v. Pair, imperforate horizontal	1,125.00	

Regular Issues

1931. ISSUE G.E. Cartier, originally intended for historical series of 1927, issued to replace No. 190. *Intaglio, perforated 11.*

209 *Sir George Etienne Cartier (1814-73), joint prime minister with MacDonald (1858-62), brought his native province of Quebec into the Confederation. He was also greatly influential in Canadian railroad expansion.*

209

		MLHVF	USEVF
10¢	**bronze green**	11.25	.20
	v. Pair, imperforate	450.00	

1932. OVERPRINT ISSUE No. 182 and airmail No. 178 overprint. Intaglio.

210 *3¢ overprint on No. 182 - King George V*

210

	MLHVF	USEVF
3¢ on 2¢ carmine red, FDD *(June 21, 1932)*	1.50	.20
Die I	3.00	1.90

Airmail Stamps

1932. OVERPRINT ISSUE No. 182 and airmail No. 178 overprinted. *Intaglio.*

211 *6¢ overprint on No. 178 - Plane over Canada*

211

		MLHVF	USEVF
6¢ on 5¢ sepia, FDD *(Feb. 22, 1932)*		9.00	3.75
v. Inverted overprint		190.00	
v1. Double overprint (F)		525.00	
v2. Triple overprint		375.00	

Commemorative Issues

1932. IMPERIAL ECONOMIC CONFERENCE ISSUE at Ottawa. *Intaglio, perforated 11.*

212 *George V*

212

		MLHVF	USEVF
3¢	**carmine red**	.95	.16

213 *Edward, Prince of Wales*

213

		MLHVF	USEVF
5¢	**blue**	7.50	2.25

214 *British Empire*

214

		MLHVF	USEVF
13¢	**green**	7.50	5.70

Airmail Stamps

1932. ISSUE Imperial Economic Conference at Ottawa. No. 202 overprinted. *Intaglio, perforated 11.*

215 *Ottawa Conference 1932 overprinted on No. 202 - Mercury and western hemisphere*

215

	MLHVF	USEVF
6¢ on 5¢ sepia	27.00	11.25

Regular Issues

1932. GEORGE V MEDALLION ISSUE *Intaglio, perforated 11.*

216-224 *George V*

216

		MLHVF	USEVF
1¢	**deep green,** FDD *(Dec. 1, 1932)*	.95	.20
	v. Pair, imperforate	1.10	
	n. Booklet pane of 4	75.00	75.00
	n1. Booklet pane of 6	25.00	25.00

217

		MLHVF	USEVF
2¢	**black brown,** FDD *(Dec. 1, 1932)*	1.15	.20
	v. Pair, imperforate	206.00	
	n. Booklet pane of 4	75.00	75.00
	n1. Booklet pane of 6	26.00	26.00

218

		MLHVF	USEVF
3¢	**deep red,** Die II	1.50	.20
	Die I	1.50	.20
	v. Pair, imperforate	206.00	
	n. Booklet pane of 4	26.00	26.00

219

		MLHVF	USEVF
4¢	**ochra**	45.00	6.75
	v. Pair, imperforate	206.00	

220

		MLHVF	USEVF
5¢	**deep blue**	9.00	.20
	v. Pair, imperforate	206.00	

221

		MLHVF	USEVF
8¢	**red orange**	30.00	3.75
	v. Pair, imperforate	206.00	

1933. GEORGE V MEDALLION ISSUE *Intaglio, horizontal, perforated 8 1/2, vertically.*

222		MLHVF	USEVF
1¢	deep green	15.00	3.00

223		MLHVF	USEVF
2¢	black brown	18.75	1.15

224		MLHVF	USEVF
3¢	deep red	15.00	.35

Special Delivery

1932. ISSUE Inscribed CENTS only. *Intaglio, perforated 11.*

225 *Canada Special Delivery Expres, inscribed CENTS only*

225		MLHVF	USEVF
20¢	henna brown	53.00	16.50
	v. Pair, imperforate	560.00	

Postage Due Stamps

1933-34. ISSUE *Intaglio, perforated 11.*

226-229 *"4 CENTS" postage due*

226		MLHVF	USEVF
1¢	dark violet, FDD *(May 5, 1934)*	13.20	6.75
	v. Pair, imperforate	375.00	

227		MLHVF	USEVF
2¢	dark violet, FDD *(Dec. 20, 1933)*	5.70	1.30

228		MLHVF	USEVF
4¢	dark violet, FDD *(Dec. 12, 1933)*	11.25	8.25

229		MLHVF	USEVF
10¢	dark violet, FDD *(Dec. 20, 1933)*	22.50	6.75

Commemorative Issues

1933. U P U EXECUTIVE COMMITTEE ISSUE Ottawa. *Intaglio, perforated 11.*

230 *Parliament buildings*

230		MLHVF	USEVF
5¢	dark blue, FDD *(May 18, 1933)*	9.00	3.40
	v. Pair, imperforate	560.00	

1933. WORLD'S GRAIN EXHIBITION AND CONFERENCE ISSUE No. 193, overprinted in blue. *Intaglio.*

231 *World's Grain Exhibition Conference overprinted in blue on No. 193 - Harvesting wheat*

231		MLHVF	USEVF
20¢	brown red, FDD *(July 24, 1933)*	15.00	37.50
	v. Pair, imperforate	560.00	

1933. FIRST TRANSATLANTIC STEAMBOAT CROSSING CENTENNIAL ISSUE 100th anniversary of the first transatlantic steamboat crossing, Aug. 17, 1933. *Intaglio, perforated 11.*

232 *The Canadian sail-steamer Royal William, first steamship to operate between Canada and England, set world record (1833), Nova Scotia to London in 25 days (after painting by S. Skilett).*

232		MLHVF	USEVF
5¢	dark blue	9.00	3.40
	v. Pair, imperforate	560.00	

1934. CARTIER'S LANDING ISSUE 400th anniversary of Cartier's landing on Canada, July 1, 1934. *Intaglio, perforated 11.*

233 Landing of Cartier *after painting by J. L. David*

233		MLHVF	USEVF
3¢	dark blue	4.50	1.50
	v. Pair, imperforate	560.00	

1934. UNITED EMPIRE LOYALISTS ISSUE 150th anniversary. *Intaglio.*

234 *Monument at Hamilton Ontario, to 40,000 United Empire Loyalists, who, during the American Revolution, emigrated from the U.S. to what is now Ontario and New Brunswick.*

234		MLHVF	USEVF
10¢	bronze green, FDD *(July 1, 1934)*	30.00	7.50
	v. Pair, imperforate	1,500.00	

1934. PROVINCE OF NEW BRUNSWICK ISSUE 150th anniversary. *Intaglio, perforated 11.*

235 *Seal of New Brunswick*

235		MLHVF	USEVF
2¢	red brown	3.00	3.25
	v. Pair, imperforate	640.00	

1935. SILVER JUBLIEE ISSUE Commerating the reign of King George V. Intaglio; perforated 12.

236 *Princess Elizabeth;*
237 *Duke of York (George VI)*

236		MLHVF	USEVF
1¢	**green**	.75	.35
	v. Pair, imperforate	225.00	

237		MLHVF	USEVF
2¢	**brown**	.75	.25
	v. Pair, imperforate	225.00	

238 *George V and Mary*

238		MLHVF	USEVF
3¢	**deep red**	2.25	.20
	v. Pair, imperforate	225.00	

239 *Prince of Wales (Edward VIII)*

239		MLHVF	USEVF
5¢	**deep blue**	6.00	3.00
	v. Pair, imperforate	225.00	

240
Windsor Castle;
241
Royal yacht Britannia

240		MLHVF	USEVF
10¢	**green**	9.00	3.00
	v. Pair, imperforate	225.00	

241		MLHVF	USEVF
13¢	**dark blue**	10.50	6.75
	v. Pair, imperforate	225.00	

Regular Issues

1935. ISSUE George V (Nos. 242-247) and pictorials. *Intaglio, perforated 8.*

242-247, 253-255 *George V*

242		MLHVF	USEVF
1¢	**green,** FDD *(June 1, 1935)*	.30	
	v. Pair, imperforate	150.00	
	n. Booklet pane of 4	55.00	55.00
	n1. Booklet pane of 6	25.00	25.00

243		MLHVF	USEVF
2¢	**brown,** FDD *(June 1, 1935)*	.45	
	v. Pair, imperforate	150.00	
	n. Booklet pane of 4	55.00	55.00
	n1. Booklet pane of 6	26.00	26.00

244		MLHVF	USEVF
3¢	**dark carmine,** FDD *(June 1, 1935)*	.75	
	v. Pair, imperforate	150.00	
	n. Booklet pane of 4	18.75	18.75

245		MLHVF	USEVF
4¢	**yellow,** FDD *(June 1, 1935)*	3.00	
	v. Pair, imperforate	150.00	

246		MLHVF	USEVF
5¢	**deep blue,** FDD *(June 1, 1935)*	3.00	
	v. Pair, imperforate	150.00	
	v1. Pair, imperforate between	225.00	

247		MLHVF	USEVF
8¢	**deep orange,** FDD *(June 1, 1935)*	3.40	
	v. Pair, imperforate	150.00	

248 *Royal Canadian Mounted Police;* 249 *Confederation Conference at Charlestown (1864)*

248		MLHVF	USEVF
10¢	**rose carmine**	7.50	.20
	v. Pair, imperforate	225.00	

249		MLHVF	USEVF
13¢	**violet,** FDD *(June 1, 1935)*	9.00	.75
	v. Pair, imperforate	225.00	

250 *Niagara Falls;* 251 *Parliament Buildings, Victoria, B.C.*

250		MLHVF	USEVF
20¢	**olive green,** FDD *(June 1, 1935)*	22.50	.55
	v. Pair, imperforate	225.00	

251		MLHVF	USEVF
50¢	**dull violet,** FDD *(June 1, 1935)*	30.00	6.00
	v. Pair, imperforate	225.00	

252 *Champlain Monument, Quebec*

252		MLHVF	USEVF
$1	**deep blue,** FDD *(June 1, 1935)*	68.00	11.25
	v. Pair, imperforate	300.00	

1935. GEORGE V COIL ISSUE *Intaglio, horizontal, perforated 8, vertically.*

253		MLHVF	USEVF
1¢	**green,** FDD *(Nov. 5, 1935)*	13.20	3.00

1935. ISSUE George V (Nos. 242-247) and pictorials. *Intaglio, perforated 8.*

254		MLHVF	USEVF
2¢	**brown,** FDD *(Oct. 14, 1935)*	11.25	.95
255		MLHVF	USEVF
3¢	**deep red,** FDD *(July 20, 1935)*	11.25	.55

Airmail Stamps

1935. ISSUE *Intaglio, perforated 12.*

256 *Daedalus*

256		MLHVF	USEVF
6¢	**red brown,** FDD *(June 1, 1935)*	3.00	1.30
	v. Pair, imperforate	600.00	

Special Delivery

1935. ISSUE *Intaglio, perforated 12.*

257 *Progress*

257		MLHVF	USEVF
20¢	**deep carmine,** FDD *(June 1, 1935)*	7.50	6.75
	v. Pair, imperforate	560.00	

Postage Due Stamps

1935-36. ISSUE *Intaglio, perforated 12.*

258-262 *"Postage Due 1 Cent"*

258		MLHVF	USEVF
1¢	**dark violet,** FDD *(Oct. 14, 1935)*	.30	.20
	red violet	1.50	.55
	v. Pair, imperforate	190.00	
259		MLHVF	USEVF
2¢	**dark violet,** FDD *(Sept. 9, 1935)*	.30	.20
	v. Pair, imperforate	190.00	
259A		MLHVF	USEVF
3¢	**dark violet,** FDD *(April 1965)*	1.90	1.50
260		MLHVF	USEVF
4¢	**dark violet,** FDD *(July 2, 1935)*	.30	.20
	v. Pair, imperforate	190.00	
261		MLHVF	USEVF
5¢	**dark violet,** FDD *(Dec. 1948)*	.35	.35

261A		MLHVF	USEVF
6¢	**dark violet,** FDD *(June 1957)*	1.90	1.70
262		MLHVF	USEVF
10¢	**dark violet,** FDD *(Sept. 16, 1935)*	.35	.20
	v. Pair, imperforate	190.00	

Commemorative Issues

1937. CORONATION OF GEORGE VI AND ELIZABETH *Intaglio, perforated 12.*

263 *King George VI & Queen Elizabeth*

263		MLHVF	USEVF
3¢	**deep rose red,** FDD *(May 10, 1937)*	.25	.20
	v. Pair, imperforate	490.00	

Regular Issues

1937-38. ISSUE George VI (Nos. 264-269) and pictorials. *Intaglio, perforated 12.*

264-269, 275-277 *George VI*

264		MLHVF	USEVF
1¢	**green,** FDD *(April 1, 1937)*	.35	.20
	v. Pair, imperforate	225.00	
	n. Booklet pane of 4	11.25	15.00
	n1. Booklet pane of 6	1.90	5.25
265		MLHVF	USEVF
2¢	**brown,** FDD *(April 3, 1937)*	.55	.20
	v. Pair, imperforate	225.00	
	n. Booklet pane of 4	13.20	15.00
	n1. Booklet pane of 6	6.00	9.00
266		MLHVF	USEVF
3¢	**carmine,** FDD *(April 3, 1937)*	.75	.20
	v. Pair, imperforate	225.00	
	n. Booklet pane of 4	2.65	3.75
267		MLHVF	USEVF
4¢	**yellow,** FDD *(May 10, 1937)*	3.00	.20
	v. Pair, imperforate	225.00	
268		MLHVF	USEVF
5¢	**blue,** FDD *(May 10, 1937)*	3.00	.20
	v. Pair, imperforate	225.00	
269		MLHVF	USEVF
8¢	**orange,** FDD *(May 10, 1937)*	3.00	.45
	v. Pair, imperforate	225.00	

270 *Memorial Chamber, Peace Tower, Ottawa, in honor of the 65,000 Canadian war dead of WWI.*

270		MLHVF	USEVF
10¢	**dark carmine,** FDD *(June 15, 1938)*	7.50	.20

| | carmine rose | 9.00 | .25 |
| | v. Pair, imperforate | 300.00 | |

271 *Entrance to Halifax Harbor*

271		**MLHVF**	**USEVF**
13¢	**blue,** FDD *(Nov. 15, 1938)*	11.25	.55
	v. Pair, imperforate	300.00	

272 *Fort Garry Gate, Winnipeg. In the Metis Rebellion (1869) it was captured by Louis Riel, leader of insurgents, and used as headquarters.*

272		**MLHVF**	**USEVF**
20¢	**light red brown,** FDD *(June 15, 1938)*	18.75	.45
	v. Pair, imperforate	225.00	

273 *Vancouver Harbor*

273		**MLHVF**	**USEVF**
50¢	**green,** FDD *(June 15, 1938)*	37.50	5.70
	v. Pair, imperforate	300.00	

274 *Chateaude Ramezay, Montreal, former residence of British governors.*

274		**MLHVF**	**USEVF**
$1	**violet,** FDD *(June 15, 1938)*	90.00	7.50
	v. Pair, imperforate	525.00	
	v1. Pair, imperforate between	3,000.00	

1937. COIL ISSUE *Intaglio, perforated 8 vertically.*

275		**MLHVF**	**USEVF**
1¢	**green,** FDD *(June 15, 1937)*	1.90	1.15
276		**MLHVF**	**USEVF**
2¢	**brown,** FDD *(June 18, 1937)*	4.90	.20
277		**MLHVF**	**USEVF**
3¢	**carmine,** FDD *(April 15, 1937)*	3.00	.35

Airmail Stamps

1938. ISSUE *Intaglio, perforated 12.*

278 *Fairchild Sekani seaplane over SS Distributor III on Mackenzie River*

278		**MLHVF**	**USEVF**
6¢	**blue,** FDD *(June 15, 1938)*	3.00	.35
	v. Pair, imperforate	—	

Special Delivery

1938-39. ISSUE *Intaglio, perforated 12.*

279, 280 *Canadian Coat of Arms*

279		**MLHVF**	**USEVF**
10¢	**deep green,** FDD *(April 1, 1939)*	4.50	4.15
	v. Pair, imperforate	560.00	
280		**MLHVF**	**USEVF**
20¢	**deep carmine,** FDD *(June 15, 1938)*	30.00	30.00
	v. Pair, imperforate	560.00	

1939. ISSUE No. 280 overprinted. *Intaglio.*

281 *No. 280 overprinted with 10¢*

281		**MLHVF**	**USEVF**
10¢ on 20¢ **deep carmine red,** FDD *(March 1, 1939)*		15.00	15.00

Regular Issues

1939. ROYAL VISIT ISSUE *Intaglio, perforated 12.*

282 *Princesses Elizabeth and Margaret Rose*

282		**MLHVF**	**USEVF**
1¢	**green & black,** FDD *(May 5, 1939)*	.25	.20
	v. Pair, imperforate	300.00	

283 *War Memorial, Ottawa*

283		**MLHVF**	**USEVF**
2¢	**brown & black,** FDD *(May 5, 1939)*	.25	.20
	v. Pair, imperforate	300.00	

284 *George VI and Elizabeth*

284		MLHVF	USEVF
3¢	**dark carmine red & black,** FDD *(May 5, 1939)*	.25	.20
	v. Pair, imperforate	300.00	

1942-43. CANADIAN WAR EFFORT ISSUE *Intaglio, perforated 12.*

285, 291 *George VI in Navy uniform*

285		MLHVF	USEVF
1¢	**green**	.35	.20
	v. Pair, imperforate	225.00	
	n. Booklet pane of 3	.95	3.40
	n1. Booklet pane of 4	3.75	3.75
	n2. Booklet pane of 6	1.50	1.50

286, 290 *George VI in Army uniform*

286		MLHVF	USEVF
2¢	**brown**	.45	.20
	v. Pair, imperforate	225.00	
	n. Booklet pane of 4	4.50	4.50
	n1. Booklet pane of 6	3.75	4.90

287		MLHVF	USEVF
3¢	**dark carmine**	.50	.20
	v. Pair, imperforate	225.00	
	n. Booklet pane of 4	1.50	1.90

288		MLHVF	USEVF
3¢	**rose violet,** T287 FDD *(June 30, 1943)*	.50	.20
	v. Pair, imperforate	225.00	
	n. Booklet pane of 3	1.90	3.40
	n1. Booklet pane of 4	1.90	2.65
	n2. Booklet pane of 6	1.50	2.65

289 *Grain elevators & freighters*

289		MLHVF	USEVF
4¢	**slate black**	1.50	.55
	v. Pair, imperforate	225.00	

290		MLHVF	USEVF
4¢	**deep rose red,** T286, FDD *(April 1, 1943)*	.50	.20
	v. Pair, imperforate	225.00	
	n. Booklet pane of 3	1.10	3.40
	n1. Booklet pane of 6	1.90	3.75

291		MLHVF	USEVF
5¢	**blue,** T285	1.30	.20
	v. Pair, imperforate	225.00	

292 *Farm scene*

292		MLHVF	USEVF
8¢	**red brown**	1.50	.55
	v. Pair, imperforate	225.00	

293 *Parliament buildings*

293		MLHVF	USEVF
10¢	**brown**	4.50	.25
	v. Pair, imperforate	375.00	

294, 295 *Ram tank, named after Rocky Mountain Ram*

294		MLHVF	USEVF
13¢	**deep blue green**	6.00	4.15

295		MLHVF	USEVF
14¢	**deep blue green,** FDD *(April 1, 1943)*	7.50	.35

296 *Corvette launching*

296		MLHVF	USEVF
20¢	**sepia**	8.25	.25

297 *Munition factory making 25-pounder field guns*

297		MLHVF	USEVF
50¢	**violet**	33.75	2.10

298 *Tribal-Class Destroyer*

298		MLHVF	USEVF
$1	**blue**	75.00	8.25

1943. CANADIAN WAR EFFORT COIL ISSUE Designs as Nos. 285-287. *Intalgio, horizontal, perforated 8, vertically.*

299		MLHVF	USEVF
1¢	**green**	1.15	.55

300		MLHVF	USEVF
2¢	brown	1.90	1.15

301		MLHVF	USEVF
3¢	dark carmine	1.90	1.25

302		MLHVF	USEVF
3¢	rose violet	3.00	.35

303		MLHVF	USEVF
4¢	dark carmine	4.50	.30

1948. CANADIAN WAR EFFORT ISSUE Designs as Nos. 285-287. *Intaglio, horizontal, perforated 9 1/2, vertically.*

304		MLHVF	USEVF
1¢	green	3.40	2.25

305		MLHVF	USEVF
2¢	brown	10.50	9.75

306		MLHVF	USEVF
3¢	rose violet	6.75	2.25

307		MLHVF	USEVF
4¢	dark carmine	8.25	2.65

Airmail Stamps

1942-43. ISSUE Harvard trainers of British Commonwealth Air Training Plan. *Intaglio, perforated 12.*

308, 309 *Harvard trainers of British Commonwealth Air Training Plan*

308		MLHVF	USEVF
6¢	blue, FDD *(July 1, 1942)*	4.50	1.15
	v. Pair, imperforate	560.00	

309		MLHVF	USEVF
7¢	blue, FDD *(April 1, 1943)*	1.15	.20
	v. Pair, imperforate	560.00	

Special Delivery

1942-43 ISSUE and airmail special delivery (Nos. 311-312). *Intaglio, perforated 12.*

310 *Canadian Coat of Arms*

310		MLHVF	USEVF
10¢	green	2.25	2.10
	v. Pair, imperforate	450.00	

311, 312 *Lockheed 14 Trans-Canada airliner over Quebec*

311		MLHVF	USEVF
16¢	ultramarine	2.25	2.10
	v. Pair, imperforate	450.00	

312		MLHVF	USEVF
17¢	ultramarine, FDD *(1943)*	3.00	2.85
	v. Pair, imperforate	560.00	

Commemorative Issues

1946. PEACE AND RECONVERSION ISSUE *Intaglio, perforated 12.*

313 *Farm scene, Ontario;* 314 *Great Bear Lake, District of Mackenzie*

313		MLHVF	USEVF
8¢	brown, FDD *(Sept. 16, 1946)*	1.50	.75

314		MLHVF	USEVF
10¢	olive green, FDD *(Sept. 16, 1946)*	1.90	.20

315 *Power station, St. Maurice River;* 316 *Combined reaper-harvester*

315		MLHVF	USEVF
14¢	black brown, FDD *(Sept. 16, 1946)*	3.00	.25

316		MLHVF	USEVF
20¢	slate, FDD *(Sept. 16, 1946)*	9.00	.20

317 *Lumbering, British Columbia;* 318 *Train ferry, Prince Edward Island*

317		MLHVF	USEVF
50¢	deep blue green, FDD *(Sept. 16, 1946)*	18.75	2.25

318		MLHVF	USEVF
$1	red purple, FDD *(Sept. 16, 1946)*	37.50	3.75

Airmail Stamps

1946. ISSUE *Intaglio, perforated 12.*

319 *Canada geese*

319		MLHVF	USEVF
7¢	**blue,** FDD *(Sept. 16, 1946)*	1.15	.20
	n. Booklet pane of 4	2.65	3.65

Special Delivery

1946-47. ISSUE No. 320 and airmail special delivery; No. 321 inscribed EXPRES, No. 322 EXPRÈS. *Intaglio, perforated 12.*

320 *Arms, laurel (Victory) & olive (Peace) branches*

320		MLHVF	USEVF
10¢	**green,** FDD *(Sept. 16, 1947)*	1.50	1.30

321, 322 *DC-4M North Star airliner over Quebec*

321		MLHVF	USEVF
17¢	**ultramarine** FDD *(Sept. 16, 1947)*	5.25	4.50
322		MLHVF	USEVF
17¢	**ultramarine,** FDD *(1947)*	5.25	4.50

Commemorative Issues

1947. ALEXANDER GRAHAM BELL ISSUE 100th anniversary of his birth. *Intaglio, perforated 12.*

323 *Alexander Graham Bell (1847-1922), inventor of the telephone, came to Canada from Scotland (1870). Later a US citizen, he always maintained a summer home in Baddeck Nova Scotia, where he died.*

323		MNHVF	UseVF
4¢	**blue,** FDD *(March 3, 1947)*	.35	.20

1947. CONFEDERATION ISSUE 80th anniversary, beginning of Canadian Citizenship. *Intaglio, perforated 12.*

324 *Person with arm reaching up*

324		MNHVF	UseVF
4¢	**blue,** FDD *(July 1, 1947)*	.35	.20

1948. PRINCESS ELIZABETH ISSUE Marriage to Lt. Philip Mountbatten. *Intaglio, perforated 12.*

325 *Princess Elizabeth*

325		MNHVF	UseVF
4¢	**blue,** FDD *(Feb. 16, 1948)*	.26	.20

1948. CANADIAN RESPONSIBLE GOVERNMENT CENTENNIAL ISSUE Parliament buildings, Ottawa, Victoria and George VI. *Intaglio, perforated 12.*

326 *Parliament Buildings, Ottawa; Victoria, George VI*

326		MNHVF	UseVF
4¢	**slate,** FDD *(Oct. 1, 1948)*	.26	.20

Official Stamps

1949-50. ISSUE No. 327 overprinted in small print O.H.M.S. on No. 285 and 290. Nos. 331-335 overprinted in large print O.H.M.S. on Nos. 314-318. *Intaglio.*

327 *O.H.M.S. (small print) overprinted on No. 285-290.*

327		MNHVF	UseVF
1¢	**green**	2.85	1.90

		MNHVF	UseVF
328			
2¢	**brown**	7.50	7.50
329		MNHVF	UseVF
3¢	**rose violet**	2.85	1.30
330		MNHVF	UseVF
4¢	**dark carmine**	2.25	.75

331-335 *O.H.M.S. overprinted (large print) on Nos. 314-318.*

331		MNHVF	UseVF
10¢	**olive green,** overprinted No. 314	3.95	.70
332		MNHVF	UseVF
14¢	**black brown,** overprinted No. 315	5.05	2.50
333		MNHVF	UseVF
20¢	**slate,** overprinted No. 316	16.90	3.60
334		MNHVF	UseVF
50¢	**deep blue green,** overprinted No. 317	225.00	110.00
335		MNHVF	UseVF
$1	**red purple,** overprinted No. 318	55.00	37.50

Airmail Stamps

1949-50. OVERPRINT ISSUE No. 319 overprint 331. *Intaglio.*

336 *No. 319 - Canada geese overprinted with large print O.H.M.S. - No. 331.*

336		MNHVF	UseVF
7¢	**blue**	13.50	4.90

Special Delivery

1949-50. ISSUE No. 320 overprint 331. *Intaglio.*

337 *No. 320 - Arms, laural (Victory) & olive (Peace) branches overprinted with large print O.H.M.S. - No. 331.*

337		MNHVF	UseVF
10¢	**green**	18.00	12.00

Commemorative Issues

1949. ENTRY OF NEWFOUNDLAND INTO CANADIAN FEDERATION ISSUE John Cabot's sailing ship, *"Matthew"*, reached the New World in 1497, landing on what is now Newfoundland. *Intaglio, perforated 12.*

338 *John Cabot's sailing ship, Matthew*

338		MNHVF	UseVF
4¢	**deep blue green** FDD *(April 1, 1949)*	.45	.20

1949. FOUNDING OF HALIFAX NOVA SCOTIA ISSUE 200th anniversary. *Intaglio, perforated 12.*

339 *Founding of Halifax, 1749: C.W. Jeffries painting*

339		MNHVF	UseVF
4¢	**deep lilac** FDD *(June 21, 1949)*	.20	.20

Regular Issues

1949-51. GEORGE VI PORTRAIT ISSUE *Intaglio, perforated 12.*

340, 347 *George VI facing left;* 341, 342, 348, 349 *George VI facing;* 343, 350 *George VI facing half left*

340		MNHVF	UseVF
1¢	**green** FDD *(Nov. 15, 1949)*	.25	.20
	n. Booklet pane of 3, horizontal, perforated 12 vertically	.60	.65
341		MNHVF	UseVF
2¢	**sepia** FDD *(Nov. 15, 1949)*	.30	.20
342		MNHVF	UseVF
2¢	**olive green,** FDD *(Aug. 11, 1951)*	.20	.20
343		MNHVF	UseVF
3¢	**rose violet** FDD *(Nov. 15, 1949)*	.35	.20
	n. Booklet pane of 3, horizontal, perforated 12 vertically	1.15	1.15
	n1. Booklet pane of 4	1.30	1.50

344

		MNHVF	UseVF
344			
4¢	**dark carmine,** FDD *(Nov. 15, 1949)*	.60	.20
	n. Booklet pane of 3, horizontal, perforated 12 vertically	9.00	9.00
	n1. Booklet pane of 6	10.50	11.25
345		MNHVF	UseVF
4¢	**orange,** FDD *(Aug. 11, 1951)*	.45	.20
	n. Booklet pane of 3, horizontal, perforated 12 vertically	1.90	2.25
	n1. Booklet pane of 6	2.25	2.25
346		MNHVF	UseVF
5¢	**blue** FDD *(Nov. 15, 1949)*	1.30	.75

1950-51. ISSUE *Intaglio, horizontal, perforated 9 1/2 vertically.*

347		MNHVF	UseVF
1¢	**green**	.45	.35
348		MNHVF	UseVF
2¢	**sepia**	3.00	1.50
349		MNHVF	UseVF
2¢	**olive green,** FDD *(1951)*	1.50	.70
350		MNHVF	UseVF
3¢	**rose violet**	1.10	.20
351		MNHVF	UseVF
4¢	**dark carmine**	14.25	.75
352		MNHVF	UseVF
4¢	**orange,** FDD *(1951)*	3.00	.75

1950. First Issue As No. 340-344 without POSTES-POSTAGE. Intaglio; perforated 12.

353 *George VI, T340-344 without POSTES - POSTAGE.*

353			MNHVF	UseVF
1¢	**green,** FDD *(Jan. 19, 1950)* T340		.20	.20
354			MNHVF	UseVF
2¢	**sepia,** FDD *(Jan. 19, 1950)* T341, 342		.45	.20
355			MNHVF	UseVF
3¢	**rose violet** FDD *(Jan. 19, 1950)* T343		.35	.20
356			MNHVF	UseVF
4¢	**dark carmine,** FDD *(Jan. 19, 1950)* T344		.45	.20
357			MNHVF	UseVF
5¢	**blue,** FDD *(Jan. 19, 1950)* T346		1.70	.95

1950. 2nd Issue *Intaglio, horizontal, perforated 9 1/2 vertically.*

358			MNHVF	UseVF
1¢	**green,** T353		.75	.30
359			MNHVF	UseVF
3¢	**rose violet,** T355		1.15	.55

Official Stamps

1949-50. Overprinted Small OHMS Issue No. 340-346, 314, 320 overprinted. No. 340, 346 overprinted 327, small OHMS. *Intaglio.*

360			MNHVF	UseVF
1¢	**green,** T353		.55	.35
361			MNHVF	UseVF
2¢	**sepia,** T354		1.35	1.35
362			MNHVF	UseVF
3¢	**rose violet,** T355		1.50	.65
363			MNHVF	UseVF
4¢	**dark carmine,** T356		1.50	.25
364			MNHVF	UseVF
5¢	**blue,** T357		2.85	1.70

1950-52. G Stamp Issue No. 340-346, 314-318 overprinted G. *Intaglio.*

365 *No. 340 - George VI, overprinted with G*

365			MNHVF	UseVF
1¢	**green,** T340		.55	.20
366			MNHVF	UseVF
2¢	**sepia,** T341		1.50	.95
367			MNHVF	UseVF
2¢	**olive green,** FDD *(Nov. 1951)* T342		.75	.20
368			MNHVF	UseVF
3¢	**rose violet,** T343		1.50	.20
369			MNHVF	UseVF
4¢	**dark carmine,** T344		1.50	.20
370			MNHVF	UseVF
4¢	**orange vermilion** FDD *(May 1, 1952)* T345		1.15	.20
371			MNHVF	UseVF
5¢	**blue,** T346		1.90	1.05
372			MNHVF	UseVF
10¢	**olive green,** T314		2.85	.55

373			MNHVF	UseVF
14¢	**black brown,** T315		7.30	.25
374			MNHVF	UseVF
20¢	**slate,** T316		18.00	1.15
375			MNHVF	UseVF
$1	**red purple,** T318		110.00	75.00

Airmail Stamps

1949-50. Overprint Issue No 319 overprint. *Intaglio.*

376 *Canada geese overprinted with G*

376			MNHVF	UseVF
7¢	**blue**		20.25	13.50

Special Delivery

1949-50. Issue No. 320 overprint. *Intaglio.*

377 *Arms, laurel (Victory) & olive (Peace) branches overprinted with G*

377			MNHVF	UseVF
10¢	**green**		30.35	20.25

Commemorative Issues

1950-52. Canada's Resources Issue *Intaglio, perforated 12.*

378 *Canada goose*

378			MNHVF	UseVF
7¢	**blue,** FDD *(Nov. 3, 1952)*		.40	.20

379 *Fur resources*

379			MNHVF	UseVF
10¢	**sepia,** FDD *(Oct. 2, 1950)*		1.05	.20

380 *Paper industry*

380		MNHVF	UseVF
20¢	slate, FDD *(April 1, 1952)*	1.80	.20

381 *Oil wells, Alberta*

381		MNHVF	UseVF
50¢	deep blue green, FDD *(March 1, 1950)*	13.20	1.30

382 *Fishing industry*

382		MNHVF	UseVF
$1	ultramarine, FDD *(Feb. 1, 1951)*	75.00	11.25

Official Stamps

1950-52. OVERPRINT G ISSUE No. 378-382 overprint 365 G. *Intaglio.*

383-387 *Overprinted with G*

383		MNHVF	UseVF
7¢	blue, FDD *(Nov. 3, 1952)* T378	4.90	1.30
384		**MNHVF**	**UseVF**
10¢	sepia, T379	1.70	.25
385		**MNHVF**	**UseVF**
20¢	slate, FDD *(April 1, 1952)* T380	3.00	.20
386		**MNHVF**	**UseVF**
50¢	deep blue green, FDD *(Oct. 2, 1950)* T381	13.50	5.45
	v. Overprint 417, FDD *(May 26, 1961)*	12.00	4.50
387		**MNHVF**	**UseVF**
$1	ultramarine, FDD *(Feb. 1, 1951)* T382	110.00	75.00

1950-52. LARGE OHMS ISSUE No. 381 overprint 331. *Intaglio.*

388 *No. 381 - Oil wells, Alberta, overprinted with large print OHMS*

388		MNHVF	UseVF
50¢	deep blue green	40.00	22.50

Commemorative Issues

1951. PRIME MINISTERS FIRST ISSUE No. 389, Sir Robert Laird Borden, conservative, 1911-1920. No. 390, William Lyon Mackenzie, liberal, 1921-1926, 1926-1930, 1935-1948. *Intaglio, perforated 12.*

389 *Sir Robert Laird Borden (1854-1937), Conservative prime minister 1911-20, fought against economic & political reciprocity with U.S.*

390 *William Lyon Mackenzie King (1874-1950), liberal prime minister, 1921-26, 1926-30 & 1935-48, joined in many defense measures with U.S. & took part in many Roosevelt-Churchill conferences.*

389		MNHVF	UseVF
3¢	turquoise, FDD *(June 25, 1951)*	.25	.20
390		**MNHVF**	**UseVF**
4¢	rose pink, FDD *(June 25, 1951)*	.25	.20

1951. FIRST CANADIAN POSTAGE STAMP CENTENNIAL ISSUE *Intaglio, perforated 12.*

391 *Trains: Bytown & Prescott (1851);* 392 *Steamships* City of Toronto & Prince George

391		MNHVF	UseVF
4¢	gray black, FDD *(Sept. 24, 1951)*	.75	.20
392		**MNHVF**	**UseVF**
5¢	deep lilac, FDD *(Sept. 24, 1951)*	1.10	1.50

393 *Stage coach & North Star plane;* 394 *Three penny beaver of 1851*

393		MNHVF	UseVF
7¢	deep blue, FDD *(Sept. 24, 1951)*	1.15	.35
394		**MNHVF**	**UseVF**
15¢	light scarlet, FDD *(Sept. 24, 1951)*	1.50	.25

1951. ROYAL VISIT TO CANADA AND US ISSUE Princess Elizabeth and the Duke of Edinburgh. *Intaglio, perforated 12.*

395 *Visit of Princess Elizabeth and the Duke of Edinburgh to Canada & U.S.*

395		MNHVF	UseVF
4¢	violet, FDD *(Oct. 26, 1951)*	.25	.20

1952. 18TH INTERNATIONAL RED CROSS CONFERENCE ISSUE
Toronto. *Intaglio, perforated 12.*

396 *Red Cross*

396		MNHVF	UseVF
4¢	**blue & scarlet,** FDD *(July 26, 1952)*	.35	.20

1952. PRIME MINISTERS SECOND ISSUE No. 397, Sir John J. C. Abbott, conservative, 1891. No. 398, Alexander Mackenzie, liberal, 1873-1878. *Intaglio, perforated 12.*

397 *Sir John J. C. Abbott (1821-93), Conservative prime minister 1891;*

398 *Alexander Mackenzie (1822-92), first liberal prime minister 1873-78.*

397		MNHVF	UseVF
3¢	**red purple,** FDD *(Nov. 3, 1952)*	.25	.20
398		MNHVF	UseVF
4¢	**red,** FDD *(Nov. 3, 1952)*	.25	.20

1953. FIRST NATIONAL WILDLIFE WEEK ISSUE *Intaglio, perforated 12.*

399 *Polar bear;* 400 *Moose;* 401 *Bighorn Sheep*

399		MNHVF	UseVF
2¢	**bright blue,** FDD *(April 1, 1953)*	.20	.20
400		MNHVF	UseVF
3¢	**sepia,** FDD *(April 1, 1953)*	.25	.20
401		MNHVF	UseVF
4¢	**slate,** FDD *(April 1, 1953)*	.25	.20

Regular Issues

1953. FIRST ISSUE *Perforated 12.*

402-406 *Elizabeth II*

402		MNHVF	UseVF
1¢	**dull purple,** FDD *(May 1, 1953)*	.20	.20
	n. Booklet pane of 3	.35	

403		MNHVF	UseVF
2¢	**green,** FDD *(May 1, 1953)*	.20	.20
404		MNHVF	UseVF
3¢	**rose,** FDD *(May 1, 1953)*	.20	.20
	n. Booklet pane of 3	.50	
	n1. Booklet pane of 4	1.30	1.30
405		MNHVF	UseVF
4¢	**violet,** FDD *(May 1, 1953)*	.25	.20
	n. Booklet pane of 3	1.90	1.50
	n1. Booklet pane of 6	1.50	1.50
406		MNHVF	UseVF
5¢	**ultramarine**	.30	.20

1953. COIL ISSUE *Horizontal perforated 9 1/2 vertically.*

407		MNHVF	UseVF
2¢	**green,** T403	1.50	1.30
408		MNHVF	UseVF
3¢	**rose,** T404	1.50	.95
409		MNHVF	UseVF
4¢	**violet,** T405	3.40	1.50

Official Stamps

1953. ISSUE Nos. 402-406 overprint No. 365, G.

410-414 *Nos. 402-406 - Elizabeth II, overprinted with G*

410		MNHVF	UseVF
1¢	**dull purple,** FDD *(Sept. 1, 1953)*	.55	
411		MNHVF	UseVF
2¢	**green,** FDD *(Sept. 1, 1953)*	.55	.20
412		MNHVF	UseVF
3¢	**rose,** FDD *(Sept. 1, 1953)*	.55	.20
413		MNHVF	UseVF
4¢	**violet,** FDD *(Sept. 1, 1953)*	.70	.20
414		MNHVF	UseVF
5¢	**ultramarine,** FDD *(Sept. 1, 1953)*	.70	.20

Commemorative Issues

1953. PICTORIAL ISSUE *Intaglio, perforated 12.*

415 *Spinning wheel*

415		MNHVF	UseVF
50¢	**blue green,** FDD *(Nov. 2, 1953)*	3.75	.35

416 *Pacific coast Indian house and totem pole*

416
$1   gray black, FDD *(Feb. 2, 1953)*   MNHVF 11.25   UseVF 1.15

Official Stamps

1953. Issue Nos. 415, 416 overprint No. 372, G.

417		MNHVF	UseVF
50¢	**blue green**	6.75	1.15
	v. Overprint 417	6.75	2.25

418		MNHVF	UseVF
$1	**gray black**	20.25	11.25

Commemorative Issues

1953. Coronation Elizabeth II Issue *Intaglio, perforated 12.*

419 *Elizabeth II*

419		MNHVF	UseVF
4¢	**violet,** FDD *(June 1, 1953)*	.20	.20

1954. Second National Wildlife Week Issue *Intaglio, perforated 12.*

420 *Walrus;*

421 *Beaver*

420		MNHVF	UseVF
4¢	**slate,** FDD *(April 1, 1954)*	.30	.20

421		MNHVF	UseVF
5¢	**ultramarine,** FDD *(April 1, 1954)*	.25	.20
	n. Booklet pane of 5	1.90	1.50

Regular Issues

1954-57. First Issue Jan. 13, 1962, phosphor issue; Nos. 422-426 vertical overprinted on face with 2 lines (one line on 4¢) for use in automatic letter-facing (ALF) machines. *Intaglio, perforated 12.*

422-427 *Elizabeth II in oval*

422		MNHVF	UseVF
1¢	**violet brown,** FDD *(June 10)*	.20	.20
	n. Booklet pane (5 + label)	1.15	
	z. phosphor tagged *(1962)*	7.50	1.30

423		MNHVF	UseVF
2¢	**green,** FDD *(June 10)*	.20	.20
	y. Miniature pane of 25	3.75	3.75
	z. phosphor tagged *(1962)*	3.75	.55

424		MNHVF	UseVF
3¢	**carmine,** FDD *(June 10)*	.25	.20
	v. Pair, imperforate vertical		
	z. phosphor tagged *(1962)*	18.75	18.75

425		MNHVF	UseVF
4¢	**violet,** FDD *(June 10)*	.25	.20

	n. Booklet pane (5 + label)	1.50	1.50
	n1. Booklet pane of 6	3.00	3.00
	z. phosphor tagged *(1962)*	11.25	2.25

426		MNHVF	UseVF
5¢	**ultramarine,** FDD *(April 1)*	.25	.20
	n. Booklet pane (5 + label)	1.15	1.15
	y. Miniature pane 20	6.75	6.75
	z. phosphor tagged *(1962)*	25.00	2.25

427		MNHVF	UseVF
6¢	**orange red,** FDD *(June 10)*	.45	.20

1954. Coil Issue As No. 422: *horizontal perforated 9 1/2 vertical.*

428		MNHVF	UseVF
2¢	**green**	.55	.20

429		MNHVF	UseVF
4¢	**violet**	1.50	.25

430		MNHVF	UseVF
5¢	**ultramarine**	2.25	.20

Official Stamps

1955-57. Issue Overprint 365, G.

431-435 *Nos. 422-426 - Elizabeth II, overprinted with G*

431		MNHVF	UseVF
1¢	**violet brown,** FDD *(1957)* T422	.55	.35

432		MNHVF	UseVF
2¢	**green,** FDD *(1956)* T423	.55	.20

No. 433 not yet assigned.

434		MNHVF	UseVF
4¢	**violet,** FDD *(1956)* T425	1.50	.25

435		MNHVF	UseVF
5¢	**ultramarine,** T426	.70	.20

No. 436 not yet assigned.

Commemorative Issues

1954. Gannet and Polaris Issue *Intaglio, perforated 12.*

437 *Gannet and Polaris*

437		MNHVF	UseVF
15¢	**slate,** FDD *(April 1, 1954)*	1.30	.20

1954. Prime Ministers Third Issue No. 438, Sir John D. Thomason, conservative, 1882 and 1892-94. No. 439, Sir Mackenzie Bowell, conservative, 1894-96. *Intaglio, perforated 12.*

438 *Sir John S. D. Thompson (1844-94), Conservative prime minister 1882 & 1892-94, successfully defended hanging of Luis Riel, Méti rebel leader, & negotiated 1887 fisheries treaty with U.S.;* 439 *Sir Mackenzie Bowell (1823-1917), Conservative prime minister 1894-96.*

438		MNHVF	UseVF
4¢	**violet,** FDD *(Nov. 1, 1954)*	.35	.20

439		MNHVF	UseVF
5¢	**ultramarine,** FDD *(Nov. 1, 1954)*	.35	.20

1955-56. PICTORIAL ISSUE *Intaglio, perforated 12.*

440 *Eskimo in kayak*

440		MNHVF	UseVF
10¢	**deep violet brown,** FDD *(Feb. 21, 1955)*	.40	.20

441 *Paper Industry*

441		MNHVF	UseVF
20¢	**green,** FDD *(Feb. 21, 1955)*	1.50	.20

442 *Chemical Industry*

442		MNHVF	UseVF
25¢	**red,** FDD *(Feb. 21, 1955)*	1.70	.20

Official Stamps

1962. ISSUE Overprint No. 372 and 374 with G.

443		MNHVF	UseVF
10¢	**deep violet brown,** T314	1.50	.20
	v. Overprint 417, FDD *(June 28, 1962)*	2.00	.90

444		MNHVF	UseVF
20¢	**green,** T316	3.75	.50
	v. Overprint 417, FDD *(June 28, 1962)*	18.00	2.50

445	
	Not assigned

Commemorative Issues

1955. THIRD NATIONAL WILDLIFE WEEK ISSUE *Intaglio, perforated 12.*

446 *Musk-ox*

446		MNHVF	UseVF
4¢	**violet,** FDD *(April 4, 1955)*	.35	.20

447 *Whooping cranes*

447		MNHVF	UseVF
5¢	**bright blue,** FDD *(April 4, 1955)*	.35	.20

1955. ICAO ISSUE 10th anniversary. *Intaglio, perforated 12.*

448 *"International Civil Aviation Organization"*

448		MNHVF	UseVF
5¢	**bright blue,** FDD *(June 1, 1955)*	.40	.20

1955. INCLUSION ALBERTA AND SASKATCHEWAN INTO CONFEDERATION ISSUE 50th anniversary. *Intaglio, perforated 12.*

449 *Pioneers before the Confederation board*

449		MNHVF	UseVF
5¢	**bright blue,** FDD *(June 30, 1955)*	.40	.20

1955. EIGHTH BOY SCOUT WORLD JAMBOREE ISSUE Niagara-on-the-Lake, Ontario. *Intaglio, perforated 12.*

450 *Boy Scout emblem*

450		MNHVF	UseVF
5¢	**light green & chestnut,** FDD *(Aug. 20, 1955)*	.40	.20

1955. PRIME MINISTERS FOURTH ISSUE *Intaglio, perforated 12.*

451 *R. B. Bennett (1870-1947), conservative prime minister (1930-35).*

451		MNHVF	UseVF
4¢	**violet,** FDD *(Nov. 8, 1955)*	.40	.20

452 *Sir Charles Tupper (1855-1927), conservative prime minister (1896), served only two months.*

452		MNHVF	UseVF
5¢	**bright blue,** FDD *(Nov. 8, 1955)*	.40	.20

1956. ICE HOCKEY ISSUE *Intaglio, perforated 12.*

453 *Ice hockey*

453		MNHVF	UseVF
5¢	**bright blue,** FDD *(Jan. 23, 1956)*	.40	.20

1956. FOURTH NATIONAL WILDLIFE WEEK ISSUE *Intaglio, perforated 12.*

454 *Caribou;*

455 *Mountain goat*

454		MNHVF	UseVF
4¢	**deep violet,** FDD *(April 12, 1956)*	.40	.20
455		MNHVF	UseVF
5¢	**bright blue,** FDD *(April 12, 1956)*	.40	.20

1956. FIRE PREVENTION PUBLICITY ISSUE *Intaglio, perforated 12.*

456 *Burning building*

456		MNHVF	UseVF
5¢	**slate & scarlet,** FDD *(Oct. 9, 1956)*	.40	.20

1957. SPORTS ISSUE *Intaglio, perforated 12, ultramarine.* Printed in sheets of 50 (10 x 5). Various combinations possible.

457 *Fishing;* 458 *Swimming*

457		MNHVF	UseVF
5¢	**ultramarine,** FDD *(March 7, 1957)*	.40	.20
458		MNHVF	UseVF
5¢	**ultramarine,** FDD *(March 7, 1957)*	.40	.20

459 *Hunting;* 460 *Skiing*

459		MNHVF	UseVF
5¢	**ultramarine,** FDD *(March 7, 1957)*	.40	.20
460		MNHVF	UseVF
5¢	**ultramarine,** FDD *(March 7, 1957)*	.40	.20
	Block of 4, #457-460	2.25	2.25

1957. FIFTH NATIONAL WILDLIFE WEEK ISSUE *Intaglio, perforated 12.*

461 *Loon*

461		MNHVF	UseVF
5¢	**black,** FDD *(April 10, 1957)*	.40	.20

1957. DAVID THOMPSON ISSUE *Intaglio, perforated 12.*

462 *David Thompson (1770-1857), explorer and geographer; map of western Canada.*

462		MNHVF	UseVF
5¢	**bright blue,** FDD *(June 5, 1957)*	.40	.20

463		MNHVF	UseVF
	Not assigned		

1957. 14TH UPU CONGRESS ISSUE *Intaglio, perforated 12.*

464 *Peace tower*

464		MNHVF	UseVF
5¢	**gray blue,** FDD *(Aug. 14, 1957)*	.40	.20

465 *Globe and postal horn*

465		MNHVF	UseVF
15¢	**gray blue,** FDD *(Aug. 14, 1957)*	2.25	1.90

1957. MINING INDUSTRY ISSUE *Intaglio, perforated 12.*

466 *Miner*

466		**MNHVF**	**UseVF**
5¢	**gray black,** FDD *(Sept. 5, 1957)*	.40	.20

1957. ROYAL VISIT ISSUE *Intaglio, perforated 12.*

467 *Elizabeth II and Prince Philip*

467		**MNHVF**	**UseVF**
5¢	**gray black,** FDD *(Oct. 10, 1957)*	.40	.20

1958. FREE PRESS ISSUE 50th anniversary The Canadian Press, news gathering organization. *Intaglio, perforated 12.*

468 *Newspaper*

468		**MNHVF**	**UseVF**
5¢	**gray black,** FDD *(Jan. 22, 1958)*	.40	.20

1958. INTERNATIONAL GEOPHYSICAL YEAR ISSUE *Intaglio, perforated 12.*

469 *Microscope and map of N. Hemisphere*

469		**MNHVF**	**UseVF**
5¢	**blue,** FDD *(March 5, 1958)*	.40	.20

1958. BRITISH COLUMBIA CENTENNIAL ISSUE *Intaglio, perforated 12.*

470 *Gold panning and Arms*

470		**MNHVF**	**UseVF**
5¢	**turquoise,** FDD *(March 8, 1958)*	.40	.20

1958. PIERRE GAULTIER DE VARENNE ISSUE *Intaglio, perforated 12.*

471 *Pierre Gaultier de Varenne, Sieur de la Verendrye, French explorer of the early 18th century, penetrated to W. Canada via Rainy River and Lake of the Woods; after monument (by Emile Brunet) at St. Boniface, Manitoba.*

471		**MNHVF**	**UseVF**
5¢	**bright ultramarine,** FDD *(June 4, 1958)*	.40	.20

1958. QUEBEC ISSUE 350th anniversary. *Intaglio, perforated 12.*

472 *Samuel de Champlain and view of Quebec*

472		**MNHVF**	**UseVF**
5¢	**deep blue green & ochre,** FDD *(June 26, 1958)*	.40	.20

1958. NATIONAL HEALTH ISSUE 50th anniversary Canadian Nurses Association. *Intaglio, perforated 12.*

473 *Portrait of nurse*

473		**MNHVF**	**UseVF**
5¢	**light purple,** FDD *(July 30, 1958)*	.40	.20

1958. DEVELOPMENT OF OIL INDUSTRY ISSUE World power conference. *Intaglio, perforated 12.*

474 *Kerosene lamp and refinery*

474		**MNHVF**	**UseVF**
5¢	**green olive & rose red,** FDD *(Sept. 10, 1958)*	.40	.20

1958. FIRST HOUSE OF REPRESENTATIVES ISSUE 200th anniversary. *Intaglio, perforated 12.*

475 *Speaker's chair and mace*

475		**MNHVF**	**UseVF**
5¢	**slate black,** FDD *(Oct. 2, 1958)*	.40	.20

1959. ISSUE 50th anniversary first flight of a powered machine in Canada, JAD McCready, pilot. *Intaglio, perforated 12.*

476 *Silver Dart and Delta Wing planes*

476
5¢   ultramarine & black, FDD *(Feb. 23, 1959)*   MNHVF .40   UseVF .20

1959. NATO ISSUE North Atlantic Treaty Organization 10th anniversary. *Intaglio, perforated 12.*

477 *Globe and dove*

477
5¢   violet blue, FDD *(April 2, 1959)*   MNHVF .40   UseVF .20

1959. ASSOCIATED COUNTRY WOMEN OF THE WORLD ISSUE *Intaglio, perforated 12.*

478 *Woman and tree*

478
5¢   apple green & black, FDD *(May 13, 1959)*   MNHVF .40   UseVF .20

1959. ROYAL VISIT ISSUE *Intaglio, perforated 12.*

479 *Queen Elizabeth II by Pietro Annigoni*

479
5¢   carmine red, FDD *(June 18, 1959)*   MNHVF .40   UseVF .20

1959. ST. LAWRENCE SEAWAY OPENING ISSUE Joint issue with the U.S. *Intaglio, perforated 12.*

480 *Maple leaf, eagle and map of Great Lakes*
480v

480
5¢   red & dull ultramarine, FDD *(June 26, 1959)*   MNHVF .40   UseVF .20
       v.   center inverted   11,250.00   9,375.00

1959. BATTLE OF THE PLAINS OF ABRAHAM ISSUE 200th anniversary, Sept. 13, 1759. *Intaglio, perforated 12.*

481 *Maple leaves between Lion (British) and Fleur-de-lis (French)*

481
5¢   red & green, FDD *(Sept. 13, 1759)*   MNHVF .40   UseVF .20

1960. CANADIAN GIRL GUIDES MOVEMENT ISSUE 50th anniversary. *Intaglio, perforated 12.*

482 *Badge of Association*

482
5¢   chestnut & ultramarine, FDD *(April 20, 1960)*   MNHVF .40   UseVF .20

1960. BATTLE OF LONG SAULT ISSUE 300th anniversary. *Intaglio, perforated 12.*

483 *Adam Dollard des Ormeaux (1635-60), French soldier, leader of small force of French and a number of Indians on an expedition up the Ottawa River; encounter with large force of Indians at Long Sault lasted an entire week, ended in the destruction of his force; battle scene in background.*

483
5¢   blue & ochre, FDD *(May 19, 1960)*   MNHVF .40   UseVF .20

1961. DEVELOPMENT OF CANADA'S NORTHLAND ISSUE *Intaglio, perforated 12.*

484 *Surveyor and earth moving machine below a compass rose*

484
5¢   green & red, FDD *(Feb. 8, 1961)*   MNHVF .40   UseVF .20

1961. BIRTH OF E.P. JOHNSON ISSUE 100th anniversary. *Intaglio, perforated 12.*

485 *Emily Pauline Johnson (1861-1913), Mohawk princess and poet*

485
5¢   green & red, FDD *(March 10, 1961)*   MNHVF .40   UseVF .20

1961. ARTHUR MEIGHEN ISSUE *Intaglio, perforated 12.*

486 *Arthur Meighen Prime Minister (1920-21, 1926)*

486		MNHVF	UseVF
5¢	**ultramarine**, FDD *(April 19, 1961)*	.40	.20

1961. TENTH ANNIVERSARY COLOMBO PLAN ISSUE *Intaglio, perforated 12.*

387 *Two engineers and dam*

487		MNHVF	UseVF
5¢	**blue & chestnut**, FDD *(June 28, 1961)*	.40	.20

1961. RESOURCES FOR TOMORROW ISSUE *Intaglio, perforated 12.*

488 *Hands holding five-spoked cogwheel symbolizing water: resources, agriculture, forestry, wildlife and fisheries*

488		MNHVF	UseVF
5¢	**brown & blue green**, FDD *(Oct. 12, 1961)*	.40	.20

1962. EDUCATION YEAR ISSUE *Intaglio, perforated 12.*

489 *Young couple and 19 symbols of fields of learning*

489		MNHVF	UseVF
5¢	**black & chestnut**, FDD *(Feb. 28, 1962)*	.40	.20

Chestnut (symbols) omitted.

1962. RED RIVER SETTLEMENT ISSUE *Intaglio, perforated 12.*

490 *Thomas George, Earl of Selkirk, founder and Scottish settler*

490		MNHVF	UseVF
5¢	**green & brown**, FDD *(May 3, 1962)*	.40	.20

1962. JEAN TALON ISSUE *Intaglio, perforated 12.*

491 *Jean Talon the great intendant of New France (1665-1668) and farm couple*

491		MNHVF	UseVF
5¢	**blue**, FDD *(June 13, 1962)*	.40	.20

1962. VICTORIA ISSUE 100th anniversary. *Intaglio, perforated 12.*

492 *Legislative building and reproduction of British Columbia and Vancouver Island No.1*

492		MNHVF	UseVF
5¢	**black & vermilion**, FDD *(Aug. 22, 1962)*	.40	.20

1962. OPENING OF TRANS-CANADA HIGHWAY ISSUE *Intaglio, perforated 12.*

493 *Coats of arms*

493		MNHVF	UseVF
5¢	**chestnut & black**, FDD *(Aug. 31, 1962)*	.40	.20

Regular Issues

1962-63. ISSUE Elizabeth (design by E. Roch). *Intaglio, perforated 12.*

494-498 *Elizabeth II and symbols of: No. 494 mining (crystals), No. 495 forestry (tree), No. 496 fishing (fish), No. 497 electrification (high tension tower), No. 498 agriculture (wheat).*

494		MNHVF	UseVF
1¢	**brown**, FDD *(Feb. 4, 1963)*	.20	.20
	n. Booklet pane of 5 plus label	3.00	2.25
	z. two phosphor bands, tagged	.20	.20
495		MNHVF	UseVF
2¢	**green**, FDD *(May 2, 1963)*	.20	.20
	y. Pane of 25	7.50	7.50
	z. two phosphor bands, tagged	.20	.20
496		MNHVF	UseVF
3¢	**purple**, FDD *(May 2, 1963)*	.20	.20
	z. two phosphor bands, tagged	.25	.20
497		MNHVF	UseVF
4¢	**red**, FDD *(Feb. 4, 1963)*	.20	.20
	n. Booklet pane of 5 plus label	3.00	2.25
	y. Pane of 25	11.25	11.25
	z. one phosphor band, tagged	3.75	3.00
498		MNHVF	UseVF
5¢	**blue**, FDD *(Oct. 3, 1962)*	.25	.20
	n. Booklet pane of 5 plus label	3.00	3.00
	y. Pane of 20	13.50	13.50
	z. two phosphor bands, tagged	.45	.25
	zy. Pane of 20	40.00	40.00

Commemorative Issues

1963. Sir Casimir Gzowski Issue 150th anniversary of his birth. *Intaglio, perforated 12.*

499 *Sir Casimir Gzowski (1813-98), Canadian engineer, soldier and educator of Polish descent. Ship, engine and bridge symbolize his widening of the Welland Canal, building of Grand Trunk Railway between Sarnia and Toronto and construction of International Bridge between Fort Erie and Buffalo.*

499		MNHVF	UseVF
5¢	**reddish purple,** FDD *(March 5, 1963)*	.30	.20

Official Stamps

1962. Issue Nos. 494-498 with overprint No. 365, G.

500 *Nos. 494-498 Elizabeth II, overprinted G*

500		MNHVF	UseVF
1¢	**brown,** FDD *(May 15, 1962)*	1.50	.75
501		MNHVF	UseVF
2¢	**green,** FDD *(May 15, 1962)*	1.50	.75
	x. Vertical pair, top G missing	750.00	
	x1. Vertical pair wide spread overprint	—	—
502		MNHVF	UseVF
4¢	**red,** FDD *(May 15, 1962)*	1.50	.75
503		MNHVF	UseVF
5¢	**blue,** FDD *(May 15, 1962)*	.75	.50

Note: Use of official stamps was discontinued Dec. 31, 1963.

Commemorative Issues

1963. Export Trade Issue *Intaglio, perforated 12.*

504 *Export crate and Mercator map*

504		MNHVF	UseVF
$1	**dull carmine,** FDD *(June 14, 1963)*	11.25	2.25

No. 505 is not assigned.

Regular Issues

1963-64. Coil Issue T495-498. *Intaglio, vertical coil perforated 9 1/2 horizontally.*

506		MNHVF	UseVF
2¢	**green,** FDD *(1964)*	4.90	2.25
507		MNHVF	UseVF
3¢	**purple,** FDD *(1964)*	3.40	1.70
508		MNHVF	UseVF
4¢	**red,** FDD *(May 15, 1963)*	4.90	2.25
509		MNHVF	UseVF
5¢	**blue,** FDD *(May 15, 1963)*	4.90	.95

Commemorative Issues

1963. Sir Martin Frobisher Issue *Intaglio, perforated 12.*

510 *Sir Martin Frobisher (1535-1594), English explorer, discovered Frobisher Bay while searching for North West Passage.*

510		MNHVF	UseVF
5¢	**ultramarine,** FDD *(Aug. 21, 1963)*	.30	.20

1963. Postal Bi-centennial Issue *Intaglio, perforated 12.*

511 *Post rider and mail route of 1763*

511		MNHVF	UseVF
5¢	**dark green & red brown,** FDD *(Sept. 25, 1963)*	.30	.20

1963. Canada Geese Issue *Intaglio, perforated 12.*

512 *Canadian geese in flight*

512		MNHVF	UseVF
15¢	**ultramarine,** FDD *(Oct. 30, 1963)*	1.90	.20

Regular Issues

1964. Issue *Intaglio, perforated 12.*

513 *Jet airliner of imaginary design over Ottawa air terminal*

513		MNHVF	UseVF
7¢	**blue,** FDD *(March 11, 1964)*	.45	.45

No. 513 w/Surcharge of 8¢: see No. 532.

Commemorative Issues

1964. Peace Stamp Issue *Intaglio and offset, perforated 12.*

514 *Peace on Earth*

			MNHVF	UseVF
514				
5¢	**turquoise blue, light blue & buff,** FDD		.30	.20
	(April 8, 1964)			

1964. CANADIAN UNITY ISSUE *Intaglio, perforated 12.*

515 Three red maple leafs insignia of Canada

			MNHVF	UseVF
515				
5¢	**blue & dark carmine,** FDD *(May 14, 1964)*		.30	.20

1964-66. PROVINICAL FLOWER AND ARMS ISSUE *Intaglio and offset, perforated 12.*

516 White trillium and arms of Ontario

			MNHVF	UseVF
516				
5¢	**red brown, buff & green,** FDD *(June 30)*		.30	.20

517 White Garden Lily and arms of Quebec

			MNHVF	UseVF
517				
5¢	**green, yellow & orange,** FDD *(June 30)*		.30	.20

518 Purple violet and arms of New Brunswick

			MNHVF	UseVF
518				
5¢	**red violet & green,** FDD *(Feb. 3, 1965)*		.30	.20

519 Mayflower and arms of Nova Scotia

			MNHVF	UseVF
519				
5¢	**blue, green & pink,** FDD *(Feb. 3, 1965)*		.30	.20

520 Dogwood and arms of British Colombia

			MNHVF	UseVF
520				
5¢	**purple, green & ochre,** FDD *(April 28, 1965)*		.30	.20

521 Prairie crocus and arms of Manitoba

			MNHVF	UseVF
521				
5¢	**red brown, purple & deep blush green,** FDD *(April 28, 1965)*		.30	.20

522 Lady slipper and arms of Prince Edward Island

			MNHVF	UseVF
522				
5¢	**violet, green & pink,** FDD *(July 21, 1965)*		.30	.20

523 Wild rose and arms of Alberta

			MNHVF	UseVF
523				
5¢	**green, rose & yellow,** FDD *(Jan. 19, 1966)*		.30	.20

524 Prairie lily and arms of Saskatchewan

			MNHVF	UseVF
524				
5¢	**brown, orange & green,** FDD *(Jan. 19, 1966)*		.30	.20

525 Pitcher plant and arms of Newfoundland

			MNHVF	UseVF
525				
5¢	**black, green & carmine,** FDD *(Feb. 23, 1966)*		.30	.20

525A Fireweed and arms of Yukon

			MNHVF	UseVF
525A				
5¢	**blue, rose & green,** FDD *(March 23, 1966)*		.30	.20

525B Mountain avens and arms of Northwest Territories

525B
5¢   **olive brown, yellow & green,** FDD *(March 23, 1966)*   MNHVF .30   UseVF .20

525C *Maple leaf and arms of Canada*

525C
5¢   **blue & red,** FDD *(June 30, 1966)*   MNHVF .30   UseVF .20

Regular Issues

1964. ISSUE No. 513 overprinted.

526 *No. 513 - Jet airliner of imaginary design over Ottawa air terminal, overprinted 8¢*

526
8¢ on 7¢ blue, FDD *(July 15, 1964)*   MNHVF .35   UseVF .35
   v. Pair, w/o overprint   .80   .80

Commemorative Issues

1964. CHARLOTTETOWN CONFERENCE CENTENNIAL ISSUE Delegates from New Brunswick, Nova Scotia, Prince Edward Island and Upper and Lower Canada met Sept. 1-9, 1864, to discuss a political union of their provinces. *Intaglio, perforated 12.*

527 *Provincial building, site of conference (at left), and modern buildings of* Fathers of Confederation Memorial *in Charlottetown, PEI.*

527
5¢   **black,** FDD *(July 29, 1964)*   MNHVF .30   UseVF .20

1964. QUEBEC CONFERENCE CENTENNIAL ISSUE *Intaglio, perforated 12.*

528 *Maple leaf and pen in hand*

528
5¢   **chocolate & light red,** FDD *(Sept. 9, 1964)*   MNHVF .30   UseVF .20

1964. ROYAL VISIT ISSUE *Intaglio, perforated 12.*

529 *Queen Elizabeth II after photograph by Anthony Buckley*

529
5¢   **purple,** FDD *(Oct. 5, 1964)*   MNHVF .30   UseVF .20

1964. CHRISTMAS ISSUE *Intaglio, perforated 12.*

530, 531 *Family and Star of Bethlehem.*

530
3¢   **carmine,** FDD *(Oct. 14, 1964)*   MNHVF .25   UseVF .20
   y. Pane of 25   7.50   7.50
   z. two phosphor bands, tagged   .75   .35
   zy. Pane of 25   11.25   11.25
531   MNHVF   UseVF
5¢   **ultramarine,** FDD *(Oct. 14, 1964)*   .25   .20
   z. two phosphor bands, tagged   1.15   .35

1964. ISSUE T513. *Intaglio, perforated 12.*

532 *Jet airliner of imaginary design over Ottawa air terminal*

532
8¢   **blue,** FDD *(Nov. 18, 1964)*   MNHVF .40   UseVF .20

1965. INTERNATIONAL COOPERATION ISSUE *Intaglio, perforated 12.*

533 *Canada's maple leaf and ICY emblem*

533
5¢   **dark green,** FDD *(March 3, 1965)*   MNHVF .25   UseVF .20

1965. SIR WILFRED GRENFELL ISSUE 100th anniversary of his birth. *Intaglio, perforated 12.*

534 *Sir Wilfred of Newfoundland coast, (see Newfoundland No. 253)*

534
5¢   **blue green,** FDD *(June 9, 1965)*   MNHVF .25   UseVF .20

1965. FLAG ISSUE *Intaglio, perforated 12.*

535 *Canadian flag adopted in 1965*

535		MNHVF	UseVF
5¢	**blue & red,** FDD *(June 30, 1965)*	.25	.20

1965. WINSTON CHURCHILL MEMORIAL ISSUE *Offset, perforated 12.*

536 *Winston Churchill*

536		MNHVF	UseVF
5¢	**chocolate,** FDD *(Aug. 12, 1965)*	.25	.20

1965. NATIONAL CAPITAL ISSUE 100th anniversary selection of Ottawa. *Intaglio, perforated 12.*

537 *Parliament buildings and Ottawa River*

537		MNHVF	UseVF
5¢	**brown,** FDD *(Sept. 8, 1965)*	.25	.20

1965. INTER-PARLIAMENTARY UNION MEETING OTTAWA ISSUE *Intaglio, perforated 12.*

538 *Peace tower, Ottawa*

538		MNHVF	UseVF
5¢	**bronze green,** FDD *(Sept. 8, 1965)*	.25	.25

1965. CHRISTMAS ISSUE *Intaglio, perforated 12.*

539, 540 *Gold, frankincense and myrrh, (The gifts of the 3 Magi)*

539		MNHVF	UseVF
3¢	**olive green,** FDD *(Oct. 13, 1965)*	.25	.20
	y. Pane of 25	6.35	6.35
	z. two phosphor bands, tagged	.25	.20
	zy. Pane of 25	9.00	8.25

540		MNHVF	UseVF
5¢	**blue,** FDD *(Oct. 3, 1965)*	.25	.20
	z. two phosphor bands, tagged	.35	.25

1966. ALOUETTE II ISSUE *Intaglio, perforated 12.*

541 Alouette II *satellite developed by Canadian Defence Research Telecommunications. Establishment and National Research Council was launched in California (1965) as part of a Canadian-American program of space research.*

541		MNHVF	UseVF
5¢	**dark blue,** FDD *(Jan. 5, 1966)*	.25	.20

No. 542 is not assigned.

Commemorative Issues

1966. LA SALLE ISSUE 300th anniversary of his arrival. *Intaglio, perforated 12.*

543 *René Robert Cavelier, Sieur de La Salle (1643-87), explorer and colonizer, founder of Louisiana*

543		MNHVF	UseVF
5¢	**deep blue green,** FDD *(April 13, 1966)*	.25	.20

1966. HIGHWAY SAFETY ISSUE *Intaglio, perforated 12.*

544 *Traffic signs*

544		MNHVF	UseVF
5¢	**black, blue & yellow,** FDD *(May 2, 1966)*	.25	.20

1966. LONDON CONFERENCE CENTENNIAL ISSUE *Intaglio, perforated 12.*

545 *Delegates to conference and London. Conference resulted in final agreement on the British North America Act*

545		MNHVF	UseVF
5¢	**red brown,** FDD *(May 26, 1966)*	.25	.20

1966. NUCLEAR-ELECTRIC POWER ISSUE Beginning of Canada's commercial large-scale production of nuclear-electric power in 1966. *Intaglio, perforated 12.*

546 *Douglas Point Nuclear Power Station on Lake Huron and symbol for heavy water atom*

546		MNHVF	UseVF
5¢	**dark blue,** FDD *(July 27, 1966)*	.25	.20

1966. COMMONWEALTH PARLIAMENTARY ASSOCIATION ISSUE
12th General Conference. *Intaglio, perforated 12.*

 547 *Parliamentary Library, Ottawa*

547		MNHVF	UseVF
5¢	**purple,** FDD *(Sept. 8, 1966)*	.25	.20

1966. CHRISTMAS ISSUE *Intaglio, perforated 12.*

 548, 549 *Albrecht Durer's* Praying Hands

548		MNHVF	UseVF
3¢	**carmine,** FDD *(Oct. 12, 1966)*	.20	.20
	y. Pane of 25	3.75	3.75
	z. two phosphor bands, tagged	.25	.20
	zy. Pane of 25	4.90	4.90
549		**MNHVF**	**UseVF**
5¢	**orange,** FDD *(Oct. 12, 1966)*	.25	.20
	z. two phosphor bands, tagged	.45	.30

1967. CENTENIAL YEAR ISSUE *Intaglio, perforated 12.*

 550 *Flag, globe and Expo emblem*

550		MNHVF	UseVF
5¢	**blue & red,** FDD *(Jan. 11, 1967)*	.25	.20
	z. two phosphor bands, tagged	.40	.30

Regular Issues

1967. PICTORIAL ISSUE *Intaglio, perforated 12, ordinary paper.*

 551 *Queen Elizabeth II and northern region*

551		MNHVF	UseVF
1¢	**brown,** FDD *(Feb. 8, 1967)*	.20	.20
	n. Booklet pane of 5 (plus label)	.35	.30
	n1. Booklet pane of 5 (plus label), 1 of #551, 4 of #611, perforated 10	.70	
	n2. Booklet pane of 10, 5 of #551, 5 of #554, perforated 10	1.15	
	v. Perforated 10 (1968)	.25	.25
	v1. Perforated 12 1/2 x 12 (1971)	.55	.25
	z. two phosphor bands, tagged	.45	.55

 552 *Queen Elizabeth II and Pacific coast*

552		MNHVF	UseVF
2¢	**green,** FDD *(Feb. 8, 1967)*	.20	.20
	z. two phosphor bands, tagged	.45	.45

 553 *Queen Elizabeth II and prairie scene*

553		MNHVF	UseVF
3¢	**slate purple,** FDD *(Feb. 8, 1967)*	.20	.20
	v. Perforated 12 1/2 x 12 (1971)	.70	.70
	z. two phosphor bands, tagged	.68	.45

 554 *Queen Elizabeth II and Mid-Canada seaway view*

554		MNHVF	UseVF
4¢	**scarlet,** FDD *(Feb. 8, 1967)*	.25	.20
	n. Booklet pane of 5 (plus label)	.95	
	n1. Booklet pane 25	4.90	
	n2. Booklet pane 25 (plus 2 labels) perforated 10	5.70	
	v. Perforated 10 (1968)	.70	.45
	z. two phosphor bands, tagged	.95	.70

 555 *Queen Elizabeth II and Atlantic coast*

555		MNHVF	UseVF
5¢	**blue,** FDD *(Feb. 8, 1967)*	.25	.20
	n. Booklet pane of 5 (plus label)	1.50	
	n1. Booklet pane of 20, perforated 10	4.15	
	v. Perforated 10 (1968)	.95	.55
	z. two phosphor bands, tagged	.70	.45

 556 Alaskan Highway, *by A. Y. Jackson*

556		MNHVF	UseVF
8¢	**brown purple,** FDD *(Feb. 8, 1967)*	.25	.25

 557 The Jack Pine, *by Tom Thomson*

557		MNHVF	UseVF
10¢	**olive green,** FDD *(Feb. 8, 1967)*	.25	.20
	z. two phosphor bands, tagged	.95	.35

558 Bylot Island, *by Lawren Harris*

558		MNHVF	UseVF
15¢	**deep purple,** FDD *(Feb. 8, 1967)*	.45	.20
	z. two phosphor bands, tagged	.95	.35

559 The Ferry, Quebec, *by James Wilson Morrice*

559		MNHVF	UseVF
20¢	**blue,** FDD *(Feb. 8, 1967)*	.55	.90
	z. two phosphor bands, tagged	1.50	.55

560 The Solemn Land, *by J.E.H. MacDonald*

560		MNHVF	UseVF
25¢	**dark blue green,** FDD *(Feb. 8, 1967)*	1.15	.20
	z. two phosphor bands, tagged	3.00	.95

561 Summer's Store, *by John Ensor*

561		MNHVF	UseVF
50¢	**orange brown,** FDD *(Feb. 8, 1967)*	3.75	.20

562 Excelsior Field, Edmonton, *by H. G. Glyde*

562		MNHVF	UseVF
$1	**scarlet,** FDD *(Feb. 8, 1967)*	7.50	.75

See also Nos. 594, 611, 651, 660.

Commemorative Issues

1967. EXPO 67 ISSUE Universal and International Exhibition EXPO 67, Montreal. *Intaglio, perforated 12.*

563 *Government Building at Expo*

563		MNHVF	UseVF
5¢	**blue & red,** FDD *(April 28, 1967)*	.25	.20

1967. WOMEN'S FRANCHISE ISSUE 50th anniversary. *Offset, perforated 12.*

564 *Symbol of woman and pedestal*

564		MNHVF	UseVF
5¢	**black & reddish purple,** FDD *(May 24, 1967)*	.25	.20

1967. ROYAL VISIT ISSUE *Intaglio, perforated 12.*

565 *Queen Elizabeth and Expo emblem*

565		MNHVF	UseVF
5¢	**orange brown & purple,** FDD *(June 30, 1967)*	.25	.20

1967. PAN-AMERICAN GAMES ISSUE Winnipeg, Manitoba. *Intaglio, perforated 12.*

566 *Track athlete in action*

566		MNHVF	UseVF
5¢	**red,** FDD *(July 19, 1967)*	.25	.20

Regular Issues

1967. COIL ISSUE T553-555. *Vertical coil perforated 9 1/2 horizontally.*

567		MNHVF	UseVF
3¢	**slate purple,** FDD *(March)*	1.50	.95
568		MNHVF	UseVF
4¢	**scarlet,** FDD *(March)*	.75	.55
569		MNHVF	UseVF
5¢	**blue,** FDD *(Feb.)*	1.50	.75

See also Nos. 595, 612, 652, 661.

Commemorative Issues

1967. THE CANADIAN PRESS ASSOCIATION ISSUE 50th Anniversary of its founding. *Intaglio, perforated 12.*

570 *Oblate spheroid form*

570		MNHVF	UseVF
5¢	**blue,** FDD *(Aug. 31, 1967)*	.45	.20

Postage Due Stamps

1967-74. POSTAGE DUE ISSUE *Offset, perforated 12. Size 20 x 17mm. Nos. 571A, 572A, 573A, 574A, 575A, 576A, 576B, 577A, 577B and 577C size 9 1/4 x 16mm.*

571-577C *Numeral*

			MNHVF	UseVF
571			MNHVF	UseVF
1¢	**red** FDC *(Feb. 8, 1967)*		.75	.35
571A			MNHVF	UseVF
1¢	**red,** FDD *(Dec. 1970)*		.35	.35
572			MNHVF	UseVF
2¢	**red** FDC *(Feb. 8, 1967)*		.70	.35
572A			MNHVF	UseVF
2¢	**red,** FDD *(Jan. 1972)*		.20	.20
573			MNHVF	UseVF
3¢	**red** FDC *(Feb. 8, 1967)*		.75	.45
573A			MNHVF	UseVF
3¢	**red,** FDD *(1974)*		.20	.20
574			MNHVF	UseVF
4¢	**red** FDC *(Feb. 8, 1967)*		1.90	1.05
574A			MNHVF	UseVF
4¢	**red,** FDD *(April 1969)*		.45	.45
575			MNHVF	UseVF
5¢	**red,** FDD *(Feb. 1967)*		3.75	3.00
575A			MNHVF	UseVF
5¢	**red,** FDD *(Feb. 1969)*		22.50	22.50
576			MNHVF	UseVF
6¢	**red** FDC *(Feb. 8, 1967)*		1.30	1.15
576A			MNHVF	UseVF
6¢	**red,** FDD *(Jan. 1972)*		.12	.12
576B			MNHVF	UseVF
8¢	**red,** FDD *(Jan. 1969)*		.45	.45
577			MNHVF	UseVF
10¢	**red** FDC *(Feb. 8, 1967)*		1.90	1.70
577A			MNHVF	UseVF
10¢	**red,** FDD *(April 1969)*		.35	.35
577B			MNHVF	UseVF
12¢	**red,** FDD *(Jan. 1969)*		.45	.45
577C			MNHVF	UseVF
16¢	**red,** FDD *(1974)*		.35	.25

Commemorative Issues

1967. VANIER MEMORIAL ISSUE *Intaglio, perforated 12.*

578 *Georges P. Vanier (1888-1967), born in Montreal, Governor-General of Canada (1959-67)*

		MNHVF	UseVF
578		MNHVF	UseVF
5¢	**gray,** FDD *(Sept. 15, 1967)*	.25	.20

1967. TORONTO CENTENNIAL ISSUE *Intaglio, perforated 12.*

579 *Toronto in 1867 and today*

		MNHVF	UseVF
579		MNHVF	UseVF
5¢	**green & rose,** FDD *(Sept. 28, 1967)*	.25	.20

1967. CHRISTMAS ISSUE *Intaglio, perforated 12.*

580, 581 *Three children singing, evergreen and Parliament Buildings Peace Tower in Ottawa*

		MNHVF	UseVF
580		MNHVF	UseVF
3¢	**red,** FDD *(Oct. 11, 1967)*	.20	.20
	y. Pane of 25	3.40	3.40
	z. two phosphor bands, tagged	.25	.20
	zy. Pane of 25	4.50	4.50
581		MNHVF	UseVF
5¢	**green,** FDD *(Oct. 11, 1967)*	.20	.20
	z. two phosphor bands, tagged	.30	.35

1968. GRAY JAYS ISSUE *Offset, perforated 12.*

582 *Gray jays*

		MNHVF	UseVF
582		MNHVF	UseVF
5¢	**green,** FDD *(Feb. 15, 1968)*	.50	.20

1968. METEOROLOGICAL ISSUE *200th anniversary of first reading. Offset, perforated 11.*

583 *Weather map and instruments*

		MNHVF	UseVF
583		MNHVF	UseVF
5¢	**multicolored,** FDD *(March 13, 1968)*	.25	.20

1968. NARWHAL ISSUE *Offset, perforated 11.*

584 *Narwhal*

		MNHVF	UseVF
584		MNHVF	UseVF
5¢	**turquoise blue, green & black,** FDD *(April 10, 1968)*	.25	.20

1968. INTERNATIONAL HYDROLOGICAL DECADE ISSUE *1965-74. Offset, perforated 11.*

585 *Rain gauge, sun and globe*

585		MNHVF	UseVF
5¢	**multicolored,** FDD *(May 8, 1968)*	.25	.20

1968. NONSUCH ISSUE 300th anniversary of voyage. *Intaglio and gravure, perforated 10.*

586 Nonsuch *against background of icebergs and aurora borealis. The tiny 43 ton 36 foot ketch sailed from Gravesend, England on June 3, and arrived in James Bay at the mouth of Rupert River on Sept. 29, 1668. Here the party wintered and after trading with friendly Cree Indians returned to London in October 1669 with a rich cargo of furs. The success of the voyage led to the founding of Hudson's Bay Company (1670).*

586		MNHVF	UseVF
5¢	**multicolored,** FDD *(June 5, 1968)*	.25	.20

1968. LACROSSE ISSUE *Intaglio and gravure, perforated 10.*

587 *Lacrosse players*

587		MNHVF	UseVF
5¢	**yellow, black & red,** FDD *(July 3, 1968)*	.25	.20

1968. GEORGE BROWN ISSUE 150th anniversary of his birth. *Intaglio and gravure, perforated 10.*

588 *George Brown (1818-80), one of Canada's Fathers of Confederation, founded* The Globe *in Toronto, (1844).*

588		MNHVF	UseVF
5¢	**multicolored,** FDD *(Aug. 21, 1968)*	.25	.20

1968. HENRI BOURASSA ISSUE 100th anniversary of his birth. *Offset and intaglio, perforated 12.*

589 *Henri Bourassa (1868-1952), politician and journalist, founded "Le Devoir," French language newspaper in Montreal (1910).*

589		MNHVF	UseVF
5¢	**red, buff & black,** FDD *(Sept. 4, 1968)*	.25	.20

1968. 1918 ARMISTICE ISSUE 50th anniversary. *Intaglio, 5¢ also offset; perforated 12.*

590 *John McCrae (1872-1918), soldier, physician and poet whose* In Flanders Fields *became one of the best known poems written by a Canadian.*

590		MNHVF	UseVF
5¢	**multicolored,** FDD *(Oct. 15, 1968)*	.25	.20

591 The Defenders and the Breaking of the Sword, *Canadian Vimy memorial near Arras, France*

591		MNHVF	UseVF
15¢	**gray,** FDD *(Oct. 15, 1968)*	1.90	1.50

1968. CHRISTMAS ISSUE *Gravure, perforated 12.*

592 Family Group, *Eskimo carving*

592		MNHVF	UseVF
5¢	**blue & gray,** FDD *(Nov. 1, 1968)*	.20	.20
	y. Pane of 10	3.00	3.00
	z. two phosphor bands, tagged	.25	.20

593 *Mother and child*

593		MNHVF	UseVF
6¢	**brown & black,** FDD *(Nov. 15, 1968)*	.25	.20
	z. two phosphor bands, tagged	.25	.20

Regular Issues

1968. REGULAR ISSUE T551, additional value. *Intaglio, perforated 10.*

594 *Queen Elizabeth II and modes of transportation*

594		MNHVF	UseVF
6¢	**red orange,** FDD *(Nov. 1, 1968)*	1.05	.55
	Perforated 10, FDD *(1968)*		1.25
	v. Perforated 12 1/2 x 12, FDD *(1969)*	.75	.35
	z. two phosphor bands, tagged	1.70	1.25
	n. Booklet pane (25 plus 2 labels)	30.00	

1968. Coil Issue *Intaglio, vertical coil perforated 10 horizontally.*

595		MNHVF	UseVF
6¢	red orange, FDD *(1969)*	.55	.30

See also Nos. 611, 612.

Commemorative Issues

1969. Curling Issue *Intaglio and gravure, perforated 10.*

596 *Curling players*

596		MNHVF	UseVF
6¢	black, red & blue, FDD *(Jan. 15, 1969)*	.25	.20

1969. Vincent Massey Issue *Offset and intaglio, perforated 12.*

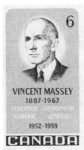

597 *Vincent Massey (1887-1967), Canada's first native-born Governor General (1952-59)*

597		MNHVF	UseVF
6¢	bistre & sepia, FDD *(Feb. 20, 1969)*	.25	.20

1969. Suzor-Cote Issue *100th anniversary of his birth. Gravure, perforated 12.*

598 *Return from the Harvest Field by Aurele de Foy Suzor-Cote (1890-1937), born at Arthabaska, Quebec.*

598		MNHVF	UseVF
50¢	multicolored, FDD *(March 14, 1969)*	3.75	2.65

1969. International Labor Organization Issue *50th anniversary. Intaglio, perforated 12 x 12 1/2.*

599 *Globe and symbols of trades*

599		MNHVF	UseVF
6¢	dark green, FDD *(May 21, 1969)*	.25	.20

1969. First Non-Stop Transatlantic Flight Issue *50th anniverary. Intaglio and gravure, perforated 12 x 12 1/2.*

600 *Twin-engined Vickers Vimy flown by Alcock & Brown from Newfoundland to Ireland, June 14-15, 1919*

600		MNHVF	UseVF
15¢	brown, green & blue, FDD *(June 13, 1969)*	1.90	1.50

1969. Sir William Osler Issue *Intaglio and gravure, perforated 12 1/2 x 12.*

601 *Sir William Osler (1849-1919), physician, author of Principles and Practice of Medicine (1892), played prominent roles in the founding of Rockefeller Institute for Medical Research, New York, and John Hopkins Medical School, Baltimore.*

601		MNHVF	UseVF
6¢	blue & brown, FDD *(June 23, 1969)*	.25	.20

1969. Bird Issue *T582, additional vertical (No. 602) or horizontal designs. Offset, perforated 12.*

602 *White-throated sparrows*

602		MNHVF	UseVF
6¢	multicolored, FDD *(July 23, 1969)*	.35	.20

603 *Ipswich sparrow*

603		MNHVF	UseVF
10¢	multicolored, FDD *(July 23, 1969)*	.75	.45

604 *Hermit thrush*

604		MNHVF	UseVF
25¢	multicolored, FDD *(July 23, 1969)*	1.90	1.70

1969. Canada Games Issue *Offset and intaglio, perforated 12.*

605 Summer and winter games flags

605		MNHVF	UseVF
6¢	**blue, green & red,** FDD *(Aug. 15, 1969)*	.25	.20

1969. CHARLOTTETOWN ISSUE 200th anniversary as capital of Prince Edward Island. *Intaglio and gravure, perforated 12 x 12 1/2.*

606 *Charlottetown location on Prince Edward Island*

606		MNHVF	UseVF
6¢	**blue, black & brown,** FDD *(Aug. 15, 1969)*	.25	.20

1969. SIR ISAAC BROCK ISSUE 200th anniversary of his birth. *Offset and intaglio, perforated 12.*

607 *Major Gen. Sir Isaac Brock (1769-1812), captured Detroit (1812), was mortally wounded during successful defense of Queenston Heights where a 190 ft. memorial column now surmounts his vault.*

607		MNHVF	UseVF
6¢	**brown, yellow & pink,** FDD *(Sept. 12, 1969)*	.25	.20

1969. CHRISTMAS ISSUE *Offset, perforated 12.*

608, 609 *Children of various races*

608		MNHVF	UseVF
5¢	**multicolored,** FDD *(Oct. 8, 1969)*	.20	.20
	n. Booklet pane of 10	3.00	3.00
	z. two phosphor bands, tagged	.20	.20
	zn. Booklet pane of 10	3.75	3.75

609		MNHVF	UseVF
6¢	**multicolored,** FDD *(Oct. 8, 1969)*	.20	.20
	v. black omitted	2,250.00	1,690.00
	z. two phosphor bands, tagged	.25	.20

1969. STEPHEN B. LEACOCK ISSUE *Intaglio and gravure, perforated 12 x 12 1/2.*

610 *Stephen Butler Leacock (1869-1944), Canadian humorist, historian, and economist and Mariposa, the fictitious Ontario community, made famous in* Leacock's Sunshine Sketches of a Little Town.

610		MNHVF	UseVF
6¢	**multicolored,** FDD *(Nov. 12, 1969)*	.25	.20

Regular Issues

1970. ISSUE T594 in changed color. *Intaglio, perforated 12 1/2 x 12, ordinary or tagged paper.*

611, 611T *Queen Elizabeth II and modes of transportation*

611		MNHVF	UseVF
6¢	**black,** FDD *(Jan. 7, 1970)*	.20	.20
	v. Perforated 10	1.00	.25
	v1. Perforated 12 1/2 x 12	.20	.20
	z. tagged paper	.20	.20
	v1z. tagged paper	.20	.20
	Booklet (25 plus 2 labels, perforated 12 1/2x12)	17.50	
	Booklet (25 plus 2 labels, perforated 10)	13.00	

611T		MNHVF	UseVF
6¢	**black, re-engraved,** FDD *(Jan. 7, 1970)*	.20	.20
	v. Perforated 10	2.00	1.00
	v1. Perforated 12 1/2 x 12	.35	.25
	z. tagged paper	.20	.20
	v1z. tagged paper	.20	.20
	n. Booklet pane of 4 (perforated 10 or 12 1/2x12)	5.00	5.00

1970. COIL ISSUE *Intaglio, vertical coil perforated 10 horizontally.*

612		MNHVF	UseVF
6¢	**black**	.20	.20

Migrating phosphor which contaminates adjoining stamps and albums pages was used on some printings of Nos. 611Tv1, 660, 667-670, 691-696 and all Nos. 665, 666.

Commemorative Issues

1970. NORTHWEST TERRITORIES CENTENNIAL ISSUE *Intaglio, perforated 12.*

613 Enchanted Owl, *print by Eskimo artist Kenojuak*

613		MNHVF	UseVF
6¢	**black & red,** FDD *(Jan. 27, 1970)*	.25	.20

1970. MANITOBA CENTENNIAL ISSUE *Offset, perforated 12.*

614		MNHVF	UseVF
6¢	**deep blue, yellow & red,** FDD *(Jan. 27, 1970)*	.25	.20
	z. phosphor bands, tagged	.30	.20

1970. INTERNATIONAL BIOLOGICAL PROGRAM ISSUE *Gravure and intaglio, perforated 12.*

615 *Microscopic view of the inside of a leaf. Tiny green bodies called chloroplasts absorb light and convert a small percentage of it into sugar.*

615		MNHVF	UseVF
6¢	**green, ochre & blue,** FDD *(Feb. 18, 1970)*	.25	.20

1970. EXPO-70 OSAKA ISSUE *Offset, perforated 12, multicolored, printed se-tenant.*

616 *British Columbia;* 617 *Canada;* 618 *Ontario;* 619 *Quebec*

616		MNHVF	UseVF
25¢	**multicolored,** FDD *(March 18, 1970)*	2.25	2.25
	z. phosphor bands, tagged	2.65	2.65

617		MNHVF	UseVF
25¢	**multicolored**	2.25	2.25
	z. phosphor bands, tagged	2.65	2.65

618		MNHVF	UseVF
25¢	**multicolored**	2.25	2.25
	z. phosphor bands, tagged	2.65	2.65

619		MNHVF	UseVF
25¢	**multicolored**	2.25	2.25
	z. phosphor bands, tagged	2.65	2.65

1970. HENRY KELSEY ISSUE *Gravure and intaglio, perforated 12 x 12 1/2.*

620 *Henry Kelsey (1670-?) apprenticed to the Hudson's Bay company in 1684, explored Canadian western plains, living and traveling with native Indian tribes for forty years.*

620		MNHVF	UseVF
6¢	**multicolored,** FDD *(April 15, 1970)*	.25	.20

1970. U.N. ISSUE 25th anniversary. *Offset, perforated 11.*

621, 622 World Divided *design*

621		MNHVF	UseVF
10¢	**blue,** FDD *(March 13, 1970)*	.75	.60
	z. phosphor bands, tagged	.95	.95

622		MNHVF	UseVF
15¢	**deep mauve & magenta,** FDD *(March 13, 1970)*	1.15	.75
	z. phosphor bands, tagged	1.50	1.50

1970. LOUIS RIEL ISSUE 100th anniversary of his death. *Gravure, perforated 12 1/2 x 12.*

623 *Louis Riel (1844-85), as leader of Red River Uprising (1865-70) negotiated Assiniboia's entry into Confederation as the province of Manitoba, was defeated during Northwest Rebellion (1885) and executed.*

623		MNHVF	UseVF
6¢	**red & blue,** FDD *(June 19, 1970)*	.25	.20

1970. SIR ALEXANDER MACKENZIE ISSUE *Intaglio, perforated 12.*

624 *Inscription on rock at Pacific Coast left by Alexander Mackenzie (1764-1820), Canadian explorer, upon completion of first overland crossing of Canada in 1793.*

624		MNHVF	UseVF
6¢	**brown,** FDD *(June 25, 1970)*	.25	.20

1970. SIR OLIVER MOWAT ISSUE 150th anniversary of his birth. *Gravure and intaglio, perforated 12 x 12 1/2.*

625 *Sir Oliver Mowat (1820-1903), delegate from Upper Canada to Quebec Conference (1864), Premier (1827) and Lieutenant-Gov. of Ontario (1897).*

625		MNHVF	UseVF
6¢	**red & black,** FDD *(Aug. 12, 1970)*	.25	.20

1970. GROUP OF SEVEN ISSUE 50th anniversary. *Offset by Ashton-Potter Ltd., Toronto, perforated 11.*

626 Isles of Spruce *by Arthur Lismer, one of seven distinguished Canadian artists who shared common interest in their approach to portraying Canadian landscape.*

626		MNHVF	UseVF
6¢	**multicolored,** FDD *(Sept. 18, 1970)*	.25	.20

1970. CHRISTMAS ISSUE T627, various drawings by children, Nos. 627-631 or Nos. 632-636. *Offset, se-tenant, Nos. 637-638, 36 x*

19mm, perforated 12, ordinary or phosphorescent paper, multicolored.

627 *Skiers;* 628 *Snowman;* 629 *Nativity;* 630 *Sleigh;* 631 *Santa Claus*

627		**MNHVF**	**UseVF**
5¢	**multicolored,** FDD *(Oct. 7, 1970)*	.30	.20
	z. ordinary or phosphorescent paper	.35	.20
628		**MNHVF**	**UseVF**
5¢	**multicolored,** FDD *(Oct. 7, 1970)*	.30	.20
	z. ordinary or phosphorescent paper	.35	.20
629		**MNHVF**	**UseVF**
5¢	**multicolored,** FDD *(Oct. 7, 1970)*	.30	.20
	z. ordinary or phosphorescent paper	.35	.20
630		**MNHVF**	**UseVF**
5¢	**multicolored,** FDD *(Oct. 7, 1970)*	.30	.20
	z. ordinary or phosphorescent paper	.35	.20
631		**MNHVF**	**UseVF**
5¢	**multicolored,** FDD *(Oct. 7, 1970)*	.30	.20
	z. ordinary or phosphorescent paper	.35	.20
	v. Strip of 5, #627-631	3.00	2.25

632 *Christmas Tree;* 633 *Toy Shop;* 634 *Christ Child;* 635 *Santa Claus;* 636 *Church*

632		**MNHVF**	**UseVF**
6¢	**multicolored,** FDD *(Oct. 7, 1970)*	.35	.20
	z. ordinary or phosphorescent paper	.40	.20
633		**MNHVF**	**UseVF**
6¢	**multicolored,** FDD *(Oct. 7, 1970)*	.35	.20
	z. ordinary or phosphorescent paper	.40	.20
634		**MNHVF**	**UseVF**
6¢	**multicolored,** FDD *(Oct. 7, 1970)*	.35	.20
	z. ordinary or phosphorescent paper	.40	.30
635		**MNHVF**	**UseVF**
6¢	**multicolored,** FDD *(Oct. 7, 1970)*	.35	.20
	z. ordinary or phosphorescent paper	.40	.30
636		**MNHVF**	**UseVF**
6¢	**multicolored,** FDD *(Oct. 7, 1970)*	.35	.20
	z. ordinary or phosphorescent paper	.40	.20
	v. Strip of 5, #632-636	3.40	.35

637 *Manger;* 638 *Snowmobile*

637		**MNHVF**	**UseVF**
10¢	**multicolored,** FDD *(Oct. 7, 1970)*	.45	.35
	z. ordinary or phosphorescent paper	.55	.45
638		**MNHVF**	**UseVF**
15¢	**multicolored,** FDD *(Oct. 7, 1970)*	1.05	.95
	z. ordinary or phosphorescent paper	1.15	1.15

1970. SIR DONALD ALEXANDER SMITH ISSUE 150th anniversary of his birth. *Offset, perforated 12.*

639 *Sir Donald Alexander Smith (1820-1914), Canadian statesman and financier drove last spike of first Canadian transcontinental railway (Nov. 7, 1885) which he indefatigably supported.*

639		**MNHVF**	**UseVF**
6¢	**dark green, lemon & black,** FDD *(Nov. 4, 1970)*	.25	.20

1971. EMILY CARR ISSUE 100th anniversary of her birth. *Offset, perforated 12.*

640 *Big Raven, by Emily Carr (1871-1945). Canadian printer & writer.*

640		**MNHVF**	**UseVF**
6¢	**multicolored,** FDD *(Feb. 12, 1971)*	.25	.20

1971. INSULIN ISSUE 50th anniversary of its discovery. *Offset, perforated 11.*

641		**MNHVF**	**UseVF**
6¢	**multicolored,** FDD *(March 3, 1971)*	.25	.20

1971. SIR ERNEST RUTHEFORD ISSUE 100th anniversary of his birth. *Offset, perforated 11.*

642 Atom *after photo by Ray Webber. Sir Ernest Rutherford (1871-1937) British physicists born at Nelson, New Zealand, developed his theory of spontaneous disintegration of atoms, as professor of physics at McGill University in Montreal (1808-1909).*

642		**MNHVF**	**UseVF**
6¢	**multicolored,** FDD *(March 24, 1971)*	.25	.20

1971. MAPLE LEAF IN FOUR SEASONS ISSUE T643, various designs. *Offset by Ashton-Potter, Toronto, perforated 11, multicolored.*

643 *Winged maple seeds, spring*

643

		MNHVF	UseVF
6¢	**multicolored** FDD *(April 14, 1971)*	.30	.20
	v. Pair, imperforate	700.00	

644 *Summer;* 645 *Autumn;* 646 *Winter*

644

		MNHVF	UseVF
6¢	**multicolored,** FDD *(June 16, 1971)*	.30	.20

645

		MNHVF	UseVF
7¢	**multicolored** FDD *(Sept. 3, 1971)*	.30	.20
	v. gray (inscribed and "6¢") omitted		

646

		MNHVF	UseVF
7¢	**multicolored** FDD *(Nov. 19, 1971)*	.30	.20

1971. L. J. PAPINEAU ISSUE 100th anniversary of his death. *Gravure and intaglio, perforated 12 1/2 x 12.*

647 *Louis Joseph Papineau (1786-1871), political reformer, leader of French Canadian Patriot Party.*

647

		MNHVF	UseVF
6¢	**multicolored,** FDD *(May 7, 1971)*	.25	.20

1971. SAMUEL HEARNE ISSUE *Gravure and intaglio, perforated 12 x 12 1/2.*

648 *Map of Copper Mine River & Canada's Arctic coast discovered by Samuel Hearne (1745-1792) of Hudson's Bay Company in 1771.*

648

		MNHVF	UseVF
6¢	**buff carmine & brown,** FDD *(May 7, 1971)*	.25	.20

1971. CENSUS CENTENNIAL ISSUE *Offset, perforated 12.*

649 *Abstract numeral "100"*

649

		MNHVF	UseVF
6¢	**black, blue & red,** FDD *(June 1, 1971)*	.25	.20

1971. RADIO CANADA INTERNATIONAL ISSUE *Offset, perforated 12.*

650 *Maple leaves*

650

		MNHVF	UseVF
15¢	**black, red & yellow,** FDD *(June 1, 1971)*	1.90	1.15
	z. tagged paper	2.65	2.25

Regular Issues

1971. COMMUNICATIONS AND TRANSPORTATION ISSUE T594, additional value. *Intaglio, perforated 12 1/2 x 12.*

651, 652 *Queen Elizabeth II*

651

		MNHVF	UseVF
7¢	**deep green,** FDD *(June 30, 1971)*	.55	.25
	z. phosphor bands, tagged	1.05	.55

1971. COMMUNICATIONS AND TRANSPORTATION COIL ISSUE *Intaglio, vertical coil perforated 10 horizontally.*

652

		MNHVF	UseVF
7¢	**deep green,** FDD *(June 30, 1971)*	.75	.35

Commemorative Issues

1971. BRITISH COLUMBIA CENTENNIAL ISSUE *Offset, perforated 12.*

653 *Canadian Confederation was extended from the Atlantic to the Pacific Ocean with entry of British Columbia as sixth province on July 20, 1871.*

653

		MNHVF	UseVF
7¢	**multicolored,** FDD *(July 20, 1971)*	.25	.20

1971. PAUL KANE ISSUE 100th anniversary of his death. Canadian painter of Indian life. *Offset, perforated 12.*

654 *Indian Encampment on Lake Huron by Paul Kane (1810-1871).*

654		MNHVF	UseVF
7¢	**multicolored,** FDD *(Aug. 11, 1971)*	.40	.20

1971. PIERRE LAPORTE ISSUE 50th anniversary of his birth. *Intaglio, perforated 12 1/2 x 12.*

655 *Pierre Laporte (1921-70), politician, assassinated by Liberation Front of Quebec.*

655		MNHVF	UseVF
7¢	**black,** FDD *(Oct. 20, 1971)*	.25	.20

1971. CHRISTMAS ISSUE Snowflakes. *Intaglio (Nos. 656, 657), offset and thermographed, perforated 12.*

656-657
Snowflakes

656		MNHVF	UseVF
6¢	**blue,** FDD *(Oct. 6, 1971)*	.25	.20
	z. phosphor bands, tagged	.26	.20
657		MNHVF	UseVF
7¢	**green,** FDD *(Oct. 6, 1971)*	.25	.20
	z. phosphor bands, tagged	.35	.20

658-659
Snowflakes

658		MNHVF	UseVF
10¢	**magenta & silver,** FDD *(Oct. 6, 1971)*	.35	.35
	z. phosphor bands, tagged	.45	.35
659		MNHVF	UseVF
15¢	**cobalt, carmal & silver,** FDD *(Oct. 6, 1971)*	.75	.75
	z. phosphor bands, tagged	.95	.95

Regular Issues

1971. ISSUE T551, additional value. *Intaglio, perforated 12 1/2 x 12.*

660, 661 *Queen Elizabeth and House of Commons Library*

660		MNHVF	UseVF
8¢	**black,** FDD *(Dec. 30, 1971)*	.55	.25
	z. phosphor bands, tagged	.95	.35

1971. COIL ISSUE *Intaglio, vertical coil perforated 10 horizontally.*

661		MNHVF	UseVF
8¢	**black,** FDD *(Dec. 30, 1971)*	.55	.25
	z. phosphor bands, tagged	.95	.35

Commemorative Issues

1972. WORLD FIGURE SKATING CHAMPIONSHIP ISSUE Calgary. *Offset, perforated 12.*

662 *Figure skaters*

662		MNHVF	UseVF
8¢	**purple,** FDD *(March 1, 1972)*	.25	.20

Regular Issues

1972. DEFINITIVES ISSUE *Offset and intaglio, perforated 11.*

663, 663A *City of Vancouver, B.C.*

663		MNHVF	UseVF
$1	**multicolored,** FDD *(March 17, 1972)*	6.00	1.90

1973. DEFINITIVES ISSUE *Gravure and intaglio, perforated 12 1/2 x 12.*

663A		MNHVF	UseVF
$1	**multicolored,** FDD *(Oct. 24, 1973)*	2.65	.55
	v. Perforated 13 1/2, FDD *(1977)*	2.65	.45

1972. DEFINITIVES ISSUE *Offset and intaglio, perforated 11.*

664 *City of Quebec*

664		MNHVF	UseVF
$2	**multicolored,** FDD *(March 17, 1972)*	4.50	2.65

Commemorative Issues

1972. WORLD HEALTH DAY ISSUE *Intaglio, perforated 12 x 12 1/2.*

665 *"Your Heart is Your Health"*

665
8¢ **carmine,** FDD *(April 7, 1972)*

	MNHVF	UseVF
	.25	.20
z. Phosphor tagged	.55	.35

1972. FRONTENAC AS GOVERNOR OF NEW FRANCE ISSUE 300th anniversary of appointment. *Gravure and intaglio, perforated 12 x 12 1/2.*

666 *Louis de Buade, Count of Frontenac*

666
8¢ **multicolored,** FDD *(May 17, 1972)*

	MNHVF	UseVF
	.25	.20
z. Phosphor tagged	.75	.75

1972-76. CANADIAN INDIANS ISSUE *T667 offset by Ashton-Potter, perforated 12 x 12 1/2; T669 gravure and intaglio by British American Bank Note Co.; perforated 12 1/2 x 12. Multicolored, both values of same se-tenant in checker board fashion.*

667 *Plains Indians artifacts: Club, feather headdress, woman's saddle, beaded saddle bag, moccasin, parfleche bag & calumet.* 668 Buffalo Chase *by George Catlin*

667
8¢ **multicolored,** FDD *(July 6, 1972)*

	MNHVF	UseVF
	.35	.20
z. tagged	.55	.30

668
8¢ **multicolored,** FDD *(July 6, 1972)*

	MNHVF	UseVF
	.35	.20
z. tagged	.55	.30

669 *Ceremonial Dress by Gerald Tailfeathers, Blackfoot Nation;* 670 Thunderbird, Plains Cree

669
8¢ **multicolored,** FDD *(Oct. 4, 1972)*

	MNHVF	UseVF
	.35	.20
z. tagged	.55	.30

670
8¢ **multicolored,** FDD *(Oct. 4, 1972)*

	MNHVF	UseVF
	.35	.20
z. tagged	.55	.30

671 *Algonkian artifacts: Birchbark basket (Tete-de-Boule Ojibwa), wooden papoose carrier (Ojibwa), snowshoes (Montagnais), birchbark basket (Malecite), birchbark box and knife (Montagnais), birchbark basket decorated with porcupine quill work (Micmac).* 672 Micmac Indians *by anonymous artist*

671
8¢ **multicolored,** FDD *(Oct. 4, 1972)*

	MNHVF	UseVF
	.35	.20

672
8¢ **multicolored,** FDD *(Oct. 4, 1972)*

	MNHVF	UseVF
	.35	.20

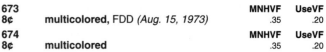

673 *Thunderbird;*

674 *Algonkians costumes*

673
8¢ **multicolored,** FDD *(Aug. 15, 1973)*

	MNHVF	UseVF
	.35	.20

674
8¢ **multicolored**

	MNHVF	UseVF
	.35	.20

675 *Pacific Coast Indians in Nootka Sound House.* 676 *Artifacts: Haida box, Nootka whale-bone club, Haida halibut hook, Haida moon mask, Salish blanket, wood carving of salmon, Haida basket, Tsimshian basket.*

675
8¢ **multicolored,** FDD *(Jan. 16, 1974)*

	MNHVF	UseVF
	.35	.20

676
8¢ **multicolored**

	MNHVF	UseVF
	.35	.20

677 *Thunderbird from painting of Kwakiutl house-front and Salish decorative pattern signifying clouds over mountains.* 678 *Chief in chilkat blanket at potlach*

677
8¢ **multicolored,** FDD *(Feb. 22, 1974)*

	MNHVF	UseVF
	.35	.20

678		MNHVF	UseVF
8¢	multicolored	.35	.20

679 *Subarctic Indian artifacts: Chippewa canoe and Montagnais-Naskapi artifacts; 680 Dance of Kutcha-Kutchin*

679		MNHVF	UseVF
8¢	multicolored, FDD *(April 4, 1975)*	.35	.20
680		MNHVF	UseVF
8¢	multicolored	.35	.20

681 *Ojibwa thunderbird;*

682 *Kutchin ceremonial dress*

681		MNHVF	UseVF
8¢	multicolored, FDD *(April 4, 1975)*	.35	.20
682		MNHVF	UseVF
8¢	multicolored	.35	.20

683

Iroquoian Indian artifacts: Corn husk mask, turtle shell rattle, false facemask, earthenware vessel & ball club; 684 Iroquian Encampment, by George Heriot

683		MNHVF	UseVF
10¢	multicolored, FDD *(Sept. 17, 1976)*	.35	.20
684		MNHVF	UseVF
10¢	multicolored	.35	.20

 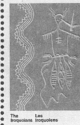

685 *Iroquoian costumes*

686 *Thunderbird*

685		MNHVF	UseVF
10¢	multicolored, FDD *(Sept. 17, 1976)*	.35	.20
686		MNHVF	UseVF
10¢	multicolored	.35	.20

1972. EARTH SCIENCES ISSUE T687, various International Congresses meeting in Canada in 1972. *Offset by Ashton-Potter Ltd, Toronto; perforated 12, ordinary or tagged paper, multicolored, se-tenant (2x2).*

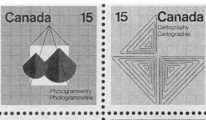
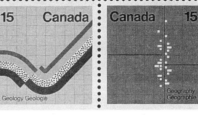

687 *Geology;* 688 *Geography;* 689 *Photogrammetry;* 690 *Cartography*

687		MNHVF	UseVF
15¢	multicolored, FDD *(Aug. 2, 1972)*	1.90	1.70
	z. tagged	2.65	2.65
688		MNHVF	UseVF
15¢	multicolored, FDD *(Aug. 2, 1972)*	1.90	1.70
	z. tagged	2.65	2.65
689		MNHVF	UseVF
15¢	multicolored, FDD *(Aug. 2, 1972)*	1.90	1.70
	z. tagged	2.65	2.65
690		MNHVF	UseVF
15¢	multicolored, FDD *(Aug. 2, 1972)*	1.90	1.70
	z. tagged	2.65	2.65

Regular Issues

1972-76. DEFINITIVES ISSUE T691, various landscapes. *Gravure and intaglio; perforated 12 1/2 x 12, or perforated 13 1/2 (Feb. 1976); two phosphor bands.*

691 *Forest of Central Canada*

691		MNHVF	UseVF
10¢	multicolored, FDD *(Sept. 8, 1972)*	.35	.20
	z. two phosphor bands, tagged	1.15	.20
	v. Perforated 12 1/2x12	.30	.20

692 *Mountain sheep*

692		MNHVF	UseVF
15¢	multicolored, FDD *(Sept. 8, 1972)*	.35	.20
	z. two phosphor bands, tagged	1.50	.95
	v. Perforated 12 1/2x12	.55	.20

693 *Prairie mosaic*

693		MNHVF	UseVF
20¢	**multicolored,** FDD *(Sept. 8, 1972)*	.45	.20
	z. two phosphor bands, tagged	.95	.90
	v. Perforated 12 1/2x12	.60	.20

694 *Polar bears*

694		MNHVF	UseVF
25¢	**multicolored,** FDD *(Sept. 8, 1972)*	.55	.20
	z. two phosphor bands, tagged	1.90	.95
	v. Perforated 12 1/2x12		

695 *Seashore*

695		MNHVF	UseVF
50¢	**multicolored** Seashore	1.15	.20
	v. Perforated 13 1/2, FDD *(1976)*	1.90	.20

Commemorative Issues

1972. CHRISTMAS ISSUE *Offset by Ashton-Potter, Toronto; perforated 12 1/2 x 12 (Nos. 696, 697), 11; multicolored, ordinary or tagged paper.*

696, 697 *Burning candles*

696		MNHVF	UseVF
6¢	**multicolored,** FDD *(Nov. 1, 1972)*	.25	.20
	z. Tagged paper	.26	.20

697		MNHVF	UseVF
8¢	**multicolored,** FDD *(Nov. 1, 1972)*	.25	.20
	z. Tagged paper	.30	.20

698, 699 *Candles, chalice and French prayerbook of 15th century open at page of announcement to shepherds.*

698		MNHVF	UseVF
10¢	**multicolored,** FDD *(Nov. 1, 1972)*	.45	.35
	z. Tagged paper	.60	.45

699		MNHVF	UseVF
15¢	**multicolored,** FDD *(Nov. 1, 1972)*	.75	.75
	z. Tagged paper	1.05	.95

1972. CENTENARY OF DEATH OF KRIEGHOFF ISSUE *Offset, perforated 12 1/2, ordinary or tagged paper.*

700 The Blacksmith's Shop *by Cornelius Krieghoff (1815-1872) leading pioneer painter.*

700		MNHVF	UseVF
8¢	**multicolored**	.30	.20
	z. Tagged paper	.35	.20

Split-door frame variety: horizontal black line in right hand door frame of barn, on every stamp in fourth vertical row of sheet. Rows 1-3 and 5 are regular.

1973. BISHOP LAVAL ISSUE *350th anniversary of his birth. Offset by Ashton-Potter, Toronto; perforated 11; tagged paper.*

701 *Francois de Montmorency-Laval (1623-1708), first bishop of Quebec (1674), founder of Quebec City Major (1663) and Minor (1668) Seminaries, elementary school for white and Indian children and St. Joachim arts and crafts school.*

701		MNHVF	UseVF
8¢	**silver, blue & gold,** FDD *(Jan. 31, 1973)*	.25	.20
	tagged		

1973. ROYAL CANADIAN MOUNTED POLICE CENTENNIAL ISSUE *T702, various designs. Offset, perforated 11.*

702 *Commissioner G.A. French and map of March West*

702		MNHVF	UseVF
8¢	**multicolored,** FDD *(March 9, 1973)*	.25	.20
	tagged		

703 *Spectrograph*

703		MNHVF	UseVF
10¢	**multicolored,** FDD *(March 9, 1973)*	.35	.35
	tagged		

704 *Musical ride*

704			MNHVF	UseVF
15¢	**multicolored,** FDD *(March 9, 1973)*		.75	.65
	tagged			
	v. Pair, imperforate		560.00	

1973. JEANNE MANCE ISSUE 300th anniversary of his death. *Offset by Ashton-Potter, perforated 11.*

705 *Jeanne Mance (1606-73), nurse and founder of Montreal's Hotel-Dieu Hospital and co-founder of Montreal (Ville-Marie) in 1642.*

705		MNHVF	UseVF
8¢	**multicolored,** FDD *(April 18, 1973)* tagged	.25	.20

1973. JOSEPH HOWE ISSUE 100th anniversary of his death. *Offset by Ashton-Potter, perforated 11.*

706 *Joseph Howe (1804-73), Premier and Lieutenant-Governor of Nova Scotia.*

706		MNHVF	UseVF
8¢	**gold & black,** FDD *(May 16, 1973)* tagged	.25	.20

1973. J.E.H. MACDONALD ISSUE 100th anniversary of his birth. *Offset by Ashton-Potter, perforated 12 1/2.*

707 *Mist Fantasy by James Edward Hervey MacDonald (1873-1932), prominent painter and member of The Group of Seven.*

707		MNHVF	UseVF
15¢	**multicolored,** FDD *(June 8, 1973)* tagged	.65	.55

1973. PRINCE EDWARD ISLAND'S ENTRY INTO CONFEDERATION ISSUE 100th anniversary. *Gravure and intaglio, perforated 12 x 12 1/2.*

708 *View of harbor from shoreline dominated by one large and three small oaks.*

708		MNHVF	UseVF
8¢	**orange and red,** FDD *(June 22, 1973)*	.25	.20
	tagged		

1973. SCOTTISH IMMIGRATION TO CANADA ISSUE 200th anniversary. *Offset, perforated perforated 12 x 12 1/2.*

709 *Landing of first Scottish settlers and ship* Hector *at Pictou, Nova Scotia, July 20, 1773.*

709		MNHVF	UseVF
8¢	**multicolored,** FDD *(July 20, 1973)* tagged	.25	.20

1973. ROYAL VISIT AND COMMONWEALTH HEADS OF GOVERNMENT ISSUE *Gravure and intaglio, perforated 12 x 12 1/2.*

710, 711 *Queen Elizabeth II*

710		MNHVF	UseVF
8¢	**silver, blue & red,** FDD *(Aug. 2, 1973)*	.25	.20
	tagged		

711		MNHVF	UseVF
15¢	**gold, black & red,** FDD *(Aug. 2, 1973)*	.70	.65
	tagged		

No. 711 light and deep shades of gold exist.

1973. NELLIE MCCLUNG ISSUE 100th anniversary of her birth. *Offset by Ashton-Potter, perforated 11.*

712 *Nellie McClung (1873-1951), pioneer feminist and writer*

712		MNHVF	UseVF
8¢	**multicolored,** FDD *(Aug. 29, 1973)* tagged	.25	.20

1973. OLYMPIC GAME ISSUE Montreal, 1976. *Offset by Ashton-Potter, perforated 12 x 12 1/2, multicolored, color of background given below.*

713, 714 *Olympic rings and "M"*

713			MNHVF	UseVF
8¢	**silver,** FDD *(Sept. 20, 1973)* tagged		.25	.20

714			MNHVF	UseVF
15¢	**gold,** FDD *(Sept. 20, 1973)* tagged		.65	.55

Regular Issues

1973-74. DEFINITIVES ISSUE T715, Prime Ministers, and Queen (No. 721). *Intaglio by Canadian Bank Note Co., perforated 12 x 12 1/2; (No. 721) British American Bank Note Co., perforated 13 x 13 1/2 also.*

715 *Sir John A. Macdonald*

715		MNHVF	UseVF
1¢	**orange,** FDD *(Oct. 17, 1973)* tagged	.20	.20
	n. Booklet pane of 6, (3 #729- 1 #720, 2 #721), FDD *(1974)*	1.30	1.15
	n1. Booklet pane of 18, 6 #715, 1 #720, 11 #721, FDD *(1975)*	1.50	1.50
	n2. Booklet pane of 10, FDD *(1976)*	—	—

716 *Sir Wilfrid Laurier*

716		MNHVF	UseVF
2¢	**green,** FDD *(Oct. 17, 1973)* tagged	.20	.20

717 *Sir Robert L. Borden*

717		MNHVF	UseVF
3¢	**red brown,** FDD *(Oct. 17, 1973)* tagged	.20	.20

718 *William Lyon Mackenzie King*

718		MNHVF	UseVF
4¢	**black,** FDD *(Oct. 17, 1973)* tagged	.20	.20

719 *Richard Bedford Bennett*

719		MNHVF	UseVF
5¢	**purple,** FDD *(Oct. 17, 1973)* tagged	.20	.20

720 *Lester B. Pearson*

720			MNHVF	UseVF
6¢	**red,** FDD *(Oct. 17, 1973)* tagged		.20	.20
	Booklet pane of 6		—	—

720A *Louis St. Laurent*

720A		MNHVF	UseVF
7¢	**brown,** FDD *(April 6, 1974)* tagged	.20	.20

721 *Queen Elizabeth II*

721		MNHVF	UseVF
8¢	**blue,** FDD *(Oct. 17,1973)* tagged	.20	.20
	v. Perforated 13 x 13 1/2, FDD *(1976)*	.75	.20
	n. Booklet pane of 6	—	—

Commemorative Issues

1973. CHRISTMAS ISSUE T722 Nos. 722, 723 and T724, various designs. *Offset, perforated 12 1/2 x 12 (Nos. 722, 723), 11; multicolored.*

722 *Ice skate*

722		MNHVF	UseVF
6¢	**multicolored,** FDD *(Nov. 7, 1973)* tagged	.20	.20

723 *Dove of Peace ornament*

723		MNHVF	UseVF
8¢	**multicolored,** FDD *(Nov. 7, 1973)* tagged	.20	.20

724 *Santa Claus*

724		MNHVF	UseVF
10¢	**multicolored,** FDD *(Nov. 7, 1973)* tagged	.30	.30

725 *Shepherd with lamb*

725
15¢   **multicolored,** FDD *(Nov. 7, 1973)* tagged   MNHVF .65   UseVF .65

1974. PRE-OLYMPIC ISSUE T726 summer activities. *Offset, perforated 12, dark blue.*

726 *Bicycling;*

727 *Hiking;*

728 *Jogging;*

729 *Diving*

726
8¢   **dark blue,** FDD *(March 22, 1974)* tagged   MNHVF .35   UseVF .20

727
8¢   **dark blue,** FDD *(March 22, 1974)* tagged   MNHVF .35   UseVF .20

728
8¢   **dark blue,** FDD *(March 22, 1974)* tagged   MNHVF .35   UseVF .20

729
8¢   **dark blue,** FDD *(March 22, 1974)* tagged   MNHVF .35   UseVF .20

1974. OLYMPIC GAME SEMI-POSTAL ISSUE *Offset, T713.*

730-732 *1976 Olympic Emblem*

730
8¢ + 2¢ copper, FDD *(April 17, 1974)* tagged   MNHVF .35   UseVF .35

731
10¢ + 5¢ silver, FDD *(April 17, 1974)* tagged   MNHVF .55   UseVF .55

732
15¢ + 5¢ gold, FDD *(April 17, 1974)* tagged   MNHVF .75   UseVF .75

1974. WINNIPEG CENTENNIAL ISSUE *Offset by Ashton-Potter, perforated 12 x 12 1/2.*

733 *Corner of Portage Ave. & Main St. in 1872*

733
8¢   **multicolored,** FDD *(May 3, 1974)* tagged   MNHVF .25   UseVF .20

1974. FREE LETTER CARRIER DELIVERY SERVICE ISSUE 100th anniversary. *Offset by Ashton-Potter, perforated 13 1/2 x 13, multicolored, No. 734-739 se-tenant in panes of 50 containing 6 blocks of all 6 designs (2x3).*

734 *Postmaster;* 735 *Mail collection;* 736 *Mail handle;* 737 *Sorting mail;* 738 *Letter carrier;* 739 *Rural delivery*

734
8¢   **multicolored,** FDD *(June 11, 1974)* tagged   MNHVF .35   UseVF .35

735
8¢   **multicolored,** FDD *(June 11, 1974)* tagged   MNHVF .35   UseVF .35

736
8¢   **multicolored,** FDD *(June 11, 1974)* tagged   MNHVF .35   UseVF .35

737
8¢   **multicolored,** FDD *(June 11, 1974)* tagged   MNHVF .35   UseVF .35

738
8¢   **multicolored,** FDD *(June 11, 1974)* tagged   MNHVF .35   UseVF .35

739
8¢   **multicolored,** FDD *(June 11, 1974)* tagged   MNHVF .35   UseVF .35
    y. se-tenant block of 6

Nos. 740-743 are not assigned.

Commemorative Issues

1974. COIL ISSUE T721. *Intaglio, horizontal coil perforated 10 vertically.*

744
8¢   **blue,** FDD *(April 1974)* tagged   MNHVF .20   UseVF .20
    v. Pair, imperforate   150.00

1974. CANADIAN AGRICULTURAL EDUCATION ISSUE *Offset   by Ashton-Potter, perforated 12 1/2.*

745 *Agricultural motifs*

745			MNHVF	UseVF
8¢	**multicolored,** FDD *(July 12, 1974)* tagged		.25	.20

1974. ALEXANDER GRAHAM BELL ISSUE 100th anniversary of the invention of the telephone. *Offset by Ashton-Potter, perforated 12 1/2.*

746 *Gallows Frame, Pedestal (Daffodil) and Contempra Phone models of telephones.*

746		MNHVF	UseVF
8¢	**multicolored,** FDD *(July 26, 1974)* tagged	.25	.20
	v. Pair, imperforate	1,500.00	

1974. WORLD CYCLING CHAMPIONSHIPS ISSUE *Gravure and intaglio, perforated 12 x 12 1/2.*

747 *Bicycle wheel*

747		MNHVF	UseVF
8¢	**black, silver & red,** FDD *(Aug. 7, 1974)* tagged	.25	.20

1974. MENNONITES ISSUE 100th anniversary of their arrival in Manitoba. *Offset by Ashton-Potter, perforated 12 1/2.*

748 *Settlers and sod hut.*

748		MNHVF	UseVF
8¢	**multicolored,** FDD *(Aug. 28, 1974)* tagged	.25	.20

1974. PRE-OLYMPIC ISSUE T749, winter activities. *Intaglio, perforated 13, carmine, No. 749-752 se-tenant (2x2).*

749 *Snowshoeing;*
750 *Skiing;*
751 *Skating;*
752 *Curling*

749		MNHVF	UseVF
8¢	**multicolored,** FDD *(Sept. 23, 1974)* tagged	.35	.20

750		MNHVF	UseVF
8¢	**multicolored,** FDD *(Sept. 23, 1974)* tagged	.35	.20

751		MNHVF	UseVF
8¢	**multicolored,** FDD *(Sept. 23, 1974)* tagged	.35	.20

752		MNHVF	UseVF
8¢	**multicolored,** FDD *(Sept. 23, 1974)* tagged	.35	.20

1974. UNIVERSAL POSTAL UNION CENTENNIAL ISSUE *Gravure and intaglio, perforated 12 x 12 1/2.*

753 *Mercury and UPU emblem*

753		MNHVF	UseVF
8¢	**violet, red & blue,** FDD *(Oct. 9, 1974)* tagged	.25	.20

754 *Mercury and UPU emblem*

754		MNHVF	UseVF
15¢	**violet, red & blue,** FDD *(Oct. 9, 1974)* tagged	1.15	.75

1974. CHRISTMAS ISSUE *Offset by Ashton-Potter, perforated 13 1/2.*

755 Nativity *by Jean Paul Lemieux*

755		MNHVF	UseVF
6¢	**multicolored,** FDD *(Nov. 1, 1974)* tagged	.20	.20

756 *Skaters in Hull by Henri Masson*

756		MNHVF	UseVF
8¢	**multicolored,** FDD *(Nov. 1, 1974)* tagged	.20	.20

757 The Ice Cone Montmorency Falls *by Robert C. Todd*

757
10¢   **multicolored,** FDD *(Nov. 1, 1974)* tagged   MNHVF .35   UseVF .30

758 Village in the Laurentian Mountains *by Clarence A. Gagnon*

758
15¢   **multicolored,** FDD *(Nov. 1, 1974)* tagged   MNHVF .65   UseVF .55

1974. MARCONI ISSUE 100th anniversary of his birth. *Offset by Ashton-Potter, perforated 13 x 13 1/2.*

759 *Guglielmo Marconi (1874-1937) and view of St. John's Harbor from Signal Hill where Marconi received first trans-Atlantic radio signal on Dec. 11, 1901.*

759
8¢   **multicolored,** FDD *(Nov. 15, 1974)* tagged   MNHVF .25   UseVF .20

1974. WILLIAM HAMILTON MERRITT ISSUE *Engraved by British American Bank Note Co., offset, perforated 13.*

760 William Hamilton Merritt, "Father of Canadian Transportation", *portrait by Robert Whale. View of Welland Canal after "Lock No. 23 Thorold" from Picturesque Canada (1882). Canal built 1824-29 connects Lakes Ontario and Erie, bypassing Niagara Falls.*

760
8¢   **multicolored,** FDD *(Nov. 29, 1974)* tagged   MNHVF .25   UseVF .20

1975. FIRST OLYMPIC GAMES ISSUE Montreal 1976. T761, various water sports. *Offset, perforated 13 1/2.*

761 *Swimming*

761
8¢ + 2¢ multicolored, FDD *(Feb. 5, 1975)* tagged   MNHVF .35   UseVF .35

762 *Rowing*

762
10¢ + 5¢ multicolored, FDD *(Feb. 5, 1975)* tagged   MNHVF .55   UseVF .55

763 *Sailing*

763
15¢ + 5¢ multicolored, FDD *(Feb. 5, 1975)* tagged   MNHVF .75   UseVF .75

1975. SECOND OLYMPIC GAMES ISSUE Montreal 1976. *Offset by Ashton-Potter, perforated 12 1/2 x 12 horizontal, 12 x 12 1/2 vertical; multicolored, color of background given below.*

764 The Sprinter *by Robert Tait McKenzie (1867-1938)*

764
$1   **dull yellow,** FDD *(March 14, 1975)* tagged   MNHVF 2.25   UseVF 2.25

765 The Plunger

765
$2   **gray,** FDD *(March 14, 1975)* tagged   MNHVF 4.50   UseVF 4.50

1975. L.M. MONTGOMERY AND L. HEMON ISSUE *Offset, perforated 13, multicolored.*

766 Anne of Green Gables *by Peter Swan, book by Maud Montgomery (1874-1942);*

766
8¢   **multicolored,** FDD *(May 15, 1975)* tagged   MNHVF .35   UseVF .25

767 Maria Chapdelaine *by Clarence Gagnon, book by Louis Hemon (1880-1913).*

767		MNHVF	UseVF
8¢	**multicolored,** FDD *(May 15, 1975)* tagged	.35	.25
	y. Se-tenant pair, #766-767	—	—

1975. M. BOURGEOYS AND A. DESJARDINS ISSUE *Offset, perforated 12 1/2 x 12.*

768 *Marguerite Bourgeoys (1620-1700), founder of Congregation de Notre-Dame, Montreal, first girls' school in Canada.*

768		MNHVF	UseVF
8¢	**multicolored,** FDD *(May 30, 1975)* tagged	.25	.20

769 *Alphonse Desjardins (1854-1920), founder of first credit union in North America.*

769		MNHVF	UseVF
8¢	**silver, carmine & chocolate,** FDD *(May 30, 1975)* tagged	.25	.20

1975. COOK AND CHOWN ISSUE *Gravure and intaglio, perforated 12 x 12 1/2.*

770 *Dr. John Cook (1805-92), first Moderator of United Presbyterian Church in Canada.*

771 *Dr. SD Chown (1853-1933), Methodist minister, founder of United Church, leader of temperance movement.*

770		MNHVF	UseVF
8¢	**multicolored,** FDD *(May 30, 1975)* tagged	.25	.20

771		MNHVF	UseVF
8¢	**multicolored,** FDD *(May 30, 1975)* tagged	.25	.20
	y. se-tenant pair		

1975. OLYMPIC TRACK AND FIELD ISSUE *Offset, perforated 12 x 12 1/2.*

772 *Pole vault*

772		MNHVF	UseVF
20¢	**multicolored,** FDD *(June 11, 1975)* tagged	.65	.55

773 *Running*

773		MNHVF	UseVF
25¢	**multicolored,** FDD *(June 11, 1975)* tagged	.75	.60

774 *Hurdles*

774		MNHVF	UseVF
50¢	**multicolored,** FDD *(June 11, 1975)* tagged	1.50	1.15

1975. CALGARY CENTENNIAL ISSUE *Offset, perforated 12 x 12 1/2.*

775 Untamed *based on photo by Walt Petrigo*

775		MNHVF	UseVF
8¢	**multicolored,** FDD *(July 3, 1975)* tagged	.25	.20

1975. INTERNATIONAL WOMEN'S YEAR ISSUE *Gravure and intaglio, perforated 13 1/2.*

776 *Female symbol*

776		MNHVF	UseVF
8¢	**yellow bistre, gray & black,** FDD *(July 14, 1975)* tagged	.25	.20

1975. PRE-OLYMPICS ISSUE T777, combat sports. *Offset, perforated 13.*

777 *Fencing*

777		MNHVF	UseVF
8¢ + 2¢	**multicolored,** FDD *(Aug. 6, 1975)* tagged	.35	.35

778 *Boxing*

778		MNHVF	UseVF
10¢ + 5¢	**multicolored,** FDD *(Aug. 6, 1975)* tagged	.55	.55

779 *Judo*

779		MNHVF	UseVF
15¢ + 5¢	**multicolored,** FDD *(Aug. 6, 1975)* tagged	.75	.75

1975. SUPREME COURT OF CANADA CENTENNIAL ISSUE *Offset by Ashton-Potter, perforated 12 1/2.*

780 Justice *by Walter S. Allward*

780		MNHVF	UseVF
8¢	**multicolored,** FDD *(Sept. 2, 1975)* tagged	.25	.20

1975. COASTAL SHIPS ISSUE *Gravure and intaglio, perforated 13.*

781 William D. Lawrence, *largest Canadian built square rigger constructed in Nova Scotia between 1872 and 1874.*

782 *Hudson's Bay Company* Beaver, *first steamship in North Pacific (1834), used in fur trade, helped preserve area for Canada.*

783 Neptune (1873) *engaged in Newfoundland sealing industry.*

784 Quadra, *names after Spanish explorer Juan Francisco de la Bodegay Quadra, served the Dept. of Maine & Fisheries (1892).*

781		MNHVF	UseVF
8¢	**brown & sepia,** FDD *(Sept. 24, 1975)* tagged	.35	.35
782		MNHVF	UseVF
8¢	**olive & dark olive,** FDD *(Sept. 24, 1975)* tagged	.35	.35
783		MNHVF	UseVF
8¢	**gray & light gray,** FDD *(Sept. 24, 1975)* tagged	.35	.35
784		MNHVF	UseVF
8¢	**brown & sepia,** FDD *(Sept. 24, 1975)* tagged	.35	.35
	y. Se-tenant block of 4	2.25	2.25

1975. CHRISTMAS ISSUE *Offset by Ashton-Potter, perforated 13, multicolored.*

785 *Santa Claus;*

786 *Skater*

785		MNHVF	UseVF
6¢	**multicolored,** FDD *(Oct. 22, 1975)* tagged	.20	.20
786		MNHVF	UseVF
6¢	**multicolored,** FDD *(Oct. 22, 1975)* tagged	.20	.20
	y. Se-tenant pair, #785-786	.30	.25

Users of this Catalog are invited to write us if they have information which they feel will supplement or correct any material contained herin. All such communications will be answered.

787 *Child;*
788 *Family*

787
		MNHVF	UseVF
8¢	**multicolored,** FDD *(Oct. 22, 1975)* tagged	.20	.20

788
		MNHVF	UseVF
8¢	**multicolored,** FDD *(Oct. 22, 1975)* tagged	.20	.20
	y. Se-tenant pair, #787-788	—	—

789 *Gift*

789
		MNHVF	UseVF
10¢	**multicolored,** FDD *(Oct. 22, 1975)* tagged	.25	.25

790 *Trees*

790
		MNHVF	UseVF
15¢	**multicolored,** FDD *(Oct. 22, 1975)* tagged	.45	.45

1975. ROYAL CANADIAN LEGION ISSUE 50th anniversary. *Gravure and intaglio, perforated 13 x 13 1/2.*

791 *Legion crest & bugle*

791
		MNHVF	UseVF
8¢	**multicolored,** FDD *(Nov. 10, 1975)* tagged	.25	.20

1976. OLYMPIC ISSUE T792, team sports and gymnastics. *Offset by Ashton-Potter, perforated 13.*

792 *Basketball player*

792
		MNHVF	UseVF
8¢ + 2¢	**multicolored,** FDD *(Jan. 7, 1976)* tagged	.35	.35

793 *Gymnastics*

793
		MNHVF	UseVF
10¢ + 5¢	**multicolored,** FDD *(Jan. 7, 1976)* tagged	.55	.55

794 *Soccer*

794
		MNHVF	UseVF
20¢ + 5¢	**multicolored,** FDD *(Jan. 7, 1976)* tagged	.95	.95

1976. OLYMPIC ART AND CULTURE ISSUE *Offset, perforated 12 x 12 1/2.*

795 *Communications arts*

795
		MNHVF	UseVF
20¢	**multicolored,** FDD *(Feb. 6, 1976)* tagged	1.30	.65

796 *Handicrafts*

796
25¢ **multicolored,** FDD *(Feb. 6, 1976)* tagged   MNHVF 1.50   UseVF .75

797 *Performing arts*

797
50¢ **multicolored,** FDD *(Feb. 6, 1976)* tagged   MNHVF 2.50   UseVF 1.30

1976. WINTER OLYMPIC ISSUE Innsbruck 1976. *Offset and embossed by Ashton-Potter, perforated 12 1/2.*

798 *Innsbruck Winter Olympics emblem*

798
20¢ **multicolored,** FDD *(Feb. 6, 1976)* tagged   MNHVF .95   UseVF .68

1976. OLYMPIC SITE ISSUE *Gravure and intaglio, perforated 13.*

799 *Notre Dame Church (1823-29) and Place Ville Marie skyscraper (1962).*

799
$1 **multicolored,** FDD *(March 12, 1976)* tagged   MNHVF 3.40   UseVF 2.25

800 *Stadium and valedrome and flags, (1976)*

800
$2 **multicolored,** FDD *(March 12, 1976)* tagged   MNHVF 5.25   UseVF 4.50

1976. HABITAT ISSUE U.N. Conference on Human Settlements. *Offset by Ashton-Potter, perforated 12 x 12 1/2.*

801 *Urban skyline and rose*

801
20¢ **multicolored,** FDD *(May 12, 1976)* tagged   MNHVF .55   UseVF .55

1976. ROYAL MILITARY COLLEGE CENTENNIAL ISSUE *Offset, perforated 12 x 12 1/2, multicolored.*

802 *Color Party, Memorial Arch;*

803 *Wing Parade, Mackenzie Building. Prime Minister Mackenzie installed the Military College on Point Frederick at Kingston in 1876.*

802
8¢ **multicolored,** FDD *(June 1, 1976)* tagged   MNHVF .20   UseVF .20
803
8¢ **multicolored,** FDD *(June 1, 1976)* tagged   MNHVF .20   UseVF .20
   y. Se-tenant pair, #802-803   .35   .35
   v. Se-tenant pair, imperforate   2,250.00

1976. US BICENTENNIAL ISSUE *Intaglio and offset, perforated 13, joint issue with the US.*

804 *Benjamin Franklin, first Deputy Postmaster General of Canada and the United States (1753-74).*

804
10¢ **cobalt, ochre & chocolate,** FDD *(June 1, 1976)* tagged   MNHVF .35   UseVF .20

1976. OLYMPIC GAME CEREMONIES ISSUE T805, various designs. *Offset by Ashton-Potter, perforated 13 1/2.*

805 *Olympic flame transmitted by satellite from Greece to Canada*

805
8¢ **multicolored,** FDD *(June 18, 1976)* tagged   MNHVF .20   UseVF .20

806 *Opening ceremony, Olympic flag*

806		MNHVF	UseVF
20¢	**multicolored,** FDD *(June 18, 1976)* tagged	.75	.65

807 *Victory ceremony*

807		MNHVF	UseVF
25¢	**multicolored,** FDD *(June 18, 1976)* tagged	.95	.75

1976. OLYMPIAD FOR THE PHYSICALLY DISABLED ISSUE *Offset, perforated 12.*

808 *Archer*

808		MNHVF	UseVF
20¢	**multicolored,** FDD *(Aug. 3, 1976)* tagged	.65	.55

1976. GUEVREMONT AND SERVICE ISSUE *Offset by Ashton-Potter, perforated 13 1/2.*

809 Le Survenant (The Outlander) 1945, author Germaine Guevremont. 810 Robert Service (1874-1958), poet; David Bierk's painting shows closing scene of The Cremation of Sam McGee.

809		MNHVF	UseVF
8¢	**multicolored,** FDD *(Aug. 17, 1976)* tagged	.20	.20

810		MNHVF	UseVF
8¢	**multicolored,** FDD *(Aug. 17, 1976)* tagged	.20	.20
	y. Se-tenant pair, #809-810	.35	.35

Regular Issues

1976. DEFINITIVE ISSUE Similar to Canada Minkus No. 721, Elizabeth II, additional value. *Perforated 12.*

811, 812 *Elizabeth II*

811		MNHVF	UseVF
10¢	**red,** FDD *(Sept. 1, 1976)*	.20	.20
	n. Booklet pane of 10, 2 of 1¢ No. 715, 4 of 2¢ No. 716, 4 of 10¢, No. 811	1.00	

1976. COIL ISSUE *Horizontal coil, perforated 10 vertically.*

812		MNHVF	UseVF
10¢	**red,** FDD *(Sept. 1, 1976)*	.20	.20

Commemorative Issues

1976. CHRISTMAS ISSUE Nativity stained glass windows. *Offset, perforated 13 1/2.*

813 *St. Michael's, Toronto*

813		MNHVF	UseVF
8¢	**multicolored,** FDD *(Nov. 3, 1976),* tagged	.20	.20

814 *St. Jude in London, Ontario*

814		MNHVF	UseVF
10¢	**multicolored,** FDD *(Nov. 3, 1976),* tagged	.20	.20

815 *Yvonne Williams' window*

815		MNHVF	UseVF
20¢	**multicolored,** FDD *(Nov. 3, 1976),* tagged	.45	.45

1976. INLAND VESSELS ISSUE *Intaglio and offset, perforated 12, No. 816-819 se-tenant (2 x 2) in various combinations.*

816 *Northcote;* 817 *Chicora;* 818 *Passport;* 819 *Arthabaska*

816			MNHVF	UseVF
10¢	**brown & black,** FDD *(Nov. 19, 1976),* tagged		.35	.35

817			MNHVF	UseVF
10¢	**blue & black,** FDD *(Nov. 19, 1976),* tagged		.35	.35

818			MNHVF	UseVF
10¢	**violet & black,** FDD *(Nov. 19, 1976),* tagged		.35	.35

819			MNHVF	UseVF
10¢	**green & black,** FDD *(Nov. 19, 1976),* tagged		.35	.35
	y. Se-tenant block of 4 #816-819		1.50	1.50

1977. SILVER JUBILEE ISSUE *Offset and embossed by Ashton-Potter, perforated 12 1/2, multicolored, color of background given below.*

820 *Queen Elizabeth II*

820			MNHVF	UseVF
25¢	**deep blue,** FDD *(Feb. 4, 1977),* tagged		.75	.55

Regular Issues

1977-1979. DEFINITIVE ISSUE *Intaglio and offset, perforated 12 x 12 1/2; No. 828: intaglio, perforated 13; No. 821v.-826v, 827, 829-831: intaglio and gravure, perforated 13; Nos. 821-826, 829-831: multicolored, color of background given below.*

821 *Gentiana andrewsii*

821			MNHVF	UseVF
1¢	**lilac,** FDD *(April 22)*		.20	.20
	v. Intaglio & gravure		.20	.20

822 *Aquilegia formosa*

822			MNHVF	UseVF
2¢	**brown,** FDD *(April 22)*		.20	.20
	v. Perforated 13, FDD *(1979)*		.20	.20

823 *Lilium canadense*

823			MNHVF	UseVF
3¢	**dull green,** FDD *(April 22)*		.20	.20
	v. Perforated 13, FDD *(1979)*		.20	.20

824 *Hepatica acutiloba*

824			MNHVF	UseVF
4¢	**gray,** FDD *(April 22)*		.20	.20
	v. Perforated 13, FDD *(1979)*		.20	.20

825 *Dodecatheon hendersonii*

825			MNHVF	UseVF
5¢	**chocolate,** FDD *(April 22)*		.20	.20
	v. Perforated 13, FDD *(1979)*		.20	.20

826 *Cxpripedium passerinum*

826			MNHVF	UseVF
10¢	**light brown,** FDD *(April 22)*		.20	.20
	v. Perforated 13, FDD *(1978)*		.25	.25

827 *Elizabeth II*

827			MNHVF	UseVF
12¢	**blue,** FDD *(Feb. 4)*		.26	.20

		1.25
n. Booklet pane of 6, 2 of 1¢ + 4 of 12¢, perforated 12 x 12 1/2 on 3 or 2 sides		
v. Perforated 12 x 12 1/2	.30	.30

828 *Parliament*

		MNHVF	UseVF
828			
12¢	**blue,** FDD *(May 3)*	.30	.20

1977. COIL ISSUE Horizontal perforated 10 vertically.

		MNHVF	UseVF
828A			
12¢	**blue,** T828, FDD *(May 3)*	.25	.10

1977-1979. DEFINITIVE ISSUE *Intaglio and offset, perforated 12 x 12 1/2; No. 828: intaglio, perforated 13; No. 821v.-826v, 827, 829-831: intaglio and gravure, perforated 13; Nos. 821-826, 829-831: multicolored, color of background given below.*

829 *Trembling Aspen*

		MNHVF	UseVF
829			
15¢	**gray green,** FDD *(Aug. 8)*	.45	.20

830 *Douglas Fir*

		MNHVF	UseVF
830			
20¢	**cobalt,** FDD *(Aug. 8)*	.35	.20

831 *Sugar Maple*

		MNHVF	UseVF
831			
25¢	**pale brown,** FDD *(Aug. 8)*	.50	.20

Additional values see Nos. 861-864, 875.

Commemorative Issues

1977. EASTERN COUGAR ISSUE *Offset by Ashton-Potter, perforated 12 1/2.*

832 *Eastern cougar (mountian lion)*

		MNHVF	UseVF
832			
12¢	**multicolored,** FDD *(March 30, 1977),* tagged	.25	.20

1977. THOMAS THOMSON ISSUE *Offset by Ashton-Potter, perforated 12, multicolored.*

833 *April;* 834 *Autumn*

		MNHVF	UseVF
833			
12¢	**multicolored,** FDD *(May 26, 1977),* tagged	.25	.20
834			
12¢	**multicolored,** FDD *(May 26, 1977),* tagged	.25	.20
	y. Se-tenant pair, #833-834		

1977. ORDER OF CANADA ISSUE 10th anniversary. *Offset and embossed by by Ashton-Potter, perforated 12.*

835 *Order of Canada instituted July 1, 1967*

		MNHVF	UseVF
835			
12¢	**multicolored,** FDD *(July 1, 1977),* tagged	.25	.20

1977. GOVERNOR GENERAL ISSUE 25th anniversary first Canadian-born governor general in modern era. *Offset by Ashton-Potter, perforated 12.*

836 *Lion and crown*

		MNHVF	UseVF
836			
12¢	**multicolored,** FDD *(June 30, 1977),* tagged	.25	.20

1977. PEACE BRIDGE ISSUE *Offset by Ashton-Potter, perforated 12 1/2.*

837 *Peace Bridge connecting Fort Erie, Ontario and Buffalo, NY, completed in 1927*

		MNHVF	UseVF
837			
12¢	**multicolored,** FDD *(Aug. 4, 1977),* tagged	.25	.20

Regular Issues

1977. DEFINITIVE ISSUE Similar to Canada Minkus No. 663A. *Intaglio, perforated 13 1/2, dull florescent paper.*

838 *English Bay, Vancouver, B.C.*

838		MNHVF	UseVF
$1	**multicolored,** FDD *(Aug. 4, 1977),* tagged	2.65	.35

Commemorative Issues

1977. FAMOUS CANADIAN MEN ISSUE *Intaglio, perforated 13.*

839 *Capt. Joseph E. Bernier (1852-1934) and CGS Arctic caught in ice during arctic expedition.*

840 *Sandford Fleming (1827-1915) and train crossing one of Intercolonial Railway bridges designed and surveyed by him.*

839		MNHVF	UseVF
12¢	**slate blue,** FDD *(Sept. 16, 1977),* tagged	.25	.20

840		MNHVF	UseVF
12¢	**brown,** FDD *(Sept. 16, 1977),* tagged	.25	.20
	y. Se-tenant pair #839-840		

1977. 23RD COMMONWEALTH PARLIAMENTARY CONFERENCE ISSUE *Offset by Ashton-Potter, perforated 12 1/2.*

841 *Peace tower of Parliament buildings, Ottawa*

841		MNHVF	UseVF
25¢	**multicolored,** FDD *(Sept. 19, 1977),* tagged	.75	.68

1977. CHRISTMAS ISSUE Ronald G. White's illustrations to *Jesus Anatonhia.* First Canadian Christmas carol composed about 1641 by Father Jean de Brebeuf, heroic missionary to Hurons, tortured and killed by Iroquois in 1649. *Offset, perforated 13 1/2.*

842 *Braves following star*

842		MNHVF	UseVF
10¢	**multicolored,** FDD *(Oct. 26, 1977),* tagged	.20	.20

843 *Angelic choir*

843		MNHVF	UseVF
12¢	**multicolored,** FDD *(Oct. 26, 1977),* tagged	.25	.20
	v. Pair, imperforat	1,000.00	

844 *Christ Child blessing chiefs*

844		MNHVF	UseVF
25¢	**multicolored,** FDD *(Oct. 26, 1977),* tagged	.45	.35

1977. SAILING VESSEL ISSUE Various ships. *Intaglio and offset, perforated 12 x 12 1/2, multicolored, No. 845-848 se-tenant (2 x 2).*

845 *Pinky;* 846 *Five-masted schooner;* 847 *Tern schooner;* 848 *Mackinaw boat*

845		MNHVF	UseVF
12¢	**multicolored,** FDD *(Nov. 18, 1977),* tagged	.25	.20

846		MNHVF	UseVF
12¢	**multicolored,** FDD *(Nov. 18, 1977),*	.25	.20

847		MNHVF	UseVF
12¢	**multicolored,** FDD *(Nov. 18, 1977)*	.25	.20

848		MNHVF	UseVF
12¢	**multicolored,** FDD *(Nov. 18, 1977)*	.25	.20
	y. Se-tenant block of 4 (Nos. 845-848)	.90	.90
	v. Vertical pair, imperforate (No. 845, 847) 3 known	1,000.00	—
	v1. Bottom margin imperforate (No. 845-848) 6 known	4,000.00	—

1977. INUIT HUNTING ISSUE *Offset by Ashton-Potter, perforated 12 x 12 1/2, multicolored. No. 849 and 850 or 851 and 852 se-tenant.*

848 *Seal hunter;* 850 *Fishing with spears;*

849		MNHVF	UseVF
12¢	multicolored, FDD *(Nov. 18, 1977),* tagged	.25	.20

850		MNHVF	UseVF
12¢	multicolored, FDD *(Nov. 18, 1977),* tagged	.25	.20
	y. Se-tenant pair, #849-850	.45	.30

851 *Caribou hunter;* 852 *Walrus hunt*

851		MNHVF	UseVF
12¢	multicolored, FDD *(Nov. 18, 1977),* tagged	.25	.20

852		MNHVF	UseVF
12¢	multicolored, FDD *(Nov. 18, 1977),* tagged	.25	.20
	y. Se-tenant pair, #851-852	.25	.25

Postage Due Stamps

1970-78. Postage Due Issue Similar to Canada Minkus No. 571A *(size: 19 1/2 x 16mm), perforated 12 1/2 x 12.*

853-858 *Postage Due*

853		MNHVF	UseVF
1¢	red FDD *(1970)*	.20	.20

854		MNHVF	UseVF
4¢	red FDD *(1977)*	.20	.20

855		MNHVF	UseVF
5¢	red FDD *(1977)*	.20	.20

855A		MNHVF	UseVF
8¢	red FDD *(1978)*	.24	.24

855B		MNHVF	UseVF
10¢	red FDD *(1977)*	.20	.20

855C		MNHVF	UseVF
12¢	red FDD *(1977)*	.27	.27

856		MNHVF	UseVF
20¢	red FDD *(1977)*	.45	.45

857		MNHVF	UseVF
24¢	red FDD *(1977)*	.54	.54

858		MNHVF	UseVF
50¢	red FDD *(1977)*	1.15	1.15

Commemorative Issues

1978. Endangered Wildlife Issue *Offset by Ashton-Potter, perforated 12 1/2.*

859 *Peregrine falcon*

859		MNHVF	UseVF
12¢	multicolored, FDD *(Jan. 18, 1978),* tagged	.26	.20

1978. CAPEX 78 Issue Canadian International Philatelic Exhibition, Toronto, June 9-18. *Intaglio and gravure, perforated 13 1/2.*

860 *Pair of 12-penny Queen Victoria of 1851*

860		MNHVF	UseVF
12¢	gray & black, FDD *(Jan. 18, 1978),* tagged	.20	.20

Regular Issues

1978. First Definitive Issue No. 861 similar to Canada Minkus No. 827 (Elizabeth II); No. 863 similar to No. 828 (Parliament); and No. 863 similar to No. 829 (Red Oak), additional values.

861 *Elizabeth II*

861		MNHVF	UseVF
14¢	carmine, black & gray, FDD *(March 7, 1978),* tagged	.26	.20
	n. Booklet pane of 25 and 2 labels	5.70	5.70

862 *Parliment buildings, Ottawa*

862		MNHVF	UseVF
14¢	red, FDD *(March 7, 1978),* tagged	.25	.20

863 *Red oak*

863		MNHVF	UseVF
30¢	multicolored, FDD *(March 7, 1978),* tagged	.55	.20

1978. Coil Issue Similar to Canada Minkus No. 862 (Parliament). Horizontal perforated 10 vertically.

864		MNHVF	UseVF
14¢	red, FDD *(March 7, 1978),* tagged	.26	.20

Commemorative Issues

1978. 11th Commonwealth Games Issue *Offset by Ashton-Potter, perforated 12 1/2.*

865 *Commonwealth Games symbol*

865		MNHVF	UseVF
14¢	**multicolored,** FDD *(March 31, 1978),* tagged	.26	.20

866 *Badmiton*

866		MNHVF	UseVF
30¢	**multicolored,** FDD *(March 31, 1978),* tagged	.53	.45

1978. CAPT. JAMES COOK ISSUE a bicentenary stamp commemorated John Cook (1728-1779), an explorer of the East and West Coasts of Canada, for his anchorage near Anchorage, June 1, 1778. *Offset, perforated 13, multicolored.*

867 James Cook *by Nathaniel Dance (1776).* 868 Nootka Sound *by John Webber, one of the official artists on Cook's third voyage. Cook sailed into Nootka Sound in March 1778 and he claimed the region for Britain.*

867		MNHVF	UseVF
14¢	**Capt. James Cook,** FDD *(April 26, 1978),* tagged	.25	.20

868		MNHVF	UseVF
14¢	**Nootka Sound,** FDD *(April 26, 1978),* tagged	.25	.20
	y. Se-tenant pair, #867-868	.50	.30

1978. RESOURCE DEVELOPMENT ISSUE *Offset by Ashton-Potter, perforated 12 1/2, multicolored, No. 869 and 870 se-tenant.*

869 *Silver mining in Cobalt;* 870 *Strip mining of the Athabasca Tar Sands*

869		MNHVF	UseVF
14¢	**Silver mining in Cobalt,** FDD *(May 19, 1978),* tagged	.25	.20

870		MNHVF	UseVF
14¢	**Strip mining of the Athabasca Tar Sands,** FDD *(May 19, 1978),* tagged	.25	.20

1978. CAPEX ISSUE Canadian International Philatelic Exhibition, Toronto, June 9-18. No. 860 pairs of PENCE issue classics No. 4-8. *Multicolored.*

871 *10p Cartier;* 872 *1/2p Victoria;* 873 *6p Albert*

871		MNHVF	UseVF
14¢	**10p Cartier, No.8,** FDD *(June 10, 1978),* tagged	.26	.20

872		MNHVF	UseVF
30¢	**1/2p Victoria, No.4,** FDD *(June 10, 1978),* tagged	.55	.35

873		MNHVF	UseVF
$1.25	**6p Albert, No.6,** FDD *(June 10, 1978),* tagged	2.10	1.15

1978. CAPEX SOUVENIR SHEET of 3 No. 871-873 *(101 x 77mm.)*

871-873 *CAPEX Souvenir sheet*

874		MNHVF	UseVF
$1.69	**Sheet of 3,** Nos. 871-873	3.20	3.20

Regular Issues

1978. FIRST DEFINITIVE ISSUE Similar to Minkus Canada No. 821 with additional values. *Intaglio, perforated 13 x 13 1/2.*

875 *Jewel weed (Impatiens capensis)*

875		MNHVF	UseVF
12¢	**multicolored,** FDD *(July 9, 1978),* tagged	.30	.20

1978. THIRD DEFINITIVE ISSUE *Offset and intaglio, perforated 13 1/2 x 13 1/2.*

876 *Main street in Prairie town*

876		MNHVF	UseVF
50¢	**multicolored,** FDD *(July 6, 1978),* tagged	1.15	.20

877 *Eastern city*

877		MNHVF	UseVF
75¢	**multicolored,** FDD *(July 6, 1978),* tagged	1.30	.30

878 *Maritime provinces*

878		MNHVF	UseVF
80¢	**multicolored,** FDD *(July 6, 1978),* tagged	1.50	.35

Commemorative Issues

1978. XI COMMONWEALTH GAMES ISSUE commemorated the 11th Commonwealth Games, Edmonton, Aug. 3-12. No. 879 various designs. *Offset by Ashton-Potter, perforated 12 1/2, multicolored.*

879 *Stadium;* 880 *Running*

879		MNHVF	UseVF
14¢	**Stadium,** FDD *(Aug. 3, 1978),* tagged	.25	.20

880		MNHVF	UseVF
14¢	**Running,** FDD *(Aug. 3, 1978),* tagged	.45	.26
	y. Se-tenant pair, #879-880		

881 *Legislature building, Edmonton;* 882 *Lawn Bowling*

881		MNHVF	UseVF
30¢	**Legislature building, Edmonton,** FDD *(Aug. 3, 1978),* tagged	.53	.53

882		MNHVF	UseVF
30¢	**Lawn Bowling,** FDD *(Aug. 3, 1978),* tagged	.53	.53
	y. Se-tenant pair, #881-882	1.05	1.15

1978. CANADIAN NATIONAL EXHIBIT CENTENNIAL ISSUE *Offset, perforated 12 1/2.*

883 *Princes' Gate, main entrance to the Canadian National Exhibition, Toronto*

883		MNHVF	UseVF
14¢	**multicolored,** FDD *(Aug. 16, 1978),* tagged	.26	.20

1978. MARGUERITE D'YOUVILLE ISSUE *Offset, perforated 13.*

884 *Marguerite d'Youville (1701-71), founder of Gray Nuns (1737) and feeding of starving people before French surrender of Montreal (1760). Mere d'Youville was beatified by Pope John XXIII in 1959.*

884		MNHVF	UseVF
14¢	**multicolored,** FDD *(Sept. 24, 1978),* tagged	.26	.20

1978. INUIT TRAVEL ISSUE commemorated the work by Eskimo artists. *Offset by Ashton-Potter, perforated 13, se-tenant.*

885 Woman Walking, *color drawing by Pitseolak;* 886 Migration *(sailing umiak) soapstone sculpture by Joe Talurinili*

885		MNHVF	UseVF
14¢	**Woman walking,** FDD *(Sept. 27, 1978),* tagged	.26	.20

886		MNHVF	UseVF
14¢	**Sailing umiak,** FDD *(Sept. 27, 1978),* tagged	.26	.20
	y. Se-tenant pair, #885, 886	.45	.30

887 Airplane over Village, *stonecut and stencil print by Pudlo;* 888 Dogteam & Sled *sculpture by Abraham Kingmeatook*

887		MNHVF	UseVF
14¢	**Airplane,** FDD *(Sept. 27, 1978),* tagged	.26	.20

888		MNHVF	UseVF
14¢	**Dogteam and sled,** FDD *(Sept. 27, 1978),* tagged	.26	.20
	y. Se-tenant pair, #887, 888	.45	.30

1978. CHRISTMAS ISSUE commemorated the Renaissance artists whose paintings are in the National Gallery in Canada. *Offset by Ashton-Potter, perforated 12 1/2.*

289 Madonna of the Flowering Pea, *(detail) by Master of Cologne, 15th century*

		MNHVF	UseVF
889			
12¢	**multicolored,** FDD *(Oct. 20, 1978),* tagged	.20	.20

890 Virgin & Child, *by Hans Memling*

		MNHVF	UseVF
890			
14¢	**multicolored,** FDD *(Oct. 20, 1978),* tagged	.25	.20

891 Virgin & Child with Goldfinch, *by Jacopo di Cione*

		MNHVF	UseVF
891			
30¢	**multicolored,** FDD *(Oct. 20, 1978),* tagged	.53	.45

1978. ICE VESSELS ISSUE No. 892, various designs. *Intaglio and offset, perforated 13, multicolored, se-tenant (2 x 2).*

892 *St. Roch;* 893 *Chief Justice Robinson;* 894 *Labrador;* 895 *Northern Light*

		MNHVF	UseVF
892			
14¢	**St. Roch,** FDD *(Nov. 15, 1978),* tagged	.30	.26

		MNHVF	UseVF
893			
14¢	**Chief Justice Robinson,** FDD *(Nov. 15, 1978),* tagged	.30	.26
894		MNHVF	UseVF
14¢	**Labrador,** FDD *(Nov. 15, 1978),* tagged	.30	.26
895		MNHVF	UseVF
14¢	**Northern Light,** FDD *(Nov. 15, 1978),* tagged	.30	.26
	y. Se-tenant block of 4 #892-895	1.20	1.15

Regular Issues

1979. DEFINITIVE ISSUE Fundy National Park, New Brunswick. *Intaglio and offset, perforated 13 1/2.*

896 *Bay of Fundy. 29 foot tides roll in and out twice a day.*

		MNHVF	UseVF
896			
$1	**multicolored,** FDD *(Jan. 24, 1979),* untagged	1.50	.55
	x. U.N. black inscription omitted	—	—
	x1. Double inscriptions	—	—

Commemorative Issues

1979. QUEBEC WINTER CARNIVAL ISSUE 25th anniversary. *Offset, perforated 13 1/2.*

897 *Carnival crowd and "Bonhomme Carnival," the jovial spirit of the festival.*

		MNHVF	UseVF
897			
14¢	**multicolored,** FDD *(Feb. 1, 1979),* tagged	.25	.20

Regular Issues

1979. SECOND DEFINITIVE ISSUE No. 898 similar to Canada Minkus No. 827 (Elizabeth II); No. 899 similar to No. 828 (Parliament); and No. 900 similar to No. 829 (Trembling Aspen). Additional values. *Perforated 13 1/2 x 13 1/2.*

		MNHVF	UseVF
898			
17¢	**green, black & gray,** FDD *(March 8, 1979),* tagged	.26	.20
899		MNHVF	UseVF
17¢	**green,** FDD *(March 8, 1979),* tagged, No. 828	.26	.20

900 *Eastern white pine*

900		MNHVF	UseVF
35¢	**multicolored,** FDD *(March 8, 1979),* tagged, No. 829	.55	.26

1979. COIL ISSUE Parliament Type of 1977, No. 899. *Horizontal, perforated 10. Vertically imperforate.*

901		MNHVF	UseVF
17¢	**green,** FDD *(March 8, 1979),* tagged, No. 828	.26	.20

1979. SECOND DEFINITIVE ISSUE Nos. 902-903 Parliament buildings. No. 904 Elizabeth II; *imperforate (1 or 2 sides), perforated 12 horizontally and 12 1/2 vertically.*

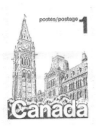

902-903
Parliament buildings

902		MNHVF	UseVF
1¢	**slate,** FDD *(March 28, 1979),* tagged, No. 828	.35	.25

903		MNHVF	UseVF
5¢	**purple,** FDD *(March 28, 1979),* tagged, No. 828	.20	.20

904 *Elizabeth II*

904		MNHVF	UseVF
17¢	**green, black & gray,** FDD *(March 28, 1979),* tagged	.75	.55
	n. Booklet pane of 25, 17¢ stamps & 2 labels	6.00	5.70

Commemorative Issues

1979. ENDANGERED WILDLIFE ISSUE *Offset by Ashton-Potter, perforated 12 1/2, multicolored.*

905 *Eastern spiny soft-shelled turtle (Trionyx Spinifera);* 906 *Bowhead whale*

905		MNHVF	UseVF
17¢	**tan,** FDD *(April 10, 1979),* tagged	.30	.20
906		MNHVF	UseVF
35¢	**blue & green,** FDD *(April 10, 1979),* tagged	.85	.53

1979. POSTAL CODE ISSUE *Offset by Ashton-Potter, perforated 13 1/2, multicolored.*

907 *Woman's hand and ribbon;*

908 *Man's hand and ribbon*

907		MNHVF	UseVF
17¢	**multicolored,** FDD *(April 27, 1979),* tagged	.26	.20

908		MNHVF	UseVF
17¢	**multicolored,** FDD *(April 27, 1979),* tagged	.26	.20
	y. Se-tenant pair, No.907-908		

Regular Issues

1979. KLUANE NATIONAL PARK ISSUE *Intaglio and offset, perforated 13 1/2.*

909 *Kluane National Park*

909		MNHVF	UseVF
$2	**multicolored,** FDD *(April 27, 1979),* tagged	3.00	1.30
	x. Silver inscription omitted	—	—

Commemorative Issues

1979. GROVE AND NELLIGAN ISSUE 100th anniversary of their birth. *Offset, perforated 13.*

910 *Frederick Philip Grove (1879-1948), born in Germany as Felix Paul Greve, writer. Stamp features scenes from his novel* Fruits of the Earth

911 *Emile Nelligan (1879-1941), poet and scene from his poem* Le Vaisseau d'or *(The Golden Ship)*

910		MNHVF	UseVF
17¢	**black & yellow,** FDD *(May 3, 1979),* tagged	.26	.20

911		MNHVF	UseVF
17¢	**multicolored,** FDC *(May 3, 1979),* tagged	.26	.20
	y. Se-tenant pair, No. 910-911		

1979. SOLDIER ISSUE *Offset by Ashton-Potter, perforated 13 1/2.*

912 *John By (1779-1836), born in England. Colonel, worked on fortifications of Quebec City and Canal at Les Cedres (1802-11), constructed Rideau Canal (1826) to secure communication between Montreal and Kingston.*

913 *Charles-Michel d'Irumberry de Salaberry (1778-1829), born at Beauport, Quebec. Repulsed advance guard of American army at Lacolle, Nov. 1812 and defeated American contingent attempting to seize Montreal at Chateaugay in 1813.*

912		MNHVF	UseVF
17¢	**multicolored,** FDD *(May 11, 1979),* tagged	.26	.20

913		MNHVF	UseVF
17¢	**multicolored,** FDD *(May 11, 1979),* tagged	.26	.20
	y. Se-tenant pair #912-913	.53	.53

1979. CANADA DAY ISSUE provincial and territorial flags. *Offset by Ashton-Potter, perforated 13 1/2.*

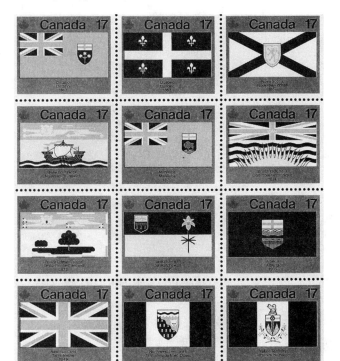

914-925

914		MNHVF	UseVF
17¢	**Ontario,** *1867,* tagged	.26	.25

915		MNHVF	UseVF
17¢	**Quebec,** *1867,* tagged	.26	.25

916		MNHVF	UseVF
17¢	**Nova Scotia,** *1867,* tagged	.26	.25

917		MNHVF	UseVF
17¢	**New Brunswick,** *1867,* tagged	.35	

918		MNHVF	UseVF
17¢	**Manitoba,** *1870,* tagged	.26	.25

919		MNHVF	UseVF
17¢	**British Columbia,** *1871,* tagged	.26	.25

920		MNHVF	UseVF
17¢	**Prince Edward Island, 1873,** tagged	.26	.25

921		MNHVF	UseVF
17¢	**Saskatchewan,** *1905,* tagged	.26	.25

922		MNHVF	UseVF
17¢	**Alberta,** *1905,* tagged	.26	.25

923		MNHVF	UseVF
17¢	**Newfoundland,** *1949,* tagged	.26	.25

924		MNHVF	UseVF
17¢	**NW Territories,** tagged	.26	.25

925		MNHVF	UseVF
17¢	**Yukon Territory,** FDD *(June 15, 1979),* tagged	.26	.25
	y. Se-tenant sheetlet of 12 (3 x 4), #914-925	3.75	3.75

1979. CANOE-KAYAK WORLD CHAMPIONSHIP ISSUE Jonquiére and Desbiens, Quebec, June 30-July 8. *Offset by Ashton-Potter, perforated 12 1/2.*

926 *White water Kayak race*

926		MNHVF	UseVF
17¢	**multicolored,** FDD *(July 3, 1979),* tagged	.30	.20

Regular Issues

1979. THIRD DEFINITIVE ISSUE *Intaglio and gravure, perforated 13.*

927 *Canada violet*

927		MNHVF	UseVF
15¢	**multicolored,** FDD *(Aug. 16, 1979),* tagged	.26	.20

Commemorative Issues

1979. WOMAN'S FIELD HOCKEY CHAMPIONSHIP ISSUE Vancouver, B.C., Aug. 16-30. *Offset by Ashton-Potter, perforated 12 1/2.*

928 *Field hockey players*

928		MNHVF	UseVF
17¢	**emerald, yellow & black,** FDD *(Aug. 16, 1979),* tagged	.30	.20

1979. INUIT SHELTERS AND COMMUNITY ISSUE *Offset by Ashton-Potter, perforated 13 1/2.*

929 Summer Tent, *print by Klakshuk;* 930 *Soapstone sculpture from Povungnituk of winter igloo*

929		**MNHVF**	**UseVF**
17¢	**multicolored,** FDD *(Sept. 13, 1979),* tagged	.26	.20

930		**MNHVF**	**UseVF**
17¢	**multicolored,** FDD *(Sept. 13, 1979),* tagged	.26	.20
	y. Se-tenant pair #929-930		

931 "The Dance," *by Kalvak of Holman Island;* 932 *Drum Dance, Repulse Bay soapstone sculpture, by Madeleine Isserkut and Jean Mapsalak*

931		**MNHVF**	**UseVF**
17¢	**multicolored,** FDD *(Sept. 13, 1979),* tagged	.26	.20

932		**MNHVF**	**UseVF**
17¢	**multicolored,** FDD *(Sept. 13, 1979),* tagged	.26	.20
	y. Se-tenant pair #931-932		

1979. CHRISTMAS ISSUE *Offset, perforated 13, multicolored, color of background given below.*

933 *Wooden train*

933		**MNHVF**	**UseVF**
15¢	**blue,** FDD *(Oct. 17, 1979),* tagged	.26	.20

934 *Horse pull toy*

934		**MNHVF**	**UseVF**
17¢	**green,** FDD *(Oct. 17, 1979),* tagged	.30	.20

935 *Knitted doll*

935		**MNHVF**	**UseVF**
35¢	**carmine,** FDD *(Oct. 17, 1979),* tagged	.60	.45
	x. gold and tagging omitted	1,250.00	

1979. INTERNATIONAL YEAR OF CHILD ISSUE *Offset by Ashton-Potter, perforated 13.*

936 *Girl nurturing Tree of Life*

936		**MNHVF**	**UseVF**
17¢	**multicolored,** FDD *(Oct. 24, 1979),* tagged	.26	.20

1979. AIRPLANE ISSUE *Offset, perforated 12 1/2.*

937 *Canadair CL-215;* 938 *Curtiss HS-2L*

937		**MNHVF**	**UseVF**
17¢	**multicolored,** FDD *(Nov. 15, 1979)*	.30	.20

938		**MNHVF**	**UseVF**
17¢	**yellow orange,** FDD *(Nov. 15, 1979)*	.30	.20
	y. Se-tenant pair #937-938	.60	.53

939 *Consolidated Canso;* 940 *Vickers Vedette*

939		**MNHVF**	**UseVF**
35¢	**multicolored,** FDD *(Nov. 15, 1979)*	.60	.53

940		**MNHVF**	**UseVF**
35¢	**multicolored,** FDD *(Nov. 15, 1979)*	.65	.53
	y. Se-tenant pair #939-940	1.25	1.25

1980. ARCTIC ISLANDS ACQUISITION CENTENNIAL ISSUE *Offset, perforated 13 1/2.*

941 *Map of Canada showing Arctic Islands*

941		**MNHVF**	**UseVF**
17¢	**multicolored,** FDD *(Jan. 23, 1980)*	.26	.20

1980. 13TH WINTER OLYMPIC GAMES ISSUE Lake Placid, N.Y., Feb. 12-24. *Offset, perforated 13 1/2.*

942 *Downhill skiing*

942
35¢   **multicolored**   MNHVF UseVF
.65 .55

1980. ROYAL CANADIAN ACADEMY OF ARTS CENTENNIAL ISSUE
Offset, perforated 13 1/2.

943 Inspiration, *bronze sculpture, by Louis-Philippe Hebert (1850-1917);* 944 Meeting of the School Trustees, *by Robert Harris*

943
17¢   **multicolored,** FDD *(March 6, 1980)*   MNHVF UseVF
.30 .20
944
17¢   **multicolored,** FDD *(March 6, 1980)*   MNHVF UseVF
.30 .20
  y. Se-tenant pair #943-944   .60 .50

945 Sunrise on the Saguenay, by Lucius O'Brien (1832-99); 946 Parliament Buildings, *by Thomas Fuller (1822-1919)*

945
35¢   **multicolored,** FDD *(March 6, 1980)*   MNHVF UseVF
.60 .53
946
35¢   **multicolored,** FDD *(March 6, 1980)*   MNHVF UseVF
.60 .53
  y. Se-tenant pair #945-946   .75 .75

1980. ENDANGERED WILDLIFE ISSUE *Offset, perforated 12 1/2.*

947 *Atlantic whitefish*

947
17¢   **multicolored,** FDD *(May 6, 1980)*   MNHVF UseVF
.35 .20

948 *Greater prairie chicken*

948
17¢   **multicolored,** FDD *(May 6, 1980)*   MNHVF UseVF
.35 .20

1980. INTERNATIONAL FLOWER SHOW ISSUE Montreal, May 17-Sept. 1. *Offset, perforated 13 1/2.*

949 *Bed of flowers*

949
17¢   **multicolored,** FDD *(May 29, 1980)*   MNHVF UseVF
.26 .20

1980. 14TH WORLD CONGRESS OF REHABILITATION INTERNATIONAL ISSUE Winnipeg, June 22-27. *Offset and embossed, perforated 1/2.*

950 *Two helping hands*

950
17¢   **ultra & gold,** FDD *(May 29, 1980)*   MNHVF UseVF
.26 .20

1980. "O CANADA" CENTENNIAL ISSUE *Offset, perforated 12 1/2.*

951 O Canada *opening bars;* 952 Composers Lavallee, Routhier and Weir

951
17¢   **multicolored,** FDD *(June 6, 1980)*   MNHVF UseVF
.26 .20
952
17¢   **multicolored,** FDD *(June 6, 1980)*   MNHVF UseVF
.26 .20
  y. Se-tenant pair #951-952   .53 .53

1980. DIEFENBAKER ISSUE *Intaglio, perforted 13 1/2.*

953 *John George Diefenbaker (1895-1979), Prime Minister, 1956-63*

953
17¢   **dark blue,** FDD *(June 20, 1980)*   MNHVF UseVF
.26 .20

1980. FAMOUS PEOPLE ISSUE *Offset, perforated 13 1/2.*

954 Emma Albani (1847-1930), soprano; 955 *Healey Willan (1880-1968), organist and composer*

954
17¢   **multicolored,** FDD *(July 4, 1980)*   **MNHVF**   **UseVF**
    .26   .20

955
17¢   **multicolored,** FDD *(July 4, 1980)*   **MNHVF**   **UseVF**
    .26   .20
    y. Se-tenant pair #954-955   .53   .53

956 *Ned Hanlan (1855-1908), oarsman*

956
17¢   **multicolored,** FDD *(July 4, 1980)*   **MNHVF**   **UseVF**
    .26   .20

1980. SASKATCHEWAN'S AND ALBERTA'S ENTRY INTO CONFEDERATION ISSUE 75th anniversary. *Offset, perforated 13 1/2.*

957 *Town and strip mining, Cowley, Alberta*

957
17¢   **multicolored,** FDD *(Aug. 27, 1980)*   **MNHVF**   **UseVF**
    .26   .20

958 *Grain elevators and wheat fields, Estlin, Saskatchewan*

958
17¢   **multicolored,** FDD *(Aug. 27, 1980)*   **MNHVF**   **UseVF**
    .26   .20

1980. DISCOVERY OF URANIUM ISSUE 80th anniversary. *Offset, perforated 13 1/2.*

959 *Uraninite Molecular Structure.*

959
35¢   **multicolored,** FDD *(Sept. 3, 1980)*   **MNHVF**   **UseVF**
    .60   .53

1980. INUIT SPIRITS ISSUE *Offset, perforated 13 1/2.*

960 Return of the Sun, *print by Kenojouak;* 961 Sedna, *stone sculpture by Ashoona Kiawak*

960
17¢   **multicolored,** FDD *(Sept. 25, 1980)*   **MNHVF**   **UseVF**
    .26   .20

961
17¢   **multicolored,** FDD *(Sept. 25, 1980)*   **MNHVF**   **UseVF**
    .26   .20
    y. Se-tenant pair #960-961   .55   .50

962 Shaman, *print by Simon;* 963 Bird Spirit, *stone sculpture by Doris Hagiolok*

962
35¢   **multicolored,** FDD *(Sept. 25, 1980)*   **MNHVF**   **UseVF**
    .55   .50

963
35¢   **multicolored,** FDD *(Sept. 25, 1980)*   **MNHVF**   **UseVF**
    .55   .50
    y. Se-tenant pair #962-963   1.15   1.15

1980. CHRISTMAS ISSUE Greeting cards, 1931. *Offset, perforated 12 1/3 x 12.*

964 "Christmas Morning" *by Frank Charles Hennessey*

964
15¢   **multicolored,** FDD *(Oct. 22, 1980)*   **MNHVF**   **UseVF**
    .25   .20

965 "Sleigh Ride" *by Joseph Sydney Hallam*

965
17¢   **multicolored,** FDD *(Oct. 22, 1980)*   **MNHVF**   **UseVF**
    .26   .20

966 "McGill Cab Stand" *by Kathleen Morris*

966
35¢   **multicolored,** FDD *(Oct. 22, 1980)*   MNHVF .50   UseVF .45

1980. MILITARY AIRCRAFT ISSUE *Offset, perforated 13 x 13 1/2.*

967 *Avro Lancaster, 1941;* 968 *Avro Canada CF-100*

967
17¢   **multicolored,** FDD *(Nov. 10, 1980)*   MNHVF .30   UseVF .20
968
17¢   **multicolored,** FDD *(Nov. 10, 1980)*   MNHVF .30   UseVF .20
    y. Se-tenant pair #967-968   .60   .50

969 *Hawker Hurrican, 1935;* 970 *Curtiss JN-4 Canuck*

969
35¢   **multicolored,** FDD *(Nov. 10, 1980)*   MNHVF .55   UseVF .50
970
35¢   **multicolored,** FDD *(Nov. 10, 1980)*   MNHVF .55   UseVF .50
    y. Se-tenant pair #969-970   1.25   1.25

1980. LACHAPELLE ISSUE *Offset, perforated 13 1/2.*

971 *Emmanuel-Persillier Lachapelle (1845-1918), physician, founded Notre Dame Hospital, Montreal, 1880, and caduceus*

971
17¢   **multicolored,** FDD *(Dec. 5, 1980)*   MNHVF .26   UseVF .20

1981. THE LOOK OF MUSIC ISSUE Rare musical instrument exhibition, Vancouver, Nov. 2, 1980-April 5, 1981. *Offset, perforated 12 1/2.*

972 *Mandora, 18th century*

972
17¢   **multicolored,** FDD *(Jan. 19, 1981)*   MNHVF .26   UseVF .20

1981. PEOPLE AND BUILDINGS ISSUE *Offset, perforated 13 x 13 1/2.*

973 *Emily Stowe (1831-1903) and Toronto General Hospital;* 974 *Idola Saint-Jean (1875-1945) and Quebec legislative building;* 975 *Louise McKinney (1868-1931) and Alberta legislative building;* 976 *Henrietta Edwards (1849-1931) clubwomen*

973
17¢   **multicolored,** FDD *(March 4, 1981)*   MNHVF .35   UseVF .25
974
17¢   **multicolored,** FDD *(March 4, 1981)*   MNHVF .35   UseVF .25
975
17¢   **multicolored,** FDD *(March 4, 1981)*   MNHVF .35   UseVF .25
976
17¢   **multicolored,** FDD *(March 4, 1981)*   MNHVF .35   UseVF .25
    y. Se-tenant block of 4 #973-976   1.35   1.35

1981. ENDANGERED WILDLIFE *Offset, perforated 13 x 13 1/2.*

977 Vancouver Island Marmot, *by Michael Dumas*

977
17¢   **multicolored,** FDD *(April 6, 1981)*   MNHVF .30   UseVF .20

978 Wood bison, *by Robert Bateman*

978
35¢   **multicolored,** FDD *(April 6, 1981)*   MNHVF .75   UseVF .68

1981. BRUNET SCULPTURE ISSUE *Offset, perforated 12 1/2.*

979 *"Lily of the Mohawks," Kateri Tekakwitha (1656-1680), first North American Indian saint, by Emile Brunet;* 980 *Marie De L'Incarnation (1599-1672), founder of Ursuline Order of Nuns*

979
17¢   **brown & pale green,** FDD *(April 24, 1981)*   MNHVF .26   UseVF .20
980
17¢   **light blue & ultra,** FDD *(April 24, 1981)*   MNHVF .26   UseVF .20
    y. Se-tenant pair #979-980   .50   .50

1981. PAINTING ISSUE *Offset, perforated 12 1/2.*

981 At Bale Saint-Paul, *by Marc-Aurele Fortin (1888-1970).*

981		MNHVF	UseVF
17¢	**multicolored,** FDD *(May 22, 1981)*	.26	.20

982 *Self-portrait, by Frederick H. Varley (1881-1969)*

982		MNHVF	UseVF
17¢	**multicolored,** FDD *(May 22, 1981)*	.25	.20
	v. Pair, imperforate	1,750.00	

1981. PAINTING ISSUE *Gravure, perforated 13.*

983 Untitled No. 6, *by Paul-Emile Borduas (1905-1960)*

983		MNHVF	UseVF
35¢	**multicolored,** FDD *(May 22, 1981)*	.60	.60

1981. MAP ISSUE *Offset, perforated 13 1/2.*

984-987 *Maps of Canada showing four provincial boundaries, 1867, 1873, 1905, 1949*

984		MNHVF	UseVF
17¢	**multicolored,** FDD *(June 30, 1981)*	.30	.25
985		MNHVF	UseVF
17¢	**multicolored,** FDD *(June 30, 1981)*	.30	.25
986		MNHVF	UseVF
17¢	**multicolored,** FDD *(June 30, 1981)*	.30	.25

987		MNHVF	UseVF
17¢	**multicolored,** FDD *(June 30, 1981)*	.30	.25
	y. Se-tenant strip of 4	1.30	1.30

1981. BOTANISTS ISSUE *Offset, perforated 12 1/2.*

988 *Frere Marie-Victorin (1885-1944); 989 John Macoun (1831-1920)*

988		MNHVF	UseVF
17¢	**multicolored,** FDD *(July 22, 1981)*	.26	.20
989		MNHVF	UseVF
17¢	**multicolored,** FDD *(July 22, 1981)*	.26	.20
	y. Se-tenant pair #988-989	.55	.50

1981. FLOWER EXHIBITION ISSUE *Offset, perforated 13 1/2.*

990 *Montreal rose*

990		MNHVF	UseVF
17¢	**multicolored,** FDD *(July 22, 1981)*	.26	.20

1981. NIAGARA-ON-THE-LAKE ISSUE First capital of Upper Canada. *Gravure and intaglio, perforated 13 1/2.*

991 *Map*

991		MNHVF	UseVF
17¢	**multicolored,** FDD *(July 31, 1981)*	.26	.20

1981. ACADIAN CONGRESS CENTENNIAL ISSUE *Offset, perforated 13 1/2.*

992 L'Acadie, *by Neree de Grace*

992		MNHVF	UseVF
17¢	**multicolored,** FDD *(Aug. 14, 1981)*	.26	.20

1981. AARON MOSHER ISSUE *Offset, perforated 13 1/2.*

993 *Aaron Mosher (1881-1959), Labor Congress founder*

993		MNHVF	UseVF
17¢	**multicolored,** FDD *(Sept. 8, 1981)*	.55	.20

1981. CHRISTMAS ISSUE Bicentennial of the first illuminated Christmas tree in Canada. *Offset, perforated 13 1/2, multicolored, color of background given below.*

994 *Christmas tree, 1781*

994		MNHVF	UseVF
15¢	**cream,** FDD *(Nov. 16, 1981)*	.55	.20

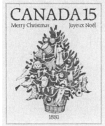

995 *Christmas tree, 1881*

995		MNHVF	UseVF
15¢	**tan,** FDD *(Nov. 16, 1981)*	.55	.20

996 *Christmas tree, 1981*

996		MNHVF	UseVF
15¢	**light blue,** FDD *(Nov. 16, 1981)*	.55	.20

1981. AIRPLANE ISSUE *Offset, perforated 12 1/2.*

997 *Canadair CL-41 Tutor* 998 *deHavilland Tiger Moth*

997		MNHVF	UseVF
17¢	**multicolored,** FDD *(Nov. 24, 1981)*	.25	.20
998		MNHVF	UseVF
17¢	**multicolored,** FDD *(Nov. 24, 1981)*	.25	.20
	y. Se-tenant pair #997-998		

999 *Avro Canada C-102* 1000 *de Havilland Canada Dash-7*

999		MNHVF	UseVF
35¢	**multicolored,** FDD *(Nov. 24, 1981)*	.60	.55
1000		MNHVF	UseVF
35¢	**multicolored,** FDD *(Nov. 24, 1981)*	.55	.45
	y. Se-tenant pair #997-1000	1.25	1.20

Regular Issues

1981. MAPLE LEAF ISSUE Canada's first non-denominational stamp inscribed "A" first-class for domestic rate. *Intaglio, perforated 13 x 13 1/2.*

1001, 1002 *Maple leaf*

1001		MNHVF	UseVF
(30¢)	**red,** FDD *(Dec. 29, 1981)*	.50	.20

1981. MAPLE LEAF COIL ISSUE Non-denominated "A" for first-class domestic rate. *Intaglio, perforated 10 vertical.*

1002		MNHVF	UseVF
(30¢)	**red & light blue,** FDD *(Dec. 29, 1981)*	.85	.20
	v. Pair, imperforate	400.00	

See Nos. 1005-1007, 1012-1013, 1038-1041.

Commemorative Issues

1982. INTERNATIONAL PHILATELIC YOUTH EXHIBITION ISSUE
Toronto, May 20-24. *Offset, perforated 13 1/2.*

1003 *Three-Penny Beaver*

1003		MNHVF	UseVF
30¢	**red,** FDD *(1982)*	.50	.25

1004 *1935 "Mountie" stamp*

1004		MNHVF	UseVF
35¢	**car rose,** FDD *(1982)*	.55	.55

Regular Issues

1982. MAPLE LEAF BOOKLET ISSUE *Intaglio, perforated 12 x 12 1/2.*

1005-1007 *Maple leaf*

1005		MNHVF	UseVF
5¢	**deep claret,** FDD *(March 1, 1982)*	.20	.20
1006		MNHVF	UseVF
10¢	**dark green,** FDD *(March 1, 1982)*	.45	.35
1007		MNHVF	UseVF
30¢	**red,** FDD *(March 1, 1982)*	.70	.30
	n. Booklet pane of 4 plus 2 labels (2 #1005, 1 #1006, 1 #1007)	1.35	

Commemorative Issues

1982. JULES LEGER ISSUE *Offset, perforated 13 1/2.*

1008 *Jules Leger (1913-1980), 26th Governor General*

1008		MNHVF	UseVF
30¢	**multicolored,** FDD *(April 2, 1982)*	.45	.20

1982. TERRY FOX ISSUE *Offset, perforated 12 1/2.*

1009 *Terry Fox (1958-1981), Marathon of Hope.*

1009		MNHVF	UseVF
30¢	**multicolored,** FDD *(April 13, 1982)*	.45	.20

1982. CONSTITUTION ISSUE *Offset, perforated 12 x 12 1/2.*

1010 *Open book*

1010		MNHVF	UseVF
30¢	**multicolored,** FDD *(April 16, 1982)*	.45	.20

Regular Issues

1982. DEFINITIVE ISSUE *Gravure and intaglio, perforated 13 x 13 1/2.*

1011 *Queen Elizabeth II*

1011		MNHVF	UseVF
30¢	**violet gray,** FDD *(May 11, 1982)*	.35	.20

1982. MAPLE LEAF ISSUE *Gravure and intaglio, perforated 13 x 13 1/2.*

1012 *Maple leaf*

1012		MNHVF	UseVF
30¢	**light blue & red,** FDD *(May 11, 1982)*	.45	.20
	n. Booklet pane of 20, perforated 12 x 12 1/2 (June 30, 1982)	11.25	
	v. Perforated 12 x 12 1/2	.75	.20

1982. MAPLE LEAF COIL ISSUE *Intaglio, perforated 10 vertical.*

1013 *Maple leaf*

1013		MNHVF	UseVF
30¢	**red,** FDD *(1982)*	.85	.20
	v. Pair, imperforate	345.00	

1982. STREET SCENE ISSUE *Offset, perforated 13 1/2.*

1014 *Street scene, Ontario City*

1014		MNHVF	UseVF
60¢	**multicolored,** *(May 11, 1982)*	1.30	.25

Commemorative Issues

1982. INTERNATIONAL PHILATELIC YOUTH EXHIBITION ISSUE Toronto, May 20-24. *Offset, perforated 13 1/2.*

1015 *1908 Champlain stamp*

1015
30¢   **red orange,** FDD *(May 20, 1982)*

	MNHVF	UseVF
	.40	.20

1016 *1928* Mount Hurd, *painting by Bell Smith known as "The Icecrowned Monarch of the Rockies."*

1016
35¢   **green,** FDD *(May 20, 1982)*

	MNHVF	UseVF
	.55	.55

1017 *1929 Bluenose schooner*

1017
60¢   **dark blue,** FDD *(May 20, 1982)*

	MNHVF	UseVF
	1.00	.90

1982. INTERNATIONAL PHILATELIC YOUTH EXHIBITION SOUVENIR SHEET

1018 *International Philatelic Youth Exhibition Souvenir Sheet*

1018
   Sheet of 5, #1003-1004, #1015-1017, FDD *(May 20, 1982)*

	MNHVF	UseVF
	3.75	3.75

Regular Issues

1982. NATIONAL PARK ISSUE *Offset, perforated 13 1/2.*

1019 *Waterton Lakes National Park*

1019
$1.50   **multicolored,** FDD *(June 18, 1982)*

	MNHVF	UseVF
	3.45	.55

Commemorative Issues

1982. SALVATION ARMY CENTENNIAL ISSUE *Offset, perforated 13.*

1020 *Salvation Army members*

1020
30¢   **multicolored,** FDD *(June 25, 1982)*

	MNHVF	UseVF
	.40	.20

1982. PAINTINGS ISSUE *Offset, perforated 12 1/2 x 12.*

1021A The Highway near Kluana Lake, *by A.Y. Jackson;* 1021B Montreal Street Scene, *by Adrien Hebert;* 1021C Breakwater, *by Christopher Pratt;* 1021D Along Great Slave Lake, *by Rene Richard;* 1021E Tea Hill, *by Molly Lamb;* 1021F Family and Rainstorm, *by Alex Colville;* 1021G Brown Shadows, *by Dorothy Knowles;* 1021H The Red Brick House, *by David Milne;* 1021I Campus Gates, *by Bruno Bobak;* 1021J Prairie Town-Early Morning, *by Illingworth Kerr;* 1021K Totems at Ninstints, *by Joe Plaskett;* 1021L Dock Snider's House, *by Lionel LeMoine FitzGerald*

1021			MNHVF	UseVF
	Miniature sheet of 12, #1021A-1021L, FDD *(June 30, 1982)*		7.50	4.50

1021A			MNHVF	UseVF
30¢	**multicolored,** FDD *(June 30, 1982)*		.60	.35

1021B			MNHVF	UseVF
30¢	**multicolored,** FDD *(June 30, 1982)*		.60	.35

1021C			MNHVF	UseVF
30¢	**multicolored,** FDD *(June 30, 1982)*		.60	.35

1021D			MNHVF	UseVF
30¢	**multicolored,** FDD *(June 30, 1982)*		.60	.35

1021E			MNHVF	UseVF
30¢	**multicolored,** FDD *(June 30, 1982)*		.60	.35

1021F			MNHVF	UseVF
30¢	**multicolored,** FDD *(June 30, 1982)*		.60	.35

1021G			MNHVF	UseVF
30¢	**multicolored,** FDD *(June 30, 1982)*		.60	.35

1021H			MNHVF	UseVF
30¢	**multicolored,** FDD *(June 30, 1982)*		.60	.35

1021I			MNHVF	UseVF
30¢	**multicolored,** FDD *(June 30, 1982)*		.60	.35

1021J			MNHVF	UseVF
30¢	**multicolored,** FDD *(June 30, 1982)*		.60	.35

1021K			MNHVF	UseVF
30¢	**multicolored,** FDD *(June 30, 1982)*		.60	.35

1021L			MNHVF	UseVF
30¢	**multicolored,** FDD *(June 30, 1982)*		.60	.35

1982. REGINA CENTENNIAL ISSUE *Offset, perforated 13 1/2 x 13.*

1022 *Legislative building*

1022		MNHVF	UseVF
30¢	**multicolored,** FDD *(Aug. 3, 1982)*	.45	.20

1982. ROYAL CANADIAN HENLEY REGATTA CENTENNIAL ISSUE
St. Catharines, Aug. 4-8. *Offset, perforated 13 1/2 x 13.*

1023 *Racing shells*

1023		MNHVF	UseVF
30¢	**multicolored,** FDD *(Aug. 4, 1982)*	.45	.20

1982. AIRPLANE ISSUE *Offset, perforated 12 1/2.*

1024 *De Havilland Canada Beaver;* 1025 *Fairchild FC-2W1*

1024		MNHVF	UseVF
30¢	**multicolored,** FDD *(Oct. 5, 1982)*	.75	.20

1025		MNHVF	UseVF
30¢	**multicolored,** FDD *(Oct. 5, 1982)*	.60	.20
	y. Se-tenant pair #1024-1025	1.75	1.15

1026 *Noorduyn Norseman;* 1027 *Fokker Super Universal*

1026		MNHVF	UseVF
60¢	**multicolored,** FDD *(Oct. 5, 1982)*	1.10	.75

1027		MNHVF	UseVF
60¢	**multicolored,** FDD *(Oct. 5, 1982)*	1.00	.75
	y. Se-tenant pair #1026-1027	2.40	2.00

Regular Issues

1982-85. FOLK ART ISSUE *Offset, perforated 14 x 13 1/2.*

1028 *Decoy*

1028		MNHVF	UseVF
1¢	**multicolored,** FDD *(Oct. 19, 1982)*	.20	.20
	Perforated 13 x 13 1/2, FDD *(Jan. 10, 1985)*	.20	.20

1029 *Fishing spear*

1029		MNHVF	UseVF
2¢	**multicolored,** FDD *(Oct. 19, 1982)*	.20	.20
	Perforated 13 x 13 1/2, FDD *(Feb 10, 1984)*	.20	.20

1030 *Stable lantern*

1030		MNHVF	UseVF
3¢	**multicolored,** FDD *(Oct. 19, 1982)*	.20	.20
	Perforated 13 x 13 1/2, FDD *(Jan. 10, 1985)*	.20	.20

1031 *Bucket*

1031		MNHVF	UseVF
5¢	**multicolored,** FDD *(Oct. 19, 1982)*	.20	.20
	Perforated 13 x 13 1/2, FDD *(July 6, 1984)*	.20	.20

1032 *Weathercock*

1032		MNHVF	UseVF
10¢	**multicolored,** FDD *(Oct. 19, 1982)*	.20	.20
	Perforated 13 x 13 1/2, FDD *(March 15, 1985)*	.20	.20

1033 *Ice skates*

1033
20¢   multicolored, FDD *(Oct. 19, 1982)* MNHVF .35 UseVF .20

Commemorative Issues

1982. CHRISTMAS ISSUE *Offset, perforated 13 1/2.*

 1034 *Holy family*

1034
30¢   multicolored, FDD *(Nov. 3, 1982)* MNHVF .45 UseVF .20
  x. red color omitted — —
  x1. printed on gum side — —
  x2. orange background (10 known) 750. —

 1035 *Shepherds*

1035
35¢   multicolored, FDD *(Nov. 3, 1982)* MNHVF .50 UseVF .45

 1036 *Three Kings*

1036
60¢   multicolored, FDD *(Nov. 3, 1982)* MNHVF .90 UseVF .75

Regular Issues

1983. NATIONAL PARK ISSUE *Offset, perforated 13 1/2.*

 1037 *Point Pelee National Park*

1037
$5   multicolored, FDD *(Jan. 10, 1983)* MNHVF 9.00 UseVF 2.00

1983. MAPLE LEAF ISSUE *Gravure and intaglio, perforated 13 x 13 1/2.*

 1038 *Maple leaf*

1038
32¢   beige, red & brown, FDD *(Feb. 10, 1983)* MNHVF .50 UseVF .60
  n. Booklet pane of 25, perforated 12 x 12 12.00 10.00
    1/2 (April 1, 1983)
  v. Perforated 12 x 12 1/2 .90 1.75
  v1. As #1038, beige omitted —

1983. MAPLE LEAF BOOKLET ISSUE *Intaglio, perforated 12 x 12 1/2.*

 1039-1040 *Maple leaf*

1039
8¢   dark blue, FDD *(Feb. 15, 1983)* MNHVF .50 UseVF .45
1040
32¢   brown, FDD *(Feb. 15, 1983)* MNHVF .50 UseVF .55
  n. Booklet pane of 4 plus 2 labels, 2 #1005, .90 1.75
    1039, 1040

1983. MAPLE LEAF COIL ISSUE *Intaglio, perforated 10 vertical.*

1041
32¢   brown, FDD *(Feb. 10, 1983)* MNHVF .55 UseVF .20
  v. Pair, imperforate 150.00

Commemorative Issues

1983. WORLD COMMUNICATIONS YEAR ISSUE *Offset, perforated 12 x 12 1/2.*

 1042 *Globe and orbits*

1042
32¢   multicolored, FDD *(March 10, 1983)* MNHVF .50 UseVF .20

1883. COMMONWEALTH DAY ISSUE *Offset, perforated 12 x 12 1/2.*

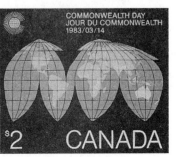 1043 *Projection of World*

1043		MNHVF	UseVF
$2	**multicolored,** FDD *(March 14, 1983)*	9.25	3.75

Regular Issue

1983. FOLK ART ISSUE *Offset, perforated 12 x 12 1/2 or 12 1/2 x 12; 26 x 20mm; multicolored, color of background given below.*

1044 *Wooden plow*

1044		MNHVF	UseVF
37¢	**green,** FDD *(April 8, 1983)*	.55	.20

1045 *Cradle*

1045		MNHVF	UseVF
48¢	**magenta,** FDD *(April 8, 1983)*	.75	.30

1046 *Wood stove*

1046		MNHVF	UseVF
64¢	**grey,** FDD *(April 8, 1983)*	1.00	.35

Commemorative Issues

1983. CANADIAN WRITERS ISSUE *Offset, perforated 13 1/2.*

1047 Mourning Woman, *scene from Angeline de Montbrun, author Laure Conan (1845-1924), painted by Rene Milot;* 1048 Sea Gulls, *by Edwin J. Pratt (1882-1966), woodcut by Claire Pratt*

1047		MNHVF	UseVF
32¢	**multicolored,** FDD *(April 22, 1983)*	.50	.20

1048		MNHVF	UseVF
32¢	**multicolored,** FDD *(April 22, 1983)*	.55	.20
	y. Se-tenant pair #1047-1048	1.10	.90
	x. color on se-tenant pair omitted	—	—

Regular Issues

1983. DEFINITIVE ISSUE *Gravure, engraved, perforated 13 x 13 1/2.*

1049 *Queen Elizabeth II*

1049		MNHVF	UseVF
32¢	**blue & gray,** FDD *(May 24, 1983)*	.50	.20

Commemorative Issues

1983. ST. JOHN AMBULANCE CENTENNIAL ISSUE *Offset, perforated 13 1/2.*

1050 *Emblem*

1050		MNHVF	UseVF
32¢	**multicolored,** FDD *(June 3, 1983)*	.50	.20

1983. WORLD UNIVERSITY GAMES ISSUE *Offset, perforated 13 1/2.*

1051, 1052 *Victory Pictogram*

1051		MNHVF	UseVF
32¢	**silver & multicolored,** FDD *(June 28, 1983)*	.50	.20

1052		MNHVF	UseVF
64¢	**gold & multicolored,** FDD *(June 28, 1983)*	1.10	.75

Every entry in this catalog has been double-checked for accuracy, but mistakes creep into any human endeavor, and we ask your assistance in eliminating them. Please call the attention of the editors to any errors in stamp descriptions found in this catalog.

1983. CANADA DAY BOOKLET ISSUE *Offset, perforated 12 1/2 x 13, multicolored. Nos. 1053-1058: 44 x 22mm; Nos. 1054-1055, 1059-1060: 36 x 22mm; Nos. 1056-1057, 1061-1062: 28 x 22mm.*

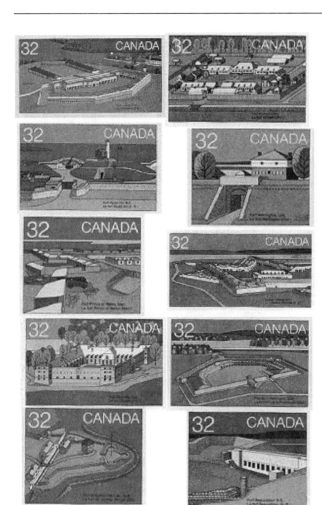

1053-1062

1053		**MNHVF**	**UseVF**
32¢	**Fort Henry, Ontario,** FDD *(June 30, 1983)*	.65	.50

1054		**MNHVF**	**UseVF**
32¢	**Fort William, Ontario,** FDD *(June 30, 1983)*	.65	.50

1055		**MNHVF**	**UseVF**
32¢	**Fort Rodd Hill, British Columbia,** FDD *(June 30, 1983)*	.65	.50

1056		**MNHVF**	**UseVF**
32¢	**Fort Wellington, Ontario,** FDD *(June 30, 1983)*	.65	.50

1057		**MNHVF**	**UseVF**
32¢	**Fort Prince of Wales, Manitoba,** FDD *(June 30, 1983)*	.65	.50

1058		**MNHVF**	**UseVF**
32¢	**Halifax Citadel, Nova Scotia,** FDD *(June 30, 1983)*	.65	.50

1059		**MNHVF**	**UseVF**
32¢	**Fort Chambly, Quebec,** FDD *(June 30, 1983)*	.65	.50

1060		**MNHVF**	**UseVF**
32¢	**Fort No. 1, Point Levis, Quebec,** FDD *(June 30, 1983)*	.65	.50

1061		**MNHVF**	**UseVF**
32¢	**Fort at Coteau-du-lac, Quebec,** FDD *(June 30, 1983)*	.65	.50

1062		**MNHVF**	**UseVF**
32¢	**Fort Beausejour, New Brunswick,** FDD *(June 30, 1983)*	.65	.50
	n. Booklet pane of 10 #1053-1062	6.75	5.00

1983. SCOUTING YEAR ISSUE *Offset, perforated 13 1/2.*

1063 *Camping scene*

1063		**MNHVF**	**UseVF**
32¢	**multicolored,** FDD *(July 6, 1983)*	.50	.20

1983. WORLD COUNCIL OF CHURCHES ASSEMBLY ISSUE Vancouver, July 24-Aug. 10. *Offset, perforated 13 1/2.*

1064 *Cross and church council emblem*

1064		**MNHVF**	**UseVF**
32¢	**tan & green,** FDD *(July 22, 1983)*	.50	.20

1983. SIR HUMPHREY GILBERT ISSUE 400th anniversary of discovery of Newfoundland. *Offset, perforated 13 1/2.*

1065 *Humphrey Gilbert (1537-1583)*

1065		**MNHVF**	**UseVF**
32¢	**multicolored,** FDD *(Aug. 3, 1983)*	.50	.20

1983. DISCOVERY OF NICKEL CENTENNIAL ISSUE Sudbury, Ontario. *Gravure and embossed, perforated 13.*

1066 *Nickel*

1066		**MNHVF**	**UseVF**
32¢	**multicolored,** FDD *(Aug. 12, 1983)*	.50	.20

1983. ANTOINE LABELLE ISSUE *Gravure and embossed, perforated 13 1/2.*

1067 *Antoine Labelle (1833-1891), Deputy Minister for Settlement*

1067		MNHVF	UseVF
32¢	multicolored, FDD *(Sept. 16, 1983)*	.50	.20

1983. JOSIAH HENSON ISSUE *Gravure and embossed, perforated 13 x 13 1/2.*

1068 *Josiah Henson (1789-1883), preacher*

1068		MNHVF	UseVF
32¢	multicolored, FDD *(Sept. 16, 1983)*	.50	.20

1983. LOCOMOTIVE ISSUE *Gravure and embossed, perforated 12 1/2 x 13.*

1069 *Dorchester 0-4-0, 1836;* 1070 *Toronto 4-4-0, 1853*

1069		MNHVF	UseVF
32¢	multicolored, FDD *(Oct. 3, 1983)*	.50	.30
1070		MNHVF	UseVF
32¢	multicolored, FDD *(Oct. 3, 1983)*	.50	.25
	y. Se-tenant pair #1069-1070	1.10	1.00

1071 *Samson 0-6-0, 1838*

1071		MNHVF	UseVF
37¢	multicolored, FDD *(Oct. 3, 1983)*	.70	.55

1072 *Adam Brown 4-4-0, 1860*

1072		MNHVF	UseVF
64¢	mutlticolored, FDD *(Oct. 3, 1983)*	1.00	.85

1983. DALHOUSIE LAW SCHOOL CENTENNIAL ISSUE *Offset, perforated 13.*

1073 *Dalhousie Law School emblem*

1073		MNHVF	UseVF
32¢	multicolored, FDD *(Oct. 28, 1983)*	.50	.20

1983. CHRISTMAS ISSUE *Offset, perforated 13 1/2.*

1074 *City church*

1074		MNHVF	UseVF
32¢	multicolored, FDD *(Nov. 3, 1983)*	.50	.20

1075 *Family going to church*

1075		MNHVF	UseVF
37¢	multicolored, FDD *(Nov. 3, 1983)*	.55	.45

1076 *Rural church*

1076		MNHVF	UseVF
64¢	multicolored, FDD *(Nov. 3, 1983)*	1.00	.75

1983. ARMY REGIMENT CENTENNIAL ISSUE *Offset, perforated 13 1/2 x 13.*

1077 *Royal Winnipeg Rifles, Royal Canadian Dragoons, 19th century uniforms;*

1078 *Royal Canadian Regiment, British Columbia Regiment, 19th century uniforms*

1077		MNHVF	UseVF
32¢	multicolored, FDD *(Nov. 10, 1983)*	.50	.20
1078		MNHVF	UseVF
32¢	multicolored, FDD *(Nov. 10, 1983)*	.55	.20
	y. Se-tenant pair #1077-1078	1.25	.90

1984. YELLOWKNIFE ISSUE *50th anniversary. Offset, perforated 13 1/2.*

1079 *Head frame and pan*

1079		MNHVF	UseVF
32¢	**multicolored,** FDD *(March 15, 1984)*	.50	.20

1984. MONTREAL SYMPHONY ORCHESTRA ISSUE 50th anniversary. *Offset, perforated 12 1/2.*

1080 *Orchestra members*

1080		MNHVF	UseVF
32¢	**multicolored,** FDD *(March 24, 1984)*	.50	.20

1984. CARTIER'S LANDING IN QUEBEC ISSUE 450th anniversary. *Gravure and intaglio, perforated 12 1/2.*

1081 *Cartier and flagship*

1081		MNHVF	UseVF
32¢	**multicolored,** FDD *(April 20, 1984)*	.50	.20

1984. VOYAGE OF TALL SHIPS ISSUE 450th anniversary of Cartier's landing in Quebec, Saint-Malo, France to Quebec. *Offset, perforated 12 x 12 1/2.*

1082 *Tall ship*

1082		MNHVF	UseVF
32¢	**multicolored,** FDD *(May 18, 1984)*	.50	.20

1984. CANADIAN RED CROSS SOCIETY ISSUE 75th anniversary. *Offset, perforated 13.*

1083 *Meritorious Service Medal*

1083		MNHVF	UseVF
32¢	**multicolored,** FDD *(May 28, 1984)*	.50	.20

1984. NEW BRUNSWICK BICENTENNIAL ISSUE *Gravure and intaglio, perforated 13.*

1084 *Oared galleys*

1084		MNHVF	UseVF
32¢	**multicolored,** FDD *(June 18, 1984)*	.50	.20

1984. ST. LAWRENCE SEAWAY ISSUE 25th anniversary. *Offset, perforated 13.*

1085 *Seaway, Lake Superior*

1085		MNHVF	UseVF
32¢	**multicolored,** FDD *(June 26, 1984)*	.50	.20

1984. CANADA DAY ISSUE *Provincial Landscapes,* by Jean Paul Lemieux (b.1904). *Offset, perforated 13.*

1086a-1086l

1086		MNHVF	UseVF
32¢	**Miniature sheet of 12,** #1068a-1086l, FDD *(June 29, 1984)*	6.75	6.00

1086a		MNHVF	UseVF
32¢	**New Brunswick**	.55	.30

1086b		MNHVF	UseVF
32¢	**British Columbia**	.55	.30

1086c		MNHVF	UseVF
32¢	**Yukon Territory**	.55	.30

1086d		MNHVF	UseVF
32¢	**Quebec**	.55	.30

1086e		MNHVF	UseVF
32¢	**Manitoba**	.55	.30

1086f		MNHVF	UseVF
32¢	**Alberta**	.55	.30

1086g		MNHVF	UseVF
32¢	**Prince Edward Island**	.55	.30

1086h		MNHVF	UseVF
32¢	**Saskatchewan**	.55	.30

1086i		MNHVF	UseVF
32¢	**Nova Scotia,** vertical	.55	.30

1086j		MNHVF	UseVF
32¢	**Northwest Territories**	.55	.30

1086k		MNHVF	UseVF
32¢	**Newfoundland**	.50	.30

1086l		MNHVF	UseVF
32¢	**Ontario,** vertical	.65	.25

Nos. 1086c and 1086j incorrectly inscribed. No. 1086c shows North-west Territories landscape; No. 1086j shows Yukon Territory church.

1984. LOYALISTS ISSUE United Empire Loyalists, American colonists who remained loyal to British throne and emigrated to Canada during American Revolution. *Offset, perforated 13.*

1087 *Loyalists and British Flag (1606-1801)*

1087		MNHVF	UseVF
32¢	**multicolored,** FDD *(July 3, 1984)*	.50	.20

Regular Issues

1984. NATIONAL PARK ISSUE *Offset, perforated 13 1/2.*

1088 *Glacier National Park*

1088		MNHVF	UseVF
$1	**multicolored,** FDD *(Aug. 15, 1984)*	1.50	.50
	v. Blue inscriptions omitted	750.00	

Commemorative Issues

1984. ROMAN CATHOLIC CHURCH ISSUE *Offset, perforated 13 1/2.*

1089 *St. John's Basilica, Newfoundland*

1089		MNHVF	UseVF
32¢	**multicolored,** FDD *(Aug. 17, 1984)*	.50	.20

1984. PAPAL VISIT ISSUE *Offset, perforated 12 1/2.*

1090, 1091 *Coat of arms and map*

1090		MNHVF	UseVF
32¢	**gold & multicolored,** FDD *(Aug. 31, 1984)*	.50	.20

1091		MNHVF	UseVF
64¢	**silver & multicolored,** FDD *(Aug. 31, 1984)*	1.10	.70

1984. LIGHTHOUSE ISSUE *Offset, perforated 12 1/2.*

1092 *Louisbourg, 1734;* 1093 *Fisgard, 1860;* 1094 *Ile Verte, 1809;* 1095 *Gibraltar Point, 1808*

1092		MNHVF	UseVF
32¢	**multicolored,** FDD *(Sept. 21, 1984)*	.50	.20

1093		MNHVF	UseVF
32¢	**multicolored,** FDD *(Sept. 21, 1984)*	.50	.20

1094		MNHVF	UseVF
32¢	**multicolored,** FDD *(Sept. 21, 1984)*	.50	.20

1095		MNHVF	UseVF
32¢	**multicolored,** FDD *(Sept. 21, 1984)*	.50	.20
	y. Se-tenant block of 4 #1092-1095	2.25	1.00

1984. STEAM LOCOMOTIVE ISSUE *Offset, perforated 12 1/2 x 13.*

1096 *Scotia;* 1097 *Countress of Dufferin*

1096		MNHVF	UseVF
32¢	**multicolored,** FDD *(Oct. 25, 1984)*	.50	.20

1097		MNHVF	UseVF
32¢	**multicolored,** FDD *(Oct. 25, 1984)*	.50	.20
	y. Se-tenant pair #1096-1097	1.10	.90

1098 *Grand Trunk Class E3*

1098		MNHVF	UseVF
37¢	**multicolored,** FDD *(Oct. 25, 1984)*	.65	.60

1099 *Canadian Pacific D10a*

1099		MNHVF	UseVF
64¢	**multicolored,** FDD *(Oct. 25, 1984)*	1.10	.90

1984. STEAM LOCOMOTIVE SOUVENIR SHEET Contains No. 1096-1099 in changed colors.

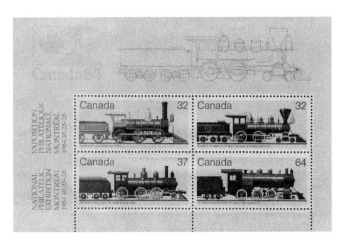

1096 *Scotia;* 1097 *Countress of Dufferin;* 1098 *Grand Trunk Class E3;* 1099 *Canadian Pacific D10a;*

1100		MNHVF	UseVF
$1.65	**Sheet of 4,** FDD *(Oct. 25, 1984)*	3.00	3.00

See Nos. 1143-1146, 1182-1185.

1984. CHRISTMAS ISSUE *Offset, perforated 13.*

1101 The Annunciation, *by Jean Dallaire*

1101		MNHVF	UseVF
32¢	**multicolored,** FDD *(Nov. 2, 1984)*	.50	.20

1102 The Three Kings, *by Simone Mary Bochard*

1102		MNHVF	UseVF
37¢	**multicolored,** FDD *(Nov. 2, 1984)*	.55	.55

1103 Snow in Bethlehem, *by David Milne*

1103		MNHVF	UseVF
64¢	**multicolored,** FDD *(Nov. 2, 1984)*	1.00	.75

1984. ROYAL CANADIAN AIR FORCE ISSUE *Offset, perforated 12 x 12 1/2.*

1104 *Pilots*

1104		MNHVF	UseVF
32¢	**multicolored,** FDD *(Nov. 9, 1984)*	.50	.20

1984. CENTENNIAL OF LA PRESSE ISSUE *La Presse,* daily French newspaper in Montreal. *Offset, perforated 13 x 13 1/2.*

1105 *Treffle Berthiaume*

1105		MNHVF	UseVF
32¢	**multicolored,** FDD *(Nov. 16, 1984)*	.50	.20

1985. INTERNATIONAL YOUTH YEAR ISSUE *Offset, perforated 12 1/2.*

1106 *Heart, arrow & jeans*

1106		MNHVF	UseVF
32¢	**multicolored,** FDD *(Feb. 8, 1985)*	.50	.20

1985. CANADIANS IN SPACE ISSUE *Offset, perforated 13 1/2.*

1107 *Astronaut*

1107		MNHVF	UseVF
32¢	**multicolored,** FDD *(March 15, 1985)*	.50	.20

1985. FAMOUS WOMEN ISSUE *Offset, perforated 13 1/2.*

1108 *Therese Casgrain (1896-1981), suffragist;* 1109 *Emily Murphy (1868-1933), writer*

1108		MNHVF	UseVF
32¢	**multicolored,** FDD *(April 17, 1985)*	.50	.20

1109		MNHVF	UseVF
32¢	**multicolored,** FDD *(April 17, 1985)*	.50	.20
	y. Se-tenant pair #1108-1109	1.10	.95

1985. GABRIEL DUMONT ISSUE Northwest Rebellion centennial. Commemorated the Metis leader, Gabriel Dumont. *Offset, perforated 14 x 13 1/2.*

1110 *Gabriel Dumont (1837-1906)*

1110		MNHVF	UseVF
32¢	**multicolored,** FDD *(May 6, 1985)*	.50	.20

Regular Issues

1985. PARLIAMENT ISSUE *Offset, perforated 13 1/2 x 13.*

1111 *Parliament*

1111		MNHVF	UseVF
34¢	**multicolored,** FDD *(Aug. 1, 1985)*	.50	.20
	n. Booklet pane of 25	12.50	
	v. Perforated 13 1/2 x 14	.50	.20
	n1. Booklet pane of 25, perforated 13 1/2 x 14	12.50	

1985. PARLIAMENT BOOKLET ISSUE *Intaglio, perforated 12 1/2 x 12.*

1112 *Parliament (East block);* 1113 *Parliament (West block);* 1114 *Parliament*

1112		MNHVF	UseVF
2¢	**myrtle green,** FDD *(June 21, 1985)*	.20	.20

1113		MNHVF	UseVF
5¢	**deep brown,** FDD *(June 21, 1985)*	.30	.20

1114		MNHVF	UseVF
34¢	**deep slate blue,** FDD *(June 21, 1985)*	1.10	.75
	n. Booklet pane of 6	1.50	1.30

1985. NATIONAL PARK ISSUE *Offset, perforated 13 1/2.*

1115 *Banff National Park, Moraine Lake*

1115		MNHVF	UseVF
$2	**multicolored,** FDD *(June 21, 1985)*	3.25	1.10
	v. Missing inscriptions	1,125.00	

Commemorative Issues

1985. CANADA DAY BOOKLET ISSUE *Offset, perforated 12 1/2 x 13. Sizes: Nos. 1116, 1121: 48 x 26mm. Nos. 1117, 1118, 1122, 1123: 40 x 26mm. Nos: 1119, 1120, 1124, 1125, 32 x 26mm.*

1116 *Lower Fort Garry, Manitoba;* 1117 *Fort Anne, Nova Scotia;* 1118 *Fort York, Ontario;* 1119 *Castle Hill, Newfoundland;* 1120 *Fort Whoop Up, Alberta;* 1121 *Fort Erie, Ontario;* 1122 *Fort Walsh, Saskatchewan;* 1123 *Fort Lennox, Quebec;* 1124 *York Redoubt, Nova Scotia;* 1125 *Fort Frederick, Ontario*

1116		MNHVF	UseVF
34¢	**multicolored,** FDD *(June 28, 1985)*	.65	.75

1117		MNHVF	UseVF
34¢	**multicolored,** FDD *(June 28, 1985)*	.65	.75

1118		MNHVF	UseVF
34¢	**multicolored,** FDD *(June 28, 1985)*	.65	.75

1119		MNHVF	UseVF
34¢	**multicolored,** FDD *(June 28, 1985)*	.65	.75

1120		MNHVF	UseVF
34¢	**multicolored,** FDD *(June 28, 1985)*	.65	.75

1121		MNHVF	UseVF
34¢	**multicolored,** FDD *(June 28, 1985)*	.65	.75

1122		MNHVF	UseVF
34¢	**multicolored,** FDD *(June 28, 1985)*	.65	.75

1123		MNHVF	UseVF
34¢	**multicolored,** FDD *(June 28, 1985)*	.65	.75

1124		MNHVF	UseVF
34¢	**multicolored,** FDD *(June 28, 1985)*	.65	.75

1125		MNHVF	UseVF
34¢	**multicolored,** FDD *(June 28, 1985)*	.65	.75
	n. Booklet pane of 10 #1116-1125	6.25	10.50

Regular Issues

1985. ELIZABETH II ISSUE *Intaglio and gravure, perforated 13 x 13 1/2.*

1126 *Elizabeth II*

1126		MNHVF	UseVF
34¢	**light blue & blue,** FDD *(July 12, 1985)*	.50	.20

1985. COIL PARLIAMENT (LIBRARY) ISSUE *Intaglio, perforated 10 horizontal.*

1127 *Parliament*

1127		MNHVF	UseVF
34¢	**dull red brown,** FDD *(Aug. 1, 1985)*	.55	.20
	v. Pair, imperforate	150.00	

1985. FOLK ART ISSUE *Offset, perforated 12 x 12 1/2.*

1128 *Settle-bed*

1128		MNHVF	UseVF
39¢	**multicolored,** FDD *(Aug. 1, 1985)*	.60	.20

1129 *Sleigh*

1129		MNHVF	UseVF
50¢	**multicolored,** FDD *(Aug. 1, 1985)*	.75	.25

1130 *Spinning wheel*

1130		MNHVF	UseVF
68¢	**multicolored,** FDD *(Aug. 1, 1985)*	1.00	.35

Commemorative Issues

1985. LOUIS HEBERT ISSUE to mark International Pharmaceutical Conference in Montreal. *Offset, perforated 12 1/2.*

1131 *Louis Hebert (1575-1627), first French Apothecary in North America 1fp*

1131		MNHVF	UseVF
34¢	**multicolored,** FDD *(Aug. 30, 1985)*	.50	.20

1985. INTERPARLIAMENTARY UNION ISSUE *Offset, perforated 13 1/2.*

1132 *Parliament Buildings*

1132		MNHVF	UseVF
34¢	**multicolored,** FDD *(Sept. 3, 1985)*	.50	.20

1985. NATIONAL GIRL GUIDES ISSUE *Gravure, perforated 13 1/2 x 13.*

1133 *Guide and brownie giving the scout sign*

1133		MNHVF	UseVF
34¢	**multicolored,** FDD *(Sept. 12, 1985)*	.50	.25

1985. LIGHTHOUSE ISSUE *Offset, perforated 13 1/2.*

1134 *Pelee Passage;* 1135 *Sisters Islets;* 1136 *Rose Blanche;* 1137 *Haut-fond Prince*

1134		MNHVF	UseVF
34¢	**multicolored,** FDD *(Oct. 3, 1985)*	.55	.25

1135		MNHVF	UseVF
34¢	**multicolored,** FDD *(Oct. 3, 1985)*	.55	.25

1136		MNHVF	UseVF
34¢	**multicolored,** FDD *(Oct. 3, 1985)*	.55	.25

1137		MNHVF	UseVF
34¢	**multicolored,** FDD *(Oct. 3, 1985)*	.55	.25
	y. Se-tenant block of 4	2.25	1.90

1985. LIGHTHOUSE SOUVENIR SHEET

1138 *Lighthouse Souvenir Sheet*

1138		MNHVF	UseVF
	Sheet of 4 #1134-1137, FDD *(Oct. 3, 1985)*	2.65	2.65

1985. CHRISTMAS ISSUE Paintings by Barbara Carroll. *Offset; No. 1139 perforated 13 1/2 on 3 sides, Nos. 1140-1142 perforated 13 1/2.*

1139 *Polar float*

1139		MNHVF	UseVF
32¢	multicolored, FDD *(Oct. 23, 1985)*	1.10	.45
	n. Booklet pane of 10	8.25	7.25

1140 *Santa Claus parade*

1140		MNHVF	UseVF
34¢	multicolored, FDD *(Oct. 23, 1985)*	.50	.20

1141 *Horse-drawn coach*

1141		MNHVF	UseVF
39¢	multicolored, FDD *(Oct. 23, 1985)*	.60	.50

1142 *Christmas tree*

1142		MNHVF	UseVF
68¢	multicolored, FDD *(Oct. 23, 1985)*	1.00	.75

1985. LOCOMOTIVE ISSUE *Offset, perforated 12 1/2 x 13.*

1143 *Grand Trunk K2;* 1144 *Canadian Pacific P2a*

1143		MNHVF	UseVF
34¢	multicolored, FDD *(Nov. 7, 1985)*	.55	.20
1144		**MNHVF**	**UseVF**
34¢	multicolored, FDD *(Nov. 7, 1985)*	.55	.20
	y. Se-tenant pair, #1143-1144	1.10	.45

1145 *Canadian Northern O10a*

1145		MNHVF	UseVF
39¢	multicolored, FDD *(Nov. 7, 1985)*	.65	.60

1146 *Canadian Govt. Railways H4D*

1146		MNHVF	UseVF
68¢	multicolored, FDD *(Nov. 7, 1985)*	1.10	.95

1985. ROYAL CANADIAN NAVY ISSUE 75th anniversary. *Offset, perforated 13 1/2 x 13.*

1147 *1910 Gunner's Mate, World War II officer and 1985 woman recruit*

1147		MNHVF	UseVF
34¢	multicolored, FDD *(Nov. 8, 1985)*	.50	.20

1985. MONTREAL MUSEUM OF FINE ARTS ISSUE 120th anniversary of Montreal Museum of Fine Arts. *Offset, perforated 13 1/2.*

1148 Old Holton House, Sherbrooke Street, Montreal, *by James Wilson Morrice (1865-1924)*

1148		MNHVF	UseVF
34¢	**multicolored,** FDD *(Nov. 15, 1985)*	.50	.20

1986. WINTER OLYMPICS ISSUE Calgary, Alberta, Feb. 13-28, 1988. *Offset, perforated 12 1/2 x 13.*

1149 *Computer map image of Southwestern Alberta*

1149		MNHVF	UseVF
34¢	**multicolored,** FDD *(Feb. 13, 1986)*	.50	.20

1986. EXPO ISSUE Vancouver, May 2-Oct. 13. *Gravure and intaglio, perforated 12 1/2 x 13.*

1150 *Canada pavilion*

1150		MNHVF	UseVF
34¢	**multicolored,** FDD *(March 7, 1986)*	.50	.20

1151 *Communications*

1151		MNHVF	UseVF
39¢	**multicolored,** FDD *(March 7, 1986)*	.70	.40

Regular Issue

1986. NATIONAL PARK ISSUE *Offset and intaglio, perforated 13 1/2.*

1152 *La Maurice National Park*

1152		MNHVF	UseVF
$5	**multicolored,** FDD *(March 14, 1986)*	8.50	2.00
	v. dark blue color, and inscription "Canada $5" omitted	2,250.00	1,125.00

Commemorative Issues

1986. MOLLY BRANT ISSUE *Offset, perforated 13 1/2.*

1153 *Molly Brant (1736-1796), Leader and Loyalist of the Iroquois*

1153		MNHVF	UseVF
34¢	**multicolored,** FDD *(April 14, 1986)*	.50	.20

1986. PHILIPPE AUBERT DE GASPE ISSUE *Offset, perforated 12 1/2.*

1154 *Philippe Aubert de Gaspe (1786-1871), novelist*

1154		MNHVF	UseVF
34¢	**multicolored,** FDD *(April 14, 1986)*	.50	.20

1986. EXPO ISSUE *Gravure and intaglio, perforated 13 x 13 1/2.*

1155 *Expo Center, Vancouver*

1155		MNHVF	UseVF
34¢	**multicolored,** FDD *(April 28, 1986)*	.50	.20

1156 *Transportation*

1156		MNHVF	UseVF
68¢	**multicolored,** FDD *(April 28, 1986)*	1.00	.55

1986. CANADIAN FORCES POSTAL SERVICE ISSUE 75th anniversary. *Offset, perforated 13 1/2.*

1157 *Soldiers handling mail*

1157		MNHVF	UseVF
34¢	**multicolored,** FDD *(May 9, 1986)*	.50	.20

1986. INDIGENOUS BIRDS ISSUE 19th International Ornithological Congress, Ottawa, June 22-29, 1986. *Offset; perforated 13 1/2.*

1158 *Great Blue Huron;* 1159 *Snow Goose;* 1160 *Great Horned Owl;* 1161 *Spruce Grouse*

1158		MNHVF	UseVF
34¢	**multicolored,** FDD *(May 22, 1986)*	.55	.30

1159		MNHVF	UseVF
34¢	**multicolored,** FDD *(May 22, 1986)*	.55	.30

1160		MNHVF	UseVF
34¢	**multicolored,** FDD *(May 22, 1986)*	.55	.30

1161		MNHVF	UseVF
34¢	**multicolored,** FDD *(May 22, 1986)*	.55	.30
	y. Se-tenant block of 4 #1158-1161	2.25	2.00

1986. CANADA DAY ISSUE Invention blueprints. *Offset, perforated 13 1/2.*

1162 *Rotary snowplow, 1869;*

1163 *Canadarm, 1986;*

1164 *Anti-gravity flight suit, 1938;*

1165 *Variable pitch propeller, 1923*

1162		MNHVF	UseVF
34¢	**multicolored,** FDD *(June 27, 1986)*	.55	.30

1163		MNHVF	UseVF
34¢	**multicolored,** FDD *(June 27, 1986)*	.55	.30

1164		MNHVF	UseVF
34¢	**multicolored,** FDD *(June 27, 1986)*	.55	.30

1165		MNHVF	UseVF
34¢	**multicolored,** FDD *(June 27, 1986)*	.55	.30
	y. Se-tenant block of 4 #1162-1165	2.25	2.00

1986. CANADIAN BROADCASTING CORP. ISSUE 50th anniversary. *Offset, perforated 12 1/2.*

 1166 *CBC logo and 5 regions of Canada*

1166		MNHVF	UseVF
34¢	**multicolored,** FDD *(July 23, 1986)*	.50	.20

1986. EXPLORATION OF CANADA ISSUE *Offset, perforated 12 1/2 x 12.*

1167 *Siberian Indians discover and inhabit America, 10,000 B.C.;* 1168 *Viking settlement, A.D. 1000;* 1169 *John Cabot lands, 1498;* 1170 *Henry Hudson pioneers Hudson Strait and Bay, 1610*

1167		MNHVF	UseVF
34¢	**multicolored,** FDD *(Aug. 29, 1986)*	.55	.30

1168		MNHVF	UseVF
34¢	**multicolored,** FDD *(Aug. 29, 1986)*	.55	.30

1169		MNHVF	UseVF
34¢	**multicolored,** FDD *(Aug. 29, 1986)*	.55	.30

1170		MNHVF	UseVF
34¢	**multicolored,** FDD *(Aug. 29, 1986)*	.55	.30
	y. Se-tenant block of 4 #1167-1170	2.25	2.00

1986. PEACEMAKERS OF THE FRONTIER ISSUE commemorated the leaders that helped prevent war between Canada and the Blackfoot during the 1870's. *Offset, perforated 13 x 13 1/2.*

1171 *James F. Macleod (1836-1894), assistant commissioner of Northwest Mounted Police;* 1172 *Chief Crowfoot (1830-1890), Blackfoot Indian Chief*

1171		MNHVF	UseVF
34¢	**indigo, gray & scarlet,** FDD *(Sept. 5, 1986)*	.50	.25

1172		MNHVF	UseVF
34¢	**scarlet, gray & indigo,** FDD *(Sept. 5, 1986)*	.50	.25
	y. Se-tenant pair #1171-1172	1.10	.90

1986. INTERNATIONAL PEACE YEAR ISSUE *Offset and embossed, perforated 13 1/2.*

1173 *Symbolic dove protecting the world*

1173		MNHVF	UseVF
34¢	**multicolored,** FDD *(Sept. 16, 1986)*	.50	.20

1986. EXPLORATION OF CANADA SOUVENIR SHEET

1174 *Souvenir sheet of #1167-1170*

1174		MNHVF	UseVF
	Sheet of 4, #1167-1170	3.00	2.65

No. 1174 issued Oct. 1 for CAPEX 87. See Nos. 1187-1190, 1240-1243, 1287-1290.

1986. WINTER OLYMPICS ISSUE Calgary, 1988. *Offset, perforated 13 1/2 x 13.*

1175 *Ice hockey;*

1176 *Biathlon*

1175		MNHVF	UseVF
34¢	**magenta,** FDD *(Oct. 15, 1986)*	.50	.25
1176		MNHVF	UseVF
34¢	**turquoise,** FDD *(Oct. 15, 1986)*	.50	.25
	y. Se-tenant pair #1175-1176	1.00	.90

See Nos. 1195-1196, 1226-1227, 1235-1238.

1986. CHRISTMAS BOOKLET ISSUE *Offset, perforated 13 1/2 horizontal; 72 x 26mm.*

1177 *Angel singing*

34

1177		MNHVF	UseVF
29¢	**multicolored,** FDD *(Oct. 29, 1986)*	1.25	.75
	n. Booklet pane of 10	11.25	12.00
	v. Perforated 12 1/2 horizontal	7.50	3.00
	n1. Booklet pane of 10, perforated 12 1/2 horizontal	75.00	60.00

No. 1177 has bar code at left, for use on covers with printed postal code matrix.

1986. CHRISTMAS ISSUE Angels. *Offset, perforated 12 1/2.*

1178 *Angel carrying crown;* 1179 *Angel playing string instrument;* 1180 *Angel carrying sash*

1178		MNHVF	UseVF
34¢	**multicolored,** FDD *(Oct. 29, 1986)*	.50	.20
1179		MNHVF	UseVF
39¢	**multicolored,** FDD *(Oct. 29, 1986)*	.60	.53
1180		MNHVF	UseVF
68¢	**multicolored,** FDD *(Oct. 29, 1986)*	1.00	.75

1986. JOHN MOLSON ISSUE *Offset, perforated 12 1/2.*

1181 *John Molson (1763-1836), Entrepreneur*

1181		MNHVF	UseVF
34¢	**multicolored,** FDD *(Nov. 4, 1986)*	.50	.20

1986. LOCOMOTIVE ISSUE Locomotives, 1925-1945. *Offset, perforated 12 1/2 x 13.*

1182 *CN V1a Locomotive;* 1183 *CP T1a Locomotive*

1182		MNHVF	UseVF
34¢	**multicolored,** FDD *(Nov. 21, 1986)*	.55	.20
1183		MNHVF	UseVF
34¢	**multicolored,** FDD *(Nov. 21, 1986)*	.55	.90
	y. Se-tenant pair #1182-1183	1.10	.90

 1184 *CN U2a Locomotive*

1184		MNHVF	UseVF
39¢	**multicolored,** FDD *(Nov. 21, 1986)*	.70	.60

1185 *CP H1c Locomotive*

1185		MNHVF	UseVF
68¢	**multicolored,** FDD *(Nov. 21, 1986)*	1.10	1.00

1987. FIRST CAPEX ISSUE *Offset and intaglio, perforated 13 x 13 1/2.*

1186 *First Toronto Post Office 1833*

1186		MNHVF	UseVF
34¢	**multicolored,** FDD *(Feb. 16, 1987)*	.50	.20

1987. EXPLORATION ISSUE Pioneers of New France. *Offset, perforated 12 1/2 x 13.*

1187 *Pierre Esprit Radisson (1636-1710) and Medard Chouart des Groseilliers (1625-1698), British expedition to Hudson Bay, 1668;* 1188 *Etienne Brule (1592-1633), first European to see the Great Lakes;* 1189 *Louis Jolliet (1645-1700) and Fr. Jacques Marquette (1637-1675), discovering the Mississippi River, 1673;* 1190 *Recollet Wilderness Mission, 1615*

1187		MNHVF	UseVF
34¢	**multicolored,** FDD *(March 13, 1987)*	.50	.30

1188		MNHVF	UseVF
34¢	**multicolored,** FDD *(March 13, 1987)*	.50	.30

1189		MNHVF	UseVF
34¢	**multicolored,** FDD *(March 13, 1987)*	.50	.30

1190		MNHVF	UseVF
34¢	**multicolored,** FDD *(March 13, 1987)*	.50	.30
	y. Se-tenant block of 4 #1187-1190	2.25	1.90

Regular Issues

1987. PARLIAMENT (LIBRARY) ISSUE *Gravure and intaglio, perforated 13 1/2 x 13.*

1191 *Parliament*

1191		MNHVF	UseVF
36¢	**dark red,** FDD *(March 30, 1987)*	.55	.20
	n. Booklet pane of 10	5.25	5.00
	n1. Booklet pane of 25 FDD *(May 19, 1987)*	13.50	12.00
	v. Perforated 13 1/2 x 14	1.20	.75
	FDD *(May 19, 1987)*		

1987. PARLIAMENT (EAST BLOCK) BOOKLET ISSUE *Intaglio, perforated 12 1/2 x 12.*

1192B *Parliament (East block)*

1192B		MNHVF	UseVF
1¢	**sage green,** FDD *(March 30, 1987)*	.20	.20

1987. PARLIAMENT (WEST BLOCK) BOOKLET ISSUE *Intaglio, perforated 12 1/2 x 12.*

1193B *Parliament (West block)*

1193B		MNHVF	UseVF
6¢	**henna brown,** FDD *(March 30, 1987)*	.20	.20

1987. PARLIAMENT (LIBRARY) BOOKLET ISSUE *Intaglio, perforated 12 1/2 x 12.*

1194B *Parliament*

1194B		MNHVF	UseVF
36¢	**dark lilac rose,** FDD *(March 30, 1987)*	.90	.75
	n. Booklet pane of 5 + label (2 #1192B, 2	1.50	1.25
	#1193B, 1 #1199B)		

Commemorative Issues

1987. OLYMPIC ISSUE *Offset, perforated 13 1/2 x 13.*

1195 *Speed skating*

1195		MNHVF	UseVF
36¢	**multicolored,** FDD *(April 3, 1987)*	.55	.20

1196 *Bobsledding*

1196
42¢ **multicolored,** FDD *(April 3, 1987)*

	MNHVF	UseVF
	.70	.60

1987. VOLUNTEER WEEK ISSUE *Offset, perforated 12 1/2 x 13.*

1197 *Volunteers*

1197
36¢ **multicolored,** FDD *(April 13, 1987)*

	MNHVF	UseVF
	.55	.20

1987. LAW DAY ISSUE Canadian Charter of Rights and Freedoms, 5th anniversary. *Offset, perforated 14 x 13 1/2.*

1198 *Coat of arms*

1198
36¢ **multicolored,** FDD *(April 15, 1987)*

	MNHVF	UseVF
	.55	.20

Regular Issues

1987. HERITAGE ARTIFACTS ISSUE Similar in type to Canada Minkus 1982-85 Folk Art Issue. *Offset, No. 1199 perforated 14 x 13 1/2, No. 1200-1202 20 x 26mm, perforated 12 x 12 1/2.*

1199 *Butter stamp*

1199
25¢ **multicolored,** FDD *(May 6, 1987)*

	MNHVF	UseVF
	.55	.20

1200 *Linen chest*

1200
42¢ **multicolored,** FDD *(May 6, 1987)*

	MNHVF	UseVF
	.90	.30

1201 *Iron kettle*

1201
55¢ **multicolored,** FDD *(May 6, 1987)*

	MNHVF	UseVF
	1.25	.30

1202 *Hand-drawn cart*

1202
72¢ **multicolored,** FDD *(May 6, 1987)*

	MNHVF	UseVF
	1.50	.40

Commemorative Issues

1987. ENGINEERING INSTITUTE ISSUE Centennial. *Offset, perforated 12 1/2 x 13.*

1203 *Engineering mofits*

1203
36¢ **multicolored,** FDD *(May 19, 1987)*

	MNHVF	UseVF
	.55	.20

Regular Issues

1987. PARLIAMENT (LIBRARY) COIL ISSUE *Intaglio, perforated 10 horizontal.*

1204 *Parliament*

1204
36¢ **dark red,** FDD *(May 19, 1987)*
   v. Pair, imperforate

	MNHVF	UseVF
	.55	.20
	275.00	

Commemorative Issues

1987. SECOND CAPEX ISSUE *Offset and intaglio, perforated 13 x 13 1/2.*

1205 *Nelson-Miramichi P.O.*

1205
36¢ **multicolored,** FDD *(June 12, 1987)*

	MNHVF	UseVF
	.55	.25

1206 *Saint Ours P.O.*

1206		MNHVF	UseVF
42¢	multicolored, FDD *(June 12, 1987)*	.65	.60

1207 *Battleford P.O.*

1207		MNHVF	UseVF
72¢	multicolored, FDD *(June 12, 1987)*	1.10	.95

1987. CAPEX SOUVENIR SHEET *Yellow green inscription.*

1208a-
1208d
*CAPEX
Souvenir
Sheet*

1208		MNHVF	UseVF
	Sheet of 4	3.00	3.00
	a. 36¢, 1st Toronto P.O.	.60	.50
	b. 36¢, Nelson-Miramichi P.O.	.60	.50
	c. 42¢, Saint Ours P.O.	.70	1.25
	d. 72¢, Battleford P.O.	1.10	1.90

1987. CANADA DAY ISSUE Commemorated inventors and communications innovations. *Offset, perforated 13 1/2.*

 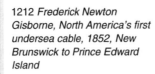

1209 *Reginald Aubrey Fessenden (1866-1932), AM radio, 1900;*

1210 *Charles Fenerty, newsprint, 1838;*

1211 *George-Edouard Desbarats and William Leggo, half-tone engraving, 1869;*

1212 *Frederick Newton Gisborne, North America's first undersea cable, 1852, New Brunswick to Prince Edward Island*

1209		MNHVF	UseVF
36¢	multicolored, FDD *(June 25, 1987)*	.60	.30
1210		MNHVF	UseVF
36¢	multicolored, FDD *(June 25, 1987)*	.60	.30
1211		MNHVF	UseVF
36¢	multicolored, FDD *(June 25, 1987)*	.60	.30
1212		MNHVF	UseVF
36¢	multicolored, FDD *(June 25, 1987)*	.60	.30
	y. Se-tenant block of 4, #1209-1212	2.65	2.25

1987. STEAMSHIP ISSUE *Offset, perforated 13 1/2 x 13. No. 1214, 51 x 22mm.*

1213 *Segwun, 1887;* 1214 *Princes Marguerite, 1948*

1213		MNHVF	UseVF
36¢	multicolored, FDD *(July 20, 1987)*	.55	.30
1214		MNHVF	UseVF
36¢	multicolored, FDD *(July 20, 1987)*	.55	.30
	y. Se-tenant pair #1213-1214	1.10	1.00

1987. SHIPWRECK ISSUE *Offset, perforated 13 1/2 x 13.*

1215 *Hamilton Scourge, 1813;* 1216 *San Juan, 1565;* 1217 *Breadalbane, 1853;* 1218 *Ericsson, 1892*

1215		MNHVF	UseVF
36¢	multicolored, FDD *(Aug. 7, 1987)*	.55	.30
1216		MNHVF	UseVF
36¢	multicolored, FDD *(Aug. 7, 1987)*	.55	.30
1217		MNHVF	UseVF
36¢	multicolored, FDD *(Aug. 7, 1987)*	.55	.30
1218		MNHVF	UseVF
36¢	multicolored, FDD *(Aug. 7, 1987)*	.55	.30
	y. Se-tenant block of 4 #1215-1218	2.25	2.25

1987. AIR CANADA ISSUE 50th anniversary. *Offset, perforated 13 1/2.*

1219 *Jet over globe*

1219		MNHVF	UseVF
36¢	multicolored, FDD *(Sept. 1, 1987)*	.55	.30

1987. SUMMIT ISSUE Second International Francophone Summit, Quebec, Sept. 2-4. *Offset, perforated 13 x 12 1/2.*

 1220 *Summit symbol*

1220		MNHVF	UseVF
36¢	multicolored, FDD *(Sept. 2, 1987)*	.55	.30

1987. COMMONWEALTH MEETING ISSUE 9th meeting, Vancouver, Oct. 13-17. *Offset, perforated 13 x 12 1/2.*

 1221 *Commonwealth emblem*

1221		MNHVF	UseVF
36¢	multicolored, FDD *(Oct. 13, 1987)*	.55	.30

1987. CHRISTMAS BOOKLET ISSUE *Offset, perforated 12 1/2 x 13.*

 1222 *Gifts and Christmas tree*

1222		MNHVF	UseVF
31¢	multicolored, FDD *(Nov. 2, 1987)*	.75	.75
	n. Booklet pane of 10	5.65	9.40

No. 1222 has bar code at left, for use on covers with printed postal code matrix. Issued in booklets only.

1987. CHRISTMAS ISSUE *Offset, perforated 13 1/2.*

1223 *Poinsettia;* 1224 *Holly wreath;* 1225 *Mistletoe and Christmas tree;*

1223		MNHVF	UseVF
36¢	multicolored, FDD *(Nov. 2, 1987)*	.55	.20
1224		**MNHVF**	**UseVF**
42¢	multicolored, FDD *(Nov. 2, 1987)*	.65	.60
1225		**MNHVF**	**UseVF**
72¢	multicolored, FDD *(Nov. 2, 1987)*	1.10	1.15

1987. OLYMPIC ISSUE Publicized the 1988 Winter Olympics in Calgary, Alberta. *Offset, perforated 13 1/2 x 13.*

  1226 *Cross-country skiing;*

1227 *Ski jumping*

1226		MNHVF	UseVF
36¢	multicolored, FDD *(Nov. 13, 1987)*	.55	.25
1227		**MNHVF**	**UseVF**
36¢	multicolored, FDD *(Nov. 13, 1987)*	.55	.25
	y. Se-tenant pair #1126-1127	1.20	.55

1987. GREY CUP ISSUE 75th, Vancouver, Nov. 29. *Offset, perforated 12 1/2.*

 1228 *Grey cup and football*

1228		MNHVF	UseVF
36¢	multicolored, FDD *(Nov. 20, 1987)*	.55	.20

Regular Issues

1987. ELIZABETH II ISSUE *Gravure and intaglio, perforated 13 x 13 1/2.*

 1229 *Elizabeth II*

1229		MNHVF	UseVF
36¢	plum, FDD *(Oct. 1, 1987)*	3.75	2.25

1987. PARLIAMENT (CENTER BLOCK) ISSUE *Offset, perforated 13 1/2 x13.*

 1230 *Parliament (Center block)*

1230		MNHVF	UseVF
37¢	multicolored, FDD *(Dec. 30, 1987)*	.75	.20
	n. Booklet pane of 10, perforated 13 1/2 x 14	7.50	7.50
	n1. Booklet pane of 25, perforated 13 1/2 x 14	18.75	15.00
	v. Single issue, perforated 13 1/2 x 14	1.20	.20

1987. ELIZABETH II ISSUE *Offset, perforated 13 1/2 x 13.*

1231 *Elizabeth II*

1231		MNHVF	UseVF
37¢	**multicolored,** FDD *(Dec. 30, 1987)*	.75	.20

1988. Mammal Issue *Offset, perforated 12 x 12 1/2.*

1232 *Lynx*

1232		MNHVF	UseVF
43¢	**multicolored,** FDD *(Jan. 18, 1988)*	1.15	.35

1233 *Killer whale*

1233		MNHVF	UseVF
57¢	**multicolored,** FDD *(Jan. 18, 1988)*	1.15	.35

1234 *Wapiti*

1234		MNHVF	UseVF
74¢	**multicolored,** FDD *(Jan. 18, 1988)*	1.50	.55

1234A *Parliament*

1234A.		MNHVF	UseVF
2¢	**slate green,** FDD *(Oct. 3, 1988)*	.20	.25
	FDD *(Jan. 18, 1989)*		

1989. Parliament Issue

1234B *Parliament*

1234B.		MNHVF	UseVF
6¢	**dark purple,** FDD *(Jan. 18, 1989)*	—	—
	FDD *(Jan. 18, 1989)*	—	—

1988. Parliament (Library) Coil Issue *Intaglio, perforated 10 horizontal.*

1234C, 1239 *Parliament*

1234C		MNHVF	UseVF
37¢	**dark blue,** FDD *(Feb. 22, 1988)*	.70	.20
	v. Pair, imperforate	170.00	

Commemorative Issues

1988. Olympic Issue *Offset, perforated 12 x 12 1/2.*

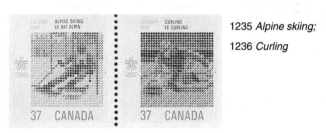

1235 *Alpine skiing;*

1236 *Curling*

1235		MNHVF	UseVF
37¢	**multicolored,** FDD *(Feb. 12, 1988)*	.60	.30

1236		MNHVF	UseVF
37¢	**multicolored,** FDD *(Feb. 12, 1988)*	.60	.30
	y. Se-tenant pair #1235-1236	1.30	.75

1237 *Figure skating*

1237		MNHVF	UseVF
43¢	**multicolored,** FDD *(Feb. 12, 1988)*	.75	.70

1238 *Luge*

1238		MNHVF	UseVF
74¢	**multicolored,** FDD *(Feb. 12, 1988)*	1.20	.90

Regular Issues

1988. Booklet Issue *Intaglio, perforated 12 1/2 x 12 on 2 or 3 sides.*

1239		MNHVF	UseVF
37¢	**dark blue,** FDD *(Feb. 3, 1988)*	.90	.30
	n. Booklet pane of 4 + 2 labels, (1 #1192b, 2 #1193b, 1 #1239)	1.10	1.10

Commemorative Issues

1988. EXPLORATION ISSUE *Offset, perforated 12 1/2 x 13.*

1240 *Anthony Henday, traveled the prairies in 1754 from Hayes River to Red Deer, Alberta.* 1241 *George Vancouver (1757-1798), circumnavigated Vancouver Island and explored the Pacific Coast, 1792-94.* 1242 *Simon Fraser (1776-1862) fur trader who discovered and navigated the Fraser River.* 1243 *John Palliser (1807-1887), geographer who determined the topographical boundry between Canada and the U.S. from Lake Superior to the Pacific Coast.*

1240		MNHVF	UseVF
37¢	**multicolored,** FDD *(March 7, 1988)*	.55	.30
1241		MNHVF	UseVF
37¢	**multicolored,** FDD *(March 7, 1988)*	.55	.30
1242		MNHVF	UseVF
37¢	**multicolored,** FDD *(March 7, 1988)*	.55	.30
1243		MNHVF	UseVF
37¢	**multicolored,** FDD *(March 7, 1988)*	.55	.30
	y. Se-tenant block of 4 #1240-1243	3.00	1.40

1988. MASTERPIECE ISSUE *Canadian art. Gravure and intaglio, perforated 13 x 13 1/2. Printed in sheets of 16.*

1244 The Young Reader, *by Ozias Leduc*

1244		MNHVF	UseVF
50¢	**multicolored,** FDD *(May 20, 1988)*	1.10	.90

See Nos. 1297, 1337, 1385, 1452, 1513, 1573, 1618, 1686, 1755.

1988. WILDLIFE AND HABITAT CONSERVATION ISSUE *Grey Owl, born Archibald Belaney, (b. 1888), conservationist; 50th anniversary Ducks Unlimited. Offset, perforated 13 x 13 1/2.*

1245 *Duck and marsh;*

1246 *Moose at marsh*

1245		MNHVF	UseVF
37¢	**multicolored,** FDD *(June 1, 1988)*	.55	.30
1246		MNHVF	UseVF
37¢	**multicolored,** FDD *(June 1, 1988)*	.55	.30
	y. Se-tenant pair #1245-1246	1.20	.75

1988. SCIENE AND TECHNOLOGY ISSUE *Offset, perforated 12 1/2 x 13.*

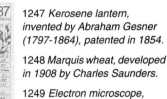

1247 *Kerosene lantern, invented by Abraham Gesner (1797-1864), patented in 1854.*

1248 *Marquis wheat, developed in 1908 by Charles Saunders.*

1249 *Electron microscope, developed in 1938 at the University of Toronto by James Hiller and Albert Prebus under the supervision of Eli Burton.*

1250 *Cobalt cancer therapy, introduced by Dr. Harold Johns and Atomic Energy of Canada Ltd., in 1951.*

1247		MNHVF	UseVF
37¢	**multicolored,** FDD *(June 17, 1988)*	.55	.30
1248		MNHVF	UseVF
37¢	**multicolored,** FDD *(June 17, 1988)*	.55	.30
1249		MNHVF	UseVF
37¢	**multicolored,** FDD *(June 17, 1988)*	.55	.30
1250		MNHVF	UseVF
37¢	**multicolored,** FDD *(June 17, 1988)*	.55	.30
	y. Se-tenant block of 4 #1247-1250	2.75	1.90

1988. BUTTERFLY ISSUE *International Entomology Congress, Vancouver. Offset, perforated 12.*

1251 *Short-tailed swallowtail;*

1252 *Northern blue;*

1253 *Macoun's Arctic;*

1254 *Canadian tiger swallowtail*

1251		MNHVF	UseVF
37¢	**multicolored,** FDD *(July 4, 1988)*	.55	.25
1252		MNHVF	UseVF
37¢	**multicolored,** FDD *(July 4, 1988)*	.55	.25

1253			MNHVF	UseVF
37¢	**multicolored,** FDD *(July 4, 1988)*		.55	.25

1254			MNHVF	UseVF
37¢	**multicolored,** FDD *(July 4, 1988)*		.55	.25
	y. Se-tenant block of 4 #1251-1254		3.00	2.00

1988. ST. JOHN'S NEWFOUNDLAND ISSUE Centennial of incorporation. *Offset, perforated 13 1/2 x 13.*

1255 *St. John's Harbor entrance & skyline*

1255			MNHVF	UseVF
37¢	**multicolored,** FDD *(July 22, 1988)*		.55	.20

1988. CANADIAN 4-H COUNCIL ISSUE 75th anniversary. *Offset, perforated 13 1/2 x 13.*

1256 *Motto, farm and young scientists*

1256			MNHVF	UseVF
37¢	**multicolored,** FDD *(Aug. 5, 1988)*		.55	.20

1988. INDUSTRIAL ISSUE Les Forges Du St. Maurice (1738-1883), Canada's first industrial complex. *Offset and intaglio, perforated 13 1/2.*

1257 *Ironworks furnace*

1257			MNHVF	UseVF
37¢	**multicolored,** FDD *(Aug. 19, 1988)*		.55	.20

1988. DOG ISSUE Canadian Kennel Club centennial. *Offset, perforated 12 1/2 x 12.*

1258 *Tahltan bear dog;* 1259 *Nova Scotia ducktolling retriever;* 1260 *Canadian Eskimo dog;* 1261 *Newfoundland*

1258			MNHVF	UseVF
37¢	**multicolored,** FDD *(Aug. 26, 1988)*		.75	.25

1259			MNHVF	UseVF
37¢	**multicolored,** FDD *(Aug. 26, 1988)*		.75	.25

1260			MNHVF	UseVF
37¢	**multicolored,** FDD *(Aug. 26, 1988)*		.75	.25

1261			MNHVF	UseVF
37¢	**multicolored,** FDD *(Aug. 26, 1988)*		.75	.25
	y. Se-tenant block of 4 #1258-1261		3.00	2.00

1988. BASEBALL ISSUE Sesquicentennial of the first baseball game played in Canada, June 4, 1838 at Beachville, Upper Canada. *Offset, perforated 13 1/2 x 13.*

1262 *Glove and diamond*

1262			MNHVF	UseVF
37¢	**multicolored,** FDD *(Sept. 14, 1988)*		.55	.20

Regular Issues

1988. WILDLIFE ISSUE *Offset, perforated 13 x 13 1/2. Sizes vary.*

1263 *Flying squirrel*

1263			MNHVF	UseVF
1¢	**multicolored,** FDD *(Oct. 3, 1988)*		.20	.20
	v. Perforated 13 x 12 3/4		2.00	.40

1264 *Prickly porcupine*

1264			MNHVF	UseVF
2¢	**multicolored,** FDD *(Oct. 3, 1988)*		.20	.20

1265 *Muskrat*

1265			MNHVF	UseVF
3¢	**multicolored,** FDD *(Oct. 3, 1988)*		.20	.20

1266 *Varying hare*

1266		**MNHVF**	**UseVF**
5¢	multicolored, FDD *(Oct. 3, 1988)*	.20	.20
	v. Pair, imperforate	925.00	

1267 *Red fox*

1267		**MNHVF**	**UseVF**
6¢	multicolored, FDD *(Oct. 3, 1988)*	.20	.20

1268 *Skunk*

1268		**MNHVF**	**UseVF**
10¢	multicolored, FDD *(Oct. 3, 1988)*	.20	.20
	v. Perforated 13 x 12 3/4	3.75	.40

1269 *Beaver*

1269		**MNHVF**	**UseVF**
25¢	multicolored, FDD *(Oct. 3, 1988)*	.35	.20

Commemorative Issues

1988. CHRISTMAS BOOKLET ISSUE *Offset, perforated 12 1/2 x 13 1/2; 35 1/2 x 21mm.*

1270 *Nativity*

1270		**MNHVF**	**UseVF**
32¢	multicolored, FDD *(Oct. 27, 1988)*	.90	.75
	n. Booklet pane of 10	7.50	9.00

Millennium of Christianity in the Ukraine. No. 1270 has bar code at left; for use on covers with printed postal code matrix.

1988. CHRISTMAS ISSUE Icons of the Eastern Church. *Offset, perforated 13 1/2.*

1271 *Conception;* 1272 *Virgin & Child;* 1273 *Virgin & Child, different*

1271		**MNHVF**	**UseVF**
37¢	multicolored, FDD *(Oct. 27, 1988)*	.65	.20

1272		**MNHVF**	**UseVF**
43¢	multicolored, FDD *(Oct. 27, 1988)*	.75	.60

1273		**MNHVF**	**UseVF**
74¢	multicolored, FDD *(Oct. 27, 1988)*	1.50	.90

1988. CHARLES INGLIS ISSUE Charles Inglis (1734-1816), Canada's first Anglican bishop and founder of the Kings-Edgehill School, Nova Scotia, and the University of King's College at Hallifax, bicentennial.
Offset, perforated 12 1/2 x 12.

1274 *Charles Inglis (1734-1816)*

1274		**MNHVF**	**UseVF**
37¢	multicolored, FDD *(Nov. 1, 1988)*	.55	.20

1988. ANGUS WALTERS ISSUE *Offset, perforated 13 1/2.*

1275 *Angus Walters (1882-1968), mariner*

1275		**MNHVF**	**UseVF**
37¢	multicolored, FDD *(Nov. 18, 1988)*	.60	.20

1988. FRANCES ANN HOPKINS ISSUE *Offset, perforated 13 1/2 x 13.*

1276 *Frances Ann Hopkins (1838-1918), painter*

1276		**MNHVF**	**UseVF**
37¢	multicolored, FDD *(Nov. 18, 1988)*	.55	.20

Regular Issues

1989. BOOKLET ISSUE *Intaglio, perforated 12 1/2 x 12 on 2 or 3 sides.*

1277 *Parliament*

1277		**MNHVF**	**UseVF**
38¢	dark blue, FDD *(Jan. 18, 1989)*	.90	.40
	n. Booklet pane of 5, 3 #1112a, 2 #1234B,	1.10	1.10

1988. ELIZABETH II ISSUE *Offset, perforated 13 x 12 1/2.*

1278 *Elizabeth II*

1278			MNHVF	UseVF
38¢	**multicolored,** FDD *(Dec. 29, 1988)*		1.50	1.50
	n.	Booklet pane of 10 + 2 labels, perforated 13 x 13 1/2	5.50	5.50
	v1.	Pane, imperforate	9.35	

1988. PARLIAMENT ISSUE *Offset, perforated 13 x 13 1/2 on 3 or 4 sides.*

1278A *Parliament*

1278A.			MNHVF	UseVF
38¢	**multicolored,** FDD *(Dec. 29, 1988)*		.60	.10
	n.	Booklet pane of 10 + 2 labels	6.00	6.00
	n1.	Booklet pane of 25 + 2 labels	18.75	18.75

1989. MAMMAL ISSUE *Offset, perforated 14 1/2 x 14.*

1279 *Walrus*

1279			MNHVF	UseVF
44¢	**multicolored,** FDD *(Jan. 18, 1989)*		1.10	.20
	v.	Perforated 12 1/2 x 13	2.25	.40
	n.	Booklet pane of 5 + label, perforated 12 1/2 x 13	9.25	5.25
	v1.	Perforated 13 1/2 x 13	280.00	30.00

1280 *Musk-ox*

1280			MNHVF	UseVF
59¢	**multicolored,** FDD *(Jan. 18, 1989)*		1.10	.35
	v.	Perforated 13	5.50	3.75

1281 *Grizzly bear*

1281			MNHVF	UseVF
76¢	**multicolored,** FDD *(Jan. 18, 1989)*		1.30	.35
	v.	Perforated 12 1/2 x 13	3.00	.75
	n.	Booklet pane of 5 + label, perforated 12 1/2 x 13	11.25	6.75
	v1.	Perforated 13	30.00	5.25

Commemorative Issues

1989. SMALL CRAFT ISSUE *Offset, perforated 13 1/2 x 13.*

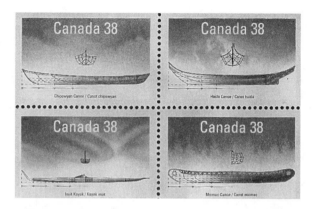

1282 *Chipewyan canoe;* 1283 *Haida canoe;* 1284 *Inuit kayak;* 1285 *Micmac canoe*

1282			MNHVF	UseVF
38¢	**multicolored,** FDD *(Feb. 1, 1989)*		.60	.35

1283			MNHVF	UseVF
38¢	**multicolored,** FDD *(Feb. 1, 1989)*		.60	.35

1284			MNHVF	UseVF
38¢	**multicolored,** FDD *(Feb. 1, 1989)*		.60	.35

1285			MNHVF	UseVF
38¢	**multicolored,** FDD *(Feb. 1, 1989)*		.60	.35
	y.	Se-tenant block of 4 #1282-1285	2.60	2.00

Regular Issues

1989. PARLIAMENT (LIBRARY) COIL ISSUE *Intaglio, perforated 10 horizontal.*

1286 *Parliament*

1286			MNHVF	UseVF
38¢	**dark green,** FDD *(Feb. 1, 1989)*		.70	.20
	v.	Pair, imperforate	375.00	

Commemorative Issues

1989. EXPLORATION ISSUE *Explorers of the North. Offset, perforated 12 1/2 x 13.*

1287 *Relics of expedition led by Sir John Franklin (1786-1847), that proved the existence of the Northwest Passage.* 1288 *Matonabbee (1737-1782), Indian guide who led first overland European expedition to the Arctic ocean.* 1289 *Vilhjalmur Stefansson (1879-1962), American ethnologist who discovered the last uncharted islands in the Arctic Archipelago.* 1290 *Relics of the discovery of the Alberta fossil bed by geologist Joseph Burr Tyrrell (1858-1957).*

1287		**MNHVF**	**UseVF**
38¢	**multicolored,** FDD *(March 22, 1989)*	.60	.35

1288		**MNHVF**	**UseVF**
38¢	**multicolored,** FDD *(March 22, 1989)*	.60	.35

1289		**MNHVF**	**UseVF**
38¢	**multicolored,** FDD *(March 22, 1989)*	.60	.35

1290		**MNHVF**	**UseVF**
38¢	**multicolored,** FDD *(March 22, 1989)*	.60	.35
	y. Se-tenant block of 4 #1287-1290	2.75	1.90

Regular Issues

1989. ARCHITECTURE ISSUE *Offset and intaglio, perforated 13 1/2.*

1291 *Runnymede Library*

1291		**MNHVF**	**UseVF**
$1	**multicolored,** FDD *(May 5, 1989)*	1.50	.50
	v. Intaglio inscriptions inverted	9,400.00	
	v1. Pair, imperforate	1,500.00	
	v2. missing inscription	1,325.00	

1292 *McAdam Railway Station*

1292		**MNHVF**	**UseVF**
$2	**multicolored,** FDD *(May 5, 1989)*	3.00	1.05
	v. Pair, imperforate	1,125.00	

A later printing of No. 1292 has more intense and clearly defined green shading on the roofline and the deep orange background extends closer to the roofline.

Commemorative Issues

1989. PHOTOGRAPHY ISSUE Photographers and their works. *Offset, perforated 12 1/2 x 12.*

1293 *William Notman (1826-1891);* 1294 *W. Hanson Boorne (1859-1945);* 1295 *Alexander Henderson (1831-1913);* 1296 *Jules-Ernest Livernois (1851-1933)*

1293		**MNHVF**	**UseVF**
38¢	**multicolored,** FDD *(June 23, 1989)*	.60	.35

1294		**MNHVF**	**UseVF**
38¢	**multicolored,** FDD *(June 23, 1989)*	.60	.35

1295		**MNHVF**	**UseVF**
38¢	**multicolored,** FDD *(June 23, 1989)*	.60	.35

1296		**MNHVF**	**UseVF**
38¢	**multicolored,** FDD *(June 23, 1989)*	.60	.35
	y. Se-tenant block of 4 #1293-1296	2.75	1.90

1989. ART ISSUE Masterpieces of Canadian Art and opening of the Museum of Civilization. Design: Ceremonial Frontlet (headpiece) worn by Tsimshian Indian Chiefs, early 20th century. *Offset, perforated 12 1/2 x 13.*

1297 *Ceremonial Frontlet*

1297		**MNHVF**	**UseVF**
50¢	**multicolored,** FDD *(June 29, 1989)*	1.10	.90

Regular Issues

1989. SELF-ADHESIVE BOOKLET LARGE FLAG OVER LANDSCAPE ISSUE *Die cut, imperforate.*

1298 *Flag over forest*

1298		**MNHVF**	**UseVF**
38¢	**multicolored,** FDD *(June 30, 1989)*	1.10	.55
	n. Booklet of 12	9.00	

Issued on peelable paper backing serving as booklet cover.

Commemorative Issues

1989. POET ISSUE *Offset, perforated 13 1/2.*

1299 *Louis Frechette (1839-1908);* 1300 *Archibald Lampman (1861-1899)*

1299		**MNHVF**	**UseVF**
38¢	**multicolored,** FDD *(July 7, 1989)*	.55	.25

1300		**MNHVF**	**UseVF**
38¢	**multicolored,** FDD *(July 7, 1989)*	.55	.25
	y. Se-tenant pair #1299-1300	1.20	.75

1989. MUSHROOM ISSUE *Offset, perforated 13 1/2.*

1301 *Clavulinopsis fusiformis;* 1302 *Boletus mirabillis;* 1303 *Cantharellus cinnabarinus;* 1304 *Morchella esculenta*

1301		MNHVF	UseVF
38¢	**multicolored,** FDD *(Aug. 4, 1989)*	.60	.35
1302		MNHVF	UseVF
38¢	**multicolored,** FDD *(Aug. 4, 1989)*	.60	.35
1303		MNHVF	UseVF
38¢	**multicolored,** FDD *(Aug. 4, 1989)*	.60	.35
1304		MNHVF	UseVF
38¢	**multicolored,** FDD *(Aug. 4, 1989)*	.60	.35
	y. Se-tenant block of 4 #1301-1304	2.75	1.90

1989. INFANTRY REGIMENT ISSUE 75th anniversary. *Offset and intaglio, perforated 13.*

1305 *Princess Patricia's Canadian light infantry*

1306 *Royal 22nd regiment*

1305		MNHVF	UseVF
38¢	**multicolored,** FDD *(Sept. 8, 1989)*	.75	.35
1306		MNHVF	UseVF
38¢	**multicolored,** FDD *(Sept. 8, 1989)*	.75	.35
	y. Se-tenant pair #1305-1306	1.50	1.10

1989. INTERNATIONAL TRADE ISSUE *Offset, perforated 13 1/2 x 12.*

1307 *World in open carton*

1307		MNHVF	UseVF
38¢	**multicolored,** FDD *(Oct. 2, 1989)*	.55	.25

1989. PERFORMING ARTS ISSUE *Offset, perforated 13 x 13 1/2.*

1308 *Royal Winnipeg Ballet 50th anniversary;*

1309 *Vancouver Opera 30th anniversary;*

1310 *National Film Board 50th anniversary;*

1311 *Confederation Center of the Arts, Charlottetown, P.E.I., 25th anniversary*

1308		MNHVF	UseVF
38¢	**multicolored,** FDD *(Oct. 4, 1989)*	.60	.30
1309		MNHVF	UseVF
38¢	**multicolored,** FDD *(Oct. 4, 1989)*	.60	.30
1310		MNHVF	UseVF
38¢	**multicolored,** FDD *(Oct. 4, 1989)*	.60	.30
1311		MNHVF	UseVF
38¢	**multicolored,** FDD *(Oct. 4, 1989)*	.60	.30
	y. Se-tenant block of 4 #1308-1311	2.70	1.90

1989. CHRISTMAS BOOKLET ISSUE Winter landscape. *Perforated 12 1/2 x 13 1/2, 35 x 21mm.*

1312 Champ-de-Mars, Winter, 1892, *by William Brymner (1855-1925)*

1312		MNHVF	UseVF
33¢	**multicolored,** FDD *(Oct. 26, 1989)*	1.50	1.50
	n. Booklet pane of 10	11.25	11.25

No. 1312 has bar code at left, for use on covers with printed postal code matrix. Booklet panes separate easily.

1989. CHRISTMAS ISSUE Winter landscapes. *Offset, #1313 perforated 13 x 13 1/2, #1314-1315 perforated 13 1/2, #1314-1315 25 x 31mm.*

1313 Bend in the Gosselin River, Arthabasca, *c.1906, by Marc-Aurele de Foy Suzor-Cote (1869-1937);* 1314 Snow II, *c.1915, by Lawren S. Harris (1885-1970);* 1315 Ste. Agnes, *c.1925-30, by Albert H. Robinson (1881-1956)*

1313		MNHVF	UseVF
38¢	**multicolored,** FDD *(Oct. 26, 1989)*	.60	.20
	n. Booklet pane of 10, perforated 13 x 12	44.00	44.00
	1/2, only 650,000 printed		
	v. Perforated 13 x 12 1/2	4.50	4.50

1314		MNHVF	UseVF
44¢	**multicolored,** FDD *(Oct. 26, 1989)*	.75	.60
	n. Booklet pane of 5 + label	15.00	15.00

1315		MNHVF	UseVF
76¢	**multicolored,** FDD *(Oct. 26, 1989)*	1.30	.90
	n. Booklet pane of 5 + label	28.50	28.50

1989. WORLD WAR II ISSUE Political and military actions taken by Canada at the outbreak of World War II. The first four stamps in a seven part World War II Canadian Achievements series. *Offset, perforated 13 1/2.*

1316 *"Convoy System Established"* 1317 *"Air Training Plan"* 1318 *"The Army Mobilizers"* 1319 *"Canada Declares War,"* 1939

1316		MNHVF	UseVF
38¢	**multicolored,** FDD *(Nov. 10, 1989)*	.60	.35

1317		MNHVF	UseVF
38¢	**multicolored,** FDD *(Nov. 10, 1989)*	.60	.35

1318		MNHVF	UseVF
38¢	**multicolored,** FDD *(Nov. 10, 1989)*	.60	.35

1319		MNHVF	UseVF
38¢	**multicolored,** FDD *(Nov. 10, 1989)*	.60	.35
	y. Se-tenant block of 4 #1316-1319	3.00	1.90

See Nos. 1365-1368, 1420-1423, 1488-1491, 1555-1558, 1610-1617.

Regular Issues

1989. FLAG AND CLOUD ISSUE *Offset, perforated 13 1/2 x 13.*

 1320 *Canadian flag and clouds*

1320		MNHVF	UseVF
39¢	**multicolored,** FDD *(Dec. 28, 1989)*	.75	.20
	n. Booklet pane of 10 + 2 labels	7.50	6.00
	n1. Booklet pane of 25 + 2 labels	22.50	18.75
	v. Perforated 12 3/4 x 13	7.50	.40

1990. ELIZABETH II ISSUE *Offset, perforated 13 x 13 1/2.*

 1321 *Elizabeth II*

1321		MNHVF	UseVF
39¢	**multicolored,** FDD *(Jan. 12, 1990)*	.75	.20
	n. Booklet pane of 10 + 2 labels	6.75	6.00
	v. Perforated 13 x 12 3/4	1.10	.20

1990. MAMMAL ISSUE *Offset, perforated 14 1/2 x 14.*

1322 *Pronghorn;* 1323 *Timberwolf;* 1324 *Beluga Whale*

1322		MNHVF	UseVF
45¢	**multicolored,** FDD *(Jan. 12, 1990)*	.90	.20
	n. Booklet pane of 5 + label, perforated 12	7.50	3.25
	1/2 x 13		
	v. Pair, imperforate	900.00	1.10
	v1. Perforated 13	13.50	1.15
	v2. Perforated 12 1/2 x 13	2.25	.40

1323		MNHVF	UseVF
61¢	**multicolored,** FDD *(Jan. 12, 1990)*	1.10	.45
	v. Perforated 13	50.00	1.90

1324		MNHVF	UseVF
78¢	**multicolored,** FDD *(Jan. 12, 1990)*	1.50	.52
	n. Booklet pane of 5, perforated 12 1/2 x 13	13.25	2.65
	v. Perforated 13 x 13	30.00	5.50
	v1. Perforated 12 1/2 x 13	3.00	.75

1990. BOOKLET FLAG ISSUE *Offset, perforated 13 1/2 x 14 on 3 sides.*

1325 *Canadian flag with yellow background;* 1326 *Canadian flag with pink background;* 1327 *Canadian flag with blue background*

1325		MNHVF	UseVF
1¢	**multicolored,** FDD *(Jan. 12, 1990)*	.20	.25
	v. Perforated 12 1/2 x 13	15.00	30.00

1326		MNHVF	UseVF
5¢	**multicolored,** FDD *(Jan. 12, 1990)*	.15	.20
	v. Perforated 12 1/2 x 13	15.00	30.00

1327		MNHVF	UseVF
39¢	**multicolored,** FDD *(Jan. 12, 1990)*	.95	.20
	n. Booklet pane of 4, No. 1325, 2 No. 1326,	1.10	.55
	1 No. 1327		
	v. Perforated 12 1/2 x 13	27.50	30.00
	n1. Booklet pane of 4, perforated 12 1/2 x	57.50	95.00
	13 (1 #1325v., 2 #1326v., 1 # 1327v.)		

1990. COIL FLAG ISSUE *Intaglio, 10 horizontal.*

 1328 *Canadian flag stamp all in violet color*

1328		MNHVF	UseVF
39¢	**violet,** FDD *(Feb. 8, 1990)*	.70	.20
	v. Pair, imperforate	150.00	

1990. SELF-ADHESIVE BOOKLET LARGE FLAG OVER LANDSCAPE ISSUE *Die cut, imperforate.*

1329 *Canadian flag with prairie scene*

1329		MNHVF	UseVF
39¢	Flag & field, FDD *(Feb. 8)*	1.10	.35
	n. Booklet of 12	9.00	

Issued on peelable paper backing serving as booklet cover.

Commemorative Issues

1990. NORMAN BETHUNE ISSUE *Offset and intaglio, perforated 13 x 13 1/2.*

1330 *Norman Bethune (1890-1939), surgeon in Canada;* 1331 *Norman Bethune, surgeon in China*

1330		MNHVF	UseVF
39¢	multicolored, FDD *(March 2, 1990)*	.60	.30

1331		MNHVF	UseVF
39¢	multicolored, FDD *(March 2, 1990)*	.60	.30
	y. Se-tenant pair #1330-1331	1.50	1.10

1990. SMALL CRAFT ISSUE *Offset, perforated 13 1/2 x 13.*

  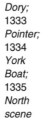

1332
Dory;
1333
Pointer;
1334
York Boat;
1335
North scene

1332		MNHVF	UseVF
39¢	multicolored, FDD *(March 15, 1990)*	.65	.35

1333		MNHVF	UseVF
39¢	multicolored, FDD *(March 15, 1990)*	.65	.35

1334		MNHVF	UseVF
39¢	multicolored, FDD *(March 15, 1990)*	.65	.35

1335		MNHVF	UseVF
39¢	multicolored, FDD *(March 15, 1990)*	.65	.35
	y. Se-tenant block of 4 #1332-1335	2.75	2.25

1990. MULTICULTURAL HERITAGE ISSUE *Offset and intaglio, perforated 13.*

1336 *Maple leaf in multicolored design*

1336		MNHVF	UseVF
39¢	multicolored, FDD *(April 5, 1990)*	.60	.25

1990. ART ISSUE Masterpieces of Canadian art. *Offset, perforated 12 1/2 x 13 1/2.*

1337 The West Wind, *by Tom Thomson*

1337		MNHVF	UseVF
50¢	multicolored, FDD *(May 3, 1990)*	.95	.75

1990. MAIL TRUCK BOOKLET ISSUE *Offset, perforated 13 1/2.*

1338, 1339 *Mail trucks*

1338		MNHVF	UseVF
39¢	multicolored, FDD *(May 3, 1990)*	.75	.50

1339		MNHVF	UseVF
39¢	multicolored, FDD *(May 3, 1990)*	.75	.50
	n. Booklet pane of 8 + printed margin, 4 each #1338-1339	6.50	6.50
	n1. Booklet pane of 9 + 3 labels, printed margin, 5 #1338, 4 # 1339	9.00	9.00

Regular Issues

1990. ARCHITECHURE ISSUE *Offset and intaglio, perforated 13 1/2.*

1340 *Bonsecours Market, Montreal*

1340		MNHVF	UseVF
$5	multicolored, FDD *(May 28, 1990)*	7.50	2.25

Commemorative Issues

1990. DOLL ISSUE *Offset, perforated 12 1/2 x 12.*

1341 *Native dolls, (1840-1916);* 1342 *Settlers' dolls, (1840-1900);* 1343 *4 Commercial dolls, (1917-1936);* 1344 *5 Commercial dolls, (1940-1960)*

1341			MNHVF	UseVF
39¢	multicolored, FDD *(June 8, 1990)*		.65	.35

1342			MNHVF	UseVF
39¢	multicolored, FDD *(June 8, 1990)*		.65	.35

1343			MNHVF	UseVF
39¢	multicolored, FDD *(June 8, 1990)*		.65	.35

1344			MNHVF	UseVF
39¢	multicolored, FDD *(June 8, 1990)*		.65	.35
	y. Se-tenant block of 4 #1341-1344		2.75	2.25

1990. NATIONAL FLAG ISSUE 25th anniversary. *Offset, perforated 13 x 12 1/2, printed in sheets of 16.*

1345 *Canadian flag and fireworks*

1345			MNHVF	UseVF
39¢	multicolored, FDD *(June 29, 1990)*		.60	.20

1990. PREHISTORIC LIFE ISSUE First four stamps in a four part Prehistoric Animal series, picturing animals of about 1900 to 10,000 years ago. *Offset and intaglio, perforated 13 x 13 1/2.*

1346 *Stromatolites (fossil algae);* 1347 *Opabinia regalis (soft invertebrate);* 1348 *Trilobite (marine arthropod, has a segmented body);* 1349 *Eurypterus remipes "Sea scorpion"*

1346			MNHVF	UseVF
39¢	multicolored, FDD *(July 12, 1990)*		.70	.35

1347			MNHVF	UseVF
39¢	multicolored, FDD *(July 12, 1990)*		.70	.35

1348			MNHVF	UseVF
39¢	multicolored, FDD *(July 12, 1990)*		.70	.35

1349			MNHVF	UseVF
39¢	multicolored, FDD *(July 12, 1990)*		.70	.35
	y. Se-tenant block of 4 #1346-1349		2.70	2.25

See Nos. 1381-1384, 1547-1550, and 1602-1605.

Please read the introduction to this catalog carefully. It contains much valuable information for all stamp collectors, and also makes the catalog easier for you to use.

1990. FOREST ISSUE *Offset, perforated 12 1/2 x 13.*

1350 *Acadian Forest;* 1351 *Great Lakes - St. Lawrence Forest;* 1352 *Coast Forest;* 1353 *Boreal Forest*

1350			MNHVF	UseVF
39¢	multicolored, FDD *(Aug. 7, 1990)*		.70	.30
	y. Sheet of 4		7.00	4.50

1351			MNHVF	UseVF
39¢	multicolored, FDD *(Aug. 7, 1990)*		.70	.30
	y. Sheet of 4		7.00	4.50

1352			MNHVF	UseVF
39¢	multicolored, FDD *(Aug. 7, 1990)*		.70	.30
	y. Sheet of 4		7.00	4.50

1353			MNHVF	UseVF
39¢	multicolored, FDD *(Aug. 7, 1990)*		.70	.30
	y. Se-tenant block of 4 #1350-1353		3.00	2.25
	y1. Sheet of 4		7.00	4.50

Sheets of four sold for $1.00 each through Petro-Canada gas stations, and for face value through the philatelic bureau. Issue date: Sept. 7.

1990. WEATHER OBSERVATION ISSUE 150th anniversary. *Offset, perforated 12 1/2 x 13 1/2.*

1354 *Rainbow in clouds*

1354			MNHVF	UseVF
39¢	multicolored, FDD *(Sept. 5, 1990)*		.60	.20

1990. INTERNATIONAL LITERACY ISSUE *Offset, perforated 13 1/2 x 13.*

1355 *Symbolic bird*

1355			MNHVF	UseVF
39¢	multicolored, FDD *(Sept. 7, 1990)*		.60	.20

1990. LEGENDARY CREATURES ISSUE First four stamps in a four part Canadian Folklore series. *Offset, perforated 12 1/2 x 13 1/2.*

1356
Sasquatch;
1357
Kraken;
1358
Werewolf;
1359
Ogopogo

1356		MNHVF	UseVF
39¢	**multicolored,** FDD *(Oct. 1, 1990)*	.75	.75
	v. Perforated 12 1/2 x 12	5.60	3.75

1357		MNHVF	UseVF
39¢	**multicolored,** FDD *(Oct. 1, 1990)*	.75	.75
	v. Perforated 12 1/2 x 12	5.60	3.75

1358		MNHVF	UseVF
39¢	**multicolored,** FDD *(Oct. 1, 1990)*	.75	.75
	v. Perforated 12 1/2 x 12	5.60	3.75

1359		MNHVF	UseVF
39¢	**multicolored,** FDD *(Oct. 1, 1990)*	.75	.75
	y. Se-tenant block of 4 #1356-1359	3.00	3.00
	y1. Se-tenant block of 4, imperforate	2,100.00	
	yv. Se-tenant block of 4, perforated 12 1/2 x 12	26.00	11.25

See also Nos. 1409-1412, 1472-1475, and 1543-1546.

1990. AGNES MACPHAIL ISSUE *Offset, perforated 13 x 13 1/2.*

1360 *Agnes Campbell Macphail (1890-1954), first woman member of Parliament*

1360		MNHVF	UseVF
39¢	**multicolored,** FDD *(Oct. 9, 1990)*	.56	.20

1990. CHRISTMAS BOOKLET ISSUE Indian art. *Offset, perforated 12 1/2 x 13 on 2 or 3 sides.*

1361 Rebirth, *by Jackson Beardy*

1361		MNHVF	UseVF
34¢	**multicolored,** FDD *(Oct. 25, 1990)*	.75	.75
	n. Booklet pane of 10	7.00	9.00

No. 1361 has bar code at left; for use on covers with printed postal code matrix.

1990. CHRISTMAS ISSUE Indian Art. *Offset, perforated 13 1/2.*

1362 Virgin Mary with Christ Child and St. John the Baptist, *by Norval Morrisseau, Ojibwa;* 1363 Mother and Child *sculpture by an Cape Dorset Inuit artist, possibly Lukta Qiatsuk;* 1364 Children of the Raven, *by Bill Reid, Haida*

1362		MNHVF	UseVF
39¢	**multicolored,** FDD *(Oct. 25, 1990)*	.75	.20
	n. Booklet pane of 10	6.25	

1363		MNHVF	UseVF
45¢	**multicolored,** FDD *(Oct. 25, 1990)*	.75	.55
	n. Booklet pane of 5 + label	3.75	

1364		MNHVF	UseVF
78¢	**multicolored,** FDD *(Oct. 25, 1990)*	1.25	.90
	n. Booklet pane of 5 + label	6.25	6.00

1990. WORLD WAR II ISSUE The second set in a seven part World War II Canadian Achievements series. *Offset, perforated 12 1/2 x 12.*

1365 *"Food Production";* 1366 *"Science and War";* 1367 *"Home Front";* 1368 *"Communal War Efforts"*

1365		MNHVF	UseVF
39¢	**multicolored,** FDD *(Nov. 9, 1990)*	.70	.35

1366		MNHVF	UseVF
39¢	**multicolored,** FDD *(Nov. 9, 1990)*	.70	.35

1367		MNHVF	UseVF
39¢	**multicolored,** FDD *(Nov. 9, 1990)*	.70	.35

1368		MNHVF	UseVF
39¢	**multicolored,** FDD *(Nov. 9, 1990)*	.70	.35
	y. Se-tenant block of 4 #1365-1368	2.75	2.25

Regular Issues

1990. BOOKLET FLAG ISSUE *Offset, perforated 13 1/2 x 14 on 3 sides.*

1369 *Canadian flag over blue sky*

1369

		MNHVF	UseVF
40¢	**multicolored,** FDD *(Dec. 28, 1990)*	.90	.20
	n. Booklet pane of 4 (2 #1325, 1 #1326, 1 #1369)	1.10	.60

1990. COIL FLAG ISSUE *Intaglio, perforated 10 horizontal.*

1370 *Canadian flag stamp all in blue gray color*

1370

		MNHVF	UseVF
40¢	**blue gray,** FDD *(Dec. 28, 1990)*	.65	.20
	v. Pair, imperforate	250.00	

1990. SMALL FLAG OVER LANDSCAPE ISSUE *Offset, perforated 13 1/2 x 13.*

1371 *Flag over mountains*

1371

		MNHVF	UseVF
40¢	**multicolored,** FDD *(Dec. 28, 1990)*	.65	.20
	n. Booklet pane of 25 + 2 labels	22.50	18.75
	n1. Booklet pane of 10 + 2 labels	7.50	6.00

1990. ELIZABETH II ISSUE *Offset, perforated 13 x 13 1/2.*

1372 *Elizabeth II*

1372

		MNHVF	UseVF
40¢	**multicolored,** FDD *(Dec. 28, 1990)*	.70	.20
	n. Booklet pane of 10 + 2 labels	7.50	6.00

1990. MAMMAL ISSUE *Offset, #1373, 1375 perforated 13, #1374 perforated 14 1/2 x 14.*

1373 *Wolverine;* 1374 *Harbor porpoise;* 1375 *Peary caribou*

1373

		MNHVF	UseVF
46¢	**multicolored,** FDD *(Dec. 28, 1990)*	.90	.25
	v. Perforated 12 1/2 x 13	1.10	.35
	n. Booklet pane of 5 + label, perforated 12 1/2 x 13	6.00	4.00
	v1. Perforated 14 1/2 x 14	4.00	.35

1374

		MNHVF	UseVF
63¢	**multicolored,** FDD *(Dec. 28, 1990)*	1.50	.35
	v. Perforated 13	6.00	.55

1375

		MNHVF	UseVF
80¢	**multicolored,** FDD *(Dec. 28, 1990)*	1.50	.55
	v. Perforated 12 1/2 x 13	3.00	.90
	n. Booklet pane of 5 + label, perforated 12 1/2 x 13	7.50	6.00
	v1. Perforated 14 1/2 x 14	4.00	.55

1991. SELF-ADHESIVE BOOKLET LARGE FLAG OVER LANDSCAPE ISSUE *Die cut, imperforate.*

1376 *Canadian flag over seacoast*

1376

		MNHVF	UseVF
40¢	**multicolored,** FDD *(Jan. 11, 1991)*	1.10	.55
	n. Booklet of 12	9.50	

Commemorative Issues

1991. PHYSICIAN ISSUE *Offset, perforated 13 1/2.*

1377 *Sir Frederick Banting (1891-1941), discoverer of insulin.*

1378 *Harold R. Griffith (1894-1985), anesthesiologist.*

1379 *Jennie K. Trout (1841-1921), first licensed Canadian woman physician.*

1380 *Wilder G. Penfield (1891-1976), neurosurgeon.*

1377

		MNHVF	UseVF
40¢	**multicolored,** FDD *(March 15, 1991)*	.70	.35

1378

		MNHVF	UseVF
40¢	**multicolored,** FDD *(March 15, 1991)*	.70	.35

1379

		MNHVF	UseVF
40¢	**multicolored,** FDD *(March 15, 1991)*	.70	.35

1380

		MNHVF	UseVF
40¢	**multicolored,** FDD *(March 15, 1991)*	.70	.35
	y. Se-tenant block of 4 #1377-1380	3.00	2.25

1991. PREHISTORIC LIFE ISSUE *The second set in a four part Prehistori Animal series. Offset, perforated 12 1/2 x 13 1/2.*

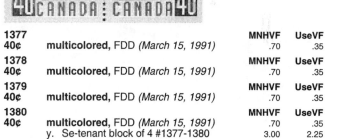

1381 *Eusthenopter on foordi (early fish);* 1382 *Hylonomus lyelli (land reptile);* 1383 *Conodants (microfossils);* 1384 *Archaeopteris (early tree)*

1381

		MNHVF	UseVF
40¢	**multicolored,** FDD *(April 5, 1991)*	.65	.35

			MNHVF	UseVF
1382				
40¢	**multicolored,** FDD *(April 5, 1991)*		.65	.35
1383				
40¢	**multicolored,** FDD *(April 5, 1991)*		.65	.35
1384				
40¢	**multicolored,** FDD *(April 5, 1991)*		.65	.35
	y. Se-tenant block of 4 #1381-1384		3.00	2.25

1991. ART ISSUE Masterpieces of Canadian art. *Offset, perforated 12 1/2 x 13.*

1385 Forest, British Columbia, *by Emily Carr*

			MNHVF	UseVF
1385				
50¢	**multicolored,** FDD *(May 7, 1991)*		.90	.90

1991. PUBLIC GARDEN BOOKLET ISSUE *Offset, perforated 13 x 12 1/2.*

1386 *The Butchart Gardens, Victoria, B.C.;* 1387 *International Peace Gardens, Boissevain, Manitoba;* 1388 *Royal Botanical Gardens, Hamilton, Ontario;* 1389 *Montreal Botanical Gardens, Quebec;* 1390 *Halifax Public Gardens, Nova Scotia*

			MNHVF	UseVF
1386				
40¢	**multicolored,** FDD *(May 22, 1991)*		.75	.35
1387				
40¢	**multicolored,** FDD *(May 22, 1991)*		.75	.35
1388				
40¢	**multicolored,** FDD *(May 22, 1991)*		.75	.35
1389				
40¢	**multicolored,** FDD *(May 22, 1991)*		.75	.35
1390				
40¢	**multicolored,** FDD *(May 22, 1991)*		.75	.35
	y. Strip of 5 #1386-1390		3.75	3.35
	n. Booklet pane 10, 2 #1386-1390		7.50	6.00

1991. CANADA DAY ISSUE *Offset, perforated 13 1/2 x 13.*

1391 *Artistic design of maple leaf*

			MNHVF	UseVF
1391				
40¢	**multicolored,** FDD *(June 28, 1991)*		.60	.20

1991. SMALL CRAFT ISSUE *Offset, perforated 13 1/2 x 13.*

1392 *Verchére rowboat;* 1393 *Touring kayak;* 1394 *Sailing dinghy;* 1395 *Cedar strip canoe*

			MNHVF	UseVF
1392				
40¢	**multicolored,** FDD *(July 18, 1991)*		.68	.30
1393				
40¢	**multicolored,** FDD *(July 18, 1991)*		.68	.30
1394				
40¢	**multicolored,** FDD *(July 18, 1991)*		.68	.30
1395				
40¢	**multicolored,** FDD *(July 18, 1991)*		.68	.30
	y. Se-tenant block of 4 #1392-1392		2.70	2.25

1991. RIVER BOOKLET ISSUE First five stamps in a four part Canadian Heritage River series. *Offset, perforated 13 x 12 1/2.*

1396 *South Nahanni River;* 1397 *Athabasca River;* 1398 *Boundary Waters-Voyageur Waterway;* 1399 *Jacques Cartier River;* 1400 *Main River*

1396		MNHVF	UseVF
40¢	**multicolored,** FDD *(Aug. 20, 1991)*	.75	.35

1397		MNHVF	UseVF
40¢	**multicolored,** FDD *(Aug. 20, 1991)*	.75	.35

1398		MNHVF	UseVF
40¢	**multicolored,** FDD *(Aug. 20, 1991)*	.75	.35

1399		MNHVF	UseVF
40¢	**multicolored,** FDD *(Aug. 20, 1991)*	.75	.35

1400		MNHVF	UseVF
40¢	**multicolored,** FDD *(Aug. 20, 1991)*	.75	.35
	y. Strip of 5 #1396-1400	3.75	3.35
	n. Booklet pane of 10	7.50	6.75

See Nos. 1441-1445, 1532-1536, 1568-1572.

1991. UKRAINIAN ISSUE Arrival of Ukrainians, cenntenial. Paintings by William Kurelek. *Offset, perforated 13 1/2 x 13.*

1401 *Leaving homeland;*

1402 *Winter in Canada;*

1403 *Clearing land;*

1404 *Growing wheat*

1401		MNHVF	UseVF
40¢	**multicolored,** FDD *(Aug. 29, 1991)*	.65	.35

1402		MNHVF	UseVF
40¢	**multicolored,** FDD *(Aug. 29, 1991)*	.65	.35

1403		MNHVF	UseVF
40¢	**multicolored,** FDD *(Aug. 29, 1991)*	.65	.35

1404		MNHVF	UseVF
40¢	**multicolored,** FDD *(Aug. 29, 1991)*	.65	.35
	y. Se-tenant block of 4 #1401-1404	2.75	2.25

1991. OCCUPATION ISSUE Dangerous public service occupations. *Offset, perforated 13 1/2.*

1405 *Ski patrol;*

1406 *Police;*

1407 *Fire fighters;*

1408 *Search & rescue*

1405		MNHVF	UseVF
40¢	**multicolored,** FDD *(Sept. 23, 1991)*	.90	.35

1406		MNHVF	UseVF
40¢	**multicolored,** FDD *(Sept. 23, 1991)*	.90	.35

1407		MNHVF	UseVF
40¢	**multicolored,** FDD *(Sept. 23, 1991)*	.90	.35

1408		MNHVF	UseVF
40¢	**multicolored,** FDD *(Sept. 23, 1991)*	.90	.35
	y. Se-tenant block of 4 #1405-1408	3.50	2.25

1991. FOLKTALE ISSUE The second set in a four part Canadian Folklore series. *Offset, perforated 13 1/2 x 12 1/2.*

1409 Chinook Wind;

1410 Buried Treasure;

1411 Witched Canoe;

1412 Orphan Boy

1409		MNHVF	UseVF
40¢	**multicolored,** FDD *(Oct. 1, 1991)*	.65	.30

1410		MNHVF	UseVF
40¢	**multicolored,** FDD *(Oct. 1, 1991)*	.65	.30

1411		MNHVF	UseVF
40¢	**multicolored,** FDD *(Oct. 1, 1991)*	.65	.30

1412		MNHVF	UseVF
40¢	**multicolored,** FDD *(Oct. 1, 1991)*	.65	.30
	y. Se-tenant block of 4 #1409-1412	2.75	2.25

1991. QUEEN'S UNIVERSITY ISSUE Kingston, Ontario, sesquicentennial. *Offset, perforated 13 x 12 1/2.*

1413 *Queen's University*

1413		MNHVF	UseVF
40¢	**multicolored,** FDD *(Oct. 16, 1991)*	.75	.30
	n. Booklet pane of 10 + 2 labels	7.50	6.00

1991. CHRISTMAS BOOKLET ISSUE *Offset, perforated 12 1/2 x 13 on 2 or 3 sides.*

1414 *Father Christmas of Great Britain with punchbowl*

1414		MNHVF	UseVF
35¢	**multicolored,** FDD *(Oct. 23, 1991)*	.65	.20
	n. Booklet pane of 10	6.50	4.00

No. 1414 has bar code at left; for use on covers with printed postal code matrix.

1991. CHRISTMAS ISSUE *Offset, perforated 13 1/2.*

1415 Santa Claus *1416 Santa claus with* *1417 Sinterklaas and*
at fireplace   *white horse and tree.* *girl of Holland*
                        Bonhomme Noel of
                        France.

1415		MNHVF	UseVF
40¢	**multicolored,** FDD *(Oct. 23, 1991)*	.75	.20
	n. Booklet pane of 10	7.50	6.00

1416		MNHVF	UseVF
46¢	**multicolored,** FDD *(Oct. 23, 1991)*	.75	.55
	n. Booklet pane of 5 + label	3.75	3.00

1417		MNHVF	UseVF
80¢	**multicolored,** FDD *(Oct. 23, 1991)*	1.25	.75
	n. Booklet pane of 5 + label	6.50	6.00

1991. BASKETBALL ISSUE Centennial. *Offset, perforated 13 x 13 1/2.*

1418 Basketball action shot

1418		MNHVF	UseVF
40¢	**multicolored,** FDD *(Oct. 25, 1991)*	.65	.25

1991. BASKETBALL SOUVENIR SHEET

1419 Souvenir sheet of 3, #1419a-1419c

1419		MNHVF	UseVF
$1.66	**Sheet of 3 #1419a-1419c,** FDD *(Oct. 25, 1991)*	3.75	2.65
	a. 40¢ Player shooting	.55	.55
	b. 46¢ Player shooting, different	.60	.75
	c. 80¢ Player dribbling	1.20	1.10

1991. WORLD WAR II ISSUE The third set in a seven part World War II Canadian Achievements series. *Offset, perforated 13 1/2.*

1420 Women's Armed Forces; *1421 War Industry;* *1422 Cadets & veterans;* *1423 Defense of Hong Kong*

1420		MNHVF	UseVF
40¢	**multicolored,** FDD *(Nov. 8, 1991)*	.60	.35

1421		MNHVF	UseVF
40¢	**multicolored,** FDD *(Nov. 8, 1991)*	.60	.35

1422		MNHVF	UseVF
40¢	**multicolored,** FDD *(Nov. 8, 1991)*	.60	.35

1423		MNHVF	UseVF
40¢	**multicolored,** FDD *(Nov. 8, 1991)*	.60	.35
	y. Se-tenant block of 4 #1420-1423	2.75	2.25

Regular Issues

1991. ELIZABETH II ISSUE *Offset, perforation 13 x 13 1/2.*

1424 Elizabeth II

1424		MNHVF	UseVF
42¢	**multicolored,** FDD *(Dec. 27, 1991)*	.75	.20
	n. Booklet pane of 10	7.50	6.00

1991. SMALL FLAG AND LANDSCAPE ISSUE *Offset, perforated 13 1/2 x 13.*

1425 Canadian flag over landscape

1425		MNHVF	UseVF
42¢	**multicolored,** FDD *(Dec. 27, 1991)*	.75	.20
	n. Booklet pane of 10	7.50	6.00
	n1. Booklet pane of 50 + 2 labels	37.50	34.00
	n2. Booklet pane of 25 + 2 labels	15.75	13.50

1991. COIL FLAG ISSUE *Intaglio, perforated 10 horizontal.*

1426 Canadian flag stamp all in red

1426		**MNHVF**	**UseVF**
42¢	**red,** FDD *(Dec. 17, 1991)*	.75	.20
	v. Pair, imperforate	170.00	

1991. TREE ISSUE *Offset, perforated 13.*

 1427 *McIntosh Apple*

1427		**MNHVF**	**UseVF**
48¢	**multicolored,** FDD *(Dec. 27, 1991)*	.95	.25
	v. Perforated 14 1/2 x 14 on 3 sides	1.30	.30
	n. Booklet pane of 5 + label, perforated 14 1/2 x 14	5.60	3.75

 1428 *Black Walnut*

1428		**MNHVF**	**UseVF**
65¢	**multicolored,** FDD *(Dec. 27, 1991)*	1.00	.30

 1429 *Stanley Plum*

1429		**MNHVF**	**UseVF**
84¢	**multicolored,** FDD *(Dec. 27, 1991)*	1.30	.35
	v. Perforated 14 1/2 x 14 on 3 sides	1.00	.30
	n. Booklet pane of 5 + label, perforated 14 1/2 x 14 on 3 sides	7.50	6.00

1992. SELF-ADHESIVE BOOKLET LARGE FLAG AND LANDSCAPE ISSUE *Die cut, imperforate.*

 1430 *Canadian flag over mountain*

1430		**MNHVF**	**UseVF**
42¢	**multicolored,** FDD *(Jan. 28, 1992)*	.95	.55
	n. Booklet of 12	8.25	

Commemorative Issues

1992. WINTER OLYMPICS BOOKLET ISSUE *Offset, perforated 12 1/2 x 13.*

 1431 *Alpine skiing*

1431		**MNHVF**	**UseVF**
42¢	**multicolored,** FDD *(Feb. 7, 1992)*	.75	.35

 1432 *Bobsledding*

1432		**MNHVF**	**UseVF**
42¢	**multicolored,** FDD *(Feb. 7, 1992)*	.75	.35

 1433 *Hockey*

1433		**MNHVF**	**UseVF**
42¢	**multicolored,** FDD *(Feb. 7, 1992)*	.75	.35

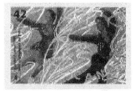 1434 *Pairs figure skating*

1434		**MNHVF**	**UseVF**
42¢	**multicolored,** FDD *(Feb. 7, 1992)*	.75	.35

 1435 *Ski jumping*

1435		**MNHVF**	**UseVF**
42¢	**multicolored,** FDD *(Feb. 7, 1992)*	.75	.35
	y. Strip of 5 #1431-1435	3.75	3.75
	n. Booklet pane of 10 #1431-1435	7.50	9.00

See Nos. 1447-1451.

1992. CITY OF MONTREAL ISSUE 350th anniversary. *Offset, perforated 13 1/2.*

1436 *City of Montreal, modern times;* 1437 *Early settlement of Montreal (Ville-Marie)*

1436		**MNHVF**	**UseVF**
42¢	**multicolored,** FDD *(March 25, 1992)*	.65	.30

1437		**MNHVF**	**UseVF**
42¢	**multicolored,** FDD *(March 25, 1992)*	.65	.30
	y. Se-tenant pair #1436-1437	1.50	.75

 1438 *"Exploration." Jacques Cartier's chart of Canada, snowshoe and ship's mast*

1438		MNHVF	UseVF
48¢	**multicolored,** FDD *(March 25, 1992)*	.75	.70

1439 *"Encounter." World map, nocturnal and Aztec calendar stone. Discovery of America, 500th anniversary.*

1439		MNHVF	UseVF
84¢	**multicolored,** FDD *(March 25, 1992)*	1.30	.90

No. 1436-1437 printed checkerwise.

1992. CITY OF MONTREAL SOUVENIR ISSUE

1440 *Souvenir sheet of 4 #1436-1439*

1440		MNHVF	UseVF
$2.16	**Sheet of 4 #1436-1439** FDD *(March 25, 1992)*	3.25	3.00

No. 1440 with engraved signatures in margin was produced in limited quantities for World Philatelic Youth Exhibition catalogue which sold for $12.

1992. RIVER BOOKLET ISSUE The second set in a four part Canadian Heritage River series. *Offset, perforated 12 1/2.*

1441 *Margaree River;* 1442 *West (Eliot) River;* 1443 *Ottawa River;* 1444 *Niagara River;* 1445 *South Saskatchewan River*

1441		MNHVF	UseVF
42¢	**multicolored,** FDD *(April 22, 1992)*	.75	.40

1442		MNHVF	UseVF
42¢	**multicolored,** FDD *(April 22, 1992)*	.75	.40

1443		MNHVF	UseVF
42¢	**multicolored,** FDD *(April 22, 1992)*	.75	.40

1444		MNHVF	UseVF
42¢	**multicolored,** FDD *(April 22, 1992)*	.75	.40

1445		MNHVF	UseVF
42¢	**multicolored,** FDD *(April 22, 1992)*	.75	.40
	y. Strip of 5 #1441-1445	4.00	3.50
	n. Booklet pane of 10, 2 each #1441-1445	9.00	9.00

1992. ALASKA HIGHWAY ISSUE 50th anniversary. *Offset, perforated 13 1/2.*

1446 *"The Alaska Highway"*

1446		MNHVF	UseVF
42¢	**multicolored,** FDD *(May 15, 1992)*	.65	.25

1992. OLYMPIC ISSUE Summer Olympics, Barcelona, Spain. *Offset, perforated 12 1/2 x 13.*

1447 *Gymnastics*

1447		MNHVF	UseVF
42¢	**multicolored,** FDD *(June 15, 1992)*	.75	.35

1448 *Running*

1448		MNHVF	UseVF
42¢	**multicolored,** FDD *(June 15, 1992)*	.75	.35

1449 *Diving*

1449		MNHVF	UseVF
42¢	**multicolored,** FDD *(June 15, 1992)*	.75	.35

1450 *Cycling*

1450		MNHVF	UseVF
42¢	**multicolored,** FDD *(June 15, 1992)*	.75	.35

1451 *Swimming*

	MNHVF	UseVF
1451		
42¢ **multicolored,** FDD *(June 15, 1992)*	.75	.35
y. Strip of 5 #1447-1451	4.50	4.50
n. Booklet pane of 10, 2 each #1447-1451	8.50	9.00

Stamps in bottom row of #1451n are in different sequence than those in #1451y.

1992. ART ISSUE Masterpieces in Canadian Art. *Offset, perforated 12 1/2 x 13.*

1452 Red Nasturtiums, *by David Milne*

	MNHVF	UseVF
1452		
50¢ **multicolored,** FDD *(June 29, 1992)*	.90	.75

1992. MINIATURE SHEET CANADA DAY ISSUE *Offset, perforated 13 x 12 1/2.*

1453 *Nova Scotia;* 1454 *Ontario;* 1455 *Prince Edward Island;* 1456 *New Brunswick;* 1457 *Quebec;* 1458 *Saskatchewan;* 1459 *Manitoba;* 1460 *North West Territories;* 1461 *Alberta;* 1462 *British Columbia;* 1463 *Yukon;* 1464 *Newfoundland*

	MNHVF	UseVF
1453		
42¢ **multicolored,** FDD *(June, 29, 1992)*	.90	.55

	MNHVF	UseVF
1454		
42¢ **multicolored,** FDD *(June, 29, 1992)*	.90	.55
1455		
42¢ **multicolored,** FDD *(June, 29, 1992)*	.90	.55
1456		
42¢ **multicolored,** FDD *(June, 29, 1992)*	.90	.55
1457		
42¢ **multicolored,** FDD *(June, 29, 1992)*	.90	.55
1458		
42¢ **multicolored,** FDD *(June, 29, 1992)*	.90	.55
1459		
42¢ **multicolored,** FDD *(June, 29, 1992)*	.90	.55
1460		
42¢ **multicolored,** FDD *(June, 29, 1992)*	.90	.55
1461		
42¢ **multicolored,** FDD *(June, 29, 1992)*	.90	.55
1462		
42¢ **multicolored,** FDD *(June, 29, 1992)*	.90	.55
1463		
42¢ **multicolored,** FDD *(June, 29, 1992)*	.90	.55
1464		
42¢ **multicolored,** FDD *(June, 29, 1992)*	.90	.55
y. Sheet of 12, #1453-1464 + 13 labels	18.75	15.00

Regular Issues

1992. EDIBLE BERRIES ISSUE *Offset, perforated 13 x 13 1/2.*

1465 *Blueberry*

	MNHVF	UseVF
1465		
1¢ **multicolored,** FDD *(Aug. 5, 1992)*	.20	.20

1466 *Wild strawberry*

	MNHVF	UseVF
1466		
2¢ **multicolored,** FDD *(Aug. 5, 1992)*	.20	.20

1467 *Black crowberry*

	MNHVF	UseVF
1467		
3¢ **multicolored,** FDD *(Aug. 5, 1992)*	.20	.20

1468 *Rose hip*

1468
5¢   **multicolored,** FDD *(Aug. 5, 1992)*   **MNHVF** **UseVF**
                                                      .20   .20

1469 Black raspberry

1469
6¢   **multicolored,** FDD *(Aug. 5, 1992)*   **MNHVF** **UseVF**
                                                      .20   .20

1470 Kinnikinnick

1470
10¢   **multicolored,** FDD *(Aug. 5, 1992)*   **MNHVF** **UseVF**
                                                       .20   .20

1471 Saskatoon berry

1471
25¢   **multicolored,** FDD *(Aug. 5, 1992)*   **MNHVF** **UseVF**
                                                       .30   .25

Commemorative Issues

1992. FOLKLORE ISSUE Legendary heroes. The third set in a four part Canadian Folklore series. *Offset, perforated 12 1/2.*

1472 Jos Monterrand, lumberjack;

1473 Laura Secord, patriot;

1474 Jerry Potts, guide, interpreter;

1475 Captain William Jackman, rescuer

1472
42¢   **multicolored,** FDD *(Sept. 8, 1992)*   **MNHVF** **UseVF**
                                                        .70   .30

1473
42¢   **multicolored,** FDD *(Sept. 8, 1992)*   **MNHVF** **UseVF**
                                                        .70   .30

1474
42¢   **multicolored,** FDD *(Sept. 8, 1992)*   **MNHVF** **UseVF**
                                                        .70   .30

1475
42¢   **multicolored,** FDD *(Sept. 8, 1992)*   **MNHVF** **UseVF**
                                                        .70   .30
           y. Se-tenant block of 4 #1472-1475   3.00   2.25

1992. MINERAL ISSUE *Offset, perforated 12 1/2.*

1476 Copper

1476
42¢   **multicolored,** FDD *(Sept. 21, 1992)*   **MNHVF** **UseVF**
                                                        .95   .40

1477 Sodalite

1477
42¢   **multicolored,** FDD *(Sept. 21, 1992)*   **MNHVF** **UseVF**
                                                        .95   .40

1478 Gold

1478
42¢   **multicolored,** FDD *(Sept. 21, 1992)*   **MNHVF** **UseVF**
                                                        .95   .40

1479 Galena

1479
42¢   **multicolored,** FDD *(Sept. 21, 1992)*   **MNHVF** **UseVF**
                                                        .95   .40

1480 Grossular

1480
42¢   **multicolored,** FDD *(Sept. 21, 1992)*   **MNHVF** **UseVF**
                                                        .95   .40
           y. Strip of 5 #1476-1480   5.00   4.00
           n. Booklet pane of 10   9.75   9.00

1992. SPACE ISSUE *Offset, perforated 13.*

 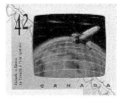

1481 *Anik E2 satellite;* 1482 *Earth and space shuttle*

1481		MNHVF	UseVF
42¢	**multicolored,** FDD *(Oct. 1, 1992)*	.75	.75
	v. Silver omitted	—	

1482		MNHVF	UseVF
42¢	**multicolored,** FDD *(Oct. 1, 1992)* 32 x 26mm	.75	.75
	y. Se-tenant pair #1481-1482	1.50	1.75

No. 1482 has a holographic image. Soaking in water may affect the hologram.

1992. HOCKEY BOOKLET ISSUE National Hockey League, 75th anniversary. *Offset, perforated 13 x 12 1/2.*

1483 *Skates, stick, puck and photograph from the early years (1917-1942)*

1483		MNHVF	UseVF
42¢	**multicolored,** FDD *(Oct. 9, 1992)*	.75	.25
	n. Booklet pane of 8 + 4 labels	5.25	5.25

1484 *Photograph and team emblems from the six-team years (1942-1967)*

1484		MNHVF	UseVF
42¢	**multicolored,** FDD *(Oct. 9, 1992)*	.75	.25
	n. Booklet pane of 8 + 4 labels	5.25	5.25

1485 *Goalie's mask, gloves and photograph from the expansion years (1967-1992)*

1485		MNHVF	UseVF
42¢	**multicolored,** FDD *(Oct. 9, 1992)*	.75	.25
	n. Booklet pane of 9 + 3 labels	7.50	6.00

1992. ORDER OF CANADA ISSUE 25th anniversary. *Offset, perforated 12 1/2.*

1486 *Daniel Roland Michener (1900-1991), governor;*

1487 *Order of Canada*

1486		MNHVF	UseVF
42¢	**multicolored,** FDD *(Oct. 21, 1992)*	.65	.25

1487		MNHVF	UseVF
42¢	**multicolored,** FDD *(Oct. 21, 1992)*	.65	.25
	y. Se-tenant pair #1486-1487	1.50	.65

Nos. 1486-1487 printed in sheets of 25 containing 16 No. 1487 and 9 No. 1486.

1992. WORLD WAR II ISSUE The fourth set in a seven part World War II Canadian Achievements series. *Offset, perforated 13 1/2.*

 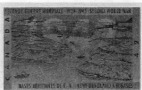

1488 *Raid on Dieppe;* 1489 *U-boats offshore;* 1490 *War reporting;* 1491 *Newfoundland air bases*

1488		MNHVF	UseVF
42¢	**multicolored,** FDD *(Nov. 10, 1992)*	.70	.30

1489		MNHVF	UseVF
42¢	**multicolored,** FDD *(Nov. 10, 1992)*	.70	.30

1490		MNHVF	UseVF
42¢	**multicolored,** FDD *(Nov. 10, 1992)*	.70	.30

1491		MNHVF	UseVF
42¢	**multicolored,** FDD *(Nov. 10, 1992)*	.70	.30
	y. Se-tenant block of 4 #1488-1491	3.00	2.25

1992. CHRISTMAS BOOKLET ISSUE *Offset, perforated 12 1/2 x 13.*

1492 *Santa Claus*

1492		MNHVF	UseVF
37¢	**multicolored,** FDD *(Nov. 13, 1992)*	.75	.75
	n. Booklet pane of 10	5.75	9.00

No. 1492 has bar code at left; for use on covers with printed postal code matrix.

1992. CHRISTMAS ISSUE *Offset, No. 1493 perforated 12 1/2, Nos. 1494-1495 perforated 13 1/2.*

1493 *Jouluvana;* 1494 *La Befana;* 1495 *Weihnachtsmann*

1493		MNHVF	UseVF
42¢	**multicolored,** FDD *(Nov. 13, 1992)*	.70	.20
	v. Perforated 13 1/2	.90	.20
	n. Booklet pane of 10, perforated 13 1/2	6.50	5.25

1494		MNHVF	UseVF
48¢	**multicolored,** FDD *(Nov. 13, 1992)*	.75	.30
	n. Booklet pane of 5 + label	4.00	4.00

1495		MNHVF	UseVF
84¢	**multicolored,** FDD *(Nov. 13, 1992)*	1.25	.60
	n. Booklet pane of 5 + label	6.50	6.00

Regular Issues

1992. TREE ISSUE *Offset, perforated 13.*

 1496 *Delicious apple*

1496		MNHVF	UseVF
49¢	**multicolored,** FDD *(Dec. 30, 1992)*	.90	.25
	v. Perforated 14 1/2 14	1.25	.30
	n. Booklet pane of 5 + 1 label, perforated 14 1/2 x 14	5.50	4.00
	n1. Booklet pane of 5 + label, perforated 13	5.50	4.00

 1497 *Beaked hazelnut*

1497		MNHVF	UseVF
67¢	**multicolored,** FDD *(Dec. 30, 1992)*	1.00	.35

 1498 *Bartlett pear*

1498		MNHVF	UseVF
86¢	**multicolored,** FDD *(Dec. 30, 1992)*	1.90	.55
	v. Perforatated 14 1/2 x 14	2.65	.55
	n. Booklet pane of 5 + 1 label, perforated 14 1/2 x 14	13.00	10.50
	n1. Booklet pane of 5 + label	9.75	7.50

1992. ELIZABETH II ISSUE *Offset, perforated 13 x 13 1/2.*

 1499 *Elizabeth II*

1499		MNHVF	UseVF
43¢	**multicolored,** FDD *(Dec. 30, 1992)*	.95	.20
	n. Booklet pane of 10	9.25	7.50

1992. SMALL FLAG AND LANDSCAPE ISSUE *Offset, perforated 13 1/2 x 13.*

 1500 *Flag & prairie*

1500		MNHVF	UseVF
43¢	**multicolored,** FDD *(Dec. 30, 1992)*	.95	.20
	n. Booklet pane of 10	7.50	6.00
	n1. Booklet pane of 25 + 2 labels	22.50	18.75
	v. Perforated 14 1/2	1.10	.20
	n2. Booklet pane of 10, perforated 14 1/2	9.25	7.50
	n3. Booklet pane of 25 + 2, perforated 14 1/2	26.00	22.50

1992. COIL FLAG ISSUE *Intaglio, perforated 10 horizontal.*

 1501 *Canadian flag stamp in green*

1501		MNHVF	UseVF
43¢	**olive green,** FDD *(Dec. 30, 1992)*	.70	.20
	v. Pair, imperforate	150.00	

1993. SELF-ADHESIVE BOOKLET LARGE FLAG AND LANDSCAPE ISSUE *Die cut, imperforated.*

 1502 *Canadian flag and shoreline*

1502		MNHVF	UseVF
43¢	**multicolored,** FDD *(Feb. 15, 1993)*	.95	.55
	n. Booklet pane of 12	8.25	

No. 1502n issued on peelable paper backing serving as booklet cover and sold for $5.25.

Every entry in this catalog has been double-checked for accuracy, but mistakes may creep into any human endeavor, and we ask your assistance in eliminating them. Please call the attention of the editors to any errors in stamp descriptions found in this catalog.

Commemorative Issues

1993. CANADIAN WOMEN ISSUE National Council of Woman of Canada and National office of YWCA centennial. *Offset, perforated 12 1/2.*

1503 *Adelaide Sophia Hoodless (1857-1910), founder of Victorian Order of Nurses.*

1504 *Marie-Joséphine Gérin-Lajoie (1890-1971), founder of Notre-Dame du Bon Conseil Institute.*

1505 *Pitseolak Ashoona (c.1904-1983), Inuit graphic artist.*

1506 *Helen Kinnear (1894-1970), first woman appointed King's Counsel and first federally appointed woman judge.*

1503		MNHVF	UseVF
43¢	**multicolored,** FDD *(March 8, 1993)*	.70	.30
1504		MNHVF	UseVF
43¢	**multicolored,** FDD *(March 8, 1993)*	.70	.30
1505		MNHVF	UseVF
43¢	**multicolored,** FDD *(March 8, 1993)*	.70	.30
1506		MNHVF	UseVF
43¢	**multicolored,** FDD *(March 8, 1993)*	.70	.30
	y. Se-tenant block of 4 #1503-1506	2.75	2.25

1993. STANLEY CUP ISSUE Centennial. *Offset, perforated 13 1/2.*

1507 *Stanley Cup*

1507		MNHVF	UseVF
43¢	**multicolored,** FDD *(April 16, 1993)*	.70	.25

1993. HANDCRAFTED TEXTILES BOOKLET ISSUE *Offset, perforated 13 x 12 1/2 on 3 sides.*

1508 *Coverlet Bed Rugg, New Brunswick;* 1509 *Patchwork quilt, Ontario;* 1510 *Doukhobor bedcover, Saskatchewan;* 1511 *Kwakwaka'wakw ceremonial robe, British Columbia;* 1512 *Boutonné coverlet, Quebec.*

1508		MNHVF	UseVF
43¢	**multicolored,** FDD *(April 30, 1993)*	.75	.35
1509		MNHVF	UseVF
43¢	**multicolored,** FDD *(April 30, 1993)*	.75	.35
1510		MNHVF	UseVF
43¢	**multicolored,** FDD *(April 30, 1993)*	.75	.35
1511		MNHVF	UseVF
43¢	**multicolored,** FDD *(April 30, 1993)*	.75	.35
1512		MNHVF	UseVF
43¢	**multicolored,** FDD *(April 30, 1993)*	.75	.35
	y. Strip of 5 #1508-1512	3.40	3.00
	n. Booklet pane of 10	6.75	7.50

Stamps in bottom row of No. 1512n are in different sequence than those in 1512y.

1993. ART ISSUE International Year of Indigenous People. *Offset, perforated 12 1/2 x 13.*

1513 *Drawing for* The Owl, *by Kenojuak Ashevak*

1513		MNHVF	UseVF
86¢	**multicolored,** FDD *(May 17, 1993)*	1.50	.75

1993. HOTEL ISSUE Historic Canadian Pacific Railway Hotels. Opening of Chateau Frontenac, in Quebec City, centennial. *Offset, perforated 13 1/2 on 3 sides.*

1514 *Empress Hotel, Victoria, B.C.*

1514		MNHVF	UseVF
43¢	**multicolored,** FDD *(June 14, 1993)*	.75	.35

1515 *Banff Springs Hotel, Alberta*

1515		MNHVF	UseVF
43¢	**multicolored,** FDD *(June 14, 1993)*	.75	.35

1516 *Royal York Hotel, Toronto, Ontario*

1516		MNHVF	UseVF
43¢	**multicolored,** FDD *(June 14, 1993)*	.75	.35

1517 *Chateau Frontenac, Quebec City, Quebec*

1517		MNHVF	UseVF
43¢	**multicolored,** FDD *(June 14, 1993)*	.75	.35

1518 *Algonquin Hotel, St. Andrews, N.B.*

1518		**MNHVF**	**UseVF**
43¢	multicolored, FDD *(June 14, 1993)*	.75	.35
	y. Strip of 5 #1514-1518	3.75	3.25
	n. Booklet pane of 10	7.50	7.50

1993. CANADA DAY SOUVENIR SHEET Provincial and Territorial Parks. Algonquin Park centennial. *Offset, perforated 13.*

1519 *Algonquin, Ontario;* 1520 *De la Gaspésie Park, Quebec;* 1521 *Cedar Dunes Park, Prince Edward Islands;* 1522 *Cape St. Mary's Seabird Ecological Reserve, Newfoundland;* 1523 *Mount Robson Park, British Columbia;* 1524 *Writint-On-Stone Park, Alberta;* 1525 *Spruce Woods Park, Manitoba* 1526 *Herschel Island Park, Yukon;* 1527 *Cypress Hills Park, Saskatchewan;* 1528 *The Rocks Park, New Brunswick;* 1529 *Blomidon Park, Nova Scotia;* 1530 *Katannilik Park, Northwest Territories*

1519		**MNHVF**	**UseVF**
43¢	multicolored, FDD *(June 30, 1993)*	.85	.50
1520		**MNHVF**	**UseVF**
43¢	multicolored, FDD *(June 30, 1993)*	.85	.50
1521		**MNHVF**	**UseVF**
43¢	multicolored, FDD *(June 30, 1993)*	.85	.50
1522		**MNHVF**	**UseVF**
43¢	multicolored, FDD *(June 30, 1993)*	.85	.50
1523		**MNHVF**	**UseVF**
43¢	multicolored, FDD *(June 30, 1993)*	.85	.50
1524		**MNHVF**	**UseVF**
43¢	multicolored, FDD *(June 30, 1993)*	.85	.50
1525		**MNHVF**	**UseVF**
43¢	multicolored, FDD *(June 30, 1993)*	.85	.50
1526		**MNHVF**	**UseVF**
43¢	multicolored, FDD *(June 30, 1993)*	.85	.50
1527		**MNHVF**	**UseVF**
43¢	multicolored, FDD *(June 30, 1993)*	.85	.50
1528		**MNHVF**	**UseVF**
43¢	multicolored, FDD *(June 30, 1993)*	.85	.50
1529		**MNHVF**	**UseVF**
43¢	multicolored, FDD *(June 30, 1993)*	.85	.50
1530		**MNHVF**	**UseVF**
43¢	multicolored, FDD *(June 30, 1993)*	.85	.50
	y. Sheet of 12 #1519-1530	15.00	7.50

1993. CITY OF TORONTO ISSUE Bicentennial. *Offset, perforated 13 1/2 x 13.*

1531 *Toronto City*

1531		**MNHVF**	**UseVF**
43¢	multicolored, FDD *(Aug. 6, 1993)*	.70	.25

1993. RIVER BOOKLET ISSUE The third set in a four part Canadian Heritage River series. *Offset, perforated 13 x 12 1/2.*

1532 *Fraser River, British Columbia;* 1533 *Yukon River, British Columbia;* 1534 *Red River, Manitoba;* 1535 *St. Lawrence River, Ontario and Quebec;* 1536 *St. John River, New Brunswick*

1532		**MNHVF**	**UseVF**
43¢	multicolored, FDD *(Aug. 10, 1993)*	.75	.35
1533		**MNHVF**	**UseVF**
43¢	multicolored, FDD *(Aug. 10, 1993)*	.75	.35
1534		**MNHVF**	**UseVF**
43¢	multicolored, FDD *(Aug. 10, 1993)*	.75	.35
1535		**MNHVF**	**UseVF**
43¢	multicolored, FDD *(Aug. 10, 1993)*	.75	.35
1536		**MNHVF**	**UseVF**
43¢	multicolored, FDD *(Aug. 10, 1993)*	.75	.35
	y. Strip of 5 #1532-1536	3.75	3.40
	n. Booklet pane of 10	7.50	7.50

1993. HISTORIC AUTOMOBILE ISSUE *Offset, perforated 12 1/2 x 13.*

1537 *1867 H.S. Taylor Steam Buggy, 35 x 22;* 1538 *1908 Russell Model L Touring Car, 35 x 22;* 1539 *1914 Ford Model T Open Touring Car, 43 x 22;* 1540 *1950 Studebaker Champion Deluxe Starlight Coupe, 43 x 22;* 1541 *1928 McLaughlin-Buick Model 28-496 Special Car, 51 x 22;* 1542 *1923-24 Gray-Dort 25-SM Luxury Sedan, 51 x 22*

1537		**MNHVF**	**UseVF**
43¢	**multicolored,** FDD *(Aug. 23, 1993)*	.75	.75

1538		**MNHVF**	**UseVF**
43¢	**multicolored,** FDD *(Aug. 23, 1993)*	.75	.75

1539		**MNHVF**	**UseVF**
49¢	**multicolored,** FDD *(Aug. 23, 1993)*	.75	.90

1540		**MNHVF**	**UseVF**
49¢	**multicolored,** FDD *(Aug. 23, 1993)*	.75	.90

1541		**MNHVF**	**UseVF**
86¢	**multicolored,** FDD *(Aug. 23, 1993)*	1.50	1.30

1542		**MNHVF**	**UseVF**
86¢	**multicolored,** FDD *(Aug. 23, 1993)*	1.50	1.30
	y. Souvenir sheet of 6, #1537-1542, 1595- 1600, 1625-1630, 1688-1718	7.50	6.00

1993. FOLK SONG ISSUE The fourth set in the four part Canadian Folklore series. *Offset, perforated 12 1/2.*

1543 *The Alberta Homesteader, Alberta;* 1544 *Les Raftmen, Quebec;* 1545 *I'se the B'y That Builds the Boat, Newfoundland;* 1546 *Onkwarro tenhanonniahkwe, Kanien'kehaka (Mohawk) (Bear Song)*

1543		**MNHVF**	**UseVF**
43¢	**multicolored,** FDD *(Sept. 7, 1993)*	.70	.30

1544		**MNHVF**	**UseVF**
43¢	**multicolored,** FDD *(Sept. 7, 1993)*	.70	.30

1545		**MNHVF**	**UseVF**
43¢	**multicolored,** FDD *(Sept. 7, 1993)*	.70	.30

1546		**MNHVF**	**UseVF**
43¢	**multicolored,** FDD *(Sept. 7, 1993)*	.70	.30
	y. Se-tenant block of 4 #1543-1546	3.00	2.25

1993. DINOSAUR ISSUE The third set in a four part Prehistoric Animal series. *Offset, perforated 13 1/2.*

1547 *Massospondylus (Jurassic period);* 1548 *Styracosaurus (Cretaceous period);* 1549 *Albertosaurus (Cretaceous period);* 1550 *Platecarpus (Cretaceous period)*

1547		**MNHVF**	**UseVF**
43¢	**multicolored,** FDD *(Oct. 1, 1993)*	.70	.30

1548		**MNHVF**	**UseVF**
43¢	**multicolored,** FDD *(Oct. 1, 1993)*	.70	.30

1549		**MNHVF**	**UseVF**
43¢	**multicolored,** FDD *(Oct. 1, 1993)*	.70	.30

1550		**MNHVF**	**UseVF**
43¢	**multicolored,** FDD *(Oct. 1, 1993)*	.70	.30
	y. Se-tenant block of 4 #1547-1550	3.00	2.25

1993. CHRISTMAS BOOKLET ISSUE *Offset, perforated 13.*

1551 *Santa Claus, North America*

1551		**MNHVF**	**UseVF**
38¢	**multicolored,** FDD *(Nov. 4, 1993)*	.75	.35
	n. Booklet pane of 10	5.50	7.50

1993. CHRISTMAS ISSUE *Offset, perforated 13 1/2.*

1552 *Swiety Mikolaj, Poland*

1552		**MNHVF**	**UseVF**
43¢	**multicolored,** FDD *(Nov. 4, 1993)*	.70	.20
	n. Booklet pane of 10	7.50	5.25

1553 *Ded Moroz, Russia*

1553		**MNHVF**	**UseVF**
49¢	**multicolored,** FDD *(Nov. 4, 1993)*	.75	.40
	n. Booklet pane of 5 + label	3.75	3.75

1554 *Father Christmas, Australia*

1554		**MNHVF**	**UseVF**
86¢	**multicolored,** FDD *(Nov. 4, 1993)*	1.25	.50
	n. Booklet pane of 5 + label	6.75	6.00

1993. WORLD WAR II ISSUE The fifth set in a seven part World War II Canadian Achievements series. *Offset, perforated 13 1/2.*

1555 *Aid to Allies;* 1556 *Canada's Bomber forces;* 1557 *Battle of the Atlantic;* 1558 *Italian campaign*

1555		**MNHVF**	**UseVF**
43¢	**multicolored,** FDD *(Nov. 8, 1993)*	.75	.35

1556		**MNHVF**	**UseVF**
43¢	**multicolored,** FDD *(Nov. 8, 1993)*	.75	.35

1557		**MNHVF**	**UseVF**
43¢	**multicolored,** FDD *(Nov. 8, 1993)*	.75	.35

1558			MNHVF	UseVF
43¢	multicolored, FDD (Nov. 8, 1993)		.75	.35
	y.	Se-tenant block of 4 #1555-1558	3.00	2.25

1994. GREETING ISSUE *Offset and die cut.*

1559 *Canada at left;* 1560 *Canada at right*

1559		MNHVF	UseVF
43¢	multicolored, FDD (Jan. 28, 1994)	.90	.45

1560		MNHVF	UseVF
43¢	multicolored, FDD (Jan. 28, 1994)	.90	.45
	n. Booklet pane, 5 each #1559-1560	9.00	

No. 1560n also contains 35 self-adhesive greeting labels in seven designs that complete the design when placed in the central circle of Nos. 1559-1560.

See Nos. 1655-1656, 1679-1680.

Regular Issues

1994. ARCHITECTURE ISSUE *Offset and intaglio, perforated 14 1/2 x 14, 48 x 40mm.*

1561 *Court House, Yorkton, Sask.*

1561		MNHVF	UseVF
$1	multicolored, FDD (Feb. 21, 1994)	1.50	.50
	v. dark blue, inscriptions omitted	1,125.00	
	v1. Perforated 13 1/2 x 13	1.75	.50

1562 *Provincial Normal School*

1562		MNHVF	UseVF
$2	multicolored, FDD (Feb. 21, 1994)	3.00	1.10
	v. dark green inscriptions omitted	1,125.00	
	v1. Intaglio inscriptions inverted	9,000.00	
	v2. Perforated 13 1/2 x 13	3.75	1.10

1994. TREE ISSUE *Offset, perforated 13.*

1563 *Snow Apple*

1563		MNHVF	UseVF
50¢	multicolored, FDD (Feb. 25, 1994)	.90	.35
	n. Booklet pane of 5 + label	5.50	4.00
	v. Perforated 14 1/2 x 14	1.35	.30
	n1. Booklet pane of 5 + label, perforated 14 1/2 x 14	5.60	4.00

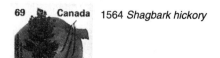

1564 *Shagbark hickory*

1564		MNHVF	UseVF
69¢	multicolored, FDD (Feb. 25, 1994)	1.10	.30

1565 *Westcot Apricot*

1565		MNHVF	UseVF
88¢	multicolored, FDD (Feb. 25, 1994)	1.50	.50
	n. Booklet pane of 5 + label	7.50	6.00
	v. Perforated 14 1/2 x 14	2.25	.75
	n1. Booklet pane of 5 + label, perforated 14 1/2 x 14	11.25	9.00

Commemorative Issues

1994. JEANNE SAUVÉ ISSUE *Offset, perforated 12 1/2 x 13. Issued se-tenant with label in sheets of 20 + 20 labels in four designs. In alternating rows, labels appear on left or right side of stamp.*

1566 *Jeanne Sauvé, (1922-93) Governor General*

1566		MNHVF	UseVF
43¢	multicolored, FDD (March 8, 1994)	.75	.30
	y. Block of 4 + 4 labels	3.75	3.00

1994. T. EATON COMPANY ISSUE *125th anniversary. Offset, perforated 13 1/2 x 13.*

1567 *Timothy Eaton Company*

1567		MNHVF	UseVF
43¢	multicolored, FDD (March 17, 1994)	.75	.30
	n. Booklet pane of 10 + 2 labels	7.50	6.00

1994. RIVER BOOKLET ISSUE *The fourth and final set in the Canadian Heritage River series. Offset, perforated 13 1/2.*

1568 *Saguenay River*

1568		MNHVF	UseVF
43¢	multicolored, FDD (April 22, 1994)	.75	.35

1569 *French River*

1569		MNHVF	UseVF
43¢	multicolored, FDD (April 22, 1994)	.75	.35

1570 *Mackenzie River*

1570		MNHVF	UseVF
43¢	multicolored, FDD *(April 22, 1994)*	.75	.35

1571 *Churchill River*

1571		MNHVF	UseVF
43¢	multicolored, FDD *(April 22, 1994)*	.75	.35

1572 *Columbia River*

1572		MNHVF	UseVF
43¢	multicolored, FDD *(April 22, 1994)*	.75	.35
	y. Strip of 5 #1568-1572	3.75	3.25
	n. Booklet pane of 10	8.25	7.50

1994. ART ISSUE *Offset, perforated 14 x 14 1/2.*

1573 Vera, *by Frederick H. Varley (1881-1969)*

1573		MNHVF	UseVF
88¢	multicolored, FDD *(May 6, 1994)*	1.50	.75

1994. FIRST XV COMMONWEALTH GAMES ISSUE *Offset, perforated 14.*

1574 *Lawn bowls;*
1575 *Lacrosse*

1574		MNHVF	UseVF
43¢	multicolored, FDD *(May 20, 1994)*	.75	.30

1575		MNHVF	UseVF
43¢	multicolored, FDD *(May 20, 1994)*	.75	.30
	y. Se-tenant pair #1574-1575	1.50	.90

1994. INTERNATIONAL YEAR OF THE FAMILY ISSUE *Offset, perforated 14.*

1576a *Mother & infant;* 1576b *Adults & children playing;* 1576c *Elderly woman & child;* 1576d *Adults & children in class;* 1576e *Judge, health care worker & child*

1576		MNHVF	UseVF
$2.15	**Sheet of 5,** FDD *(June 2, 1994)*	3.75	3.00
	a. Mother & infant 43¢	.60	.34
	b. Adults & children playing 43¢	.60	.34
	c. Elderly woman & child 43¢	.60	.34
	d. Adults & children in class 43¢	.60	.34
	e. Judge, health care worker & child 43¢	.60	.34

1994. CANADA DAY ISSUE Maple trees. *Offset, perforated 13 x 13 1/2. Sheet of 12.*

1577 *Bigleaf Maple;* 1578 *Sugar Maple;* 1579 *Silver Maple;* 1580 *Striped Maple;* 1581 *Norway Maple;* 1582 *Manitoba Maple;* 1583 *Black Maple;* 1584 *Douglas Maple;* 1585 *Mountain Maple;* 1586 *Vine Maple;* 1587 *Hedge Maple;* 1588 *Red Maple*

1577		MNHVF	UseVF
43¢	multicolored, FDD *(June 30, 1994)*	.75	.40

1578		MNHVF	UseVF
43¢	multicolored, FDD *(June 30, 1994)*	.75	.40

1579		MNHVF	UseVF
43¢	multicolored, FDD *(June 30, 1994)*	.75	.40

1580		MNHVF	UseVF
43¢	multicolored, FDD *(June 30, 1994)*	.75	.40

1581		MNHVF	UseVF
43¢	multicolored, FDD *(June 30, 1994)*	.75	.40

		MNHVF	UseVF
1582		**MNHVF**	**UseVF**
43¢	**multicolored,** FDD *(June 30, 1994)*	.75	.40
1583		**MNHVF**	**UseVF**
43¢	**multicolored,** FDD *(June 30, 1994)*	.75	.40
1584		**MNHVF**	**UseVF**
43¢	**multicolored,** FDD *(June 30, 1994)*	.75	.40
1585		**MNHVF**	**UseVF**
43¢	**multicolored,** FDD *(June 30, 1994)*	.75	.40
1586		**MNHVF**	**UseVF**
43¢	**multicolored,** FDD *(June 30, 1994)*	.75	.40
1587		**MNHVF**	**UseVF**
43¢	**multicolored,** FDD *(June 30, 1994)*	.75	.40
1588		**MNHVF**	**UseVF**
43¢	**multicolored,** FDD *(June 30, 1994)*	.75	.40
	a. Sheet of 12	9.00	7.50

1994. SECOND XV COMMONWEALTH GAMES ISSUE *Offset, perforated 14.*

1589 *Wheelchair marathon;* 1590 *High jump*

1589		**MNHVF**	**UseVF**
43¢	**multicolored,** FDD *(Aug. 5, 1994)*	.75	.30
1590		**MNHVF**	**UseVF**
43¢	**multicolored,** FDD *(Aug. 5, 1994)*	.75	.30
	y. Se-tenant pair #1589-1590	1.50	.65

1591 *Diving*

1591		**MNHVF**	**UseVF**
50¢	**multicolored,** FDD *(Aug. 5, 1994)*	.90	.50

1592 *Cycling*

1592		**MNHVF**	**UseVF**
88¢	**multicolored,** FDD *(Aug. 5, 1994)*	1.50	.60

1994. FAMOUS PEOPLE ISSUE *Offset, perforated 13.*

1593 *William Avery Bishop (1894-1956), fighter ace;* 1594 *Mary Travers, "La Bolduc" (1894-1941), folk singer*

1593		**MNHVF**	**UseVF**
43¢	**multicolored,** FDD *(Aug. 12, 1994)*	.70	.30
1594		**MNHVF**	**UseVF**
43¢	**multicolored,** FDD *(Aug. 12, 1994)*	.70	.30
	y. Se-tenant pair #1593-1594	1.50	.90

1994. HISTORIC VEHICLES ISSUE *Offset, perforated 12 1/2 x 13. Miniature sheet.*

1595 *1942 Ford F60L-AMB military ambulance;* 1596 *1925 Reo Police Wagon;* 1597 *1927 Sicard Snow Remover/Snowblower;* 1598 *1936 Bickle Chieftain Fire Engine;* 1599 *1894 Ottawa Car Company Streetcar;* 1600 *1950 Motor Coach Industries Courier 50 Skyview bus*

1595		**MNHVF**	**UseVF**
43¢	**multicolored,** FDD *(Aug. 19, 1994)*	.70	.70
1596		**MNHVF**	**UseVF**
43¢	**multicolored,** FDD *(Aug. 19, 1994)*	.70	.70
1597		**MNHVF**	**UseVF**
50¢	**multicolored,** FDD *(Aug. 19, 1994)*	.75	.75
1598		**MNHVF**	**UseVF**
50¢	**multicolored,** FDD *(Aug. 19, 1994)*	.75	.75
1599		**MNHVF**	**UseVF**
88¢	**multicolored,** FDD *(Aug. 19, 1994)*	1.50	1.10
1600		**MNHVF**	**UseVF**
88¢	**multicolored,** FDD *(Aug. 19, 1994)*	1.50	1.10
	a. Sheet of 6 #1595-1600	6.00	5.25

1994. ICAO ISSUE International Civil Aviation 50th anniversary. *Offset, perforated 13.*

1601 *Jet aircraft*

1601		**MNHVF**	**UseVF**
43¢	**multicolored,** FDD *(Sept. 16, 1994)*	.70	.25

1994. DINOSAUR ISSUE The fourth and final set in the Prehistoric Animal series. *Offset, perforated 13.*

1602 *Short-faced bear;* 1603 *Woolly mammoth;* 1604 *Coryphodon;* 1605 *Megacerops*

1602		**MNHVF**	**UseVF**
43¢	**multicolored,** FDD *(Sept. 26, 1994)*	.70	.30

1603		MNHVF	UseVF
43¢	**multicolored,** FDD *(Sept. 26, 1994)*	.70	.30
1604		MNHVF	UseVF
43¢	**multicolored,** FDD *(Sept. 26, 1994)*	.70	.30
1605		MNHVF	UseVF
43¢	**multicolored,** FDD *(Sept. 26, 1994)*	.70	.30
	y. Se-tenant block of 4 #1602-1605	3.00	2.25

1994. CHRISTMAS BOOKLET ISSUE *Offset, perforated 13. Bar code at left, for use on covers with printed postal code matrix.*

 1606 *Soloist*

1606		MNHVF	UseVF
38¢	**multicolored,** FDD *(Nov. 3, 1994)*	.75	.35
	n. Booklet pane of 10	6.00	9.50

1994. CHRISTMAS ISSUE *Offset, perforated 13 1/2.*

 1607 *Family singing carols*

1607		MNHVF	UseVF
43¢	**multicolored,** FDD *(Nov. 3, 1994)*	.70	.20
	n. Booklet pane of 10	7.00	6.00

 1608 *Choir*

1608		MNHVF	UseVF
50¢	**multicolored,** FDD *(Nov. 3, 1994)*	.75	.35
	n. Booklet pane of 5 + label	4.00	4.50

 1609 *Outdoor caroling*

1609		MNHVF	UseVF
88¢	**multicolored,** FDD *(Nov. 3, 1994)*	1.50	.60
	n. Booklet pane of 5 + label	7.00	6.00

1994. WORLD WAR II ISSUE The sixth set in a seven part World War II Canadian Achievements series. *Offset, perforated 13 1/2.*

1610 *D-Day beachhead;* 1611 *Artillery-Normandy;* 1612 *Tactical Air Forces;* 1613 *Walcheren and the Scheldt*

1610		MNHVF	UseVF
43¢	**multicolored,** FDD *(Nov. 7, 1994)*	.70	.35
1611		MNHVF	UseVF
43¢	**multicolored,** FDD *(Nov. 7, 1994)*	.70	.35
1612		MNHVF	UseVF
43¢	**multicolored,** FDD *(Nov. 7, 1994)*	.70	.35
1613		MNHVF	UseVF
43¢	**multicolored,** FDD *(Nov. 7, 1994)*	.70	.35
	y. Se-tenant block of 4 #1610-1613	2.75	1.35

1995. WORLD WAR II ISSUE The seventh and final set in the World War II Canadian Achievements series. *Offset, perforated 13 1/2.*

1614 *Freeing the POW;* 1615 *Veterans Return Home;* 1616 *Liberation of Civilians;* 1617 *Crossing the Rhine*

1614		MNHVF	UseVF
43¢	**multicolored,** FDD *(March 20, 1995)*	.70	.45
1615		MNHVF	UseVF
43¢	**multicolored,** FDD *(March 20, 1995)*	.70	.45
1616		MNHVF	UseVF
43¢	**multicolored,** FDD *(March 20, 1995)*	.70	.45
1617		MNHVF	UseVF
43¢	**multicolored,** FDD *(March 20, 1995)*	.70	.45
	y. Se-tenant block of 4 #1614-1615	2.70	1.90

1995. ART ISSUE *Offset, perforated 13.*

 1618 Floraison, *by Alfred Pellan (1906-88)*

1618		MNHVF	UseVF
88¢	**multicolored,** FDD *(April 21, 1995)*	1.50	.55

1995. FLAG ISSUE Thirtieth anniversary of the Canadian flag. *Offset, perforated 13 1/2 x 13.*

 1619 *Flag over lake*

1619		MNHVF	UseVF
43¢	**multicolored,** FDD *(May 1, 1995)*	.70	.25

No. 1619 was valued at the first class domestic letter rate on day of issue.

1995. LOUISBOURG ANNIVERSARY ISSUE 275th anniversary of the founding of the Fortress of Louisbourg. *Offset, perforated 12 1/2 x 13. Nos. 1620, 1624, 48 x 32mm. No. 1621, 32 x 32mm. No. 1622, 40 x 32mm. No. 1623, 56 x 32mm.*

1620 *Louisbourg Harbor, ships near Dauphin Gate;* 1621 *Walls, streets and buildings of Louisbourg;* 1622 *Museum behind King's Bastion;* 1623 *Drawing of King's Garden Convent, hospital & barracks;* 1624 *Partially eroded fortifications*

1620		MNHVF	UseVF
43¢	multicolored, FDD *(May 5, 1995)*	.75	.35
1621		MNHVF	UseVF
43¢	multicolored, FDD *(May 5, 1995)*	.75	.35
1622		MNHVF	UseVF
43¢	multicolored, FDD *(May 5, 1995)*	.75	.35
1623		MNHVF	UseVF
43¢	multicolored, FDD *(May 5, 1995)*	.75	.35
1624		MNHVF	UseVF
43¢	multicolored, FDD *(May 5, 1995)*	.75	.35
	y. Strip of 5, #1620-1624	3.75	3.75
	n. Booklet pane of 10	7.50	6.00

Nos. 1620-1624 were valued at the first class domestic letter rate on day of issue. No. 1624y is a continuous design.

1995. HISTORIC VEHICLE ISSUE Farm and frontier vehicles. *Miniature sheet. Offset, perforated 12 1/2 x 13; 35 x 22mm or 43 x 22 mm.*

1625 *1950 Cockshutt "30" farm tractor, 35 x 22mm;* 1626 *1970 Bombardier Ski-Doo Olympique 335 snowmobile, 35 x 22mm;* 1627 *Bombardier B-12 CS multi-passenger snowmobile, 43 x 22mm;* 1628 *1924 Gotfredson Model 20 farm truck, 43 x 22mm;* 1629 *1962 Robin-Nodwell RN 110 tracked carrier, 43 x 22mm;* 1630 *1942 Massey-Harris No. 21 self-propelled combine, 43 x 22mm*

1625		MNHVF	UseVF
43¢	multicolored, FDD *(May 26, 1995)*	.60	.60
1626		MNHVF	UseVF
43¢	multicolored, FDD *(May 26, 1995)*	.60	.60
1627		MNHVF	UseVF
50¢	multicolored, FDD *(May 26, 1995)*	.75	.75
1628		MNHVF	UseVF
50¢	multicolored, FDD *(May 26, 1995)*	.75	.75
1629		MNHVF	UseVF
88¢	multicolored, FDD *(May 26, 1995)*	1.50	.90
1630		MNHVF	UseVF
88¢	multicolored, FDD *(May 26, 1995)*	1.50	.90
	a. Sheet of 6 #1625-1630	6.00	5.25

1995. GOLF BOOKLET ISSUE National Golf Week, Canadian Amateur Golf Championship centennial and Royal Canadian Golf Association centennial. *Offset, perforated 13 1/2 x 13 on 3 sides.*

1631 *Banff Springs Golf Club, Alberta;* 1632 *Riverside Country Club, New Brunswick;* 1633 *Glen Abbey Golf Club, Ontario;* 1634 *Victoria Golf Club, British Columbia;* 1635 *Royal Montreal Golf Club, Quebec*

1631		MNHVF	UseVF
43¢	multicolored, FDD *(June 6, 1995)*	.75	.40
1632		MNHVF	UseVF
43¢	multicolored, FDD *(June 6, 1995)*	.75	.40
1633		MNHVF	UseVF
43¢	multicolored, FDD *(June 6, 1995)*	.75	.40
1634		MNHVF	UseVF
43¢	multicolored, FDD *(June 6, 1995)*	.75	.40
1635		MNHVF	UseVF
43¢	multicolored, FDD *(June 6, 1995)*	.75	.40
	y. Strip of 5 #1631-1635	3.75	3.75
	n. Booklet pane of 10	7.50	6.00

1995. PAINTINGS SOUVENIER ISSUE *Offset; perforated 13.*

1636a *October Gold, by Franklin Carmichael;* 1636b *From the North Shore, Lake Superior, by Lawren Harris;* 1636c *Evening, Les Eboulements, Quebec, by A. Y. Jackson*

1636		MNHVF	UseVF
$1.29	Sheet of 3, multicolored, FDD *(June 29, 1995)* #1636a-1636c	2.50	2.25
	a. *October Gold,* by Franklin Carmichael 43¢	.75	.75
	b. *From the North Shore, Lake Superior,* by Lawren Harris 43¢	.75	.75
	c. *Evening, Lee Eboulements, Quebec,* by A. Y. Jackson 43¢	.75	.75

1637a *Sereniy, Lake of the Woods, by Frank H. Johnston;* 1637b *A September Gale, Georgian Bay, by Arthur Lismer;* 1637c *Falls, Montreal River, by J. E. H. MacDonald;* 1637d *Open Window, by Frederick Horsman Varley*

1637		MNHVF	UseVF
$1.72	**Sheet of 4, multicolored,** FDD *(June 29, 1995)* #1637a-1637d	3.25	3.00
	a. *Serenity, Lake of the Woods,* by Frank H. Johnston 43¢	.75	.75
	b. *A September Gale, Georgian Bay,* by Arthur Lismer 43¢	.75	.75
	c. *Falls, Montreal River,* by J. E. H. MacDonald 43¢	.75	.75
	d. *Open Window,* by Frederick Horsman Varley 43¢	.75	.75

1638a Mill Houses, *by Alfred J. Casson;* 1638b Pembina Valley, *by Lionel LeMoine FitzGerald;* 1638c The Lumberjack, *by Edwin Headley Holgate*

1638		MNHVF	UseVF
$1.29	**Sheet of 3, multicolored,** FDD *(June 29, 1995)* #1638a-1638c	2.40	2.25
	a. *Mill Houses,* by Alfred J. Casson 43¢	.75	.75
	b. *Pembina Valley,* by Lionel LeMoine FitzGerald 43¢	.75	.75
	c. *The Lumberjack,* by Edwin Headley Holgate 43¢	.75	.75

1995. LUNENBURG ACADEMY ISSUE Centennial of the Lunenberg Academy in Nova Scotia. *Offset, perforated 13.*

 1639 *Lunenburg Academy*

1639		MNHVF	UseVF
43¢	**multicolored,** FDD *(June 29, 1995)*	.60	.25

1995. MANITOBA ISSUE 125th anniversary of entry into Confederation. *Offset, perforated 13 1/2 x 13.*

 1640 *"1870 Manitoba 1995"*

1640		MNHVF	UseVF
43¢	**multicolored,** FDD *(July 14, 1995)*	.60	.25

Regular Issues

1995. SMALL FLAG AND LANDSCAPE ISSUE *Offset, perforated 14 1/2.*

 1641 *Flag & buildings*

1641		MNHVF	UseVF
45¢	**multicolored,** FDD *(July 31, 1995)*	.75	.20
	n. Booklet pane of 10	9.25	7.50
	Complete booklet, #1641n	9.75	
	n1. Booklet pane of 25 + 2 labels	28.00	20.00
	Complete booklet, #1641n1	18.75	
	v. Perforated 13 1/2 x 13	.75	.20
	n2. Booklet pane of 10, perforated 13 1/2 x 13	7.50	6.00
	Complete booklet, #1641n2	8.25	
	n3. Booklet pane of 25 + 2 labels, perforated 13 1/2 x 13	18.25	15.00
	Complete booklet, #1641n3	18.75	

1995. COIL FLAG ISSUE *Intaglio, perforated 10 horizontal.*

1642		MNHVF	UseVF
45¢	**blue green,** FDD *(July 31, 1995)*	.75	.20
	v. Pair, imperforate	150.00	

1995. ELIZABETH II ISSUE *Offset, perforated 13 x 13 1/2.*

 1643 *Elizabeth II*

1643		MNHVF	UseVF
45¢	**multicolored,** FDD *(July 31, 1995)*	.75	.20
	n. Booklet pane of 10	7.50	6.00
	Complete booklet, No. 1643n	8.25	

1995. TREE ISSUE *Offset, perforated 13.*

 1644 *Gravenstein Apple*

1644		MNHVF	UseVF
52¢	**multicolored,** FDD *(July 31, 1995)*	.85	.25
	n. Booklet pane of 5 + label	5.50	4.50
	Complete booklet, No. 1644n	6.00	
	v. Perforated 14 1/2 x 14	1.15	.30
	n1. Booklet pane of of 5 + label, perforated 14 1/2 x 14	5.60	4.50
	Complete booklet, 1644n1	6.00	

 1645 *American Chestnut*

1645		MNHVF	UseVF
71¢	**multicolored,** FDD *(July 31, 1995)*	1.10	.30
	v. Perforated 14 1/2 x 14	2.25	.50

 1646 *Elberta Peach*

1646		MNHVF	UseVF
90¢	**multicolored,** FDD *(July 31, 1995)*	1.40	.45
	n. Booklet pane of 5 + label	7.50	6.00
	Complete booklet, No. 1646n	8.25	
	v. Perforated 14 1/2 x 14	2.25	.50

n1. Booklet pane of 5 + label, perforated 14 9.25 7.50
1/2 x 14
Complete booklet, No. 1646n1 9.25

Commemorative Issues

1995. MIGRATORY WILDLIFE ISSUE *Offset, perforated 13 x 12 1/2.*

1647 *Belted Kingfisher;*

1648 *Monarch butterfly;*

1649 *Hoary bat;*

1650 *Northern pintail*

1647		MNHVF	UseVF
45¢	**multicolored,** FDD *(Aug. 15, 1995)*	.75	.40

1648		MNHVF	UseVF
45¢	**multicolored,** FDD *(Aug. 15, 1995)*	.75	.25

1649		MNHVF	UseVF
45¢	**multicolored,** FDD *(Aug. 15, 1995)*	.75	.25

1650		MNHVF	UseVF
45¢	**multicolored,** FDD *(Aug. 15, 1995)*	.75	.25
	y. Se-tenant block of 4 #1647-1650	3.00	1.90

No. 1647 inscribed "aune."

1995. BRIDGE ISSUE *Offset, perforated 12 1/2 x 13.*

1651 *Quebec Bridge, Quebec;* 1652 *Highway 403-401-410 interchange, Ontario;* 1653 *Hartland covered wooden bridge, New Brunswick;* 1654 *Alex Fraser Bridge, British Columbia*

1651		MNHVF	UseVF
45¢	**multicolored,** FDD *(Sept. 1, 1995)*	.75	.30

1652		MNHVF	UseVF
45¢	**multicolored,** FDD *(Sept. 1, 1995)*	.75	.30

1653		MNHVF	UseVF
45¢	**multicolored,** FDD *(Sept. 1, 1995)*	.75	.30

1654		MNHVF	UseVF
45¢	**multicolored,** FDD *(Sept. 1, 1995)*	.75	.30
	y. Se-tenant block of 4 #1651-1654	3.00	1.90

1995. GREETING ISSUE *Die cut, self-adhesive.*

1655 *"Canada" at left;* 1656 *"Canada" at right*

1655		MNHVF	UseVF
45¢	**green & multicolored,** FDD *(Sept. 1, 1995)*	.75	.45

1656		MNHVF	UseVF
45¢	**green & multicolored,** FDD *(Sept. 1, 1995)*	.75	.45
	n. Booklet pane, 5 each #1655-1656	9.00	

No. 1656n by its nature is a complete booklet. The peelable backing serves as a booklet cover. It also contains 15 self-adhesive greeting labels in four designs that complete the design when placed in the central circle of Nos. 1655-1656. It exists with special cover and labels commemorating the 50th anniversary of Canadian Chiropractic Memorial College, Toronto.

1995. CANADIAN ARCTIC BOOKLET ISSUE *Offset, perforated 13 x 12 1/2.*

 1657 *Polar bear & caribou*

1657		MNHVF	UseVF
45¢	**multicolored,** FDD *(Sept. 15, 1995)*	.75	.30

 1658 *Arctic Poppy & cargo canoe*

1658		MNHVF	UseVF
45¢	**multicolored,** FDD *(Sept. 15, 1995)*	.75	.30

 1659 *Inuk man, igloo & sled dogs*

1659		MNHVF	UseVF
45¢	**multicolored,** FDD *(Sept. 15, 1995)*	.75	.30

 1660 *Dogsled team & ski plane*

1660		MNHVF	UseVF
45¢	**multicolored,** FDD *(Sept. 15, 1995)*	.75	.30

 1661 *Children*

1661		MNHVF	UseVF
45¢	**multicolored,** FDD *(Sept. 15, 1995)*	.75	.30
	y. Strip of 5, #1657-1661	3.75	3.75
	n. Booklet pane 10	7.50	6.75

Stamps in bottom row of 1661n are in different sequence.

1995. MIGRATORY WILDLIFE REVISED INSCRIPTION ISSUE

 1662 *Belted Kingfisher*

1662		MNHVF	UseVF
45¢	**multicolored,** FDD *(Sept. 26, 1995)*	.95	.40
	y. Se-tenant block of 4, #1648, 1649-1650, 1662	3.75	1.90

No. 1662 inscribed "Faune."

1995. Comic Book Character Booklet Issue *Offset, perforated 13 x 12 1/2.*

1663 *Superman*

1663
45¢ **multicolored,** FDD *(Oct. 2, 1995)* | MNHVF .75 | UseVF .30

1664 *Johnny Canuck*

1664
45¢ **multicolored,** FDD *(Oct. 2, 1995)* | MNHVF .75 | UseVF .30

1665 *Nelvana*

1665
45¢ **multicolored,** FDD *(Oct. 2, 1995)* | MNHVF .75 | UseVF .30

1666 *Captain Canuck*

1666
45¢ **multicolored,** FDD *(Oct. 2, 1995)* | MNHVF .75 | UseVF .30

1667 *Fleur de Lys*

1667
45¢ **multicolored,** FDD *(Oct. 2, 1995)* | MNHVF .75 | UseVF .30
y. Strip of 5, #1663-1667 | 3.75 | 3.75
n. Booklet pane 10 | 7.50 | 6.75

Stamps in the bottom row of No. 1667n are in different sequence.

1995. U.N. Issue 50th anniversary. *Offset, perforated 13 1/2.*

1668 *Prime Minister William Lyon Mackenzie King signing the U.N. Charter in San Francisco*

1668
45¢ **blue & multicolored,** FDD *(Oct. 24, 1995)* | MNHVF .75 | UseVF .30

No. 1668 printed in sheets of 10 with top label equal to 10 stamps. Label shows details of Canadian participation in UN activities. UN emblem is stamped in blue foil.

1995. Christmas Booklet Issue *Offset, perforated 12 1/2 x 13.*

1669 *Holly*

1669
40¢ **multicolored,** FDD *(Nov. 2, 1995)* | MNHVF .75 | UseVF .75
n. Booklet pane of 10 | 6.40 | 9.50

1995. Christmas Issue Capital Sculptures by Emile Brunet (1893-1977). *Offset, perforated 13 1/2.*

1670 The Nativity

1670
45¢ **multicolored,** FDD *(Nov. 2, 1995)* | MNHVF .70 | UseVF .20
n. Booklet pane of 10 | 7.25 | 6.00
Complete booklet, 1670n | 7.50 |

1671 The Annunciation

1671
52¢ **multicolored,** FDD *(Nov. 2, 1995)* | MNHVF .75 | UseVF .40
n. Booklet pane of 5 + label | 4.00 | 4.00
Complete booklet, 1671n | 4.50 |

1672 Flight to Egypt

1672
90¢ **multicolored,** FDD *(Nov. 2, 1995)* | MNHVF 1.50 | UseVF .60
n. Booklet pane of 5 + label | 7.50 | 6.75
Complete booklet, #1672n | 8.25 |

1995. La Francophonie's Agency Issue Cultural and technical cooperation, 25th anniversary. *Offset, perforated 13 x 13 1/2.*

1673 *"la francophonie 1970, 1975"*

1673
45¢ **multicolored,** FDD *(Nov. 6, 1995)* | MNHVF .75 | UseVF .25

1995. HOLOCAUST ISSUE End of Holocaust 50th anniversary. *Offset, perforated 12 1/2 x 13.*

1674 *Photographs of people from the Holocaust*

1674		MNHVF	UseVF
45¢	**multicolored,** FDD *(Nov. 9, 1995)*	.75	.25

1996. BIRD ISSUE *Offset, perforated 13 1/2. Issued in panes of 12 stamps, printed checkerwise and in uncut sheets of 5 panes.*

1675 *American kestrel*

1675		MNHVF	UseVF
45¢	**multicolored,** FDD *(Jan. 9, 1996)*	.75	.30

1676 *Atlantic puffin*

1676		MNHVF	UseVF
45¢	**multicolored,** FDD *(Jan. 9, 1996)*	.75	.30

1677 *Pileated woodpecker*

1677		MNHVF	UseVF
45¢	**multicolored,** FDD *(Jan. 9, 1996)*	.75	.30

1678 *Ruby-throated hummingbird*

1678		MNHVF	UseVF
45¢	**multicolored,** FDD *(Jan. 9, 1996)*	.75	.30
	y. Se-tenant strip of 4, #1675-1678	2.75	2.25

See also Nos. 1751-1754.

1996. GREETINGS ISSUE *Offset, die cut, self-adhesive, 51 x 24mm.*

1679 *'greeting' quick stick Canada at left;* 1680 *'greeting' quick stick Canada at right*

1679		MNHVF	UseVF
45¢	**green & multicolored,** FDD *(Jan. 15, 1996)*	.75	.35

1680		MNHVF	UseVF
45¢	**green & multicolored,** FDD *(Jan. 15, 1996)*	.75	.35
	n. Booklet pane, 5 each No. 1679-1680	9.00	9.00

By its nature No. 1680n is a complete booklet. The peelable backing serves as a booklet cover. It also contains 35 self-adhesive greeting labels in seven designs that complete the design when placed in the central circle of Nos. 1679-1680.

Nos. 1679-80 are similar in appearance to Nos. 1655-56 but are larger.

1996. HIGH TECHNOLOGY BOOKLET ISSUE *Offset, perforated 13 1/2 on 3 sides.*

1681 *Ocean technology;* 1682 *Aerospace technology;* 1683 *Information technology;* 1684 *Biotechnology*

1681		MNHVF	UseVF
45¢	**multicolored,** FDD *(Feb. 15, 1996)*	.95	.40

1682		MNHVF	UseVF
45¢	**multicolored,** FDD *(Feb. 15, 1996)*	.95	.40

1683		MNHVF	UseVF
45¢	**multicolored,** FDD *(Feb. 15, 1996)*	.95	.40

1684		MNHVF	UseVF
45¢	**multicolored,** FDD *(Feb. 15, 1996)*	.95	.40
	n. Booklet pane of 12, 3 each #1681-1684	9.00	10.50
	Complete Booklet, #1684n	9.75	

Regular Issues

1996. ARCHITECTURE ISSUE *Offset and intaglio, perforated 13 1/2 x 13.*

1685 *Carnegie Public Library, Victoria*

1685		MNHVF	UseVF
$5	**multicolored,** FDD *(Feb. 29, 1996)*	7.50	2.25

Commemorative Issues

1996. ART ISSUE Issued for the opening of Canada's National Art Gallery. *Offset, perforated 12 1/2 x 13.*

1686 The Spirit of Haida Gwaii, *by Bill Reid*

1686		MNHVF	UseVF
90¢	**multicolored,** FDD *(April 30, 1996)*	1.50	.50

1996. AIDS AWARENESS ISSUE for the 11th International Conference on AIDS, held in Vancouver, B.C., July 1996. *Offset, perforated 13 1/2.*

1687 One World, One Hope, *by Joe Average*

1687		MNHVF	UseVF
45¢	**multicolored,** FDD *(May 8, 1996)*	.70	.25

1996. HISTORIC VEHICLE ISSUE *Offset, perforated 12 1/2 x 13.* Nos. 1692-1693, 1704-1707, 1718 are 51 x 22mm; Nos. 1708-1717 are 43 x 21mm.

1688 *(1899) Still Motor Co. Ltd. Electric Van 45¢;* 1689 *(1914) Waterous Engine Works Road Roller 45¢;* 1690 *(1938) International D-35 Delivery Truck 52¢;* 1691 *(1936) Champion Road Grader 52¢;* 1692 *(1947) White Model WA 122 Tractor-Trailer 90¢;* 1693 *(1975) Hayes HDX 45-115 Logging Truck 90¢*

1688		MNHVF	UseVF
45¢	**multicolored,** FDD *(June 8, 1996)*	.70	.70
1689		MNHVF	UseVF
45¢	**multicolored,** FDD *(June 8, 1996)*	.70	.70
1690		MNHVF	UseVF
52¢	**multicolored,** FDD *(June 8, 1996)*	.75	.75
1691		MNHVF	UseVF
52¢	**multicolored,** FDD *(June 8, 1996)*	.75	.75
1692		MNHVF	UseVF
90¢	**multicolored,** FDD *(June 8, 1996)*	1.50	1.50
1693		MNHVF	UseVF
90¢	**multicolored,** FDD *(June 8, 1996)*	1.50	1.50
	y. Souvenir sheet of 6, #1688-1693 ($3.74)	5.75	4.00

1996. HISTORIC LAND VEHICLES COLLECTION ISSUE Issued for CAPEX 96. *Offset, perforated 12 1/2 x 13.*

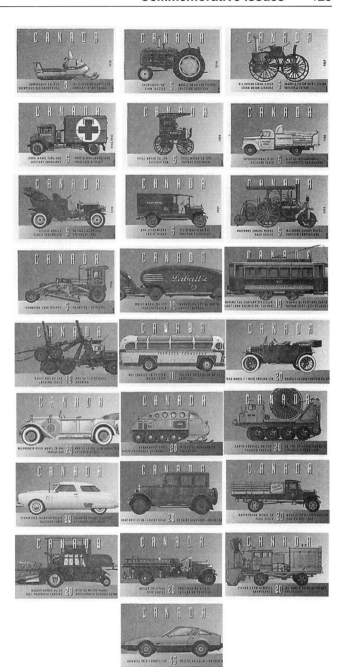

1694 *5¢ (1970) Bombardier Ski-Doo Olympique 335 snowmobile;* 1695 *5¢ (1950) Cockshutt "30" farm tractor;* 1696 *5¢ (1867) H.S. Taylor Steam Buggy;* 1697 *5¢ (1942) Ford F60L-AMB military ambulance;* 1698 *5¢ (1899) Still Motor Co. Ltd. Electric Van;* 1699 *(1938) International D-35 Delivery Truck;* 1700 *5¢ (1908) Russell Model L Touring Car;* 1701 *5¢ (1925) Reo Speed Wagon/ Police Wagon;* 1702 *5¢ (1914) Waterous Engine Works Road Roller;* 1703 *5¢ (1936) Champion Road Grader;* 1704 *10¢ (1947) White Model WA 122 Tractor Trailer;* 1705 *10¢ (1894) Ottawa Car Company Streetcar;* 1706 *10¢ (1975) Hayes HDX 45-115 Logging Truck;* 1707 *10¢ (1950) Motor Coach Industries Courier 50 Skyview bus;* 1708 *20¢ (1914) Ford Model T Open Touring Car;* 1709 *20¢ (1928) Mc-Laughlin Buick Model 28-496 Special Car;* 1710 *20¢ (1948) Bombardier B-12 CS multi-passenger snowmobile;* 1711 *20¢ (1962) Robin-Nodwell RN 110 tracked carrier;* 1712 *20¢ (1950) Studebaker Champion Deluxe Starlight Coupe;* 1713 *20¢ (1923-24) Gray-Dort 25-SM Luxury Sedan;* 1714 *20¢ (1924) Gotfredson model 20 farm truck;* 1715 *20¢ (1942) Massey-Harris No. 21 self-propelled combine;* 1716 *20¢ (1936) Bickle Chiefton Fire Engine;* 1717 *20¢ (1927) Sicard Snow Remover/ Snowblower;* 1718 *45¢ (1975) Bricklin SV-1 Sports Car*

1694		MNHVF	UseVF
5¢	1970 Bombardier Ski-Doo Olympique 335 snowmobile	.15	.15

1695		MNHVF	UseVF
5¢	1950 Cockshutt "30" farm tractor	.15	.15

1696		MNHVF	UseVF
5¢	1867 H.S. Taylor Steam Buggy	.15	.15

1697		MNHVF	UseVF
5¢	1942 Ford F60L-AMB military ambulance	.15	.15

1698		MNHVF	UseVF
5¢	1899 Still Motor Co. Ltd. Electric Van	.15	.15

1699		MNHVF	UseVF
5¢	1938 International D-35 Delivery Truck	.15	.15

1700		MNHVF	UseVF
5¢	1908 Russell Model L Touring Car	.15	.15

1701		MNHVF	UseVF
5¢	1925 REO Speed Wagon Police Wagon	.15	.15

1702		MNHVF	UseVF
5¢	1914 Waterous Engine Works Road Roller	.15	.15

1703		MNHVF	UseVF
5¢	1936 Champion Road Grader	.15	.15

1704		MNHVF	UseVF
10¢	1947 White Model WA 122 Tractor Trailer	.50	.50

1705		MNHVF	UseVF
10¢	1894 Ottawa Car Company Streetcar	.50	.50

1706		MNHVF	UseVF
10¢	1975 Hayes HDX 45-115 Logging Truck	.50	.50

1707		MNHVF	UseVF
10¢	1950 Motor Coach Industries Courier 50 Skyview bus	.50	.50

1708		MNHVF	UseVF
20¢	1914 Ford Model T Open Touring Car	.50	.50

1709		MNHVF	UseVF
20¢	1928 Mc-Laughlin Buick Model 28-496 Special Car	.50	.50

1710		MNHVF	UseVF
20¢	1948 Bombardier B-12 CS multi-passenger snowmobile	.50	.50

1711		MNHVF	UseVF
20¢	1962 Robin-Nodwell RN 110 tracked carrier	.50	.50

1712		MNHVF	UseVF
20¢	1950 Studebaker Champion Deluxe Starlight Coupe	.50	.50

1713		MNHVF	UseVF
20¢	1923-24 Gray-Dort 25-SM Luxury Sedan	.50	.50

1714		MNHVF	UseVF
20¢	1924 Gotfredson model 20 farm truck	.50	.50

1715		MNHVF	UseVF
20¢	1942 Massey-Harris No. 21 self-propelled combine	.50	.50

1716		MNHVF	UseVF
20¢	1936 Bickle Cheifton Fire Engine	.50	.50

1717		MNHVF	UseVF
20¢	1927 Sicard Snow Remover/Snowblower	.50	.50

1718		MNHVF	UseVF
45¢	1975 Bricklin SV-1 Sports Car	.75	.60
	a. Souvenir sheet of 25, #1694-1718	6.00	6.00

1996. YUKON GOLD RUSH ISSUE CAPEX '96. Commemorated the centennial of the Yukon Gold Rush. *Offset, perforated 13 x 13 1/2.*

1719 *"Skookum" Jim Mason's discovery on Rabbit Creek, 1896;* 1720 *Miners trekking to gold fields, boats on Lake Laberge;* 1721 *Supr. Sam Steele, North West Mounted Police, Alaska-Yukon border;* 1722 *Dawson City, Yukon, boom town, city of entertainment;* 1723 *Klondike gold fields*

1719		MNHVF	UseVF
45¢	multicolored, FDD *(June 13, 1996)*	.70	.30

1720		MNHVF	UseVF
45¢	multicolored, FDD *(June 13, 1996)*	.70	.30

1721		MNHVF	UseVF
45¢	multicolored, FDD *(June 13, 1996)*	.70	.30

1722		MNHVF	UseVF
45¢	multicolored, FDD *(June 13, 1996)*	.70	.30

1723		MNHVF	UseVF
45¢	multicolored, FDD *(June 13, 1996)*	.70	.30
	y. Strip of 5, #1719-1723	3.50	1.50

CAPEX 1996. Nos. 1719-1723 issued in panes of 10 stamps.

1996. CANADA DAY ISSUE *Offset, straight die cut, self-adhesive.*

1724 *Maple leaf quilt*

1724		MNHVF	UseVF
45¢	multicolored, FDD *(June 28, 1996)*	.70	.25
	y. Pane of 12	9.00	2.75

1996. OLYMPIC GOLD MEDALISTS BOOKLET ISSUE *Offset and typographed, perforated 13 x 12 1/2.*

1725 *Ethel Catherwood, high jump, 1928;* 1726 *Étienne Desmarteau, 56 lb. weight throw, 1904;* 1727 *Fanny Rosenfeld, 100m & 400m relay, 1928;* 1728 *Gerald Ouellette, smallbore rifle, prone, 1956;* 1729 *Percy Williams, 100m & 200m, 1928*

1725		MNHVF	UseVF
45¢	multicolored, FDD *(July 8, 1996)*	.70	.30

1726		MNHVF	UseVF
45¢	multicolored, FDD *(July 8, 1996)*	.70	.30

1727		MNHVF	UseVF
45¢	multicolored, FDD *(July 8, 1996)*	.70	.30

1728		MNHVF	UseVF
45¢	multicolored, FDD *(July 8, 1996)*	.70	.30

1729		MNHVF	UseVF
45¢	multicolored, FDD *(July 8, 1996)*	.70	.30
	y. Strip of 5, No. 1725-1729	3.00	1.50
	n. Booklet pane 10	6.75	3.00
	Complete booklet, No. 1729n	9.75	

1996. BRITISH COLUMBIA ISSUE 125th anniversary into Confederation. *Offset, perforated 13 x 12 1/2.*

1730 *British Columbia City*

1730		MNHVF	UseVF
45¢	multicolored, FDD *(July 19, 1996)*	.70	.25

1996. CANADIAN HERALDRY ISSUE Honored the 22nd International Congress of Geneological and Heraldic Sciences held in Aug. 1996, at Ottawa. *Offset, perforated 12 1/2 x 12.*

1731 *Heraldic symbols*

1731		MNHVF	UseVF
45¢	**multicolored,** FDD *(Aug. 19, 1996)*	.70	.25

1996. MOTION PICTURES ISSUE Film strips from motion pictures. *Offset, straight die cut, self-adhesive.*

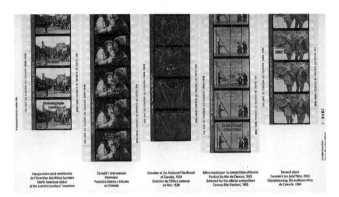

1732a-1732e *Film strips from motion pictures*

1732		MNHVF	UseVF
$2.25	**Sheet of 5, multicolored,** FDD *(Aug. 22, 1996)*	3.50	2.75
	a. 45¢ L'arrivée d'un train en gare, Lumiére cimematography, 1896	.65	.45
	b. 45¢ Back to God's Country, Nell & Ernest Shipman, 1919	.65	.45
	c. 45¢ Hen Hop, Norman McLaren, 1942	.65	.45
	d. 45¢ Pur la suite du monde, Pierre Perrault, Michael Brault, 1963	.65	.45
	e. 45¢ Goin' Down the Road, Don Shebib, 1970	.65	.45

1733		MNHVF	UseVF
$2.25	**Sheet of 5, multicolored,** FDD *(Aug. 22, 1996)*	3.50	2.75
	a. 45¢ Mon oncle Antoine, Claude Jutra, 1971	.70	.45
	b. 45¢ The Apprenticeship of Duddy Kravitz, Ted Kotcheff, 1974	.70	.45
	c. 45¢ Les Ordres, Michael Brault, 1974	.70	.45
	d. 45¢ Les Bons Débarras, Francis Mankiewiez, 1980	.70	.45
	e. 45¢ The Grey Fox, Philip Borsos, 1982	.70	.45

1996. LITERACY SEMI-POSTAL ISSUE has die cut opening in center to represent a missing puzzle piece. Surcharge donated to ABC CANADA literacy organization. *Offset, perforated 13 x 12 1/2.*

1734 *Puzzle pieces*

1734		MNHVF	UseVF
45¢+5¢	**multicolored,** FDD *(Sept. 9, 1996)*	1.25	.75
	n. Booklet pane of 10	10.50	10.50

1996. ÉDOUARD MONTPETIT ISSUE *Offset, perforated 12 x 12 1/2.*

1735 *Édouard Montpetit (1881-1954) educator*

1735		MNHVF	UseVF
45¢	**multicolored,** FDD *(Sept. 26, 1996)*	.70	.25

1996. WALT DISNEY ISSUE Souvenir story booklet to honor Walt Disney World's 25th anniversary. *Offset, perforated 12 1/2 x 13.*

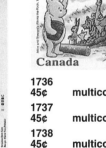

1736 *Winnie and Lt. Colebourn, 1914;* 1737 *Winnie and Christopher Robin, 1925;* 1738 *Milne and Shepard's Winnie the Pooh, 1926;* 1739 *Winnie the Pooh at Walt Disney World, 1996*

1736		MNHVF	UseVF
45¢	**multicolored,** FDD *(Oct. 1, 1996)*	.75	.35

1737		MNHVF	UseVF
45¢	**multicolored,** FDD *(Oct. 1, 1996)*	.75	.35

1738		MNHVF	UseVF
45¢	**multicolored,** FDD *(Oct. 1, 1996)*	.75	.35

1739		MNHVF	UseVF
45¢	**multicolored,** FDD *(Oct. 1, 1996)*	.75	.35
	y. Se-tenant block of 4, #1736-1739	3.00	2.75
	n. Booklet pane of 16	12.00	11.25

No. 1739y. was issued in panes of 16 stamps, with the halves of the pane printed tete-beche. 1739n was used as a cover for a souvenir story booklet.

1996. WALT DISNEY SOUVENIR SHEET 25th anniversary Walt Disney World.

1740 *Souvenir sheet of #1736-1739*

1740		MNHVF	UseVF
	Sheet of 4, #1736-1739	7.50	7.25

1996. CANADIAN AUTHOR BOOKLET ISSUE *Offset and intaglio, perforated 13 1/2 x 13 on 3 sides.*

1741 *Margaret Laurence (1926-87)*; 1742 *Donald Creighton (1902-79)*; 1743 *Gabrielle Roy (1909-83)*; 1744 *Felix-Antoine Savard (1896-1982)*; 1745 *Thomas C. Hailburton (1796-1865)*

1741		MNHVF	UseVF
45¢	**multicolored,** FDD *(Oct. 10, 1996)*	1.25	.25

1742		MNHVF	UseVF
45¢	**multicolored,** FDD *(Oct. 10, 1996)*	1.25	.25

1743		MNHVF	UseVF
45¢	**multicolored,** FDD *(Oct. 10, 1996)*	1.25	.25

1744		MNHVF	UseVF
45¢	**multicolored,** FDD *(Oct. 10, 1996)*	1.25	.25

1745		MNHVF	UseVF
45¢	**multicolored,** FDD *(Oct. 10, 1996)*	1.25	.25
	y. Strip of 5, #1741-1745	4.50	5.25
	n. Booklet pane of 10	10.50	10.50
	Complete booklet	11.25	

1996. CHIRSTMAS ISSUE 50th anniversary of UNICEF. *Offset, #1746 and #1748 perforated 13 1/2 x 13 1/2, #1747 12 1/2 x 12 1/2.*

1746 *Children on snowshoes and sled;* 1747 *Santa Claus skiing;* 1748 *Children skating*

1746		MNHVF	UseVF
45¢	**multicolored,** FDD *(Nov. 1, 1996)*	.70	.25
	n. Booklet pane of 10	7.25	6.00
	Complete booklet	9.00	

1747		MNHVF	UseVF
52¢	**multicolored,** FDD *(Nov. 1, 1996)*	.75	.25
	n. Booklet pane of 5 + label	4.25	3.00
	Complete booklet	4.50	

1748		MNHVF	UseVF
90¢	**multicolored,** FDD *(Nov. 1, 1996)*	1.50	.50
	n. Booklet pane of 5 + label	7.50	7.25
	Complete booklet	5.00	

1997. CHINESE NEW YEAR ISSUE Year of the ox. *Offset, perforated 13 x 12 1/2.*

1749 *Ox*

1749		MNHVF	UseVF
45¢	**multicolored,** FDD *(Jan. 7, 1997)*	.70	.25

1997. CHINESE NEW YEAR SOUVENIR SHEET ISSUE Year of the ox fan shaped Souvenir sheet.

1750 *Souvenir sheet with 2 #1749 ox stamps*

1750		MNHVF	UseVF
90¢	**Sheet of 2** #1749 FDD *Jan. 7, 1997*	2.25	2.25
	x. As #1750, gold omitted	—	
	v. Hong Kong overprint	7.50	7.50

No. 1749A is fan shaped.

1997. BIRD ISSUE *Offset, perforated 12 1/2 x 13.*

1751 *Mountain Bluebird;* 1752 *Western Grebe;* 1753 *Northern Gannet;* 1754 *Scarlet Tanager*

1751		MNHVF	UseVF
45¢	**multicolored,** FDD *(Jan. 10, 1997)*	.70	.25

1752		MNHVF	UseVF
45¢	**multicolored,** FDD *(Jan. 10, 1997)*	.70	.25

1753		MNHVF	UseVF
45¢	**multicolored,** FDD *(Jan. 10, 1997)*	.70	.25

1754		MNHVF	UseVF
45¢	**multicolored,** FDD *(Jan. 10, 1997)*	.70	.25
	y. Se-tenant block of 4, #1751-1754	2.75	2.25

Nos. 1751-1754 were issued in sheets of 20, 5 each, printed checker-wise to contain 4 complete blocks of 5 strips.

1997. ART ISSUE *Offset, perforated 12 1/2 x 13.*

1755 York Boat on Lake Winnipeg, *by Walter Joseph Phillips*

1755		MNHVF	UseVF
90¢	**gold & multicolored,** FDD *(Feb. 17, 1997)*	1.50	.50

1997. CANADIAN TIRE ISSUE 75th anniversary. *Offset, perforated 13 x 13 1/2.*

1756 *Canadian Tire principals, advertising photo*

1756		MNHVF	UseVF
45¢	**multicolored,** FDD *(March 3, 1997)*	.70	.25

1997. FATHER GADBOIS ISSUE *Offset, perforated 13 1/2 x 13.*

1757 *Father Charles-Emile Gadbois (1906-81), musicologist*

1757		MNHVF	UseVF
45¢	**multicolored,** FDD *(March 20, 1997)*	.70	.25

1997. INTERNATIONAL HORTICULTURAL BOOKLET ISSUE Celebrated the international horticultural exhibition, Quebec en Fleur 97, held in Quebec City. *Offset, perforated 13 x 12 1/2 on 3 sides.*

1758 Blue Poppy, *by Claude A. Simard*

1758		MNHVF	UseVF
45¢	**multicolored,** FDD *(April 4, 1997)*	.75	.25
	n. Booklet pane of 12	7.50	3.00
	Complete booklet	9.00	

1997. NURSE ISSUE Victorian Order of Nurses for Canada, Centennial. *Offset, perforated 12 1/2 x 13.*

1759 *Nurse and patient above, below century of means of transporation*

1759		MNHVF	UseVF
45¢	**multicolored,** FDD *(May 12, 1997)*	.70	.25

1997. LAW SOCIETY ISSUE Law Society of Upper Canada Bicentennial. *Offset, perforated 13 x 13.*

1760 *Osgoode Hall*

1760		MNHVF	UseVF
45¢	**multicolored,** FDD *(May 23, 1997)*	.70	.25

1997. SALT WATER FISH ISSUE *Offset, perforated 12 1/2 x 13.*

1761 *Great White Shark;* 1762 *Pacific Halibut;* 1763 *Atlantic Sturgeon;* 1764 *Bluefin Tuna*

1761		MNHVF	UseVF
45¢	Great white shark	.70	.25
1762		MNHVF	UseVF
45¢	Pacific halibut	.70	.25
1763		MNHVF	UseVF
45¢	Atlantic sturgeon	.70	.25
1764		MNHVF	UseVF
45¢	Bluefin tuna	.70	.25
	y. Se-tenant block of 4, #1761-1764	2.75	2.00

1997. BRIDGE ISSUE Opening of the Confederation Bridge. *Offset, perforated 12 1/2 x 13.*

1765 *Lighthouse and bridge* 1766 *Bridge and bird*

1765		MNHVF	UseVF
45¢	**multicolored,** FDD *(May 31, 1997)*	.70	.25
1766		MNHVF	UseVF
45¢	**multicolored,** FDD *(May 31, 1997)*	.70	.25
	y. Se-tenant pair, #1765-1766 + label	1.50	.50

1997. CAR RACING ISSUE Honored race car driver Gilles Villeneuve. *Offset, perforated 12 1/2 x 13.*

1767 *Gilles Villeneuve (1950-82), Formula One race car driver, winning race in Ferrari T-4*

1767		MNHVF	UseVF
45¢	**multicolored,** FDD *(June 12, 1997)*	.70	.25

1768 *Close-up of Villeneuve racing in Number 12 Ferrari T-3*

1768		MNHVF	UseVF
90¢	**multicolored,** FDD *(June 12, 1997)*	1.50	.50
	y. Se-tenant pair, #1767-1768	2.00	.75
	y1. Souvenir Sheet of 8	7.50	

1997. JOHN CABOT ISSUE 500th anniversary voyage to Canada. Commemorated the 1497 voyage of John Cabot and his crew. The *Matthew* is featured near the shore of Newfoundland. This stamp was a joint issue with Italy. *Offset, unwatermarked, perforated 12 1/2 x 13.*

1769 *The* Matthew *near the shore of Newfoundland, with map*

1769		MNHVF	UseVF
45¢	**multicolored,** FDD *(June 24, 1997)*	.70	.25

1997. SCENIC HIGHWAY ISSUE This se-tenant block of four celebrated Canada Day it is the first in a multi-year set which honored Scenic Highways: Nova Scotia's Cabot Trail, Ontario's Wine Route, Saskatchewan's Big Muddy, and British Columbia's Sea to Sky Highway were depicted. *Offset, unwatermarked, perforated 12 1/2 x 13.*

1770 *The Cabot Trail, Nova Scotia;* 1771 *Sea to Sky Highway, British Columbia;* 1772 *The Big Muddy, Saskatchewan;* 1773 *The Wine Route, starting in Ontario*

1770		MNHVF	UseVF
45¢	**multicolored,** FDD *(June 30, 1997)*	.70	.25
1771		MNHVF	UseVF
45¢	**multicolored,** FDD *(June 30, 1997)*	.70	.25
1772		MNHVF	UseVF
45¢	**multicolored,** FDD *(June 30, 1997)*	.70	.25
1773		MNHVF	UseVF
45¢	**multicolored,** FDD *(June 30, 1997)*	.70	.25
	y. Se-tenant block of 4 #1770-1773	2.75	1.50

1997. INDUSTRIAL DESIGN ISSUE The 1997 Congress of the International Council of Societies of Industrial Design shows four examples of Canadian design which have had their effect on the lives of Canadians and others throughout the world. This celebrated the 50th anniversary and 20th International Congress of International Council of Societies of Industrial Design held in Toronto, Aug. 1997. *Offset, unwatermarked, perforated 12 1/2 x 13.*

1774 *Industrial designs*

1774		MNHVF	UseVF
45¢	**multicolored,** FDD *(July 23, 1997)*	.70	.30

No. 1774 was issued with se-tenant label in sheets of 24 + 24 labels. The 12 different labels each appear twice in different colors. In alternating rows, labels appear on left or right side of stamp.

1997. HIGHLAND GAMES ISSUE The sport, music and dance of Highland Culture was celebrated on this commemorative it celebrating the 50th anniversary of the Glengarry Highland Games. Originating in Ireland and nurtured in Scotland the games were brought to Canada by migrating Scots. *Offset, unwatermarked, perforated 12 1/2 x 13.*

1775 *Scottish people in dress, Maxville, Ontario*

1775		MNHVF	UseVF
45¢	**multicolored,** FDD *(Aug. 1, 1997)*	.70	.25

1997. KNIGHTS OF COLUMBUS ISSUE The centennial of the Knights of Columbus in Canada is honored with a depiction of their logo. *Offset, unwatermarked, perforated 13.*

1776 *Knights of Columbus logo*

1776		MNHVF	UseVF
45¢	multicolored, FDD *(Aug. 5, 1997)*	.80	.25

Commemorative Issues

1997. PTTI ISSUE Postal, Telegrah and Telephone International of World Congress. Montreal was host to the 28th World Congress of the PTTI. It is one of the world's largest and most important labor movements. *Offset, unwatermarked, perforated 13.*

1777 *"28th PTTI World Congress"*

1777		MNHVF	UseVF
45¢	multicolored	.70	.40

1997. YEAR OF ASIA PACIFIC ISSUE In 1997, Canada was chair of the APEC Forum. Over 2,500 business and political leaders from 18 participating economies attended the meetings and explored trade in the Asia Pacific region. *Offset, unwatermarked, perforated 13 1/2.*

1778 *Symbolic dove formed from Canadian leaf symbol, in flight over industries*

1778		MNHVF	UseVF
45¢	multicolored	.70	.40

1997. TEAM CANADA VICTORY ISSUE The 25th anniversary of the Team Canada victory over the Soviet hockey team is depicted on this se-tenant pair with views of the last-minute victory and celebration. *Offset, unwatermarked, perforated 12 1/2 x 13.*

1779, 1780 *Views of the last-minute victory and celebration of Team Canada*

1779		MNHVF	UseVF
45¢	multicolored	.70	.40
1780		MNHVF	UseVF
45¢	multicolored	.70	.40
	y. Se-tenant pair #1779-1778	.70	.40

1997. PROMINENT POLITICIANS ISSUE These federal politicians, Martha Black, Lionel Chevrier, Judy LaMarsh and Réal Caouette are honored with these se-tenant portrait stamps. *Offset, unwatermarked, perforated 12 1/2 x 13.*

1781 *Marha Black (1856-1957);*

1782 *Lionel Chevrier (1903-1987);*

1783 *Judy LaMarsh (1924-1980)*

1784 *Réal Caouette (1917-1976)*

1781		MNHVF	UseVF
45¢	multicolored	.70	.40
1782		MNHVF	UseVF
45¢	multicolored	.70	.40
1783		MNHVF	UseVF
45¢	multicolored	.70	.40
1784		MNHVF	UseVF
45¢	multicolored	.70	.40
	y. Se-tenant block of 4 #1781-1784	2.80	1.60

1997. THE SUPERNATURAL ISSUE *Offset, unwatermarked, perforated 12 1/2 x 13.*

1785-1788 *Depictions of the supernatural — vampire, werewolf, ghost and goblin*

1785		MNHVF	UseVF
45¢	multicolored	.70	.40
1786		MNHVF	UseVF
45¢	multicolored	.70	.40
1787		MNHVF	UseVF
45¢	multicolored	.70	.40
1788		MNHVF	UseVF
45¢	multicolored	.70	.40
	y. Se-tenant block of 4 #1785-1788	2.80	1.60

Regular Issues

1997. GRIZZLY BEAR ISSUE Third new high denomination regular issue was a finely engraved rendering of the grizzly bear. *Offset and intaglio, unwatermarked, perforated 13.*

1789 *Grizzly bear*

1789		MNHVF	UseVF
$8.00	multicolored, FDD *(Oct. 15, 1997)*	10.00	5.00

Commemorative Issues

1997. CHRISTMAS STAINED GLASS ISSUE These three stained glass views of Madonna and Child depict windows from Holy Rosary Cathedral in Vancouver, B.C.; The United Church in Leith, Ontario; and St. Stephen's Ukrainian Byzantine Rite Roman Catholic Church in Calgary, Alberta. *Offset, unwatermarked, perforated 12 1/2 x 13.*

1790 *Madonna and Child depicted window from Holy Rosary Cathedral in Vancouver, B.C.*

1790		MNHVF	UseVF
45¢	multicolored	.70	.40

1791 *Madonna and Child depicted window from The United Church in Leith, Ontario*

1791		MNHVF	UseVF
52¢	multicolored	.80	.50

1792 *Madonna and Child depicted window from St. Stephen's Ukrainian Byzantine Rite Roman Catholic Church in Calgary, Alberta*

1792		MNHVF	UseVF
90¢	multicolored	1.40	.70

1997. ROYAL AGRICULTURAL WINTER FAIR ISSUE Toronto's Royal Agricultural Winter Fair is the largest indoor equestrian and agricultural competition. This issue celebrated the 75th anniversary of the Fair. *Offset, unwatermarked, perforated 13 x 12 1/2.*

1793 *Depiction of Toronto's Royal Agricultural Winter Fair*

1793		MNHVF	UseVF
45¢	multicolored	.70	.35

1998. YEAR OF THE TIGER ISSUE Celebrated the Lunar Year of the Tiger. *Offset, unwatermarked, perforated 13 x 12 1/2.*

1794 *Year of the Tiger*

1794a *Lunar Year of the Tiger Souvenir sheet without inscription in very outer border*

1794b *Lunar Year of the Tiger Souvenir sheet with Ashton-Potter inscription and Designer names in the very outer border at the bottom*

1794		MNHVF	UseVF
45¢	multicolored, FDD *(Jan. 8, 1998)*	.70	.35
	a. Souvenir sheet of 2 (no inscription) 90¢	1.50	.85
	b. Souvenir sheet of 2 (printer inscription and designer names in border) 90¢	2.00	1.00

Regular Issues

1998. FLAG AND BUILDING ISSUE Definitive featuring the flag of Canada issued in booklets of 10. *Offset, unwatermarked, perforated 13 x 12 1/2.*

1795 *Canadian flag and building*

1795		MNHVF	UseVF
45¢	**multicolored,** FDD *(Feb. 2, 1998)*	.70	.35
	n. Booklet of 10	7.50	4.25

Commemorative Issues

1998. PROVINCIAL PREMIERS ISSUE Pane of 10 stamps honoring 20th century Provincial premiers. *Offset, unwatermarked, perforated 13 1/2.*

1796a *John Robarts of Ontario;* 1796b *Jean Lesage of Quebec;* 1796c *John B. McNair of New Brunswick;* 1796d *Tommy Douglas of Saskatchewan;* 1796e *Joey Smallwood of Newfoundland;* 1796f *Angus L. Macdonald of Nova Scotia;* 1796g *W.A.C. Bennett of British Columbia;* 1796h *Ernest Manning of Alberta;* 1796i *John Bracken of Manitoba;* 1796j *J. Walter Jones of Prince Edward Island*

1796		MNHVF	UseVF
$4.50	**Pane of 10, multicolored** FDD *(Feb. 18, 1998)*	7.50	4.25
	a. John Robarts of Ontario 45¢	.70	.35
	b. Jean Lesage of Quebec 45¢	.70	.35
	c. John B. McNair of New Brunswick 45¢	.70	.35
	d. Tommy Douglas of Saskatchewan 45¢	.70	.35
	e. Joey Smallwood of Newfoundland 45¢	.70	.35
	f. Angus L. Macdonald of Nova Scotia 45¢	.70	.35
	g. W.A.C. Bennett of British Columbia 45¢	.70	.35
	h. Ernest Manning of Alberta 45¢	.70	.35
	i. John Bracken of Manitoba 45¢	.70	.35
	j. J. Walter Jones of Prince Edward Island 45¢	.70	.35

1998. BIRDS OF CANADA ISSUE Birds of Canada series. *Offset, unwatermarked, perforated 13 x 13 1/2.*

1797 *Hairy woodpecker;* 1798 *Great crested flycatcher;* 1799 *Eastern screech owl;* 1800 *Gray-crowned rosy finch*

1797		MNHVF	UseVF
45¢	**multicolored,** FDD *(March 13, 1998)*	.70	.35

1798		MNHVF	UseVF
45¢	**multicolored,** FDD *(March 13, 1998)*	.70	.35

1799		MNHVF	UseVF
45¢	**multicolored,** FDD *(March 13, 1998)*	.70	.35

1800		MNHVF	UseVF
45¢	**multicolored,** FDD *(March 13, 1998)*	.70	.35
	y. Block of 4 #1797-1800	3.25	2.00

Regular Issues

1998. MAPLE LEAF ISSUE *Self-adhesive experimental automatic teller machine (ATM) sheetlet of 18. Offset, unwatermarked, straight die cut.*

1801 *Canadian maple leaf*

1801		MNHVF	UseVF
45¢	**multicolored,** FDD *(April 14, 1998)*	.90	.45
	n. Pane of 18	16.50	8.00

Commemorative Issues

1998. FISHING FLIES BOOKLET ISSUE Stamps depict five tied flies used by anglers. *Offset, unwatermarked, perforated 12 1/2 x 13.*

1802 *Cosseboom Special;* 1803 *Coho Blue;* 1804 *Lady Amherst;* 1805 *Dark Montréal;* 1806 *Steelhead Bee;* 1807 *Coquihalla Orange*

1802		MNHVF	UseVF
45¢	**multicolored,** FDD *(April 16, 1998)*	.70	.35
1803		MNHVF	UseVF
45¢	**multicolored,** FDD *(April 16, 1998)*	.70	.35
1804		MNHVF	UseVF
45¢	**multicolored,** FDD *(April 16, 1998)*	.70	.35
1805		MNHVF	UseVF
45¢	**multicolored,** FDD *(April 16, 1998)*	.70	.35
1806		MNHVF	UseVF
45¢	**multicolored,** FDD *(April 16, 1998)*	.70	.35
1807		MNHVF	UseVF
45¢	**multicolored,** FDD *(April 16, 1998)*	.70	.35
	n. Booklet of 12 with 2 images of each of the 6 flies	9.00	5.25

1998. CANADIAN INSTITUTE OF MINING, METALLURGY & PETRO-LEUM ISSUE Centennial of the organization is commemorated with views of mining, foundry and deep sea oil platform. *Offset, unwatermarked, perforated 12 1/2.*

1808 *Views of mining, foundry and deep sea oil platform*

1808		MNHVF	UseVF
45¢	**multicolored,** FDD *(May 4, 1998)*	.70	.35

1998. IMPERIAL PENNY POSTAGE ISSUE The institution of British penny postage in 1898 is commemorated with the depiction of Canada's "XMAS" Empire map stamp (88) and Sir William Mulock. *Offset, unwatermarked, perforated 12 1/2 x 13.*

1809 *Empire map*

1809		MNHVF	UseVF
45¢	**multicolored,** FDD *(May 29, 1998)*	.70	.35

1998. SUMO WRESTLING ISSUE Showed action in the sport with two labels flanking. *Offset and embossed, unwatermarked, perforated 12 1/2 x 13.*

1810 *Wrestlers grappling*

1811 *Single wrestler bowing*

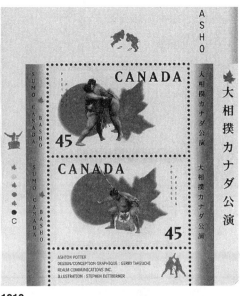

1811a *Souvenir sheet*

1810		MNHVF	UseVF
45¢	**multicolored,** FDD *(June 5, 1998)*	.70	.40
1811		MNHVF	UseVF
45¢	**multicolored,** FDD *(June 5, 1998)*	.70	.40
	a. Souvenir sheet of #1810-1811	2.00	1.00
	y. Se-tenant pair #1810-1811	1.45	.85

1998. CANALS OF CANADA RECREATIONAL RESTORATIONS IS-SUE Built for the transport of goods from the Great Lakes to the St. Lawrence for commercial purposes in the 19th century. The locks and canals now also support a thriving recreational use multi-season. *Booklet of 10 se-tenant stamps showed man-made waterways and location map. Offset, unwatermarked, perforated 12 1/2.*

1812 *St. Peters Canal*

1812		MNHVF	UseVF
45¢	**multicolored,** FDD *(June 17, 1998)*	.70	.45

1813 *St. Ours Canal*

1813		MNHVF	UseVF
45¢	**multicolored,** FDD *(June 17, 1998)*	.70	.45

1814 *Port Carling Lock*

1814		MNHVF	UseVF
45¢	**multicolored,** FDD *(June 17, 1998)*	.70	.45

1815 *Rideau Canal (with boat)*

1815		**MNHVF**	**UseVF**
45¢	**multicolored,** FDD *(June 17, 1998)*	.70	.45

1816 *Trent-Severn Waterway (with locks)*

1816		**MNHVF**	**UseVF**
45¢	**multicolored,** FDD *(June 17, 1998)*	.70	.45

1817 *Chambly*

1817		**MNHVF**	**UseVF**
45¢	**multicolored,** FDD *(June 17, 1998)*	.70	.45

1818 *Lachine*

1818		**MNHVF**	**UseVF**
45¢	**multicolored,** FDD *(June 17, 1998)*	.70	.45

1819 *Rideau Canal (with people)*

1819		**MNHVF**	**UseVF**
45¢	**multicolored,** FDD *(June 17, 1998)*	.70	.45

1820 *Trent-Severn Waterway (with boat)*

1820		**MNHVF**	**UseVF**
45¢	**multicolored,** FDD *(June 17, 1998)*	.70	.45

1821 *Sault Ste. Marie Canal*

1821		**MNHVF**	**UseVF**
45¢	**multicolored,** FDD *(June 17, 1998)*	.70	.45
	n. Booklet of 10	7.00	4.50

1998. HEALTH PROFESSIONALS ISSUE Single stamp with metallic embossing of the staff of a aesculapius and the medical cross. Honored Canadian health-care workers. *Offset and embossed, unwatermarked, perforated 12 1/2.*

1822 *Staff of a aesculapius and the medical cross*

1822		**MNHVF**	**UseVF**
45¢	**multicolored,** FDD *(June 25, 1998)*	.70	.35

1998. ROYAL CANADIAN MOUNTED POLICE ISSUE Honored the RCMP on its 125th anniversary. Tabs that flank the designs include the mounties' crest, mounted officers, and mounted officers with maple leaf background. *Offset and embossed, unwatermarked, perforated 12 1/2 x 13.*

1823 *Old-time male officer;* 1824 *Modern-era female officer*

1824a *Souvenir sheet of 2 RCMP stamps separated by Maple leaf tab*

1824b *Souvenir sheet with Portugal 98 logo upper left*

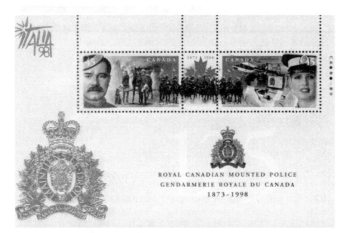

1824c *Souvenir sheet with Italia 98 logo upper left*

1824d *Souvenir sheet with signature of Lt. Col. French*

1823		MNHVF	UseVF
45¢	multicolored, FDD *(July 3, 1998)*	.70	.35

1824		MNHVF	UseVF
45¢	multicolored, FDD *(July 3, 1998)*	.70	.35
	y. Se-tenant pair #1823-1824	1.45	.75
	a. Souvenir sheet of 2 stamps separated by Maple leaf tab 90¢	1.75	1.00
	b. Souvenir sheet with Portugal 98 logo upper left 90¢	2.25	1.25
	c. Souvenir sheet with Italia 98 logo upper left 90¢	2.25	1.25
	d. Souvenir sheet with printed signature of Lt. Col. French 90¢	1.75	1.00

1998. WILLIAM ROUÉ ISSUE The designer of the famed racing schooner *Bluenose* is honored, along with a depiction of the boat, set in a partial frame based on the design of the 50¢ stamp of 1929 (#174). *Offset and intaglio, unwatermarked, perforated 13.*

1826 *William Roue*

1825		MNHVF	UseVF
45¢	multicolored, FDD *(July 24, 1998)*	.70	.35

1998. SCENIC HIGHWAYS ISSUE Diverse scenes from Canada's highways are shown in this se-tenant set of four, the second in a series. *Offset, unwatermarked, perforated 12 1/2 x 13.*

1826 *Dempster Highway, Yukon;* 1827 *Dinosaur Trail, Alberta;* 1828 *Blue Heron Route, Prince Edward Island;* 1829 *River Valley Drive, New Brunswick*

1826		MNHVF	UseVF
45¢	multicolored, FDD *(July 28, 1998)*	.75	.40

1827		MNHVF	UseVF
45¢	multicolored, FDD *(July 28, 1998)*	.75	.40

1828		MNHVF	UseVF
45¢	multicolored, FDD *(July 28, 1998)*	.75	.40

1829		MNHVF	UseVF
45¢	multicolored, FDD *(July 28, 1998)*	.75	.40
	y. Block of 4 #1826-1829	3.00	1.65

1998. LES AUTOMATISTES ISSUE Seven Montreal artists, who developed a method of surrealist painting based on the notion of automation in the middle of this century are honored with depictions of their work. *Self-adhesive booklet of 7. Offset, unwatermarked, straight die-cut.*

1830 *Jean-Paul Riopelle*

1830		MNHVF	UseVF
45¢	multicolored, FDD *(Aug. 7, 1998)*	.70	.45

1831 *Fernand Leduc*

1831		MNHVF	UseVF
45¢	**multicolored,** FDD *(Aug. 7, 1998)*	.70	.45

1832 *Jean-Paul Mousseau*

1832		MNHVF	UseVF
45¢	**multicolored,** FDD *(Aug. 7, 1998)*	.70	.45

1833 *Pierre Gaurreau*

1833		MNHVF	UseVF
45¢	**multicolored,** FDD *(Aug. 7, 1998)*	.70	.45

1834 *Paul-Emile Borduas*

1834		MNHVF	UseVF
45¢	**multicolored,** FDD *(Aug. 7, 1998)*	.70	.45

1835 *Marcelle Farron*

1835		MNHVF	UseVF
45¢	**multicolored,** FDD *(Aug. 7, 1998)*	.70	.45

1836 *Marcel Barbeau*

1836		MNHVF	UseVF
45¢	**multicolored,** FDD *(Aug. 7, 1998)*	.70	.45
	n. Booklet of 7 #1830-1836	5.00	3.50

1998. LEGENDARY CANADIANS ISSUE Four notable participants in Canadian sport are honored. *Offset, unwatermarked, perforated 13.*

1837 *Napléon-Alexandre Comeau, known as the King of the North Shore*

1837		MNHVF	UseVF
45¢	**multicolored,** FDD *(Aug. 15, 1998)*	.70	.40

1838 *Phyllis Munday, who first reached the highest summit in the Rocky Mountains*

1838		MNHVF	UseVF
45¢	**multicolored,** FDD *(Aug. 15, 1998)*	.70	.40

1839 *Harry "Red" Foster, a radio sports announcer and founder of the Canadian Special Olympics*

1839		MNHVF	UseVF
45¢	**multicolored,** FDD *(Aug. 15, 1998)*	.70	.40

1840 *Bill Mason, a successful filmmaker and outdoorsman*

1840		MNHVF	UseVF
45¢	**multicolored,** FDD *(Aug. 15, 1998)*	.70	.40
	y. Block of 4 #1837-1840	3.00	1.75

1998. ART CANADA ISSUE *The Farmer's Family,* part of a 1970 triptych by New Brunswick painter Bruno Bobak. *Offset, unwatermarked, perforated 13 .*

1841 The Farmer's Family, *by painter Bruno Bobak*

1841		MNHVF	UseVF
90¢	**multicolored,** FDD *(Sept. 8, 1998)*	1.45	.85

1998. HOUSING ISSUE The evolution of habitation is traced. *Offset, unwatermarked, perforated 13.*

1842 *Native Peoples Housing;* 1843 *Settler Housing;* 1844 *Regional Housing;* 1845 *Heritage Preservation Housing;* 1846 *Multiple Unit Housing;* 1847 *Prefabricated Housing;* 1848 *Veterans' Housing;* 1849 *Planned Community Housing;* 1850 *Innovative Housing*

1842		MNHVF	UseVF
45¢	**multicolored,** FDD *(Sept. 23, 1998)*	.70	.35
1843		MNHVF	UseVF
45¢	**multicolored,** FDD *(Sept. 23, 1998)*	.70	.35
1844		MNHVF	UseVF
45¢	**multicolored,** FDD *(Sept. 23, 1998)*	.70	.35
1845		MNHVF	UseVF
45¢	**multicolored,** FDD *(Sept. 23, 1998)*	.70	.35
1846		MNHVF	UseVF
45¢	**multicolored,** FDD *(Sept. 23, 1998)*	.70	.35
1847		MNHVF	UseVF
45¢	**multicolored,** FDD *(Sept. 23, 1998)*	.70	.35
1848		MNHVF	UseVF
45¢	**multicolored,** FDD *(Sept. 23, 1998)*	.70	.35
1849		MNHVF	UseVF
45¢	**multicolored,** FDD *(Sept. 23, 1998)*	.70	.35
1850		MNHVF	UseVF
45¢	**multicolored,** FDD *(Sept. 23, 1998)*	.70	.35
	y. Block of 9 #1842-1850	6.50	3.15

1998. UNIVERSITY OF OTTAWA ISSUE Commemorated the 150th anniversary of North America's largest bilingual university. *Offset, unwatermarked, perforated 13.*

1851 *University of Ottawa*

1851		MNHVF	UseVF
45¢	**multicolored,** FDD *(Sept. 25, 1998)*	.70	.35

Regular Issues

1998. MAPLE LEAF ISSUE *Self-adhesive coil with serrated die-cut, embossed gold foil imprint outline. Offset, unwatermarked, perforated 13.*

1852 *Maple Leaf*

1852		MNHVF	UseVF
45¢	**multicolored,** FDD *(Sept. 30, 1998)*	1.25	.75

Commemorative Issues

1998. CIRCUS ISSUE Clown portraits on a four-stamp souvenir sheet are set against a background of animal acts, acrobats, an animal trainer and a human tower. *Offset, unwatermarked, perforated 13.*

1853a-1853d *Souvenir sheet of clown portraits: Animal acts, Acrobats, Animal trainer, and a Human tower*

1853		MNHVF	UseVF
45¢	**multicolored,** FDD *(Oct. 1, 1998)*	2.80	1.50
	a. Animal acts 45¢	.70	.40
	b. Acrobats 45¢	.70	.40
	c. Animal trainer 45¢	.70	.40
	d. Human tower 45¢	.70	.40

1998. CIRCUS ISSUE Clown stamps have the same image as 18523a-d but have one straight edge. *Offset, unwatermarked, perforated 13 on 3 sides.*

1854		MNHVF	UseVF
45¢	**multicolored,** FDD *(Oct. 1, 1998)*	.70	.40

1855		MNHVF	UseVF
45¢	**multicolored,** FDD *(Oct. 1, 1998)*	.70	.40

1856		MNHVF	UseVF
45¢	**multicolored,** FDD *(Oct. 1, 1998)*	.70	.40

1857		MNHVF	UseVF
45¢	**multicolored,** FDD *(Oct. 1, 1998)*	.70	.40
	n. Booklet of 12 #1854-1857	8.50	4.85

1998. JOHN HUMPHREY ISSUE The New Brunswick native who drafted the United Nations' Universal Declaration of Human Rights in 1948 is honored on the 50th anniversary of that document. *Offset, unwatermarked, perforated 13.*

1858 *John Humphrey*

1858		MNHVF	UseVF
45¢	**multicolored,** FDD *(Oct. 7, 1998)*	.70	.40

Regular Issues

1998. LOON ISSUE Canadian Wildlife series. Designed by Ralph Carmichael, who also designed the $1 coin that pictures a loon. *Offset and intaglio, unwatermarked, perforated 13.*

1859 *Loon*

1859		MNHVF	UseVF
$1	**multicolored,** FDD *(Oct. 27, 1998)*	2.00	1.00

1989. POLAR BEAR ISSUE Canadian Wildlife series. Designed by Brent Townsend, who also designed the $2 coin that pictures a polar bear. *Offset and intaglio, unwatermarked, perforated 13.*

1860 *Polar Bear*

1860		MNHVF	UseVF
$2	**multicolored,** FDD *(Oct. 27, 1998)*	4.00	2.00

Commemorative Issues

1998. NAVAL RESERVE ISSUE Two se-tenant stamps honored the 75th anniversary of the Canadian Naval Reserve, featuring the HMCS Sackville and HMCS Shawinigan and images of sailors in old and contempory uniforms. *Offset, unwatermarked, perforated 13.*

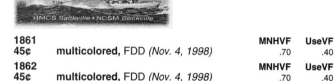

1861 *HMCS Sackville with images of sailors in old and contempory uniforms; 1862 HMCS Shawinigan with images of sailors in old and contempory uniforms*

1861		MNHVF	UseVF
45¢	**multicolored,** FDD *(Nov. 4, 1998)*	.70	.40

1862		MNHVF	UseVF
45¢	**multicolored,** FDD *(Nov. 4, 1998)*	.70	.40
	y. Se-tenant pair #1861-1862	1.45	.85

1998. CHRISTMAS ANGELS ISSUE *Issued in panes of 50 of each image. Offset, unwatermarked, perforated 13.*

1863 *Trumpeting Angel of the Last Judgement*

1863		MNHVF	UseVF
45¢	**multicolored,** FDD *(Nov. 6, 1998)*	.70	.35

1864 *Standing Adoring Angel*

1864		MNHVF	UseVF
52¢	**multicolored,** FDD *(Nov. 6, 1998)*	.75	.40

1865 *Kneeling Adoring Angel*

1865		MNHVF	UseVF
90¢	**multicolored,** FDD *(Nov. 6, 1998)*	1.25	1.00

1998. CHRISTMAS ANGELS BOOKLET ISSUE Gilt wooden angels, same design as 1863-1865 but with one straight edge. Issued in booklets of 10 for domestic-rate version, booklets of 5 for higher-value version. *Offset, unwatermarked, perforated 13 on 3 sides.*

1866

		MNHVF	UseVF
45¢	**multicolored,** FDD *(Nov. 6, 1998)*	.70	.35
	n. Booklet of 10	7.00	3.50

1867

		MNHVF	UseVF
52¢	**multicolored,** FDD *(Nov. 6, 1998)*	.75	.40
	n. Booklet of 5	3.75	2.00

1868

		MNHVF	UseVF
90¢	**multicolored,** FDD *(Nov. 6, 1998)*	1.25	1.00
	n. Booklet of 5	6.25	5.00

Regular Issues

1998. FLAG OVER ICEBERG ISSUE Canadian flag waves over a rocky coastline and Newfoundland iceberg in background. Cancellation site of OFDC was at site of first flag raising in 1965, Ottawa. *Offset, unwatermarked, perforated 13.*

1869, 1871 *Flag over Iceberg*

1869

		MNHVF	UseVF
46¢	**multicolored,** FDD *(Dec. 28, 1998)*	.65	.30
	n. Booklet of 10	6.50	3.00

1998. FLAG SELF-ADHESIVE BOOKLET ISSUE *Booklet of 30, straight die-cut, offset, unwatermarked.*

1870

		MNHVF	UseVF
46¢	**multicolored,** FDD *(Dec. 28, 1998)*	.65	.35
	n. Booklet of 30	20.00	10.50
	n1. Booklet of 30 (2000)	20.00	10.50

1998. FLAG COIL ISSUE *Vertical coil of 100 engraved, printed in red and white. Offset, unwatermarked, straight die cut.*

1871 *Canadian flag*

1871

		MNHVF	UseVF
46¢	**multicolored,** FDD *(Dec. 28, 1998)*	.70	.40

1998. MAPLE LEAF ISSUE Maple leaf has been an official symbol of Canada's country since 1860. *Offset, unwatermarked, perforated 13.*

1872 *Maple leaf*

1872

		MNHVF	UseVF
55¢	**black & orange,** FDD *(Dec. 28, 1998)*	.75	.45
	n. Booklet of 5	3.75	3.25

1998. MAPLE LEAF ISSUE Second step domestic rate, yellow leaf, bordered in silver, violet background. *Offset, unwatermarked, perforated 13.*

1873 *Maple leaf*

1873

		MNHVF	UseVF
73¢	**violet & yellow,** FDD *(Dec. 28, 1998)*	.85	.60

1998. MAPLE LEAF ISSUE International rate, green leaf, gold border, orange background. *Offset, unwatermarked, perforated 13.*

1874 *Maple leaf*

1874

		MNHVF	UseVF
95¢	**orange & green,** FDD *(Dec. 28, 1998)*	1.00	.75
	n. Booklet of 5	5.00	3.75

1998. MAPLE LEAF ISSUE *Offset, unwatermarked, straight die cut.*

1875 *Maple leaf*

1875

		MNHVF	UseVF
46¢	**green & red,** FDD *(Dec. 28, 1998)*	1.00	.75
	n. Booklet of 18	18.00	13.50

1998. QUEEN ELIZABETH II Regal portrait by Canadian photographer Yousuf Karsh, first used in a 1987 stamp but updated with new colors and printed smaller. *Offset, unwatermarked, perforated 13 1/2 x 13.*

1876 *Queen Elizabeth II*

1876

		MNHVF	UseVF
46¢	**multicolored,** FDD *(Dec. 28, 1998)*	.60	.30

Commemorative Issues

1999. YEAR OF THE RABBIT ISSUE Celebrated the Lunar New Year with the Rabbit. Designed by Ken Koo, a native of Hong Kong, the third in a 12-year cycle of the Chinese zodiac. *Offset, unwatermarked, perforated 13 1/2.*

1877 *Rabbit*

1877

		MNHVF	UseVF
46¢	**multicolored,** FDD *(Jan. 8, 1999)*	.60	.30

1999. YEAR OF THE RABBIT SOUVENIR SHEET in a round format. *Offset, unwatermarked, perforated 12 1/2 x 13.*

1878 *Year of the Rabbit souvenir sheet*

1878		MNHVF	UseVF
95¢	**multicolored,** FDD *(Jan. 8, 1999)*	1.30	.60
	y. Souvenir sheet	1.50	.75
	y1. Overprinted for China 99	1.50	.75

1999. THEATRE DU RIDEAU ISSUE Commemorated the 50th anniversary of Canada's first professional French-language theater ensemble, founded in 1949 in Montreal. Stamp designed by Marie Rouleau and Yves Paquin of Montreal shows traditional tragic and comedic masks of theater merging with sketchy portraits of the company's founders and the "Green Curtain" after which the theater takes its name. *Pane of 16 offset by Canadian Bank Note Co., unwatermarked, perforated 13 1/4 x 12.*

1879 *Theatre du Rideau*

1879		MNHVF	UseVF
46¢	**multicolored,** FDD *(Feb. 17, 1999)*	.60	.20

1999. BIRDS OF CANADA ISSUE This fourth annual series of four stamps features portraits of birds by artist Pierre Leduc. *Gummed stamps offset by Ashton-Potter Canada Ltd. (Self-adhesive stamps in a booklet of 12 have the same illustrations.) Perforated 12 1/2 x 13.*

1880 *Northern goshawk;* 1881 *Red-winged blackbird;* 1882 *American goldfinch;* 1883 *Sandhill crane*

1880		MNHVF	UseVF
46¢	**multicolored,** FDD *(Feb. 24, 1999)*	.60	.20

1881		MNHVF	UseVF
46¢	**multicolored,** FDD *(Feb. 24, 1999)*	.60	.20
1882		MNHVF	UseVF
46¢	**multicolored,** FDD *(Feb. 24, 1999)*	.60	.20
1883		MNHVF	UseVF
46¢	**multicolored,** FDD *(Feb. 24, 1999)*	.60	.20
	y. Block of 4 #1880-1883	2.50	1.25

1999. BIRDS OF CANADA BOOKLET ISSUE *Self-adhesive stamps in a booklet of 12 have the same illustrations as #1880-1883. Offset by Ashton-Potter Canada Ltd., die-cut perforated 11 1/2.*

1884		MNHVF	UseVF
46¢	**multicolored,** FDD *(Feb. 24, 1999)*	.80	.35
1885		MNHVF	UseVF
46¢	**multicolored,** FDD *(Feb. 4, 1999)*	.80	.35
1886		MNHVF	UseVF
46¢	**multicolored,** FDD *(Feb. 24, 1999)*	.80	.35
1887		MNHVF	UseVF
46¢	**multicolored,** FDD *(Feb. 24, 1999)*	.80	.35
	y. Booklet of 12	9.50	—

1999. MUSEUM OF ANTHROPOLOGY ISSUE Commemorated the University of British Columbia Museum of Anthropology's 50th anniversary. The stamp showed the exterior of the building and a carving, *The Raven and the First Men,* by renowned Haida artist Bill Reid. *Offset by Canadian Bank Note Co., unwatermarked, perforated 13 1/4 x 13.*

1888 *University of British Columbia Museum of Anthropology*

1888		MNHVF	UseVF
46¢	**multicolored,** FDD *(March 9, 1999)*	.60	.30

1999. MARCO POLO ISSUE Commemorated a speed-record-setting 19th century ship built in St. John, New Brunswick. *Offset by Ashton-Potter Canada Ltd., perforated 13 x 12 1/2.*

1889 *Painting by J. Franklin Wright of a port-quarter view of Marco Polo under sail and leaving St. John*

1889		MNHVF	UseVF
46¢	**multicolored,** FDD *(March 19, 1999)*	.60	.30

Users of this Catalog are invited to write us if they have information which they feel will supplement or correct any material contained herein. All such communications will be answered.

1999. MARCO POLO SOUVENIR SHEET ISSUE Joint-issue souvenir sheet with 85¢ Australian stamp, a port view of the three-masted ship, both superimposed on a global projection, showing the ship's route from Canada to Australia, which it navigated in 15 days in 1851. *Offset, unwatermarked, perforated 13.*

1890 *Marco Polo Souvenir sheet with Australian 85¢ stamp and Canadian 46¢ stamp*

1890		MNHVF	UseVF
$1.25	**multicolored,** FDD *(March 19, 1999)*	1.65	.75
	v. Single stamp image of ship *Marco Polo* 46¢	.75	.45

1999. SCENIC HIGHWAYS ISSUE Third year series-ending stamps of scenic highways in Canada. *Offset by Ashton-Potter Canada Ltd., unwatermarked, perforated 12 1/2 x 13.*

1891 *Route 132 in Quebec;* 1892 *Dempster Highway in the Northwest Territories;* 1893 *Yellowhead Highway in Manitoba;* 1894 *Discovery Trail in Newfoundland*

1891		MNHVF	UseVF
46¢	**multicolored,** FDD *(March 31, 1999)*	.60	.20
1892		MNHVF	UseVF
46¢	**multicolored,** FDD *(March 31, 1999)*	.60	.20
1893		MNHVF	UseVF
46¢	**multicolored,** FDD *(March 31, 1999)*	.60	.20
1894		MNHVF	UseVF
46¢	**multicolored,** FDD *(March 31, 1999)*	.60	.20
	y. Block of 4 #1891-1894	2.40	1.20

1999. NUNAVUT ISSUE Marked the creation of a Canadian territory in the eastern Arctic, *"Our Land"* in the Inukitut language. On the stamp Inuit children represent the promise of the future, and native stone cairns represent the past. Nunavut, carved from the Northwest Territories, encompasses roughly one-fifth of Canada. Its area is home to more than 25,000 Inuit, whose ancestors have lived there for 1,000 years. *Offset, unwatermarked, perforated 12 1/2 x 13.*

 1895 *Inuit children and landscape*

1895		MNHVF	UseVF
46¢	**multicolored,** FDD *(April 1, 1999)*	.60	.30

1999. INTERNATIONAL YEAR OF OLDER PERSONS ISSUE Celebrated the United Nations International Year of Older Persons. *Offset by Canadian Bank Note Co., unwatermarked, perforated 13 1/2.*

 1896 *Allegorical illustration of an elderly couple walking down the road of life*

1896		MNHVF	UseVF
46¢	**multicolored,** FDD *(April 12, 1999)*	.60	.30

1999. SIKH CANADIANS ISSUE Issued in conjunction with the 300th anniversary of Sikh Baisakhi, the beginning of a new religious year, the stamp features repeating images of a Khanda, a central symbol of the faith. It is a double-edged sword that cleaves truth from falsehood, superimposed on a perfect circle representing God. *Offset by Canadian Bank Note Co. in panes of 16, unwatermarked, perforated 13.*

 1897 *Double-edged sword superimposed on a perfect circle representing God*

1897		MNHVF	UseVF
46¢	**multicolored,** FDD *(April 19, 1999)*	.60	.30

1999. ORCHIDS ISSUE Four se-tenant stamps help promote the World Orchid Conference in Vancouver. Four wild Canadian orchids are featured in the expressive paintings of Poon-Kuen Chow and Yukman Lai. *Offset by Ashton-Potter Canada Ltd., unwatermarked, perforated 13 x 12 1/2.*

 1898 *Dragon's Mouth (Arethusa bulbosa);* 1899 *Small Round-Leaved Orchid (Amerrorchis rotundifolia);* 1900 *Small Purple Fringed Orchid (Platanthera psycodes);* 1901 *Greater Yellow Lady's Slipper (Cypripedium pubescens)*

1898		MNHVF	UseVF
46¢	**multicolored,** FDD *(April 27, 1999)*	.75	.35
1899		MNHVF	UseVF
46¢	**multicolored,** FDD *(April 27, 1999)*	.75	.35
1900		MNHVF	UseVF
46¢	**multicolored,** FDD *(April 27, 1999)*	.75	.35
1901		MNHVF	UseVF
46¢	**multicolored,** FDD *(April 27, 1999)*	.75	.35

y. Souvenir sheet of 4	3.00	1.15
y1. Souvenir sheet overprinted for China 1999 (also see Year of the Rabbit SS)	3.00	1.15
n. Booklet of 12	9.00	4.75

Regular Issues

1999. TRADITIONAL TRADES DEFINITIVES ISSUE Multicolored stamps were intended to meet the need for low-value stamps. They consist of a circular motif at the top of the design showing the material being crafted by hand at the bottom. Designed by Monique Dufour and Sophie Lafortune, photography by Jean-Pierre Beaudin. Panes of 100 stamps. *Offset by Ashton-Potter Ltd., unwatermarked, perforated 13.*

1902 *Bookbinding*

1902		**MNHVF**	**UseVF**
1¢	**multicolored,** FDD *(April 29, 1999)*	.20	.20

1903 *Decorative Ironwork*

1903		**MNHVF**	**UseVF**
2¢	**multicolored,** FDD *(April 29, 1999)*	.20	.20

1904 *Glass Blowing*

1904		**MNHVF**	**UseVF**
3¢	**multicolored,** FDD *(April 29, 1999)*	.20	.20

1905 *Oyster Farming*

1905		**MNHVF**	**UseVF**
4¢	**multicolored,** FDD *(April 29, 1999)*	.20	.20

1906 *Weaving*

1906		**MNHVF**	**UseVF**
5¢	**multicolored,** FDD *(April 29, 1999)*	.20	.20

1907 *Quilting*

1907		**MNHVF**	**UseVF**
9¢	**multicolored,** FDD *(April 29, 1999)*	.20	.20

1908 *Artistic Woodworking*

1908		**MNHVF**	**UseVF**
10¢	**multicolored,** FDD *(April 29, 1999)*	.20	.20

1909 *Leatherworking*

1909		**MNHVF**	**UseVF**
25¢	**multicolored,** FDD *(April 29, 1999)*	.20	.20

Commemorative Issues

1999. CANADIAN HORSES ISSUE Four famous horses are featured in se-tenant commemoratives. *Offset by Ashton-Potter Canada Ltd., unwatermarked, perforated 13 x 13 1/4.*

1910, 1914 *Northern Dancer*, the first Canadian horse to win the Kentucky Derby; 1911, 1915 *Kingsway Skoal*, who bucked his way to every major rodeo award; 1912, 1916 *Big Ben*, a jumper who became the second non-human in Canada's Sports Hall of Fame; 1913, 1917 *Ambro Flight*, the greatest money-winning trotting mare in North America

1910		**MNHVF**	**UseVF**
46¢	**multicolored,** FDD *(June 2, 1999)*	.60	.20
1911		**MNHVF**	**UseVF**
46¢	**multicolored,** FDD *(June 2, 1999)*	.60	.20
1912		**MNHVF**	**UseVF**
46¢	**multicolored,** FDD *(June 2, 1999)*	.60	.20
1913		**MNHVF**	**UseVF**
46¢	**multicolored,** FDD *(June 2, 1999)*	.60	.20
	y. Pane of 16	2.40	1.00

1999. CANADIAN HORSES BOOKLET ISSUE Same designs as #1910-1913 in a self-adhesive booklet. *Offset by Ashton-Potter Canada Ltd., unwatermarked, perforated 11 1/2.*

1914		**MNHVF**	**UseVF**
46¢	**multicolored,** FDD *(June 2, 1999)*	.85	.35

1915		MNHVF	UseVF
46¢	multicolored, FDD *(June 2, 1999)*	.85	.35

1916		MNHVF	UseVF
46¢	multicolored, FDD *(June 2, 1999)*	.85	.35

1917		MNHVF	UseVF
46¢	multicolored, FDD *(June 2, 1999)*	.85	.35
	y. Booklet of 12	9.00	—

1999. BARREAU DU QUEBEC ISSUE Commemorated the 150th anniversary of the Quebec Bar Association. *Offset by Canadian Bank Note Co., unwatermarked, perforated 12 1/2 x 13.*

 1918 *Symbol for Quebec Bar Association*

1918		MNHVF	UseVF
46¢	multicolored, FDD *(May 31, 1999)*	.60	.20

1999. MASTERPIECES OF CANADIAN ART ISSUE Twelfth in a series depicting a significant piece of Canadian art, the 1952 painting *Coq Licorne* by Quebec artist Jean Dallaire (1916-1965) within a frame of platinum foil. The subject is a rooster, symbol of France, with a unicorn's horn. Issued July 3, 1999 in conjunction with the Philexfrance stamp exhibition in Paris, France. *Pane of 16, offset and foil stamping by Ashton-Potter, unwatermarked, perforated 12 1/2 x 13.*

 1919 *A rooster with a unicorn's horn, symbol of France*

1919		MNHVF	UseVF
95¢	multicolored, FDD *(July 3, 1999)*	1.25	.40

1999. PAN-AMERICAN GAMES ISSUE Four se-tenant stamps promoted the athletic competition, the world's largest multi-sport event outside of the Olympics, held in 1999 in Winnepeg, Manitoba. The games feature 41 sports and 42 countries. *Pane of 16, offset by Ashton-Potter, unwatermarked, perforated 13 1/2.*

1920 *Track & Field;*
1921 *Cycling;*
1922 *Swimming;*
1923 *Soccer*

1920		MNHVF	UseVF
46¢	multicolored, FDD *(July 12, 1999)*	.60	.25

1921		MNHVF	UseVF
46¢	multicolored, FDD *(July 12, 1999)*	.60	.25

1922		MNHVF	UseVF
46¢	multicolored, FDD *(July 12, 1999)*	.60	.25

1923		MNHVF	UseVF
46¢	multicolored, FDD *(July 12, 1999)*	.60	.25
	y. Block of 4 #1920-1923	2.25	1.20

1999. WORLD ROWING CHAMPIONSHIPS ISSUE Promoted the 23rd international championship competition held in 1999 in St. Catharines, Ontario. *Pane of 20, offset by Ashton-Potter, unwatermarked, perforated 12 1/2 x 13.*

 1924 *Person rowing in competition*

1924		MNHVF	UseVF
46¢	multicolored, FDD *(Aug. 22, 1999)*	.60	.25

1999. UNIVERSAL POSTAL UNION ISSUE Commemorated the 125th anniversary of the international postal association. *Pane of 20, offset by Canadian Bank Note Co., unwatermarked, perforated 12 1/2 x 13.*

 1925 *UPU symbol superimposed on world map*

1925		MNHVF	UseVF
46¢	multicolored, FDD *(Aug. 26, 1999)*	.60	.25

1999. ROYAL CANADIAN AIR FORCE ISSUE Commemorated the 75th anniversary of the military organization. Some of the aircraft shown were used before the granting of the "Royal" designation in 1924. *Se-tenant pane of 16, offset in 10 colors by Canadian Bank Note Co., unwatermarked, perforated 12 1/2 x 13.*

 1926 *De Haviland Mosquito*

1926		MNHVF	UseVF
46¢	multicolored, FDD *(Sept. 4, 1999)*	.60	.25

 1927 *Sopwith Camel*

1927		MNHVF	UseVF
46¢	multicolored, FDD *(Sept. 4, 1999)*	.60	.25

 1928 *De Haviland Canada DHC-3 Otter*

1928		MNHVF	UseVF
46¢	multicolored, FDD *(Sept. 4, 1999)*	.60	.25

1929 *De Haviland Canada CC-108 Caribou*

1929
46¢ **multicolored,** FDD *(Sept. 4, 1999)*

	MNHVF	UseVF
	.60	.25

1930 *Canadair CL-28 Argus*

1930
46¢ **multicolored,** FDD *(Sept. 4, 1999)*

	MNHVF	UseVF
	.60	.25

1931 *Canadair (North American) F-86 Sabre 6*

1931
46¢ **multicolored,** FDD *(Sept. 4, 1999)*

	MNHVF	UseVF
	.60	.25

1932 *McDonnell Douglas CF-18*

1932
46¢ **multicolored,** FDD *(Sept. 4, 1999)*

	MNHVF	UseVF
	.60	.25

1933 *Sopwith 5.F.1 Dolphin*

1933
46¢ **multicolored,** FDD *(Sept. 4, 1999)*

	MNHVF	UseVF
	.60	.25

1934 *Armstrong Whitworth Siskin IIIA*

1934
46¢ **multicolored,** FDD *(Sept. 4, 1999)*

	MNHVF	UseVF
	.60	.25

1935 *Canadian Vickers (Northrup) Delta II*

1935
46¢ **multicolored,** FDD *(Sept. 4, 1999)*

	MNHVF	UseVF
	.60	.25

1936 *Sikorsky CH-124A Sea King*

1936
46¢ **multicolored,** FDD *(Sept. 4, 1999)*

	MNHVF	UseVF
	.60	.25

1937 *Vickers-Armstrong Wellington Mk. II*

1937
46¢ **multicolored,** FDD *(Sept. 4, 1999)*

	MNHVF	UseVF
	.60	.25

1938 *Avro Anson Mk. 1*

1938
46¢ **multicolored,** FDD *(Sept. 4, 1999)*

	MNHVF	UseVF
	.60	.25

1939 *Canadair (Lockheed) CF-104G Starfighter*

1939
46¢ **multicolored,** FDD *(Sept. 4, 1999)*

	MNHVF	UseVF
	.60	.25

1940 *Burgess-Dunne*

1940
46¢ **multicolored,** FDD *(Sept. 4, 1999)*

	MNHVF	UseVF
	.60	.25

1941 *Avro 504K*

1941
46¢ **multicolored,** FDD *(Sept. 4, 1999)*
y. Pane of 16

	MNHVF	UseVF
	.60	.25
	10.00	5.00

1999. CANADIAN INTERNATIONAL AIR SHOW ISSUE Highlighted the 50th anniversary of the annual event at the Canadian National Exhibition in Toronto. A formation of nine RCAF Snowbirds extends over three of the stamps. *Se-tenant commemoratives on a souvenir sheet. Offset by Canadian Bank Note Co., unwatermarked, perforated 12 1/2 x 13.*

1942 Fokker Dr.1 triplane, a replica of the Red Baron's fighter; 1943 H101 Salto sailplane; 1944 Vampire MKIII flown by the RCAF at the first CIAS in 1949; 1945 Daredevil wing-walker on a Stearman A-75

1942			MNHVF	UseVF
46¢	multicolored, FDD *(Sept. 4, 1999)*		.60	.25

1943			MNHVF	UseVF
46¢	multicolored, FDD *(Sept. 4, 1999)*		.60	.25

1944			MNHVF	UseVF
46¢	multicolored, FDD *(Sept. 4, 1999)*		.60	.25

1945			MNHVF	UseVF
46¢	multicolored, FDD *(Sept. 4, 1999)*		.60	.25
	y. Block of 4 #1942-1945		2.50	1.25

1999. MILLENNIUM COLLECTION BOOK ISSUE 68 46¢ stamps included in a hardcover book. They were reprinted later in 4-stamp sheetlets. The individual stamps in the book are not itemized here. *Offset by Ashton-Potter, unwatermarked, perforated 12 1/2 x 13.*

1946			MNHVF	UseVF
46¢	multicolored, FDD *(Sept. 15, 1999)*		50.00	—

1999. NORTH ATLANTIC TREATY ORGANIZATION ISSUE 50th anniversary of NATO noted with the flags of member states. *Pane of 16 stamps, offset by Ashton-Potter, unwatermarked, perforated 12 1/2 x 13.*

1947 Flags of NATO member states

1947			MNHVF	UseVF
46¢	multicolored, FDD *(Sept. 21, 1999)*		.60	.25

1999. FRONTIER COLLEGE ISSUE Noted the 100th anniversary of the Ontario educational institution conceived to bring literacy to laborers in remote logging, mining and railway camps but now active in urban settings also. *Pane of 16 stamps, offset by Canadian Bank Note Co., unwatermarked, perforated 13 x 13 1/2.*

1948 Frontier College

1948			MNHVF	UseVF
46¢	multicolored, FDD *(Sept. 24, 1999)*		.60	.25

1999. KITES ISSUE Topical stamps issued for Stamp Collecting Month featured four stamps with different shapes and distinctive die-cut simulated perforations. *Se-tenant stamps in self-adhesive booklets of 8, offset by Ashton-Potter, unwatermarked, perforated 13.*

1949 Master Control Sport Kite in a triangle shape

1949			MNHVF	UseVF
46¢	multicolored, FDD *(Oct. 1, 1999)*		.75	.40

1950 Gibson Girl box kite on a vertical rectangle

1950			MNHVF	UseVF
46¢	multicolored, FDD *(Oct. 1, 1999)*		.75	.40

1951 Dragon Centipede on an elipse shape

1951			MNHVF	UseVF
46¢	multicolored, FDD *(Oct. 1, 1999)*		.75	.40

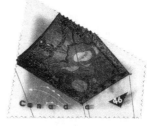

1952 Indian Garden Flying Carpet Edo Kite on a stamp with four straight but unequal sides

1952			MNHVF	UseVF
46¢	multicolored, FDD *(Oct. 1, 1999)*		.75	.40
	n. Booklet of 8 #1949-1952		7.00	3.50

1999. DOVES ISSUE 1999-2000 and Dove Hologram from self-adhesive souvenir sheet of 1 (1953y) or 4 (1953y1) with die-cut simulated perforations. *Offset and hologram by Ashton-Potter, Crown Canada and Gravure Choquet Inc., unwatermarked, straight die-cut.*

1953 Dove Hologram

1953y
Dove
souven
ir sheet

1955 Dove on Branch

1999. DOVE ON BRANCH ISSUE Souvenir sheet of 1 (1955y) or 4 (1955y1). *Intaglio by Canadian Bank Note Co., unwatermarked, perforated 12 3/4.*

1953		MNHVF	UseVF
46¢	**multicolored,** FDD *(Oct. 12, 1999)*	.65	.35
	y. Souvenir sheet of 1	.65	.35
	y1. Block of 4	2.75	1.75

1999. DOVE AND CHILD ISSUE Souvenir sheet of 1 (1954y) or 4 (1954y1). *Offset by Ashton-Potter, unwatermarked, perforated 13 1/2.*

1954 Dove and Child

1955y
Souvenir
sheet of
1 Dove
on
Branch

1955		MNHVF	UseVF
95¢	**multicolored,** FDD *(Oct. 12, 1999)*	1.25	1.25
	y. Souvenir sheet of 1	1.25	1.25
	y1. Block of 4	6.00	6.00

1999. CHRISTMAS VICTORIAN ANGELS ISSUE Christmas issue portrayed Victorian-era angels. *50-stamp panes, offset by Canadian Bank Note Co., unwatermarked, perforated 13 1/4.*

1956 Angel with drum

1956		MNHVF	UseVF
46¢	**multicolored,** FDD *(Nov. 4, 1999)*	.70	.35
	n. Booklet of 10	3.50	1.75

1954y
Dove
and
Child
souvenir
sheet

1957 Angel with toys

1954		MNHVF	UseVF
55¢	**multicolored,** FDD *(Oct. 12, 1999)*	.75	.40
	y. Souvenir sheet of 1	.75	.40
	y1. Block of 4	3.00	1.75

1957		MNHVF	UseVF
55¢	**multicolored,** FDD *(Nov. 4, 1999)*	.75	.40
	n. Booklet of 5	3.75	2.00

 1958 *Angel with candle and bells*

1958
95¢   **multicolored,** FDD *(Nov. 4, 1999)*   MNHVF 1.25   UseVF .80
n. Booklet of 5   6.25   4.00

1999. MILLENNIUM COLLECTION OF ENTERTAINMENT ISSUE

1959 *Calgary Stampede;*

1960 *A World of Fun;*

1961 *Hockey Night in Canada;*

1962 *Live From the Forum*

1959
46¢   **multicolored,** FDD *(Dec. 17, 1999)*   MNHVF .60   UseVF .25
1960
46¢   **multicolored,** FDD *(Dec. 17, 1999)*   MNHVF .60   UseVF .25
1961
46¢   **multicolored,** FDD *(Dec. 17, 1999)*   MNHVF .60   UseVF .25
1962
46¢   **multicolored,** FDD *(Dec. 17, 1999)*   MNHVF .60   UseVF .25
y. Minisheet of 4 #1959-1962   2.50   1.00

1999. MILLENNIUM COLLECTION OF PERFORMERS ISSUE *Offset, unwatermarked, perforated 13 1/4.*

1963 *Portia White;*

1964 *Glenn Gould;*

1965 *Guy Lombardo;*

1966 *Felix Leclerc*

1963
46¢   **multicolored,** FDD *(Dec. 17, 1999)*   MNHVF .60   UseVF .25
1964
46¢   **multicolored,** FDD *(Dec. 17, 1999)*   MNHVF .60   UseVF .25
1965
46¢   **multicolored,** FDD *(Dec. 17, 1999)*   MNHVF .60   UseVF .25
1966
46¢   **multicolored,** FDD *(Dec. 17, 1999)*   MNHVF .60   UseVF .25
y. Minisheet of 4 #1963-1966   2.50   1.00

1999. MILLENNIUM COLLECTION OF TECHNOLOGY ISSUE *Offset, unwatermarked, perforated 13 1/4.*

 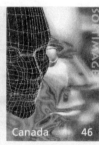

1967 *Imax Movies;*

1968 *SoftImage;*

1969 *Ted Rogers Sr.;*

1970 *Sir William Stephenson*

1967
46¢   **multicolored,** FDD *(Dec. 17, 1999)*   MNHVF .60   UseVF .25
1968
46¢   **multicolored,** FDD *(Dec. 17, 1999)*   MNHVF .60   UseVF .25
1969
46¢   **multicolored,** FDD *(Dec. 17, 1999)*   MNHVF .60   UseVF .25
1970
46¢   **multicolored,** FDD *(Dec. 17, 1999)*   MNHVF .60   UseVF .25
y. Minisheet of 4 #1967-1970   2.50   1.00

1999. MILLENNIUM COLLECTION OF MEDIA GROUPS ISSUE *Offset, unwatermarked, perforated 13 1/4.*

1971 *Royal Canadian Academy of Arts;*

1972 *Canada Council;*

1973 *National Film Board;*

1974 *Canada Broadcasting Co.*

1971		MNHVF	UseVF
46¢	**multicolored,** FDD *(Dec. 17, 1999)*	.60	.25

1972		MNHVF	UseVF
46¢	**multicolored,** FDD *(Dec. 17, 1999)*	.60	.25

1973		MNHVF	UseVF
46¢	**multicolored,** FDD *(Dec. 17, 1999)*	.60	.25

1974		MNHVF	UseVF
46¢	**multicolored,** FDD *(Dec. 17, 1999)*	.60	.25
	y. Minisheet of 4 #1971-1974	2.50	1.00

Commemorative Issues

2000. MILLENNIUM PARTNERSHIP PROGRAM ISSUE Honored a government program to promote local, national, and international partnerships to leave a positive legacy. The program's logo is a stylized human figure in front of a maple leaf and with a hand of flame. *Unwatermarked, perforated 13 x 12 1/2.*

1975 *Stylized human figure*

1975		MNHVF	UseVF
46¢	**multicolored,** FDD *(Jan. 1, 2000)*	.60	.25

2000. YEAR OF THE DRAGON ISSUE The fourth in a 12-year cycle of the Chinese zodiac, part of the Lunar New Year series. *Panes of 25, offset and embossed by Ashton-Potter Canada Ltd., unwatermarked, perforated 12 1/2.*

1976 *Dragon*

1976		MNHVF	UseVF
46¢	**multicolored,** FDD *(Jan. 8, 2000)*	.60	.25

2000. YEAR OF THE DRAGON SOUVENIR SHEET ISSUE *Offset and embossed by Ashton-Potter Canada Ltd. Unwatermarked, perforated 13 1/2.*

1977 *Souvenir sheet of Dragon*

1977		MNHVF	UseVF
95¢	**multicolored,** FDD *(Jan. 8, 2000)*	1.30	

2000. MEDICAL INNOVATORS ISSUE *Unwatermarked, perforated 13 1/4.*

Millennium souvenir sheet: 1978 *Frederick Banting, discoverer of insulin;* 1979 *Armand Frappier founded studies in immunology;* 1980 *Hans Selye advanced knowledge of the biology of stress;* 1981 *Dr. Maude Abbott was a world authority on heart defects*

1978		MNHVF	UseVF
46¢	**multicolored,** FDD *(Jan. 17, 2000)*	.60	.25

1979		MNHVF	UseVF
46¢	**multicolored,** FDD *(Jan. 17, 2000)*	.60	.25

1980		MNHVF	UseVF
46¢	**multicolored,** FDD *(Jan. 17, 2000)*	.60	.25

1981		MNHVF	UseVF
46¢	**multicolored,** FDD *(Jan. 17, 2000)*	.60	.25
	y. Sheetlet of 4	2.50	1.00

2000. SOCIAL PROGRESS ISSUE *Unwatermarked, perforated 13 1/4.*

Millennium souvenir sheet: 1982 *Religious health care orders to Medicare;* 1983 *"Women are Persons";* 1984 *Alphonse and Doremene Desjardins: small savings, big results;* 1985 *Moses Coady: social betterment through adult education*

1982		MNHVF	UseVF
46¢	**multicolored,** FDD *(Jan. 17, 2000)*	.60	.25

1983		MNHVF	UseVF
46¢	**multicolored,** FDD *(Jan. 17, 2000)*	.60	.25

1984		MNHVF	UseVF
46¢	**multicolored,** FDD *(Jan. 17, 2000)*	.60	.25

1985		MNHVF	UseVF
46¢	**multicolored,** FDD *(Jan. 17, 2000)*	.60	.25
	y. Sheetlet of 4	2.50	1.00

2000. HEARTS OF GOLD ISSUE *Unwatermarked, perforated 13 1/4.*

Millennium souvenir sheet: 1986 Canadian International Development Agency; 1987 Lucille Teasdale ran a hospital in Uganda for 30 years; 1988 Terry Fox founded the Marathon of Hope; 1989 Meals on Wheels for the homebound

			MNHVF	UseVF
1986				
46¢	**multicolored,** FDD *(Jan. 17, 2000)*		.60	.25
1987			MNHVF	UseVF
46¢	**multicolored,** FDD *(Jan. 17, 2000)*		.60	.25
1988			MNHVF	UseVF
46¢	**multicolored,** FDD *(Jan. 17, 2000)*		.60	.25
1989			MNHVF	UseVF
46¢	**multicolored,** FDD *(Jan. 17, 2000)*		.60	.25
	y. Sheetlet of 4		2.50	1.00

2000. HUMANITARIANS AND PEACEKEEPERS ISSUE *Unwatermarked, perforated 13 1/4.*

Millennium souvenir sheet: 1990 Raoul Dandurand was president of the Assembly of the League of Nations; 1991 Pauline Vanier was a Red Cross volunteer in Paris in World War II; Elizabeth Smellie headed Army nursing services in both world wars and organized the Canadian Women's Army Corps.; 1992 Lester B. Pearson won a Nobel Prize for his efforts in seeking Middle East peace; 1993 The Ottawa Convention prohibited the use of anti-personnel land mines

			MNHVF	UseVF
1990				
46¢	**multicolored,** FDD *(Jan. 17, 2000)*		.60	.25
1991			MNHVF	UseVF
46¢	**multicolored,** FDD *(Jan. 17, 2000)*		.60	.25
1992			MNHVF	UseVF
46¢	**multicolored,** FDD *(Jan. 17, 2000)*		.60	.25

			MNHVF	UseVF
1993				
46¢	**multicolored,** FDD *(Jan. 17, 2000)*		.60	.25
	y. Sheetlet of 4		2.50	1.00

2000. 50TH NATIONAL HOCKEY LEAGUE ALL-STAR GAME ISSUE
Honored six past and present NHL stars in a souvenir sheet of six stamps showing them in action. Portraits of the six are on attached tabs. *Unwatermarked, perforated 13 1/4.*

1994 Wayne Gretzky; 1995 Gordie Howe; 1996 Maurice Richard; 1997 Doug Harvey; 1998 Bobby Orr

			MNHVF	UseVF
1994				
46¢	**multicolored,** FDD *(Feb. 5, 2000)*		.60	.25
1995			MNHVF	UseVF
46¢	**multicolored,** FDD *(Feb. 5, 2000)*		.60	.25
1996			MNHVF	UseVF
46¢	**multicolored,** FDD *(Feb. 5, 2000)*		.60	.25
1997			MNHVF	UseVF
46¢	**multicolored,** FDD *(Feb. 5, 2000)*		.60	.25
1998			MNHVF	UseVF
46¢	**multicolored,** FDD *(Feb. 5, 2000)*		.60	.25
1999			MNHVF	UseVF
46¢	**multicolored,** FDD *(Feb. 5, 2000)*		.60	.25
	y. Sheetlet of 6		3.75	1.90

2000. ABORIGINAL PEOPLES ISSUE *Unwatermarked, perforated 13 1/4.*

Millennium souvenir sheet: 2000 Odawa leader Pontiac persuaded the British to recognize Indian land rights; 2001 Onondaga Tom Longboat was the fastest runner over 15 miles in the early 1900s; 2002 The Powers of the Inuit Shamans; 2003 Healing from Within

			MNHVF	UseVF
2000				
46¢	**multicolored,** FDD *(Feb. 17, 2000)*		.60	.25

2001		MNHVF	UseVF
46¢	**multicolored,** FDD *(Feb. 17, 2000)*	.60	.25

2002		MNHVF	UseVF
46¢	**multicolored,** FDD *(Feb. 17, 2000)*	.60	.25

2003		MNHVF	UseVF
46¢	**multicolored,** FDD *(Feb. 5, 2000)*	.60	.25
	y. Sheetlet of 4	2.50	1.00

2000. CULTURAL FABRIC ISSUE *Unwatermarked, perforated 13 1/4.*

Millennium souvenir sheet: 2004 L'Anse aux Meadows, the oldest known European settlement in the New World; 2005 Halifax's Pier 21, a symbol of hope for immigrants; 2006 The Neptune Theatre in Halifax; 2007 Ontario's Stratford Festival: Canada's "Midsummer Night's Dream"

2004		MNHVF	UseVF
46¢	**multicolored,** FDD *(Jan. 17, 2000)*	.60	.25

2005		MNHVF	UseVF
46¢	**multicolored,** FDD *(Feb. 17, 2000)*	.60	.25

2006		MNHVF	UseVF
46¢	**multicolored,** FDD *(Feb. 17, 2000)*	.60	.25

2007		MNHVF	UseVF
46¢	**multicolored,** FDD *(Feb. 17, 2000)*	.60	.25
	y. Sheetlet of 4	2.50	1.00

2000. LITERARY GREATS ISSUE *Unwatermarked, perforated 13 1/4.*

Millennium souvenir sheet: 2008 W.O. Mitchell, author of Who Has Seen the Wind; 2009 Gratien Gelinas, the father of contemporary Quebec theater; 2010 Pierre Tisseyre promoted the French-language literary tradition; 2011 Harlequin Books titles appear in 24 languages

2008		MNHVF	UseVF
46¢	**multicolored,** FDD *(Feb. 17, 2000)*	.60	.25

2009		MNHVF	UseVF
46¢	**multicolored,** FDD *(Feb. 17, 2000)*	.60	.25

2010		MNHVF	UseVF
46¢	**multicolored,** FDD *(Feb. 17, 2000)*	.60	.25

2011		MNHVF	UseVF
46¢	**multicolored,** FDD *(Feb. 17, 2000)*	.60	.25
	y. Sheetlet of 4	2.50	1.00

2000. GREAT THINKERS ISSUE *Unwatermarked, perforated 13 1/4.*

Millennium souvenir sheet: 2012 Marshall McLuhan, a pioneer pop philosopher; 2013 Northrup Frye, literary critic; 2014 Roger Lemlin, patriarch of the fictional Plouffe family; 2015 Hilda Marion Neatby, head of the Saskatchewan University history department

2012		MNHVF	UseVF
46¢	**multicolored,** FDD *(Feb. 17, 2000)*	.60	.25

2013		MNHVF	UseVF
46¢	**multicolored,** FDD *(Feb. 17, 2000)*	.60	.25

2014		MNHVF	UseVF
46¢	**multicolored,** FDD *(Feb. 17, 2000)*	.60	.25

2015		MNHVF	UseVF
46¢	**multicolored,** FDD *(Feb. 17, 2000)*	.60	.25
	y. Sheetlet of 4	2.50	1.00

2000. PHILANTHROPY ISSUE *Unwatermarked, perforated 13 1/4.*

Millennium souvenir sheet: 2016 The Massey Foundation founded by farm equipment maker Hart Massey; 2017 The Killam Legacy of Izaak Walton Killam and his wife Dorothy Killam; 2018 Eric Lafferty Harvie assisted diverse organizations; 2019 Macdonald Stewart Foundation of Sir William Macdonald

2016		MNHVF	UseVF
46¢	**multicolored,** FDD *(Feb. 17, 2000)*	.60	.25

2017		MNHVF	UseVF
46¢	**multicolored,** FDD *(Feb. 17, 2000)*	.60	.25

2018		MNHVF	UseVF
46¢	multicolored, FDD *(Feb. 17, 2000)*	.60	.25

2019		MNHVF	UseVF
46¢	multicolored, FDD *(Feb. 17, 2000)*	.60	.25
	y. Sheetlet of 4	2.50	1.00

2000. BIRDS OF CANADA ISSUE Fifth set of four stamps illustrated by Pierre Leduc, a wildlife artist from Stoneham, Quebec. *Gummed stamps offset by Ashton-Potter Canada Ltd., unwatermarked, perforated 12 1/2 x 13.*

2020 *Canadian warbler, a song bird;* 2021 *Osprey, a bird of prey sometimes called a fish hawk;* 2022 *Pacific loon, a protected species smaller than the common loon;* 2023 *Blue jay, an omniverous bird with bright plumage and crest*

2020		MNHVF	UseVF
46¢	multicolored, *FDD (March 1, 2000)*	.60	.25

2021		MNHVF	UseVF
46¢	multicolored, *FDD (March 1, 2000)*	.60	.25

2022		MNHVF	UseVF
46¢	multicolored, *FDD (March 1, 2000)*	.60	.25

2023		MNHVF	UseVF
46¢	multicolored, *FDD (March 1, 2000)*	.60	.25
	y. Block of 4	2.50	1.25

2000. BIRDS OF CANADA BOOKLET ISSUE *Self-adhesive booklets of 12 stamps offset by Ashton-Potter Canada Ltd., unwatermarked, 11 1/2 straight die cut.*

2024		MNHVF	UseVF
46¢	multicolored, *FDD (March 1, 2000)*	.80	.35

2025		MNHVF	UseVF
46¢	multicolored, *FDD (March 1, 2000)*	.80	.36

2026		MNHVF	UseVF
46¢	multicolored, *FDD (March 1, 2000)*	.80	.37

2027		MNHVF	UseVF
46¢	multicolored, *FDD (March 1, 2000)*	.80	.38
	y. Booklet of 12	9.50	

2000. TECHNOLOGICAL MARVELS ISSUE *Unwatermarked, perforated 13 1/4.*

Millennium souvenir sheet: 2028 *Rogers Pass, the longest tunnel in North America;* 2029 *Manic Dams harness the power of Quebec's Manicouagan River;* 2030 *Canadian Space Program;* 2031 *Toronto's CN Tower, world's tallest free-standing structure*

2028		MNHVF	UseVF
46¢	multicolored, FDD *(March 17, 2000)*	.60	.25

2029		MNHVF	UseVF
46¢	multicolored, FDD *(March 17, 2000)*	.60	.25

2030		MNHVF	UseVF
46¢	multicolored, FDD *(March 17, 2000)*	.60	.25

2031		MNHVF	UseVF
46¢	multicolored, FDD *(March 17, 2000)*	.60	.25
	y. Sheetlet of 4	2.50	1.00

2000. INVENTIONS ISSUE *Unwatermarked, perforated 13 1/4.*

Millennium souvenir sheet: 2032 *George Klein, Canada's most prolific modern inventor, headed the design of Canada's first nuclear reactor;* 2033 *Abraham Gesner created kerosene in 1846;* 2034 *Alexander Graham Bell invented more than just the telephone;* 2035 *Joseph Armand Bombardier changed winter recreation with his snowmobile*

2032		MNHVF	UseVF
46¢	multicolored, FDD *(March 17, 2000)*	.60	.25

2033		MNHVF	UseVF
46¢	multicolored, FDD *(March 17, 2000)*	.60	.25

2034		MNHVF	UseVF
46¢	multicolored, FDD *(March 17, 2000)*	.60	.25

2035		MNHVF	UseVF
46¢	multicolored, FDD *(March 17, 2000)*	.60	.25
	y. Sheetlet of 4	2.50	1.00

2000. FOOD ISSUE *Unwatermarked, perforated 13 1/4.*

Millennium souvenir sheet: 2036 *Sir Charles Saunders developed the Marquis strain of wheat;* 2037 *Frederick Tisdall and collaborators developed the ready-to-eat baby cereal, Pablum;* 2038 *Archibald Gowanlock Huntsman pioneered methods of packaging frozen fish fillets;* 2039 *McCain Foods is a leader in frozen foods*

2036		MNHVF	UseVF
46¢	multicolored, FDD *(March 17, 2000)*	.60	.25

2037		MNHVF	UseVF
46¢	multicolored, FDD *(March 17, 2000)*	.60	.25

2038		MNHVF	UseVF
46¢	multicolored, FDD *(March 17, 2000)*	.60	.25

2039
46¢ multicolored, FDD *(March 17, 2000)* | MNHVF .60 | UseVF .25
y. Sheetlet of 4 | 2.50 | 1.00

2000. ENTERPRISING GIANTS ISSUE *Unwatermarked, perforated 13 1/4.*

Millennium souvenir sheet: 2040 Hudson's Bay Company, former fur traders, now is a retailing giant; 2041 Bell Canada Enterprises has communications clients in 150 countries; 2042 Rose-Anna Vachon has been tantalyzing taste buds since 1923; 2043 George Weston Ltd. has become the country's largest food distributor

2040
46¢ multicolored, FDD *(March 17, 2000)* | MNHVF .60 | UseVF .25
2041
46¢ multicolored, FDD *(March 17, 2000)* | MNHVF .60 | UseVF .25
2042
46¢ multicolored, FDD *(March 17, 2000)* | MNHVF .60 | UseVF .25
2043
46¢ multicolored, FDD *(March 17, 2000)* | MNHVF .60 | UseVF .25
y. Sheetlet of 4 | 2.50 | 1.00

2000. SUPREME COURT ISSUE commemorated the 125th anniversary of the Canadian high court. It featured an illustration by Quebec artist Claude le Sauteur of nine red-robed justices against the Supreme Court of Canada building. *Offset by Canadian Bank Note Co., unwatermarked, perforated 12 1/2 x 13.*

2044 *Supreme Court justices*

2044
46¢ multicolored, FDD *(April 10, 2000)* | MNHVF .60 | UseVF .25

2000. THE CALLING OF AN ENGINEER ISSUE Honored the professional ritual, which began 75 years previously at the University of Toronto with the assistance of author Rudyard Kipling. The unifying theme of the tete-beche pair of stamps is an iron ring. Four engineering achievements are pictured: The CP High Level Bridge in Lethbridge, Alberta; the synthetic rubber plant of Polysar Ltd. in Sarnia, Ontario; a tower in the Trans-Canada Microwave Radio Relay System; and the cardiac pacemaker, developed at the National Research Council in 1949. *Unwatermarked, perforated 12 1/2 x 13.*

2045 *Engineering achievements*

2045
46¢ multicolored, FDD (April 25, 2000) | MNHVF .60 | UseVF .25
y. Tete beche pair | 1.20 | .50

2000. RURAL MAILBOXES ISSUE Featured decorated rural mailboxes, highlighting a different region of Canada in different seasons. The booklet of 12 se-tenant stamps was issued to coincide with the annual convention of the Royal Philatelic Society of Canada. *Offset by Ashton-Potter Canada Ltd., unwatermarked, perforated 12 1/2 x 13.*

2046 *Spring scene, fish head;* 2047 *Summer scene, cow head;* 2048 *Fall scene, tractor;* 2049 *Winter scene, goose head*

2046
46¢ multicolored, FDD *(April 28, 2000)* | MNHVF .60 | UseVF .25
2047
46¢ multicolored, FDD *(April 28, 2000)* | MNHVF .60 | UseVF .25
2048
46¢ multicolored, FDD *(April 28, 2000)* | MNHVF .60 | UseVF .25
2049
46¢ multicolored, FDD *(April 28, 2000)* | MNHVF .60 | UseVF .25
y. Block of 4 | 2.40 | 1.00
n. Booklet of 12 | 7.25 | .30

2000. GREETINGS (PICTURE POSTAGE) ISSUE Featured self-adhesive, scallop-edged golden stamp frames into which could be affixed generic greetings labels in a five-stamp booklet or personalized photos in 25-stamp panes. *Offset by Ashton Potter Canada Ltd., unwatermarked.*

2050 *Generic greeting golden frames*

2050
46¢ multicolored, FDD *(April 28, 2000)* | MNHVF .60 | UseVF .25
n. Booklet of 5 | 3.00 | 1.25

2000. QUEEN MOTHER ISSUE Celebrated the 100th birthday of the British Royal Family's Queen Mother Elizabeth, the "Queen Mum," who was born Aug. 4, 1900. *Offset by Canada Bank Note Co. in a commemorative pane of nine stamps, unwatermarked.*

2051 *Queen Mother Elizabeth*

2051		**MNHVF**	**UseVF**
95¢	**multicolored,** FDD *(May 23, 2000)*	1.20	.50
	y. Pane of 9	10.80	4.50

2000. FRESH WATERS ISSUE (U.S. rate). Featured officially unidentified Canadian lakes and rivers in two five-stamp self-adhesive booklets. Two photos, separated by a gutter of water droplets, are on each stamp. *Offset by Canadian Bank Note Co., unwatermarked.*

2052-2056 *Canadian lakes and rivers*

2052		**MNHVF**	**UseVF**
55¢	**multicolored**	.70	.30
2053		**MNHVF**	**UseVF**
55¢	**multicolored**	.70	.30
2054		**MNHVF**	**UseVF**
55¢	**multicolored**	.70	.30
2055		**MNHVF**	**UseVF**
55¢	**multicolored**	.70	.30
2056		**MNHVF**	**UseVF**
55¢	**multicolored**	.70	.30
	y. Pane of 5	3.50	1.50

2000. FRESH WATERS ISSUE (International rate).

2057		**MNHVF**	**UseVF**
95¢	**multicolored,** FDD *(May 23, 2000)*	1.20	.50
2058		**MNHVF**	**UseVF**
95¢	**multicolored,** FDD *(May 23, 2000)*	1.20	.50
2059		**MNHVF**	**UseVF**
95¢	**multicolored,** FDD *(May 23, 2000)*	1.20	.50
2060		**MNHVF**	**UseVF**
95¢	**multicolored,** FDD *(May 23, 2000)*	1.20	.50
2061		**MNHVF**	**UseVF**
95¢	**multicolored,** FDD *(May 23, 2000)*	1.20	.50
	y. Pane of 5	6.00	2.50

2000. BOYS AND GIRLS CLUBS ISSUE Celebrated the centennial of the organization for youth. *Offset by Canadian Bank Note Co.*

2062 *Boys and girls*

2062
46¢   **multicolored,** FDD *(June 1, 2000)*   MNHVF .60   UseVF .25

2000. SEVENTH DAY ADVENTISTS ISSUE Coincided with the 57th International General Conference Session of the Protestant church in St. John, New Brunswick.

2063 *Landscape and church symbol*

2063
46¢   **multicolored,** FDD *(June 29, 2000)*   MNHVF .60   UseVF .25

2000. STAMPIN' THE FUTURE ISSUE Featured the four winning artworks by Canadian youth in an international competition. Winners were Rosalie Anne Nardelli, Montreal, Quebec; Sarah Lutgen, Vernon, British Columbia; Andrew Wright, Collingwood, Ontario; and Christine Weera, Edmonton, Alberta. *Offset by Canadian Bank Note Co.*

2064-2067 *Canadian youth artwork*

2064
46¢   **multicolored,** FDD *(July 1, 2000)*   MNHVF .60   UseVF .25

2065
46¢   **multicolored,** FDD *(July 1, 2000)*   MNHVF .60   UseVF .25

2066
46¢   **multicolored,** FDD *(July 1, 2000)*   MNHVF .60   UseVF .25

2067
46¢   **multicolored,** FDD *(July 1, 2000)*   MNHVF .60   UseVF .25
        y. Block of 4   2.40   1.00

2000. MASTERPIECES OF CANADIAN ART ISSUE Featured *The Artist at Niagara, 1858* by the popular 19th century artist, Cornelius Krieghoff. It is the 13th issue in an annual series. *Gummed, offset and with platinum foil stamping border by Ashton-Potter Canada Ltd.*

2068 *The Artist at Niagara, 1858, by Cornelius Krieghoff*

2068
95¢   **multicolored,** FDD *(July 13, 2000)*   MNHVF 1.20   UseVF .50

2000. TALL SHIPS ISSUE Helped to promote a visit of tall sailing ships to Halifax, Nova Scotia. The two se-tenant self-adhesive stamps on an illustrated pane of 10 show 12 unidentified ships. *Offset by Ashton-Potter Canada Ltd., scallop-edged.*

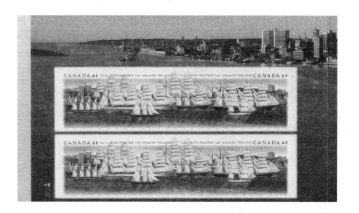

2069 *Skyline and "Canada 46" on left;* 2070 *Skyline and "Canada 46" on right*

2069
46¢   **multicolored,** FDD *(July 19, 2000)*   MNHVF .60   UseVF .25

2070
46¢   **multicolored,** FDD *(July 19, 2000)*   MNHVF .60   UseVF .25
        y. Se-tenant pair   1.20   .50
        y1. Pane of 10   6.00   —

2000. DEPARTMENT OF LABOUR ISSUE Hailed the centennial of the government department. *Offset by Canadian Bank Note Co.*

2071 *Department of Labour*

2071
46¢   **multicolored,** FDD *(Sept. 1, 2000)*   MNHVF .60   UseVF .25

2000. PETRO-CANADA ISSUE Saluted the 25th anniversary of the government oil and gas company with a montage of photos. *Offset by Canadian Bank Note Co. in self-adhesive booklets of 12 with straight die-cuts except for two V-shaped roulette cuts on each margin.*

2072 *Oil and gas company symbols*

2072		MNHVF	UseVF
46¢	**multicolored,** FDD *(Sept. 13, 2000)*	.60	.25
	y. Pane of 12	7.20	—

2000. WHALES ISSUE Pictured four species of whales in an illustrated sheetlet for Stamp Collecting Month.

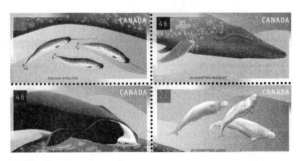

2073 *Narwhal;* 2074 *Blue Whale;* 2075 *Bow Head Whale;* 2076 *Beluga Whale*

2073		MNHVF	UseVF
46¢	**multicolored,** FDD *(Oct. 1, 2000)*	.60	.25
2074		MNHVF	UseVF
46¢	**multicolored,** FDD *(Oct. 1, 2000)*	.60	.25
2075		MNHVF	UseVF
46¢	**multicolored,** FDD *(Oct. 1, 2000)*	.60	.25
2076		MNHVF	UseVF
46¢	**multicolored,** FDD *(Oct. 1, 2000)*	.60	.25
	y. Sheetlet of 16	9.60	4.00
	y1. Block of 4	2.40	1.00

2000. PICTURE POSTAGE - CHRISTMAS ISSUE Featured a spray of holly in the frame border and a choice of 5 holiday labels.

2077 *Golden frame, spray of holly in the border*

2077		MNHVF	UseVF
46¢	**multicolored**	.60	.25
	n. Booklet of 5 plus 5 labels	3.00	1.25

2000. NATIVITY SCENES ISSUE Featured Christmas art works by disabled artists. Susie Matthias, London, Ontario, born without arms or legs, painted the 46¢ Nativity scene by holding a paintbrush in her mouth. Michel Guillemette, Sainte-Foy, Quebec, paralyzed from the neck down, painted the 55¢ stamp of the manger. David Allan Carter, Dartmouth, Nova Scotia, also paralyzed from the neck down, painted Joseph and Mary on the journey to Bethlehem, where Christ was born. *Offset by Ashton-Potter Canada Ltd.*

2078-2080 *Christmas art works by disabled artists*

2078		MNHVF	UseVF
46¢	**multicolored,** FDD *(Nov. 3, 2000)*	.60	.25
	n. Booklet of 10	6.00	2.50
2079		MNHVF	UseVF
55¢	**multicolored,** FDD *(Nov. 3, 2000)*	.70	.30
	n. Booklet of 6	4.20	1.80
2080		MNHVF	UseVF
95¢	**multicolored,** FDD (Nov. 3, 2000)	1.20	.50
	n. Booklet of 6	7.20	3.00

2000. CANADIAN REGIMENTS ISSUE Honored two historic military regiments. Les Voltigeurs de Quebec, the oldest French-Canadian regiment, was formed in 1862 of six existing rifle companies. The image is of a regimental drummer. Lord Strathcona's Horse was a calvary regiment organized for service in 1900 for the Boer War. The image is of Sir Samuel Steele, its first commander and a legendary lawman of the Canadian West.

2081 *Lord Strathcona's Horse,* 2082 *Les Voltigeurs de Quebec*

2081		MNHVF	UseVF
46¢	**multicolored,** FDD (Nov. 11, 2000)	.60	.25
2082		MNHVF	UseVF
46¢	**multicolored,** FDD (Nov. 11, 2000)	.60	.25

Every entry in this catalog has been double-checked for accuracy, but mistakes may creep into any human endeavor, and we ask your assistance in eliminating them. Please call the attention of the editors to any errors in stamp descriptions found in this catalog.

Official Stamps

1911-31. LARGE OHMS PERFIN ISSUE Perfin 112, large OHMS (5 holes in vertical bars of H) sporadically applied by some departments of government from 1912-1939, was of optional use; not sold to public at Post Office.

O112 *Five holes in vertical bars of H*

			UseF
O112	1¢	yellow	25.00
O113	2¢	carmine	25.00
O114	2¢	green	18.75
O115	3¢	brown	22.50
O116	3¢	deep red	25.00
O117	3¢	deep rose red	25.00
O118	4¢	olive bistre	25.00
O119	5¢	dark blue	30.00
O120	5¢	violet	25.00
O121	7¢	yellow ochre	45.00
O122	7¢	red brown	37.50
O123	8¢	blue	45.00
O124	10¢	plum	45.00
O125	10¢	blue	30.00
O126	10¢	bistre brown	20.00
O127	20¢	olive green	30.00
O128	50¢	brown black	52.50
O129	$1	brown orange	75.00

1927. LARGE OHMS PERFIN ISSUE No. 156-159 perfin 112, large OHMS.

			UseF
O156	1¢	brown orange	25.00
O157	2¢	green	37.50
O158	3¢	deep rose red	45.00
O159	5¢	slate purple	30.00

1927. LARGE OHMS PERFIN ISSUE No. 162 perfin 112, large OHMS.

			UseF
O162	5¢	slate purple	30.00

1928-29. LARGE OHMS PERFIN ISSUE No. 165-175, perfin 112, large OHMS. *Intaglio.*

			UseF
O165	1¢	yellow orange	35.00
O166	2¢	green	22.50
O167	3¢	dark carmine	52.50
O168	4¢	bistre	70.00
O169	5¢	violet	22.50
O170	8¢	blue	65.00
O171	10¢	green	20.00
O172	12¢	slate black	200.00
O173	20¢	deep rose red	55.00
O174	50¢	deep blue	190.00
O175	$1	olive green	150.00

1928. SMALL OHMS PERFIN ISSUE perfin 264, small OHMS; perfin 112, large OHMS. *Intaglio.*

			UseF
O178	5¢	sepia	10.00

1930-32. LARGE OHMS PERFIN ISSUE No. 180-195 perfin 112, large OHMS. No. 186 and some low values of the subsequent issues printed by both flat plate and rotary press. the gum of rotary stamps has a striped appearance. *Gravure.*

			UseF
O179	1¢	orange	35.00
O180	1¢	deep green	15.00
O181	2¢	dull green	55.00
O182	2¢	deep red	22.50
O183	2¢	brown	25.00
O184	3¢	deep red	20.00
O185	4¢	yellow bistre	55.00
O186	5¢	dull violet	40.00
O187	5¢	dull blue	35.00
O188	8¢	dark blue	60.00
O189	8¢	red orange	52.50
O190	10¢	olive green	25.00
O191	12¢	gray black	120.00
O192	13¢	slate violet	60.00
O193	20¢	red	55.00
O194	50¢	blue	75.00

O195

		UseF
$1	drab olive	190.00

1931. LARGE OHMS PERFIN ISSUE Perfin 112, large OHMS. *Intaglio.*

O209

		UseF
10¢	bronze green	25.00

1932. LARGE OHMS PERFIN ISSUE Perfin 112, large OHMS. *Intaglio.*

O210

		UseF
3¢	carmine red	60.00

1932. LARGE OHMS PERFIN ISSUE No. 212, 213 perfin 112, large OHMS. *Intaglio.*

O212

		UseF
3¢	carmine red	22.50

O213

		UseF
5¢	blue	37.50

O214

		UseF
13¢	green	225.00

1932. LARGE OHMS PERFIN ISSUE No. 216-221 perfin 112, large OHMS. *Intaglio.*

O215

		UseF
6¢ on 5¢		170.00

O216

		UseF
1¢	dark green	20.00

O217

		UseF
2¢	black brown	20.00

O218

		UseF
3¢	deep red, Die II	20.00

O219

		UseF
4¢	ochre	60.00

O220

		UseF
5¢	dark blue	30.00

O221

		UseF
8¢	red orange	60.00

1933. LARGE OHMS PERFIN ISSUE No. 230 perfin 112, large OHMS. *Intaglio.*

O230

		UseF
5¢	dark blue	55.00

1933. LARGE OHMS PERFIN ISSUE No. 231 perfin 112, large OHMS. *Intaglio.*

O231

		UseF
20¢	brown red	60.00

1933. LARGE OHMS PERFIN ISSUE No. 232, perfin 112, large OHMS. *Intaglio.*

O232

		UseF
5¢	dark blue	55.00

1934. LARGE OHMS PERFIN ISSUE No. 233 perfin 112, large OHMS. *Intaglio.*

O233

		UseF
3¢	dark blue	60.00

1935. LARGE OHMS PERFIN ISSUE No. 248, 251, perfin 263, small OHMS (4 holes in vertical bars of H). No. 244, 248, 249, 251 perfin 112, large OHMS. *Intaglio.*

O244

		UseF
3¢	deep rose red	37.50

1935. SMALL OHMS PERFIN ISSUE

O248

		MLHF	UseF
10¢	rose red	75.00	55.00

1935. LARGE OHMS PERFIN ISSUE No. 248, 251, perfin 263, small OHMS (4 holes in vertical bars of H). No. 244, 248, 249, 251 perfin 112, large OHMS. *Intaglio.*

O248A

		UseF
10¢	rose red	25.00

O249

		UseF
13¢	slate red violet	60.00

1935. SMALL OHMS PERFIN ISSUE

O251

		MLHF	UseF
50¢	slate violet	95.00	55.00

1935. LARGE OHMS PERFIN ISSUE No. 248, 251, perfin 263, small OHMS (4 holes in vertical bars of H). No. 244, 248, 249, 251 perfin 112, large OHMS. *Intaglio.*

O251A

		UseF
50¢	slate violet	75.00

1935. SMALL OHMS PERFIN AIRMAIL ISSUE Perfin 263, small OHMS. *Intaglio.*

O256

		MLHF	UseF
6¢	red brown	70.00	60.00

1937-38. SMALL OHMS PERFIN ISSUE No. 264-274 (4 holes in vertical bars of H).

From June 30 1939 all stamps used by Government depts had to be perf OHMS (On His Majesty's Service) with 4 holes in vertical bars of H (perfin 264). These stamps were available to collectors from the Philatelic Division, Ottawa. The sale of these perfins was discontinued in 1948. *Intaglio.*

O264 *Four holes in vertical bars of H*

O264

		MLHF	UseF
1¢	green		1.50

1937-38. LARGE OHMS PERFIN ISSUE Perfin 112. *Intaglio.*

O264A

		MLHF	UseF
1¢	green		3.40

1937-38. SMALL OHMS PERFIN ISSUE No. 264-274 (4 holes in vertical bars of H).

O265

		MLHF	UseF
2¢	brown	1.90	.20

1937-38. LARGE OHMS PERFIN ISSUE Perfin 112. *Intaglio.*

O265A

		MLHF	UseF
2¢	brown		6.50

1937-38. Small OHMS Perfin Issue No. 264-274 (4 holes in vertical bars of H).

O266		MLHF	UseF
3¢	deep red rose	1.90	.20

1937-38. Large OHMS Perfin Issue Perfin 112. *Intaglio.*

O266A		MLHF	UseF
3¢	deep red rose		2.25

1937-38. Small OHMS Perfin Issue No. 264-274 (4 holes in vertical bars of H).

O267		MLHF	UseF
4¢	orange yellow	4.50	2.75

1937-38. Large OHMS Perfin Issue Perfin 112. *Intaglio.*

O267A		MLHF	UseF
4¢	orange yellow	35.00	11.00

1937-38. Small OHMS Perfin Issue No. 264-274 (4 holes in vertical bars of H).

O268		MLHF	UseF
5¢	blue	3.75	.25

1937-38. Large OHMS Perfin Issue Perfin 112. *Intaglio.*

O268A		MLHF	UseF
5¢	red orange		18.00

1937-38. Small OHMS Perfin Issue No. 264-274 (4 holes in vertical bars of H).

O269		MLHF	UseF
8¢	red orange	15.00	6.00

1937-38. Large OHMS Perfin Issue Perfin 112. *Intaglio.*

O269A		MLHF	UseF
8¢	red orange		23.00

1937-38. Small OHMS Perfin Issue No. 264-274 (4 holes in vertical bars of H).

O270		MLHF	UseF
10¢	deep rose red, 4 holes		70.00
O270a		MLHF	UseF
10¢	red carmine, 4 holes	100.00	3.75

1937-38. Large OHMS Perfin Issue Perfin 112. *Intaglio.*

O270ab		MLHF	UseF
10¢	red carmine, 5 holes		40.00
O270b		MLHF	UseF
10¢	deep rose red, 5 holes		30.00

1937-38. Small OHMS Perfin Issue No. 264-274 (4 holes in vertical bars of H).

O271		MLHF	UseF
13¢	blue	100.00	65.00

1937-38. Large OHMS Perfin Issue Perfin 112. *Intaglio.*

O271A		MLHF	UseF
13¢	blue		60.00

1937-38. Small OHMS Perfin Issue No. 264-274 (4 holes in vertical bars of H).

O272		MLHF	UseF
20¢	light red brown	30.00	2.00

1937-38. Large OHMS Perfin Issue Perfin 112. *Intaglio.*

O272A		MLHF	UseF
20¢	light red brown		35.00

1937-38. Small OHMS Perfin Issue No. 264-274 (4 holes in vertical bars of H).

O273		MLHF	UseF
50¢	green	35.00	10.00
O274		MLHF	UseF
$1	slate red violet	140.00	50.00

1938. Small OHMS Perfin Issue No. 264, small OHMS. *Intaglio.*

O278		MLHF	UseF
6¢	blue, FDD *(1938)*	3.00	1.00

1938. Large OHMS Perfin Issue Perfin 112, large OHMS. *Intaglio.*

O278A		MLHF	UseF
6¢	blue, FDD *(1938)*		40.00

1938-39. Small OHMS Perfin Issue 264. small OHMS. *Intaglio.*

O279		MLHF	UseF
10¢	deep green, FDD *(April 1, 1939)*	15.00	6.00

1938-39. Large OHMS Perfin Issue 112, large OHMS. *Intaglio.*

O279A		MLHF	UseF
10¢	deep green, FDD *(April 1, 1939)*		55.00

1939. Large OHMS Perfin Issue Nos. 282-384 perfin 112, large OHMS or perfin 264, small OHMS (not available to public and rare). *Intaglio.*

O282		MLHF	UseF
1¢	green & black		55.00
O283		MLHF	UseF
2¢	brown & black		75.00
O284		MLHF	UseF
3¢	dark carmine red & black		55.00

1942-48. Small OHMS Perfin Issue Nos.285-298 perfin 264, small OHMS. *Intaglio.* For officials No. 285-298 overprinted, see No. 327-335.

O285		MLHF	UseF
1¢	green	.35	.20
O286		MLHF	UseF
2¢	brown	.55	.20
O287		MLHF	UseF
3¢	deep rose red	1.50	.40
O288		MLHF	UseF
3¢	red purple	.65	.20
O289		MLHF	UseF
4¢	slate black	3.00	1.00
O290		MLHF	UseF
4¢	deep rose red	.60	.20

O291		MLHF	UseF
5¢	blue	1.00	.20

O292		MLHF	UseF
8¢	red brown	7.00	3.00

O293		MLHF	UseF
10¢	brown	4.00	.20

O294		MLHF	UseF
13¢	deep blue green	5.00	4.00

O295		MLHF	UseF
14¢	deep blue green	7.00	1.00

O296		MLHF	UseF
20¢	sepia	9.50	1.00

O297		MLHF	UseF
50¢	violet	37.50	6.00

O298		MLHF	UseF
$1	blue	120.00	3.75

1942-43. SMALL OMHS PERFIN AIRMAIL ISSUE Nos. 308, 309 perfin 264, small OHMS. *Intaglio.*

O308		MLHF	UseF
6¢	blue	3.00	1.50

O309		MLHF	UseF
7¢	blue	3.00	.40

1942-43. SMALL OHMS PERFIN ISSUE No. 310-312 perfin 264, small OHMS. *Intaglio.*

O310		MLHF	UseF
10¢	green	15.00	9.00

O311		MLHF	UseF
16¢	ultramarine	22.50	20.00

O312		MLHF	UseF
17¢	ultramarine	15.00	15.00

1946. SMALL OHMS PERIN ISSUE Nos. 313-318 perfin 264, small OHMS. *Intaglio.*

O313		MLHF	UseF
8¢	brown	11.25	3.75

O314		MLHF	UseF
10¢	olive green	3.00	.20

O315		MLHF	UseF
14¢	black brown	3.75	.75

O316		MLHF	UseF
20¢	slate	4.50	.75

O317		MLHF	UseF
50¢	deep blue green	25.00	6.25

O318		MLHF	UseF
$1	red purple	70.00	22.50

1946. SMALL OHMS PERFIN AIRMAIL ISSUE No. 319 perfin 264, small OHMS. *Intaglio.*

O319		MLHF	UseF
7¢	blue	2.25	.60

1946-47. SMALL OHMS PERFIN ISSUE Nos. 320-322 perfin 264, small OHMS. *Intaglio, perforated 12.*

O320		MLHF	UseF
10¢	green	7.50	7.50

O321		MLHF	UseF
17¢	ultramarine	37.50	35.00

O322		MLHF	UseF
17¢	ultramarine	75.00	75.00

1949-51. SMALL OHMS PERFIN ISSUE No. 341, 343 perfin 264. *Intaglio.*

O341		MLHF	UseF
2¢	black brown	.75	.75

O343		MLHF	UseF
3¢	red purple	.75	.75

British Columbia / Vancouver Island

Regular Issues

1860. PERFORATE ISSUE *Typography, perforated 14.*

1, N1 *Queen Victoria*

		UnFVF	UseFVF
1			
2 1/2p	**red rose**	475.00	375.00
N1		UnFVF	UseFVF
2 1/2p	**pale dull red,** imperforate	3,900.00	

Note: *No. 1 was sold for 3p and used as a 3p provisional from June 20, 1864 to Nov. 1, 1865. Though inscribed* VANCOUVER, *it was mainly used in British Columbia.*

1865. SEAL ISSUE *Typography, perforated 14.*

2 *British Columbia seal*

		UnFVF	UseFVF
2			
3p	**blue**	120.00	100.00
	a. light blue, 1867	120.00	100.00
	FDC *(Nov. 1, 1865)*		

1865. IMPERFORATE ISSUE *Typography, watermark K1, imperforate.*

3, 4 Queen Victoria

		UnFVF	UseFVF
3			
5¢	**rose**	40,000.00	19,500.00
4		UnFVF	UseFVF
10¢	**light blue**	3,000.00	2,400.00

1865. PERFORATE ISSUE *Perforated 14.*

		UnFVF	UseFVF
5			
5¢	**rose**	300.00	285.00
6		UnFVF	UseFVF
10¢	**light blue**	300.00	285.00

1868-71. FIRST OVERPRINT ISSUE Overprinted in black, blue, green, red, and violet, with new values in CENTS. *Watermark K1, perforated 12 1/2.*

7 *"5.CENTS.5" overprint*

5:CENTS 5

	UnFVF	UseFVF
7	1,200.00	1,200.00
5¢ on 3p venetian red (black)		

8, 9 Overprint

	UnFVF	UseFVF
8	1,100.00	1,100.00
10¢ on 3p lake blue (blue)	UnFVF	UseFVF
9	700.00	700.00
25¢ on 3p orange yellow, (violet)		

10, 11 Overprint

	UnFVF	UseFVF
10	900.00	900.00
50¢ on 3p mauve (red)	UnFVF	UseFVF
11	1,750.00	1,750.00
$1 on 3p apple green, (green)		

1868-71. SECOND OVERPRINT ISSUE *Perforated 14.*

12 *"TWO CENTS" overprint*

TWO CENTS

	UnFVF	UseFVF
12	120.00	120.00
2¢ on 3p yellow brown (black)		
13	UnFVF	UseFVF
5¢ on 3p venetian red (black)	220.00	220.00
FDD *(May 1869)*		
N14	UnFVF	UseFVF
10¢ on 3p lake (blue)	1,600.00	
15	UnFVF	UseFVF
25¢ on 3p orange yellow (violet)	225.00	225.00
FDD *(July 1869)*		
16	UnFVF	UseFVF
50¢ on 3p mauve (red)	700.00	700.00
FDD *(Feb. 1871)*		
N17	UnFVF	UseFVF
$1 on 3p apple green (green)	1,400.00	

Since 1871: Stamps of Canada.

New Brunswick

Regular Issues

1851. CROWN AND FLOWERS ISSUE Royal Crown and heraldic flowers. *Intaglio, imperforated, blue paper.*

1, 2, 3, *Crown and heraldic flowers*

		UnFVF	UseFVF
1			
3p	**red,** FDD *(Sept. 1851)*	3,400.00	730.00
	a. bright red	2,900.00	650.00
	bisect		4,000.00

		UnFVF	UseFVF
2			
6p	**yellow,** FDD *(Sept. 1851)*	5,400.00	4,000.00
	bisect		3,000.00

		UnFVF	UseFVF
3			
1s	**purple,** FDD *(Sept. 1851)*	25,000.00	6,000.00
	a. red purple	20,000.00	7,500.00

Reprints of 1890, on stout white paper: #1 orange, #2 and #3 violet black: $25 ea.

1860. PICTORIALS ISSUE *Intaglio, perforated 12, white or yellow paper.*

4 *Locomotive*

		UnFVF	UseFVF
4			
1c	**dull claret,** FDD *(May 15, 1860)*	35.00	34.00
	a. brown purple	70.00	55.00
	v. Horizontal pair, imperforate between	550.00	

There is a Minkus stamp album to meet the need of every collector — beginner or advanced. Write for free list.

5 *Queen Victoria*

		UnFVF	UseFVF
5			
2c	**orange, '63,** FDD *(May 15, 1860)*	15.00	15.00
	v. Vertical pair, imperforate between	600.00	

6 *When Charles Connell, postmaster general, submitted (1860) a 5¢ stamp using his own picture, the resulting legislative furor led to his resignation and virtual retirement from all public life. The stamp was withdrawn but not before a limited number had been sold.*

		UnFVF	UseFVF
6			
5c	**brown,** FDD *(May 15, 1860)*	6,000.00	

7 *Queen Victoria*

8 *Queen Victoria*

		UnFVF	UseFVF
7			
5c	**green,** FDD *(May 15, 1860)*	15.00	15.00
	a. blue green	15.00	15.00
	b. bronze green	155.00	32.00
8		UnFVF	UseFVF
10c	**red,** FDD *(May 15, 1860)*	45.00	43.00
	bisect		900.00

9 *Combination sailing - steam ship*

		UnFVF	UseFVF
9			
12 1/2c	**indigo,** FDD *(May 15, 1860)*	75.00	75.00

10 *Prince of Wales (Edward VII)*

		UnFVF	UseFVF
10			
17c	**black,** FDD *(May 15, 1860)*	45.00	45.00

Since March 1868: Stamps of Canada.

Nova Scotia

Regular Issues

1851-57. ISSUE *Intaglio, imperforate, bluish paper.*

1 *Queen Victoria*

1		**UnFVF**	**UseFVF**
1p	**red brown**	6,000.00	1,000.00
	Bisect		
	FDC *(May 12, 1853)*		

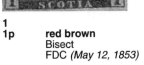

2 *Crown and heraldic flowers*

2		**UnFVF**	**UseFVF**
3p	**blue**	2,000.00	375.00
	a. deep blue	4,000.00	825.00
	b. light blue (1857)	2,000.00	375.00
	y. Bisect		1,900.00
	FDC *(Sept. 1, 1851)*		

3 *Crown and heraldic flowers*

3		**UnFVF**	**UseFVF**
6p	**yellow green**	10,000.00	
	y. Bisect (yellow green)		10,000.00
	y1. Bisect (dark blue green) (1857)		9,000.00
	a. deep blue green	20,000.00	2,000.00
	FDC *(Sept. 1, 1851)*		

4 *Crown and heraldic flowers*

4		**UnFVF**	**UseFVF**
1s	**red violet**	45,000.00	20,000.00
	a. violet (1857)	32,000.00	8,000.00
	y. Bisect		25,000.00
	FDC *(Sept. 1, 1851)*		

1851. ISSUE REPRINTS OF 1890 *Thin hard paper, colors slightly different, imperforated.*

4A		**UnFVF**	**UseFVF**
1p	**red brown**	40.00	

4B		**UnFVF**	**UseFVF**
3p	**blue**	50.00	

4C		**UnFVF**	**UseFVF**
6p	**yellow green**	50.00	

4D		**UnFVF**	**UseFVF**
1s	**red violet**	50.00	

1851. ISSUE REPRODUCTION OF 1950 Souvenir sheet of four different stamps for London International Stamp Exhibition.

4E		**UnFVF**	**UseFVF**
1s	**red violet**		

1860-66. ISSUE *Intaglio, perforated 12, white paper unless noted.*

5 *Queen Victoria*

5		**UnFVF**	**UseFVF**
1¢	**black**	7.50	22.50
	p. yellowish paper	7.50	22.50
	v. Horizontal pair, imperforate between	285.00	
	v1. Pair	2,300.00	

6		**UnFVF**	**UseFVF**
2¢	**dull purple**	22.00	25.00
	p. yellowish paper	9.00	25.00
	v. Pair	9,000.00	

7		**UnFVF**	**UseFVF**
5¢	**deep blue**	275.00	30.00
	p. yellowish paper	275.00	30.00

8 *Queen Victoria*

		UnFVF	UseFVF
8			
8-1/2¢	**green**	6.75	13.50
	p. yellowish paper	30.00	35.00
9		**UnFVF**	**UseFVF**
10¢	**orange red**	25.00	30.00
	p. yellowish paper	9.00	30.00
	v. Pair	2,500.00	
10		**UnFVF**	**UseFVF**
12-1/2¢	**black**	42.00	27.00
	p. yellowish paper	35.00	30.00

Since 1868: Stamps of Canada.

Prince Edward Island

Regular Issues

1861. ISSUE *Typographed, perforated 9, yellowish paper.*

1, 5 *Queen Victoria*

		UnFVF	UseFVF
1			
2p	**carmine rose**	275.00	175.00
	FDC *(Jan. 1, 1861)*		

2, 6 *Queen Victoria*

		UnFVF	UseFVF
2			
3p	**blue**	675.00	285.00
	v. Double impression	2,400.00	
	y. Bisect	2,500.00	
	FDC *(Jan. 1, 1861)*		

3, 8 *Queen Victoria*

		UnFVF	UseFVF
3			
6p	**yellow green**	900.00	400.00
	FDC *(Jan. 1, 1861)*		

1861-68. ISSUE *Typographed, yellowish, bluish white paper unless noted, perforated 11 1/2 to 12.*

4 *Queen Victoria*

		UnFVF	UseFVF
4			
1p	**yellow orange**	20.00	22.00
	v. Perforated 11	50.00	135.00
	v1. Compound perforated 11 & 11 1/2 - 12	125.00	50.00
	v2. Horizontal pair, imperforate between	425.00	
	v3. Pair, imperforate	250.00	
	y. Bisect		750.00

		UnFVF	UseFVF
5			
2p	**deep rose**	13.50	19.00
	v. Compound perforated 11 & 11 1/2 - 12	200.00	95.00
	v1. Pair, imperforate between	150.00	
	v2. Pair, imperforate	125.00	
	y. Bisect		
	p. white paper	15.00	22.50
	p1. *TWC* for *TWO*	60.00	

		UnFVF	UseFVF
6			
3p	**blue**	25.00	30.00
	v. Compound perforated 11 & 11 1/2 - 12	200.00	100.00
	v1. Pair, imperforate between	200.00	
	v2. Pair, imperforate	150.00	
	y. Bisect		
	p. white paper	10.00	22.00
	p1. white paper, imperforate pair	150.00	

7 *Queen Victoria*

		UnFVF	UseFVF
7			
4p	**black**	30.00	40.00
	v. Compound imerforated 11 & 11 1/2 - 12	200.00	200.00
	v1. Pair, imperforate between	160.00	
	y. Bisect		
	p. white paper	8.00	60.00
	p1. white paper, pair, imperforate between	160.00	
	p2. white paper, imperforate pair	100.00	
	FDC *(1868)*		

		UnFVF	UseFVF
8			
6p	**blue green**	40.00	40.00
	v. Compound perforated 11 & 11 1/2 - 12	200.00	180.00
	y. Bisect		

9 *Queen Victoria*

		UnFVF	UseFVF
9			
9p	**rose lilac**	35.00	40.00
	v. Perforated 11	40.00	50.00
	v1. Compound imperforated 11 & 11 1/2 - 12	200.00	190.00
	v2. Pair, imperforate between	300.00	
	v3. Pair	300.00	
	y. Bisect		

1870. ISSUE *Intaglio, perforated 12.*

10 *Queen Victoria*

10
4-1/2p   yellow brown

	UnFVF	UseFVF
	30.00	40.00

No. 10 "STG" indicated st(erlin)g, "CY", local c(urrenc)y at either of which stamps could be purchased.

1872. ISSUE *Typographed, Nos. 12, 14-16 perforated 12 to 12 1/4, Nos. 11, 13 perforated 11 1/2 to 12.*

11 *Queen Victoria*

11
1¢   yellow orange

	UnFVF	UseFVF
	3.75	16.50
v. Perforated 12 1/2 - 13	25.00	
v1. Compound perforated 11 1/2 - 13	60.00	72.00
v2. Pair, imperforate	100.00	
FDC *(Jan. 1, 1872)*		

12 *Queen Victoria*

12
2¢   gray blue

	UnFVF	UseFVF
	7.00	40.00
y. Bisect		
FDC *(Jan. 1, 1872)*		

13 *Queen Victoria*

13
3¢   dull carmine rose

	UnFVF	UseFVF
	10.00	15.00
v. Perforated 12 1/2 - 13	20.00	20.00

v1. Compound perforated 11 1/2 - 13	75.00	65.00
v2. Pair, imperforate between	225.00	
v3. Pair, imperforate	160.00	
y. Bisect		
FDC *(Jan. 1, 1872)*		

14 *Queen Victoria*

14
4¢   yellow green

	UnFVF	UseFVF
	3.50	25.00
v. Pair, imperforate	4.00	25.00
FDC *(Jan. 1, 1872)*		

15 *Queen Victoria*

15
6¢   black

	UnFVF	UseFVF
	4.00	25.00
v. Perforated 12 1/2 - 13		300.00
v1. Horizontal pair, imperforate between	175.00	
v2. Pair, imperforate	175.00	
y. Bisect		500.00
FDC *(Jan. 1, 1872)*		

16 *Queen Victoria*

16
12¢   rose violet

	UnFVF	UseFVF
	4.50	50.00
v. Pair, imperforate	175.00	
FDC *(Jan. 1, 1872)*		

Since July 1, 1873: Stamps of Canada.

Newfoundland

Regular Issue

1857. HERALDIC FLOWERS ISSUE *Intaglio, imperforate, thick wove paper.*

1 *Crown and heraldic flowers*

5 *Crown and heraldic flowers*

		UnFVF	UseFVF
5			
5p	violet brown	360.00	540.00

		UnFVF	UseFVF
1			
1p	brown purple	120.00	210.00

2 *Heraldic flowers*

6 *Heraldic flowers*

		UnFVF	UseFVF
6			
6p	scarlet vermilion	22,000.00	6,000.00
	Bisect		10,000.00

		UnFVF	UseFVF
2			
2p	scarlet vermilion	27,000.00	13,500.00

7 *Heraldic flowers*

3 *Rose, thistle and shamrock*

		UnFVF	UseFVF
7			
6 1/2p	scarlet vermilion	4,500.00	5,400.00

		UnFVF	UseFVF
3			
3p	green	675.00	825.00

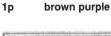

4 *Heraldic flowers*

8 *Heraldic flowers*

		UnFVF	UseFVF
8			
8p	scarlet vermilion	480.00	600.00
	Bisect		10,000.00

		UnFVF	UseFVF
4			
4p	scarlet vermilion	10,500.00	6,750.00
	Bisect		10,000.00

Users of this Catalog are invited to write to us if they have information which they feel will supplement or correct any material contained herein. All such communications will be answered.

9 Heraldic flowers

9		UnFVF	UseFVF
1s	**scarlet vermilion**	33,000.00	10,000.00
	Bisect		20,000.00

1860-63. DESIGNS OF HERALDIC FLOWERS ISSUE All values known with paper maker's watermark. STACEY WISE 1858 in double-line letters. Faked cancellations and bisects exist.

Designs of Nos. 1-9 on thin to medium wove paper. *Intaglio imperforate.*

10		UnFVF	UseFVF
1p	**purple brown**, FDD *(1863)*	180.00	325.00
	a. Red brown	7,500.00	

11		UnFVF	UseFVF
2p	**red orange**	475.00	600.00

12		UnFVF	UseFVF
2p	**rose**, FDD *(1863)*	225.00	750.00

13		UnFVF	UseFVF
3p	**green**, FDD *(1863)*	75.00	200.00

14		UnFVF	UseFVF
4p	**orange vermilion** FDD *(1863)*	4,200.00	2,000.00
	Bisect		

15		UnFVF	UseFVF
4p	**rose** FDD *(1863)*	32.50	165.00
	Bisect		

16		UnFVF	UseFVF
5p	**purple brown** FDD *(1863)*	60.00	500.00
	a. Chestnut	45.00	300.00

17		UnFVF	UseFVF
6p	**orange vermilion**	5,000.00	2,300.00

18		UnFVF	UseFVF
6p	**rose** FDD *(1863)*	25.00	200.00
	Bisect		

19		UnFVF	UseFVF
6 1/2p	**rose** FDD *(1863)*	90.00	800.00

20		UnFVF	UseFVF
8p	**rose** FDD *(1863)*	90.00	800.00
	Bisect		

21		UnFVF	UseFVF
1s	**orange vermilion**	60,000.00	22,500.00

22		UnFVF	UseFVF
1s	**rose** FDD *(1863)*	40.00	350.00
	Bisect		

1865-94. 1ST CENT ISSUE Queen Victoria and pictorials. *Intaglio, perforated 12.*

23 Die I: Prince of Wales (Edward VII) in Highland costume; 24, 37 *Die II*

23		UnFVF	UseFVF
1¢	**slate purple**, FDD *(1868)*	80.00	60.00

24		UnFVF	UseFVF
1¢	**pale purple brown 'II'** FDD *(May 1871)*	90.00	60.00

25, 38 Codfish

25		UnFVF	UseFVF
2¢	**blue green**	270.00	190.00
	Bisect		4,500.00
	p. Thin yellowish paper	270.00	50.00

26, 30, 31, 39 Queen Victoria

26		UnFVF	UseFVF
3¢	**vermilion** FDD *(July 1870)* Victoria	270.00	50.00

27		UnFVF	UseFVF
3¢	**blue** FDD *(April 1, 1873)* Victoria	425.00	27.50

28, 29, 40 Harp Seal

28		UnFVF	UseFVF
5¢	**brown**	1,100.00	350.00
	Bisect		3,500.00

29		UnFVF	UseFVF
5¢	**black** FDD *(1868)*	325.00	150.00

30		UnFVF	UseFVF
6¢	**dull brown lake** FDD *(July 1870)* Victoria	25.00	20.00

31		UnFVF	UseFVF
6¢	**carmine lake**, Victoria	24.00	24.00

Color change of 1894.

32 Prince Consort Albert (1819-61)

32		UnFVF	UseFVF
10¢	**black**	200.00	60.00
	p. Thin yellowish paper	425.00	115.00
	Bisect		3,500.00

33, 34 *Queen Victoria*

33		**UnFVF**	**UseFVF**
12¢	**light red brown**	54.00	48.00
	Bisect		3,200.00
	p. Thin yellowish paper	600.00	360.00

34		**UnFVF**	**UseFVF**
12¢	**dark yellow brown** FDD *(1894)*	36.00	42.00

Color change of 1893.

35 *Coastal schooner*

35		**UnFVF**	**UseFVF**
13¢	**orange yellow**	100.00	95.00

36 *Queen Victoria*

36		**UnFVF**	**UseFVF**
24¢	**deep blue on yellowish**	42.00	42.00

1876-79. ROULETTED ISSUE (Designs of 1868-73).

37		**UnFVF**	**UseFVF**
1¢	**pale purple brown II** FDD *(1877)*	85.00	48.00

38		**UnFVF**	**UseFVF**
2¢	**deep blue green** FDD *(1879)*	240.00	150.00

39		**UnFVF**	**UseFVF**
3¢	**blue** FDD *(1877)*	240.00	15.00

40		**UnFVF**	**UseFVF**
5¢	**blue** FDD *(1876)*	300.00	18.00

1880-96. QUEEN VICTORIA & PICTORIALS ISSUE new designs. Shades of each value exist. The 1896 varieties are reissues printed in brighter colors with clearer impressions and yellowish instead of white gum. No. 49 on pink paper is from a shipment recovered from the sea; salt water affected the paper. *Intaglio, perforated 12.*

41, 42 *Newfoundland dog*

41		**UnFVF**	**UseFVF**
1/2¢	**rose red** FDD *(1896)*	7.50	7.50
	a. FDD *(1896)*, orange red	60.00	75.00

42		**UnFVF**	**UseFVF**
1/2¢	**black** FDD *(1894)*	4.75	4.75
	FDD *(Nov. 1894)*, black		

43, 44 *Prince of Wales*

43		**UnFVF**	**UseFVF**
1¢	**dull brown** FDD *(1896)*	18.00	15.00
	a. deep brown	30.00	20.00

44		**UnFVF**	**UseFVF**
1¢	**deep green** FDD *(1896)*	3.75	3.75
	a. green, FDD *(1896)*	6.00	4.50

45 Codfish

45		**UnFVF**	**UseFVF**
2¢	**yellow green** FDD *(1896)*	48.00	15.00
	a. green, FDD *(1896)*	24.00	22.50

46		**UnFVF**	**UseFVF**
2¢	**orange** FDD *(1887)* Codfish	8.25	6.50
	v. Imperforate pair	400.00	

47, 48, 49 *Queen Victoria*

47		**UnFVF**	**UseFVF**
3¢	**pale dull blue** FDD *(1896)*	48.00	12.00
	a. deep blue, FDD *(1896)*	24.00	15.00

48		**UnFVF**	**UseFVF**
3¢	**deep brown** FDD *(1896)*	15.00	6.75
	a. chocolate brown, FDD *(1896)*	45.00	32.00

49		**UnFVF**	**UseFVF**
3¢	**slate** FDD *(1890)*	13.00	3.50
	v. Imperforate between	1,200.00	

50 Seal

50		**UnFVF**	**UseFVF**
5¢	**pale dull blue** FDD *(1887)*	275.00	15.00
	a. deep blue, FDD *(1887)*	72.00	7.50
	b. bright blue	15.00	8.25

51 *Grand Banks fishing boat*

51		**UnFVF**	**UseFVF**
10¢	black	42.00	36.00

1897. 400TH ANNIVERSARY ISSUE discovery of Newfoundland and 60th year reign of Victoria. *Intaglio, perforated 12.*

52 *Queen Victoria in 1897*

52		**UnFVF**	**UseFVF**
1¢	green	4.25	4.25

53 *John Cabot's son Sebastian (Holbein painting)*

53		**UnFVF**	**UseFVF**
2¢	bright rose	4.25	4.25

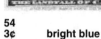

54 *Cape Bonavista, Cabot's landfall (June 24, 1497)*

54		**UnFVF**	**UseFVF**
3¢	bright blue	6.00	3.75

55 *Caribou hunting*

55		**UnFVF**	**UseFVF**
4¢	olive green	8.50	7.50

56 *Mining (copper discovery, 1864, followed by that of iron ore and lead)*

56		**UnFVF**	**UseFVF**
5¢	violet	8.50	7.50

57 *Logging (chiefly pine and spruce)*

57		**UnFVF**	**UseFVF**
6¢	red brown	8.50	7.50

58 *Fishing*

58		**UnFVF**	**UseFVF**
8¢	brown orange	22.50	15.00

59 Matthew *(same illustration appeared on 1893 3¢ Columbian issue of United States)*

59		**UnFVF**	**UseFVF**
10¢	sepia	24.00	15.00

60 *Ptarmigan (snow partridge)*

60		**UnFVF**	**UseFVF**
12¢	deep blue	36.00	15.00

61 *Seals*

61		UnFVF	UseFVF
15¢	orange red	36.00	16.50

62 *Fishing of Atlantic salmon in Newfoundland streams*

62		UnFVF	UseFVF
24¢	dull violet blue	27.00	24.00

63 *Seal of Colony, granted admiralty for use on the Union flag.* Motto: Haec Tibi Dona Fero *(these Gifts I Bring Thee)*

63		UnFVF	UseFVF
30¢	slate black	54.00	36.00

64 *Iceberg off St. John's*

64		UnFVF	UseFVF
35¢	red	84.00	78.00

65 King Henry VII *(Holbein painting). Henry gave Cabot a Charter and £10 for his discovery.*

65		UnFVF	UseFVF
60¢	black	28.00	30.00

Input from stamp collectors regarding the content of this catalog and ideas to make it more useful are eagerly sought. Send your comments to:
Minkus Catalog Editor
Krause Publications
700 E. State St.
Iola, WI 54990

1897. ONE CENT OVERPRINT ISSUE No. 49 overprinted, found on stamps of various shades. *Intaglio.*

66 *Overprint on Queen Victoria (No. 49)*

ONE CENT   ONE CENT   **ONE CENT**

Overprint 1, Overprint 2, Overprint 3

66		UnFVF	UseFVF
1¢ on 3¢	Slate purple, overprint 1 in black		
	v. Overprint 2 in black	115.00	115.00
	v1. Overprint 3 in black	600.00	575.00
	v2. Overprinted doubled one diagonal	2,400.00	

1897-1908. ROYAL PORTRAITS ISSUE *Intaglio, perforated 12.*

67 *Duke of Windsor (Edward VIII) as a child*

67		UnFVF	UseFVF
1/2¢	olive	5.25	5.25
	v. Pair, imperforate	425.00	

68, 69 *Queen Victoria*

68		UnFVF	UseFVF
1¢	carmine FDD *(Dec. 1897)*	5.25	5.25

69		UnFVF	UseFVF
1¢	yellow green, FDD *(June 1898)*	4.50	.35
	v. Vertical pair imperforate horizontally	300.00	
	v1. Pair, imperforate betweeen	350.00	

70, 71 *Prince of Wales (Edward VII)*

75 *Duke of York (George V)*

70		UnFVF	UseFVF
2¢	**brown orange,** FDD *(Dec. 1897)*	4.50	4.25
	v. Pair, imperforate		475.00

71		UnFVF	UseFVF
2¢	**red,** FDD *(June 1898)*	9.00	1.00
	v. Pair, imperforate	350.00	
	v1. Pair, imperforate between	550.00	

75		UnFVF	UseFVF
5¢	**blue,** FDD *(June 1899)*	22.50	5.25

1910. 300TH ANNIVERSARY COLONIZATION ISSUE *Offset, perforated 12.*

72 *Map of Newfoundland*

76 *King James I (1566-1625) granted the charter. King James version of Bible dedicated to him.*

72		UnFVF	UseFVF
2¢	**deep carmine red,** FDD *(Sept. 1908)*	25.00	1.75

73 *Princess of Wales (Queen Alexandra)*

76		UnFVF	UseFVF
1¢	**dull green,** FDD *(Aug. 15, 1910)*	4.50	2.75
	v. NFW for NEW (12 x 12)	75.00	65.00
	v1. Perforated 12 x 11	2.50	1.50
	v2. Perforated 12 x 14	3.00	2.50
	v9. NFW on V2	75.00	60.00
	v3. Horizontal pair, imperforate between, 12 x 14	300.00	
	v11. NFW on v3	550.00	
	v4. Horizontal pair, imperforate between (12 x 12)	340.00	
	v10. NFW on v4	600.00	600.00
	v5. Horizontal pair, imperforate between (12 x 11)	275.00	
	v8. NFW on v5	475.00	
	v6. Vertical pair, imperforate between (12 x 11)	275.00	
	v7. NFW for NEW (12 x 11)	70.00	55.00
	v12. Vertical pair, imperforate between	500.00	

Note: *"NFW" variety is due to a transfer flaw.*

73		UnFVF	UseFVF
3¢	**red orange,** FDD *(June 1898)*	8.25	1.00
	p. on bluish paper	16.50	5.25
	v. Pair, imperforate	350.00	
	v1. Vertical pair, imperforate between	500.00	

77 *Arms granted to the Colony by Charles I in 1637 and adopted by government of Newfoundland in 1928.*

74 *Duchess of York (Queen Mary)*

77		UnFVF	UseFVF
2¢	**rose red**	6.00	1.75
	v. Perforated 12 x 11 1/2	475.00	440.00
	v1. Perforated 12 x 14	4.75	1.75
	v2. Horizontal pair, imperforate between	425.00	
	FDD *(Aug. 15, 1910)*		

74		UnFVF	UseFVF
4¢	**dull violet,** FDD *(Oct. 1901)*	20.00	6.00
	v. Pair, imperforate	425.00	

Every entry in this catalog has been double-checked for accuracy, but mistakes may creep into any human endeavor, and we ask your assistance in eliminating them. Please call the attention of the editors to any errors in stamp descriptions found in this catalog.

78 *John Guy, mayor of Bristol, obtained grant that included land between St. Mary's and Baravista Bays, sailed in 3 ships with about 40 colonists and settled at Cupids. The colony ceased to exist by 1628.*

78		UnFVF	UseFVF
3¢	olive	16.00	18.00
	FDD *(Aug. 15, 1910)*		

79 *Guy's flagship* Endeavour

79		UnFVF	UseFVF
4¢	violet	22.50	24.00
	FDD *(Aug. 15, 1919)*		

80 *View of Cupids on Conception Bay, the site of Guy's colony*

80		UnFVF	UseFVF
5¢	bright blue	16.00	15.00
	v. Perforated 14 x 12	10.00	7.25
	FDD *(Aug. 15, 1910)*		

81, 87 *Francis Bacon, Lord Chancellor to James I, was instrumental in securing the charter for Guy's company, in which Bacon was a shareholder.*

81		UnFVF	UseFVF
6¢	lake	30.00	36.00
	v. COLONISATION	40.00	40.00
	v1. Pair, imperforate	400.00	
	FDD *(Aug. 15, 1910)*		

82, 88 *View of Mosquito, branch colony founded by Guy*

82		UnFVF	UseFVF
8¢	bistre brown	57.50	60.00
	FDD *(Aug. 15, 1910)*		

83, 89 *Logging camp on Red Indian Lake*

83		UnFVF	UseFVF
9¢	olive green	54.00	57.50
	FDD *(Aug. 15, 1910)*		

84, 90 *Paper mills at Grand Falls*

84		UnFVF	UseFVF
10¢	purple slate	72.00	72.00
	FDD *(Aug. 15, 1910)*		

85, 91 *Edward VII (1841-1910), eldest son of Queen Victoria, was king 1901-10.*

85		UnFVF	UseFVF
12¢	pale red brown	65.00	72.00
	FDD *(Aug. 15, 1910)*		
	v. Pair, imperforate	475.00	

86, 92 *George V (1865-1936), the second son of Edward VII, was king 1910-36. In 1916 he gave up all German titles and changed the name of the royal house from Saxe-Coburg-Gotha to Windsor.*

86		UnFVF	UseFVF
15¢	black	60.00	60.00
	FDD *(Aug. 15, 1910)*		

1911. ISSUE Nos. 81-86 new colors. *Intaglio, perforated 14.*

87		UnFVF	UseFVF
6¢	brown purple, FDD *(Jan. 31, 1911)*	25.00	25.00
	v. Pair, imperforate	400.00	
	v1. Horizontal pair, imperforate vertically	475.00	

88		UnFVF	UseFVF
8¢	brown bistre, FDD *(Feb. 7, 1911)*	70.00	70.00
	v. Pair, imperforate	475.00	
	v1. Horizontal pair, imperforate vertically	475.00	

89		UnFVF	UseFVF
9¢	olive green, FDD *(Feb. 7, 1911)*	60.00	60.00
	v. Pair, imperforate	475.00	
	v1. Horizontal pair, imperforate vertically	475.00	

90		UnFVF	UseFVF
10¢	violet black, FDD *(Feb. 7, 1911)*	115.00	115.00
	v. Pair, imperforate	450.00	
	v1. Horizontal pair, imperforate vertically	475.00	

91		UnFVF	UseFVF
12¢	**bistre brown,** FDD *(Feb. 7, 1911)*	75.00	75.00
	v. Pair, imperforate	400.00	
	v1. Horizontal pair, imperforate vertically	475.00	

92		UnFVF	UseFVF
15¢	**green slate,** FDD *(Feb. 7, 1911)*	75.00	75.00
	v. Pair, imperforate	350.00	
	v1. Horizontal pair, imperforate vertically	475.00	

1911. CORONATION OF KING GEORGE V ISSUE *Intaglio, perforated 13 1/2 x 14, Nos. 98, 99, 100, 102, 103 perforated 14.*

93 *Queen Mary (1867-1953), queen consort of George V and mother of Edward VIII and George VI.*

93		UnFVF	UseFVF
1¢	**green**	4.25	.45
	v. Pair, imperforate	250.00	

94 *George V*

94		UnFVF	UseFVF
2¢	**carmine red,** FDD *(1916)*	3.00	.35
	a. rose red	7.50	1.00
	v. Pair, imperforate	250.00	

95 *Prince of Wales (1894-1972) became King Edward VIII in January 1936 and became the only British King to abdicate the throne on Dec. 10, 1936. He married twice-divorced American Wallis Simpson in June 1937.*

95		UnFVF	UseFVF
3¢	**red brown**	30.00	30.00

96 *Prince Albert (1895-1952) became King George VI (1936-52) when his brother, Edward VIII, abdicated.*

96		UnFVF	UseFVF
4¢	**purple**	27.00	27.00

97 *Princess Mary*

97		UnFVF	UseFVF
5¢	**ultramarine**	12.00	12.00
	v. Pair, imperforate	250.00	

98 *Prince Henry (Duke of Gloucester)*

98		UnFVF	UseFVF
6¢	**gray black**	35.00	35.00

99 *Prince George (Duke of Kent)*

99		UnFVF	UseFVF
8¢	**deep turquoise green**	135.00	135.00
	a. Slate blue	100.00	100.00

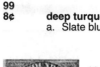

100 *Prince John*

100		UnFVF	UseFVF
9¢	**violet blue**	27.50	27.50

101 *Queen Mother Alexandra*

101		UnFVF	UseFVF
10¢	**deep green**	40.00	40.00

102 *Duke of Connaught*

102		UnFVF	UseFVF
12¢	**plum**	35.00	35.00

103 *Seal of the Colony*

103		UnFVF	UseFVF
15¢	**deep red purple**	33.00	33.00
	v. Pair, imperforate	100.00	

1919. NEWFOUNDLAND REGIMENT & NAVAL FORCES ISSUE
Traced actions by Newfoundland armed forces in World War I. Head
of Caribou and names of actions: 1¢ Suvla Bay, Gallipoli, September
1915; (Following actions on Western Front): 3¢ Gueudecourt, Oct. 12,
1916; 4¢ Beaumont Hamel, July 1, 1916; 6¢ Monchy, April 1, 1917;
10¢ Steenbeck, Aug. 16, 1917; 15¢ Langmarck, Winter 1916; 24¢
Cambrai, Nov. 20-Dec. 5, 1917; 36¢ Combles, Feb. 1917. *Ubique*
("Everywhere"): 2¢, 5¢, 8¢, and 12¢. *Intaglio.* Perforated 14, shades
issued Jan. 12, 1919.

 104 *Suvla Bay*

115 *Combles*

104		UnFVF	UseFVF
1¢	green	2.40	.60
	v. Pair, imperforate	250.00	

105		UnFVF	UseFVF
2¢	rose red	3.00	1.25
	v. Pair, imperforate	250.00	

106		UnFVF	UseFVF
3¢	brown	3.00	1.00
	v. Pair, imperforate	250.00	

107		UnFVF	UseFVF
4¢	purple	3.60	2.50
	v. Pair, imperforate	250.00	

108		UnFVF	UseFVF
5¢	bright blue	4.75	2.40
	v. Pair, imperforate	250.00	

109		UnFVF	UseFVF
6¢	slate gray	30.00	30.00
	v. Pair, imperforate	250.00	

110		UnFVF	UseFVF
8¢	bright magenta	20.00	20.00
	v. Pair, imperforate	250.00	

111		UnFVF	UseFVF
10¢	gray green	15.00	7.75
	v. Pair, imperforate	250.00	

112		UnFVF	UseFVF
12¢	orange	65.00	57.50
	v. Pair, imperforate	250.00	

113		UnFVF	UseFVF
15¢	indigo	30.00	30.00
	v. Pair, imperforate	250.00	

114		UnFVF	UseFVF
24¢	bistre brown	42.00	42.00
	v. Pair, imperforate	250.00	

115		UnFVF	UseFVF
36¢	sage green	30.00	30.00
	v. Pair, imperforate	250.00	

Air Mail Issues

1919. HAWKER ISSUE for Harry G. Hawker's unsuccessful attempt
to cross the Atlantic. *No. 106 overprinted intaglio.*

 116 *Overprint*

FIRST
TRANS-
ATLANTIC
AIR POST,
April, 1919.

116   3c brown

116		UnFVF	UseFVF
3¢	brown FDD *(April 12, 1919)*	27,000.00	24,000.00

Early Transatlantic Air Mail.

*Because of its location, Newfoundland became (1919) the takeoff point
for many transatlantic flight attempts. A $10,000 prize offered by the*
London Daily Mail *for the first succesful crossing was won June 14 by
Alcock & Brown, (see No. 117). Between 1919, when Newfoundland
was the first British possession to issue an airmail stamp, until 1931,
when the first regular airmails were issued, various provisionals franked
the mail carried on these flights. The stamp sales often helped to pay
the costs of the ventures.*

*Many flights, for which no special stamps were issued, can be identified
only by postmarks and sometimes cachets. These include flights by
Australia's Major Cotton; Floyd Bennett's search for Nungesser & Coli,
who were lost between France and New York; the unsuccessful Bremen flight of Von Hunefeld, Koehl & Fitzmaurice; Duke Schiller's rescue
of the* Bremen's *crew; and successful crossings by Amelia Earhart,
Wilmer Stutz, Lou Gordon and Sir Charles Kingsford-Smith. Letters carried on these flights are among the rarest of airmail items.*

1919. MORGAN-RAYNHAM ISSUE for use on correspondence carried on the abortive Morgan-Raynham Trans-Atlantic flight. *No. 106
overprinted in manuscript Aerial/Atlantic/Mail/JAR. Intaglio.*

116A.		UnFVF	UseFVF
3¢	deep brown FDD *(April 19, 1919)*	60,000.00	

1919. ALCOCK & BROWN ISSUE for the first successful flight by Alcock & Brown from St. John's to Clifden, Ireland (June 14-15, 1919)
and on other flights. *No. 61 overprinted, intaglio.*

117		UnFVF	UseFVF
$1 on 15¢	bright scarlet FDD *(June 7, 1919)*	250.00	250.00
	v. no comma after POST	425.00	450.00
	v1. as v. no period after 1919	900.00	900.00

1920. AIRMAIL ISSUE *No. 63 with overprint 118, No. 61, 64 with
overprint 119 (bars 13 1/2mm apart) in gray black or intense black. Intaglio*

 118 *Overprint*

TWO
CENTS

118		UnFVF	UseFVF
2¢ on 30¢	slate black FDD *(Sept. 11, 1920)*	9.75	9.00
	v. Overprint inverted	825.00	

 119 *Overprint*

THREE
CENTS

119		UnFVF	UseFVF
3¢ on 15¢	orange red FDD *(Sept. 11, 1929)*	12.00	12.00
	v. Bars 10 1/2mm apart	150.00	150.00
	v1. No. 119 inverted overprint	1,200.00	

120

		UnFVF	UseFVF
3¢ on 35¢ **red** FDD *(Sept. 11, 1920)*		12.00	12.00
v. Inverted overprint			
v1. No lower bar		225.00	240.00
v2. THREE omitted		2,100.00	

1921. HALIFAX AIRMAIL ISSUE for flights between St. John's and Halifax Nova Scotia. *No. 64 overprinted. Intaglio.*

121
Overprint

**AIR MAIL
to Halifax, N.S.
1921.**

121

		UnFVF	UseFVF
35¢	**red** FDD *(Nov. 16, 1921)*	210.00	180.00
	v. period after 1921	225.00	200.00
	v1. Inverted overprint, as v. but w/period	5,000.00	
	v2. Inverted overprint, w/period after 1921		

Regular Issue

1923-24. PICTORIAL ISSUES *Intaglio, perforated 14.*

122 *Twin Hills, Tor's Cove*

122

		UnFVF	UseFVF
1¢	**green**	3.00	.60
	v. Pair, imperforate	350.00	
	n. Booklet Pane of 8	500.00	

123 *South West Arm, Trinity*

123

		UnFVF	UseFVF
2¢	**carmine red**	3.00	.60
	v. Pair, imperforate	350.00	
	n. Booklet Pane of 8	275.00	

124 *War memorial, St. John's*

124

		UnFVF	UseFVF
3¢	**deep brown**	3.00	3.00

125 *Humber River*

125

		UnFVF	UseFVF
4¢	**dark purple**	3.60	3.60
	v. Pair, imperforate	350.00	

126 *Coast of Trinity*

126

		UnFVF	UseFVF
5¢	**ultramarine**	7.25	7.25
	v. Pair, imperforate	350.00	

127 *Upper Steadies, Humber River*

127

		UnFVF	UseFVF
6¢	**gray black**	7.25	7.25
	v. Pair, imperforate	350.00	

128 *Quidi Vidi, near St. John's*

128

		UnFVF	UseFVF
8¢	**dull purple**	7.25	7.25
	v. Pair, imperforate	350.00	

129 *Caribou crossing lake*

129		UnFVF	UseFVF
9¢	**dark gray green**	36.00	36.00
	v. Pair, imperforate	350.00	

130 *Humber River Canyon*

130		UnFVF	UseFVF
10¢	**red violet**	9.00	9.00
	v. Pair, imperforate	350.00	

131 *Shell Bird Island*

131		UnFVF	UseFVF
11¢	**olive green**	10.00	10.00
	v. Pair, imperforate	350.00	

132 *Mt. Moriah, Bay of Islands*

132		UnFVF	UseFVF
12¢	**lake**	15.00	15.00
	v. Pair, imperforate	350.00	

133 *Humber River near Little Rapids*

133		UnFVF	UseFVF
15¢	**deep blue**	18.00	18.00
	v. Pair, imperforate	350.00	

134 *Placentia, near Mt. Pleasant*

134		UnFVF	UseFVF
20¢	**red brown,** FDD *(April 29, 1924)*	18.00	18.00

135 *Topsail Falls near St. John's*

135		UnFVF	UseFVF
24¢	**sepia,** FDD *(April 22, 1924)*	75.00	75.00

Air Mail Issue

1927. AIRMAIL ISSUE for De Pinedo's return flight to Rome. 300 copies of No. 65 overprinted in red (66 unused copies known). *Intaglio.*

136 *"De Pinedo" overprint*

Air Mail
DE PINEDO
1927

136		UnFVF	UseFVF
60¢	**black** FDD *(May 18, 1927)*	40,000.00	17,500.00

Regular Issue

1929. REGULAR ISSUE No. 127 overprinted in red. *Intaglio.*

THREE
CENTS

137 *Upper Steadies, Humber River overprinted in red*

137		UnFVF	UseFVF
3¢ on 6¢ gray black		4.75	4.75
	v. Inverted overprint	750.00	
	v1. Black overprint	1,350.00	

No. 137 with black overprint, 3mm or 5mm spacing; essay.

1928-31. NEWFOUNDLAND-LABRADOR SERIES ISSUE issued when Privy council decided in favor of Newfoundland's claims to territory in Quebec. *Intaglio by Whitehead Morris Ltd.; perforated 13 to 14; no watermark, No. 152; Size 19 1/2 x 24 1/2mm.*

138 *New map of Newfoundland; original engraving top; re-engraved bottom*

		UnFVF	**UseFVF**
138			
1¢	**deep blue green**	1.75	1.00

139 *Steamer* Caribou *operating between Port-aux-Basques and New Sydney, Nova Scotia. Original engraving left; re-engraved right.*

		UnFVF	**UseFVF**
139			
2¢	**deep rose red**	2.75	1.25
	v. Pair, imperforate	250.00	

140 *King George V & Queen Mary. Original engraving left; re-engraved shaded pearls right.*

		UnFVF	**UseFVF**
140			
3¢	**brown**	3.75	.90

141 *Prince of Wales (Edward VIII), original engraving top; re-engraved, "4" shaded horizontally bottom.*

		UnFVF	**UseFVF**
141			
4¢	**red purple**	6.00	6.00

142 *Express steam train running between St. John's and Port-aux-Basques (547 miles). Original engraving; re-engraved with spur.*

		UnFVF	**UseFVF**
142			
5¢	**deep gray green**	9.00	9.00

143 *Newfoundland hotel, St. John's. Original engraving; re-engraved (also no period after St. Johns).*

		UnFVF	**UseFVF**
143			
6¢	**ultramarine**	8.25	8.25

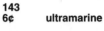

144 *Heart's content, relay station for cables from England to Canada and U.S.*

		UnFVF	**UseFVF**
144			
8¢	**light red brown**	12.00	12.00

145 *Cabot Tower, St. Johns, built 1897 on Signal Hill, site of Amherst's victory, followed by French surrender of North American possessions except St. Pierre and Miquelon. 1st transatlantic telephone (1858) and radio (Marconi, 1901) messages were received here. Original engraving left; re-engraved right (also no period after St. Johns).*

		UnFVF	**UseFVF**
145			
9¢	**dull green**	15.00	15.00

146 *War memorial, St. John's on Kings Beach, where Sir Humphrey Gilbert took possession of the island in the name of Queen Elizabeth (1583).*

		UnFVF	**UseFVF**
146			
10¢	**brown violet**	12.00	12.00

147, 151 *General Post Office, St. John's*

		UnFVF	**UseFVF**
147			
12¢	**brown red**	9.00	9.00

148 Cabot Tower, St. Johns

		UnFVF	UseFVF
148			
14¢	**brown purple,** FDD *(Aug. 28),*	10.50	10.50

149 *Alcock & Brown's bomber, Vickers-Vimy, converted World War I plane, leaving Lester's Field, St. John's, for first non-stop transatlantic flight (1919). Original engraving top; re-engraved bottom.*

		UnFVF	UseFVF
149			
15¢	**deep blue**	11.25	11.25

 150 *Colonial building. Original engraving, top; re-engraved botom.*

		UnFVF	UseFVF
150			
20¢	**greenish black**	8.25	9.00

		UnFVF	UseFVF
151			
28¢	**gray green,** FDD *(Aug. 28)*	27.00	25.00

152 *Grand Falls on Hamilton River, Labrador (300-foot drop)*

		UnFVF	UseFVF
152			
30¢	**olive brown**	11.25	11.25

1929-31. 2ND NEWFOUNDLAND-LABRADOR ISSUE *re-engraved by Perkins, Bacon. Intaglio, perforated 13 1/2 x 14; no watermark.*

		UnFVF	UseFVF
153			
1¢	**green,** FDD *(Sept. 26, 1929)*	3.00	1.00
	v. Double impression	900.00	
	v1. Pair, imperforate	250.00	
	v2. Vertical pair, imperforate between	250.00	
154		**UnFVF**	**UseFVF**
2¢	**scarlet,** FDD *(Aug. 10, 1929)*	3.00	.60
	v. Pair, imperforate	150.00	
155		**UnFVF**	**UseFVF**
3¢	**red brown,** FDD *(Aug. 10, 1929)*	3.60	.60
	v. Pair, imperforate	275.00	
156		**UnFVF**	**UseFVF**
4¢	**claret,** FDD *(Aug. 26, 1929)*	4.75	1.75
	v. Pair, imperforate	250.00	
157		**UnFVF**	**UseFVF**
5¢	**gray green,** FDD *(Sept. 14, 1929)*	6.00	6.00
158		**UnFVF**	**UseFVF**
6¢	**ultramarine,** FDD *(Nov. 8, 1929)*	18.00	18.00
159		**UnFVF**	**UseFVF**
10¢	**dull violet,** FDD *(Oct. 5, 1929)*	9.00	4.25
160		**UnFVF**	**UseFVF**
15¢	**gray blue,** FDD *(Jan. 1930)*	50.00	50.00
161		**UnFVF**	**UseFVF**
20¢	**greenish black,** FDD *(Jan. 1, 1931)*	65.00	35.00

1931. 3RD NEWFOUNDLAND-LABRADOR ISSUE *Re-engraved by Perkins, Bacon. Intaglio, perforated 13 1/2 x 14, watermark No. 162. No. 168, 2 horizontal lines above EIGHT CENTS: No. 172 size 19 x 25mm.*

 162 *Newfoundland map*

162 *Watermark*

162		UnFVF	UseFVF
1¢	**green,** FDD *(July 1931)*	4.75	1.65
	v. Horizontal pair, Imperforate between	650.00	

163		UnFVF	UseFVF
2¢	**scarlet,** FDD *(July 1931)*	5.75	2.00

164		UnFVF	UseFVF
3¢	**red brown,** FDD *(July 1931)*	5.75	1.50

165		UnFVF	UseFVF
4¢	**claret,** FDD *(March 25)*	9.00	3.00

166		UnFVF	UseFVF
5¢	**gray green,** FDD *(April 1)*	13.50	12.75

167		UnFVF	UseFVF
6¢	**ultramarine,** FDD *(April 1)*	27.00	25.00

168		UnFVF	UseFVF
8¢	**red brown,** FDD *(July 1931)*	27.00	25.00

169		UnFVF	UseFVF
10¢	**dull violet,** FDD *(July 1931)*	12.00	11.00

170		UnFVF	UseFVF
15¢	**gray blue,** FDD *(July 1931)*	42.00	40.00

171		UnFVF	UseFVF
20¢	**greenish black,** FDD *(July 1931)*	54.00	18.00

172		UnFVF	UseFVF
30¢	**sepia,** FDD *(July 1931)*	36.00	33.00

Air Mail Issues

1930. AIRMAIL ISSUE for flight on Oct. 10-11 by Capt. Errol Boyd on the Bellanca monoplane, Miss Columbia, to the Scilly Islands, near Land's End, England. *No. 115 overprinted.*

Dangerous forgeries of overprint known. Copies should be accompanied by Certificate of a recognized Expert Committee.

173 *Overprint*

Trans-Atlantic
AIR MAIL
By B. M.
"Columbia"
September
1930
Fifty Cents

173		UnFVF	UseFVF
50¢ on 36¢ sage green		9,000.00	9,000.00

1931. AIRMAIL ISSUE regular airmail service started in Spring 1931. *No watermark, perforated 14.*

174 *Dogsled and airplane*

174		UnFVF	UseFVF
15¢	**bistre brown**	12.00	12.75
	v. Horizontal pair, imperforate between	1,000.00	
	v1. Vertical pair, imperforate between	1,000.00	
	v2. Pair, imperforate	550.00	

175 *Early transoceanic mail packet ship and Vickers-Vimy biplane carrying transatlantic mail*

175		UnFVF	UseFVF
50¢	**green**	24.00	25.00
	v. Horizontal pair, imperforate between	1,500.00	1,000.00
	v1. Vertical pair, imperforate between	1,500.00	1,000.00
	v2. Pair, imperforate	900.00	

176 *Historic transatlantic flights*

176		UnFVF	UseFVF
$1	**blue**	65.00	65.00
	v. Vertical pair, imperforate between	1,000.00	
	v1. Horizontal pair, imperforate between	1,000.00	
	v2. Pair, imperforate	900.00	

1931. 2ND AIRMAIL ISSUE *Watermark 162, arms (sideways).*

177		UnFVF	UseFVF
15¢	**bistre brown**	10.50	11.25
	v. Pair, imperforate	725.00	
	v1. Horizontal pair, imperforate between	1,000.00	
	v2. Vertical pair, imperforate between	1,200.00	

178		UnFVF	UseFVF
50¢	**green**	35.00	39.00
	v. Pair, imperforate	900.00	
	v1. Horizontal pair, imperforate between	1,000.00	
	v2. Vertical pair, imperforate between	1,000.00	

179		UnFVF	UseFVF
$1	**blue**	95.00	105.00
	v. Pair, imperforate	700.00	
	v1. Horizontal pair, imperforate between	1,100.00	
	v2. Vertical pair imperforate between	1,100.00	

No. 177-179 no watermark exist; collected only paired with watermarked stamp.

Regular Issue

1932. PICTORIALS ISSUE No. 187, antlers of equal height; No. 188 antler under T higher. *Watermark 162 arms, intaglio, perforated 13 1/2.*

180, 181 *Codfish*

180		UnFVF	UseFVF
1¢	**green,** FDD *(Jan. 1)*	2.75	.90
	n. Booklet Pane of 4 perforated 13	150.00	

181		UnFVF	UseFVF
1¢	**gray black**	.90	.60
	v. Perforated 14	30.00	22.50
	v1. Pair, imperforate	175.00	
	n. Booklet Pane of 4, perforated 13 1/2	110.00	
	n1. Booklet Pane of 4, perforated 14	150.00	

182, 183 *George V*

182
2¢   **rose,** FDD *(Jan 1)*
    n. Booklet Pane of 4, perforated 13

	UnFVF	UseFVF
rose	2.40	.90
Booklet Pane of 4, perforated 13	100.00	

183
2¢   **dull green**
    v. Imperforate pair
    v1. Horizontal pair, imperforate between
    n. Booklet Pane of 4, perforated 13 1/2
    n1. Booklet Pane of 4, perforated 14

	UnFVF	UseFVF
dull green	1.50	.60
Imperforate pair	32.50	10.00
Horizontal pair, imperforate between	200.00	
Booklet Pane of 4, perforated 13 1/2	25.00	
Booklet Pane of 4, perforated 14	175.00	

184 *Queen Mary*

184
3¢   **yellow brown,** FDD *(Jan. 1)*
    v. Imperforate pair
    v1. Vertical pair, Imperforate between
    n. Booklet Pane of 4, perforated 13
    n1. Booklet Pane of 4, perforated 13 1/2
    n2. Booklet Pane of 4, perforated 14

	UnFVF	UseFVF
yellow brown	1.50	.90
Imperforate pair	135.00	90.00
Vertical pair, Imperforate between	250.00	
Booklet Pane of 4, perforated 13	150.00	
Booklet Pane of 4, perforated 13 1/2	100.00	
Booklet Pane of 4, perforated 14	400.00	

185, 186 *Edward VII, Prince of Wales*

185
4¢   **deep lilac,** FDD *(Jan. 1)*

	UnFVF	UseFVF
deep lilac	7.75	2.40

186
4¢   **rose carmine**
    v. Perforated 14
    v1. Pair, imperforate
    v2. Vertical pair, imperforate between

	UnFVF	UseFVF
rose carmine	1.50	.60
Perforated 14	13.50	4.50
Pair, imperforate	200.00	
Vertical pair, imperforate between	325.00	

187, 188 *Caribou*

187
5¢   **violet brown,** FDD *(Jan. 1)*
    v. Pair, imperforate

	UnFVF	UseFVF
violet brown	19.00	1.25
Pair, imperforate	200.00	

188   UnFVF   UseFVF

5¢   **brown violet, 20mm wide**
    v. Die II: 20 1/2mm wide
    v1. Perforated 14
    v2. Horizontal pair, imperforate between
    v3. Pair, imperforate

	UnFVF	UseFVF
brown violet, 20mm wide	1.75	.60
Die II: 20 1/2mm wide	19.00	1.25
Perforated 14	100.00	
Horizontal pair, imperforate between		
Pair, imperforate	325.00	

189 *Princess Elizabeth (born April 21, 1926), the first child of George VI and Elizabeth, then the Duke and Duchess of York.*

189
6¢   **slate blue,** FDD *(Jan. 1)*

	UnFVF	UseFVF
slate blue	25.00	25.00

190 *Duchess of York (Queen Mother Elizabeth). When she celebrated her 100th birthday Aug. 4, 2000, she was hailed as England's favorite grandmother.*

190
7¢   **red brown**

	UnFVF	UseFVF
red brown	2.40	3.00

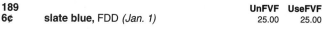

191 *Corner Brook paper mills*

191
8¢   **brown red**

	UnFVF	UseFVF
brown red	2.40	1.75

192 *Salmon leaping*

192
10¢   **olive black,** FDD *(Jan 1)*
    v. Pair, imperforate

	UnFVF	UseFVF
olive black	2.40	1.25
Pair, imperforate	200.00	

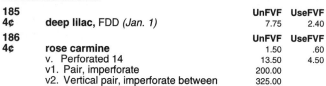

193 *Newfoundland dog*

193
14¢   **black,** FDD *(Jan 1)*
    v. Pair, imperforate

	UnFVF	UseFVF
black	4.25	3.50
Pair, imperforate	325.00	

194 *Northern Seal Baby Whitecoat*

194		**UnFVF**	**UseFVF**
15¢	**plum,** FDD *(Jan. 1)*	4.25	3.50
	v. Perforated 14	30.00	60.00

195 *Transatlantic beacon at Cape Race*

195		**UnFVF**	**UseFVF**
20¢	**dull green,** FDD *(Jan. 1)*	4.75	2.40
	v. Perforated 14	120.00	
	v1. Pair, imperforate	88.00	

196v *Loading iron ore at Bell Island*

196		**UnFVF**	**UseFVF**
24¢	**light blue**	6.00	6.00
	v. Pair, imperforated	225.00	

197 *Sealing fleet*

197		**UnFVF**	**UseFVF**
25¢	**slate black,** FDD *(Jan. 1)*	6.00	4.25
	v. Perforated 14	55.00	
	v1. Pair, imperforate	400.00	
	v2. Horizontal pair, imperforate between		
	v3. Vertical pair, Imperforate between	700.00	

198, 199 *Fishing fleet*

198		**UnFVF**	**UseFVF**
30¢	**ultramarine,** FDD *(Jan. 1)*	42.00	54.00
	v. Pair, imperforate	750.00	

199		**UnFVF**	**UseFVF**
48¢	**red brown,** FDD *(Jan. 1, 1938)*	9.50	6.00
	v. Pair, imperforate	200.00	

Air Mail Issues

1932. AIRMAIL ISSUE for the flight of the air liner Dornier DO-X to Southhampton England, May 21-23. No. 179 overprinted in red. *Intaglio.*

```
TRANS-ATLANTIC
WEST TO EAST
Per Dornier DO-X
May, 1932.
One Dollar and Fifty Cents
```
200 *Overprint*

200		**UnFVF**	**UseFVF**
$1.50 on $1 blue		675.00	675.00
	v. Inverted overprint	12,000.00	

1933. AIRMAIL OVERPRINT ISSUE vertical L & S Post. & bars, for regular (land & sea) postal use. *Intaglio.*

201 *L.& S. Post*

201		**UnFVF**	**UseFVF**
15¢	**bistre brown**	11.00	13.50
	v. Overprint reading up	1,800.00	

1933. REGULAR ISSUE Labrador. *Intaglio, perforated 11 1/2, 14 (No. 202, 204, 206), watermark 162, arms.*

202 *Plane flushing covey of ptarmigan*

202		**UnFVF**	**UseFVF**
5¢	**red brown**	20.00	20.00
	v. Pair, imperforate	450.00	

203 *Seaplane & trout fishers*

203		**UnFVF**	**UseFVF**
10¢	**orange yellow**	25.00	25.00
	v. Pair, imperforate	375.00	

Users of this Catalog are invited to write us if they have information which they feel will supplement or correct any material contained herein. All such communications will be answered.

204 *Plane reporting a herd of seals*

204
30¢ **blue**   UnFVF   UseFVF
                             50.00   50.00
   v. Pair, imperforate   900.00

205 *Mail delivery to fishing boats*

205
60¢ **deep yellow green**   UnFVF   UseFVF
                             90.00   90.00
   v. Pair, imperforate   900.00

206 *Plane over gold miners in Labrador*

206
75¢ **yellow brown**   UnFVF   UseFVF
                             90.00   90.00
   v. Pair, imperforate   675.00

1933. REGULAR ISSUE Balbo's mass formation flight from Chicago to Rome. No. 206 overprinted. *Intaglio.*

1933
GEN. BALBO
FLIGHT.
$4.50

207 *Gen. Balbo Flight overprint*

207
$4.50 on 75¢ yellow brown   UnFVF   UseFVF
                             900.00   900.00
   v. inverted surcharge (8 known)   17,500.00

Regular Issue

1933. 350TH ANNIVERSARY FORMAL ANNEXATION ISSUE by Sir Humphrey Gilbert. *Intaglio, perforated 13 1/2, 14, watermark 167, arms.*

208 *Sir Humphrey Gilbert from travel book Huroolgia (1620)*

208
1¢ **slate black**   UnFVF   UseFVF
                             2.25   1.35
   v. Pair, imperforate   50.00

209 *Compton castle, Devon, England, home of Gilbert family*

209
2¢ **green**   UnFVF   UseFVF
                             2.25   1.35
   v. Pair, imperforate   70.00

210 *Gilbert arms & crest with squirrel after which one ship was named (see No. 218). Motto: Quid non (Why not)*

210
3¢ **chestnut**   UnFVF   UseFVF
                             2.85   1.85
   v. Pair, imperforate   40.00

211 *Eton college. Gilbert was educated at Eton & Oxford*

211
4¢ **carmine red**   UnFVF   UseFVF
                             2.85   1.25
   v. Pair, imperforate   50.00

212 *Token sent by Queen Elizabeth on the eve of departure*

212
5¢ **dark rose lilac**   UnFVF   UseFVF
                             3.75   2.25
   v. Pair, imperforate   35.00

213 *Sir Humphrey receiving Royal Colonization Patents (June 11, 1578)*

213
7¢ **turquoise blue**   UnFVF   UseFVF
                             16.50   16.50

214 *Flagship Raleigh & Delight, Golden Hind, Swallow, Squirrel leaving Plymouth (1583); Raleigh soon turned back*

214
8¢ **orange red**   UnFVF   UseFVF
                             15.00   15.00

215 *The 4 vessels passing through The Narrows at St. John's (Aug. 3, 1583)*

215		UnFVF	UseFVF
9¢	**ultramarine**	13.50	13.50
	v. Pair, imperforate	160.00	

216 *Annexation of Newfoundland (Aug. 5, 1583); original settlers presenting cut sod as token of annexation*

216		UnFVF	UseFVF
10¢	**red brown**	12.00	8.25
	v. Pair, imperforate	300.00	

217 *Arms of England with "I have engraven there the Arms of England", a quotation from Sir Humphrey's report on annexation (No. 216)*

217		UnFVF	UseFVF
14¢	**black**	25.00	25.00

218 *The 10 ton* Squirrel *in storm off the Azores with Sir Humphrey crying out to the* Hind, *"We are as near to heaven by sea as by land." He perished with his ship a few hours later (Sept. 9, 1583)*

218		UnFVF	UseFVF
15¢	**purple brown**	35.00	35.00

219 *Map of Newfoundland from* Golden Fleece *(1624)*

219		UnFVF	UseFVF
20¢	**dull green**	20.00	18.00

220 *Queen Elizabeth*

220		UnFVF	UseFVF
24¢	**violet brown**	40.00	40.00
	v. Pair, imperforate	120.00	

221 *Sir Humphrey's statue at Truro Cathedral, Devonshire*

221		UnFVF	UseFVF
32¢	**olive black**	42.00	42.00

Commemoratives

1935. SILVER JUBILEE ISSUE George V, *KT3. Perforated 11 x 12, watermark K4, multicolored pair script CA.*

222-25 *George V and Windsor castle*

222		UnFVF	UseFVF
4¢	**rose carmine**	1.75	1.75

223		UnFVF	UseFVF
5¢	**red lilac**	2.00	2.00

224		UnFVF	UseFVF
7¢	**deep blue**	3.75	3.75

225		UnFVF	UseFVF
24¢	**yellow olive**	10.00	10.00

1937. CORONATION ISSUE *KT4, perforated 11 x 11 1/2, watermark K4, multicolored pair script CA.*

226-228 *Queen Elizabeth and King George VI*

226		UnFVF	UseFVF
2¢	**deep blue green**	1.25	1.25

227		UnFVF	UseFVF
4¢	**carmine rose**	1.25	1.25

		UnFVF	UseFVF
228			
5¢	**red lilac**	1.90	1.90

1937. CORONATION ISSUE additional values in new design and larger size.

229 *Codfish*

229
1¢ **gray black** UnFVF UseFVF
   .75   .35
v. Perforated 13 24.00 27.00
v1. no watermark 27.00

230 *Newfoundland map*

230
3¢ **orange brown** UnFVF UseFVF
 1.75 .75
v. Perforated 13 2.00 .90
v1. Vertical pair, imperforate **between, die II** 950.00
v2. no watermark 70.00
v3. Die II, course impression 1.75 1.00

231 *Caribou*

231
7¢ **blue** UnFVF UseFVF
 24.00 2.25
v. Perforated 13 120.00

232 *Corner Brook, Paper Mill*

232
8¢ **red** UnFVF UseFVF
 2.40 2.25
v. Pair, imperforate 350.00
v1. no watermark 45.00

233 *Salmon*

233
10¢ **olive black** UnFVF UseFVF
 5.25 4.50
v. Double impression
v1. no watermark 80.00

234 *Newfoundland dog*

234
14¢ **black** UnFVF UseFVF
 4.50 4.25
v. no watermark 50.00

235 *Northern seal*

235
15¢ **rose lake** UnFVF UseFVF
 6.75 6.00
v. no watermark 50.00

236 *Transatlantic Beacon*

236
20¢ **dull green** UnFVF UseFVF
 4.50 4.25
v. no watermark 135.00

237 *Loading iron ore at Bell Island*

237
24¢ **turquoise** UnFVF UseFVF
 5.75 5.25
v. no watermark 135.00

238 *Sealing fleet*

238
25¢ **slate black** UnFVF UseFVF
 5.75 5.25
v. no watermark 70.00

239 *Fishing fleet leaving for the banks*

239
48¢ **dark purple** UnFVF UseFVF
 7.25 6.75
v. no watermark 135.00

1938. 1ST ANNIVERSARY CORONATION ISSUE George VI. *Intaglio, perforated 13 1/2, watermarked, 162, arms.*

240 *George VI*

240		UnFVF	UseFVF
2¢	dull green	4.25	.30
	v. no watermark	250.00	

241 *Queen Elizabeth*

241		UnFVF	UseFVF
3¢	carmine red	4.25	.35
	v. no watermark	350.00	

242 *Princess Elizabeth*

242		UnFVF	UseFVF
4¢	light blue	4.50	.35
	v. no watermark	165.00	

243 *Queen Mary*

243		UnFVF	UseFVF
7¢	gray blue	3.25	2.75

For same designs, perforated 12 1/2, see No. 225-259.

1939. ROYAL VISIT ISSUE *Intaglio, perforated 13 1/2.*

244 *Queen Elizabeth and King George VI*

244		UnFVF	UseFVF
5¢	dark blue	2.00	2.00

1939. OVERPRINT ISSUE No. 244 overprinted in brown, red.

245 *Overprint*

245		UnFVF	UseFVF
2¢ on 5¢ No. 244 overprint in blue		2.85	2.85

246 *Overprint*

246		UnFVF	UseFVF
4¢ on 5¢ No. 244 overprint in red		2.00	2.00

Postage Due

1939-49. POSTAGE DUE ISSUE *Offset, perforated 10 1/4 (1939), 11 (1946-49), 11 x 9.*

247 *"Postage Due"*

247		UnFVF	UseFVF
1¢	pale green, perforated 10	3.00	3.00
	v. Perforated 11	5.25	5.25
248		UnFVF	UseFVF
2¢	red, perforated 10	8.25	8.25
	v. Perforated 11 x 9	8.25	8.25
249		UnFVF	UseFVF
3¢	blue, perforated 10	12.75	12.75
	v. Perforated 11 x 9	12.75	12.75
	v1. Perforated 9		
250		UnFVF	UseFVF
4¢	yellow orange, perforated 10	7.50	7.50
	v. Perforated 11 x 9	12.75	12.75
251		UnFVF	UseFVF
5¢	brown, perforated 10	2.50	2.50
	v. Perforated 10 1/4	5.25	5.25
252		UnFVF	UseFVF
10¢	slate purple, perforated 10	2.50	2.50
	v. watermark 162	5.00	8.00

Commemoratives

1941. 50TH ANNIVERSARY GRENFELL MISSION ISSUE in Newfoundland and Labrador. *Intaglio, perforated 12.*

253 *Sir Wilfred Grenfell on the bridge of Strathcona II, watching his hospital ship Maravel*

253		UnFVF	UseFVF
5¢	blue	.90	.75

Regular Issue

1941-44. PICTORIAL ISSUES *No. 181, 199, 240-243, intaglio, perforated 12 1/2, watermark 162, arms.*

		MNHVF	UseVF
254			
1¢	black, codfish	.45	.25
255		MNHVF	UseVF
2¢	dull green, George VI	.60	.20
256		MNHVF	UseVF
3¢	carmine red, Queen Elizabeth	.75	.20
	v. no watermark	70.00	

257		MNHVF	UseVF
4¢	**light blue,** Princess Elizabeth	1.35	.20

258		MNHVF	UseVF
5¢	**red violet** (Die I), Caribou	1.35	.20

259		MNHVF	UseVF
7¢	**gray blue,** Queen Mary	2.00	2.00
	v. watermark	180.00	

260		MNHVF	UseVF
8¢	**red,** Corner Brook Paper Mill	2.00	1.50

261		MNHVF	UseVF
10¢	**brown black,** Salmon	2.00	1.25

262		MNHVF	UseVF
14¢	**black,** Newfoundland dog	3.00	2.85

263		MNHVF	UseVF
15¢	**plum,** Northern seal	3.75	3.00

264		MNHVF	UseVF
20¢	**dull green,** Transatlantic Beacon	3.25	2.50

265		MNHVF	UseVF
24¢	**deep blue,** Loading iron ore, Bell Island	5.25	4.25

266		MNHVF	UseVF
25¢	**gray black,** Sealing fleet	5.25	4.25

267		MNHVF	UseVF
48¢	**red brown,** Leaving for the banks	7.50	4.50

Commemorative

1943. MEMORIAL UNIVERSITY COLLEGE ISSUE St. John's. *Intaglio, perforated 12.*

268 *Memorial University College*

268		MNHVF	UseVF
30¢	**carmine red**	4.25	2.85

Air Mail Issues

1943. REGULAR ISSUE *Intaglio, perforated 12.*

269 *Lockheed 14 airline over St. John's*

269		MNHVF	UseVF
7¢	**bright blue**	1.00	.75

1946. REGULAR ISSUE No. 268 overprinted. *Intaglio.*

 270 *Overprint*

270		MNHVF	UseVF
2¢ on 30¢ carmine red		.90	.90

Commemoratives

1947. ELIZABETH'S BIRTHDAY ISSUE on her 21st birthday, April 27, 1947. *Intaglio, perforated 12 1/2, watermark 162.*

721 *Princess Elizabeth, heir presumptive to the throne of England*

271		MNHVF	UseVF
4¢	**light Prussian blue**	.90	.35

1947. 450TH ANNIVERSARY DISCOVERY OF NEWFOUNDLAND ISSUE *Intaglio, perforated 12 1/2, watermark 162, arms (sideways).*

722 *Cabot on the* Matthew *off Cape Bonavista, 1497*

272		MNHVF	UseVF
5¢	**red lilac**	1.25	1.25
	v. Horizontal pair, imperforate between	1,500.00	

Since April 1, 1949: Stamps of Canada.

UNITED NATIONS

The United Nations evolved out of the failed efforts of its predecessor, the ill-fated League of Nations, to keep the peace. The term "United Nations" was first used by President Franklin Roosevelt in his  "Declaration by United Nations" on Jan. 1, 1942, when 26 nations signed a pledge to not stop fighting until the Axis powers of Nazi Germany, Imperial Japan and Fascist Italy had been defeated.

The process of formally creating the United Nations as an organization began in 1944 at a conference of Allied statesmen at Dumbarton Oaks outside Washington, D.C. Because membership in the organization required a declaration of war against the Axis, the result was that by the time the first meeting of the organization was formally convened in San Francisco, 50 nations signed the charter on June 26, 1945 in a special ceremony that took place at the Veterans War Memorial Building in San Francisco. The organization formally came into being on Oct. 24, 1945, when a majority of the signatories, including all five great powers, deposited their ratifications.

The original structure of the organizations consisted of a Security Council, a General Assembly, a Trusteeship Council, and an Economic and Social Council. The executive branch was the Secretariat, presided over by a Secretary General, who was in effect the CEO of the organization.

The most powerful part of the U.N. was and still is the Security Council. It consists of five permanent members, the above mentioned "great powers" of the USA, the USSR (now Russia), Great Britain, France and China. There are also 10 other temporary members who serve two-year terms and are chosen by the General Assembly. According to the Charter, the U.N. can undertake military and other peace-keeping and political actions only with the unanimous concurrence of all five permanent members of the Security Council. Other than this, the U.N. can act in an advisory capacity only, and its recommendations do not carry the force of law unless the Security Council approves.

Following its establishment, the organization immediately became a Cold War battleground. Actions advocated by the U.S. were largely stymied by the veto (Security Council "no" vote) of the Soviet Union. Despite this, the U.N. did manage to undertake peacekeeping operations, most notable of which was the Korean War, which, although it was fought mostly with U.S. troops, was officially a U.N. operation to deter aggression by North Korea against South Korea. U.N. forces also were involved in the Middle East in the Suez crisis of 1956 and Lebanon in 1958, in the Congo during its post-independence upheavals in 1960 and in Cyprus in 1964. Most recently the U.N. attempted to insert itself into the ethnic conflicts of a disintegrating Yugoslavia with varying success.

The United Nations also has many smaller specialized agencies, some of which predate the organization. Some of the more familiar ones are the Universal Postal Union (1874), the International Telecommunications Union (1865), the International Labor Organization (1920), the Food and Agricultural Organization (FAO), and the World Health Organization (WHO).The World Court at the Hague in the Netherlands, created in 1899, was also formally attached to the UN. In addition there was a Trusteeship Council that oversaw former League of Nations mandated territories administered by the victorious Allied powers. When the last of the Trust Territories, the U.S. supervised nations of Marshall Islands, Micronesia and Palau, became independent in the 1980s, the Trusteeship Council went out of existence.

The major trend in a changing United Nations after 1960 was the explosion of new members, as large numbers of former colonies of European nations, especially in Africa, attained independence. U.N. membership increased from its original 51 members to almost 200 as of 1999. While none of these members acquired any meaningful extra power as result of their membership, their presence in the General Assembly in which all member nations are represented, allowed them an international forum to state their positions on a number of issues.

Stamps of the United Nations

The United Nations established its own postal system and began issuing stamps in 1951. Its postal system was run by the U.S. Post Office and its stamps were good only on mail originating at U.N. headquarters in New York. The USPS was, and still is, compensated by the U.N. for all mail carried by it orginating at U.N. headquarters.

Starting on Oct. 4, 1969, the U.N. began issuing stamps denominated in Swiss currency for use on mail originating at its European headquarters, the old League of Nations building in Geneva. By agreement with Swiss postal authorities, all mail originating there is carried by the Swiss postal system, for which the Swiss are also compensated.

Ten years later, stamps denominated in Austrian currency were issued by the U.N. for use by its two agencies located in Vienna, the International Atomic Energy Commission and the U.N. Industrial Development Organization. An agreement similar to that with Switzerland and the USA provided for handling of this mail by the Austrian Post Office.

In addition, Switzerland issues special stamps for use by the various other U.N. specialized agencies located within its borders. Also, the Netherlands provided special postal emissions for use on mail originating at the International Court of Justice in the Hague. The governmetn of India oversaw a U.N. International Control Commission for Indochina from 1954 until the 1960s and issued special postal adhesives for use by Commission personnel in Laos, Cambodia and Vietnam.

Denis J. Norrington

Regular Issues

1951. REGULAR ISSUE *Perforated 13x12 1/2, (horizontal stamps), 12 1/2x13 (vertical stamps).*

1 Peoples of the World, *designed by O. C. Metronti, U.K.; engraved by J. C. Evans and A. B. Crossett; printed by Thomas de la Rue, U.K.*

		MNHVF	UseVF
1			
1¢	**rose magenta**	.25	.20
	FDC *(Oct. 24, 1951)*		1.00
	Inscription block of 4	1.00	

2 *View of U.N. buildings, designed by Leon Helguera, Mexico; engraved by K. Seisinger; printed by Joh. Enschedé and Sons, Netherlands.*

		MNHVF	UseVF
2			
1-1/2¢	**deep blue green**	.25	.20
	FDC *(Oct. 24, 1951)*		1.00
	Inscription block of 4	.75	
	v. Precanceled		35.00

3 *"Peace, Justice, Security," designed by J. F. Doeve, Netherlands; engraved by C. A. Mechelse; printed by Joh. Enschedé and Sons, Netherlands.*

		MNHVF	UseVF
3			
2¢	**purple**	.25	.20
	FDC *(Nov. 16, 1951)*		1.00
	Inscription block of 4	1.00	
	v. Precanceled		35.00

4 *U.N. Flag, designed by Ole Hamann, Denmark; engraved by B. S. Cresser; printed by Thomas de la Rue, U.K. Photogravure center.*

		MNHVF	UseVF
4			
3¢	**magenta & bright blue**	.25	.20
	FDC *(Oct. 24, 1951)*		1.00
	Inscription block of 4	1.00	

5 *Helping hand, U.N. International Children's Emergency Fund, designed by S. L. Hartz, Netherlands; engraved by S. L. Hartz; printed by Joh. Enschedé and Sons, Netherlands.*

		MNHVF	UseVF
5			
5¢	**deep cobalt**	.25	.20
	FDC *(Oct. 24, 1951)*		1.00
	Inscription block of 4	1.00	

6 Peoples of the World, *designed by O. C. Meronti, U.K.; engraved by J. C. Evans and A. B. Crossett; printed by Thomas de la Rue, U.K.*

		MNHVF	UseVF
6			
10¢	**dark chocolate**	.30	.25
	FDC *(Nov. 16, 1951)*		1.00
	Inscription block of 4	1.50	

7 *U.N. Flag, designed by Ole Hamann, Denmark; engraved by B. S. Cresser; printed by Thomas de la Rue, U.K. Photogravure center.*

		MNHVF	UseVF
7			
15¢	**deep violet & bright blue**	.40	.20
	FDC *(Nov. 16, 1951)*		1.00
	Inscription block of 4	1.50	

8 *World Unity, designed by Hubert Woyty-Wimmer, U.K.; engraved by Hubert Woyty-Wimmer and B. S. Cresser; printed by Thomas de la Rue, U.K.*

		MNHVF	UseVF
8			
20¢	**dark bistre brown**	1.00	.60
	FDC *(Nov. 16, 1951)*		1.00
	Inscription block of 4	4.00	

9 *U.N. Flag, designed by Ole Hamann, Denmark; engraved by B. S. Cresser; printed by Thomas de la Rue, U.K. Photogravure center.*

		MNHVF	UseVF
9			
25¢	**deep slate & bright blue**	.75	.60
	FDC *(Oct. 24, 1951)*		1.00
	Inscription block of 4	3.00	

10 *U.N. headquarters, New York, designed by Leon Helguera, Mexico; engraved by K. Seisinger; printed by Joh. Enschedé and Sons, Netherlands.*

		MNHVF	UseVF
10			
50¢	**deep violet blue**	6.50	5.00
	FDC *(Nov. 16, 1951)*		1.00
	Inscription block of 4	27.50	

11 *"Peace, Justice, Security" and U.N. emblem, designed by J. F. Doeve, Netherlands; engraved by C. A. Mechelse; printed by Joh. Enschedé and Sons, Netherlands.*

11		MNHVF	UseVF
$1.00	scarlet	2.50	1.75
	FDC (Oct. 24, 1951)		1.00
	Inscription block of 4	10.00	

Airmail Issues

1951. AIRMAIL ISSUE *Intaglio by Thomas de la Rue, U.K. Perforated 14.*

12, 13 *Plane and gull, designed by Ole Hamann, Denmark; engraved by B. S. Cresser.*

12		MVF	UseVF
6¢	dark red (2,500,000 printed)	.25	.20
	FDC (Dec. 14, 1951)		3.00
	v. Pair, imperforate	1,750.00	

13		MVF	UseVF
10¢	bright blue green (2,750,000 printed)	.25	.20
	FDC (Dec. 14, 1951)		5.00

14, 15 *Swallows and U.N. emblem, designed by Olav Mathiesen, Denmark; engraved by A. B. Crossett.*

14		MVF	UseVF
15¢	blue ultramarine (3,250,000 printed)	.30	.25
	FDC (Dec. 14, 1951)		7.00
	a. Prussian blue (error)	90.00	
	v. Pair, imperforate	—	

15		MVF	UseVF
25¢	gray black (2,500,000 printed)	.90	.40
	FDC (Dec. 14, 1951)		10.00
v.	Pair, imperforate	—	

Commemorative Issues

1952. U.N. DAY ISSUE Seventh anniversary of the U.N. charter signing. Designed by Jean van Noten, Belgium. *Printed by American Bank Note Co., U.S. Perforated 12.*

16 *Verteran's War Memorial Building, San Francisco, Calif. Birthplace of Charter signed June 26, 1945.*

16		MNHVF	UseVF
5¢	light gray blue (1,274,670)	.25	.20
	FDC (Oct. 24, 1952)		1.00
	Inscription block of 4	1.25	

1952. HUMAN RIGHTS DAY ISSUE Designed by Hubert Woyty-Wimmer, U.K. Engraved by A. B. Crossett. *Printed by Thomas de la Rue, U.K. Perforated 14.*

17, 18 *Flame surrounded by "Human Rights" in 5 official languages*

17		MNHVF	UseVF
3¢	deep blue green (1,554,312)	.25	.20
	FDC (Dec. 10, 1952)		1.00
	Inscription block of 4	1.50	

18		MNHVF	UseVF
5¢	blue ultramarine (1,126,371)	.25	.25
	FDC (Dec. 10, 1952)		1.00
	Inscription block of 4	1.50	

1953. PROTECTION FOR REFUGEES ISSUE Designed by Olav Mathiesen, Denmark. Engraved by A. B. Crossett. *Printed by Thomas de la Rue, U.K. Perforated 12 1/2x13.*

19, 20 *Refugee family*

19		MNHVF	UseVF
3¢	deep red brown (1,299,793)	.30	.35
	FDC (April 24, 1953)		1.00
	Inscription block of 4	1.75	

20		MNHVF	UseVF
5¢	indigo (969,224)	.50	.30
	FDC (April 24, 1953)		1.00
	Inscription block of 4	2.00	

1953. UNIVERSAL POSTAL UNION ISSUE The UPU agency of the U.N. was established in 1875 to improve international postal services. Designed by Hubert Woyty-Wimmer, U.K. Engraved by A. B. Crossett. *Printed by Thomas de la Rue, U.K. Perforated 13.*

21, 22 *Envelopes over map*

21		MNHVF	UseVF
3¢	sepia *(1,259,689)*	.20	.20
	FDC *(June 12, 1953)*		1.00
	Inscription block of 4	2.00	

22		MNHVF	UseVF
5¢	deep blue *(907,312)*	.75	.60
	FDC *(June 12, 1953)*		1.00
	Inscription block of 4	3.50	

1953. TECHNICAL ASSISTANCE ISSUE Designed by Olav Mathiesen, Denmark. Engraved by B. S. Cresser. *Printed by Thomas de la Rue, U.K. Perforated 13x12 1/2.*

23, 24 *Enmeshed cog-wheels*

23		MNHVF	UseVF
3¢	greenish black *(1,184,346)*	.30	.35
	FDC *(Oct. 24, 1953)*		1.00
	Inscription block of 4	1.75	

24		MNHVF	UseVF
5¢	dark blue green *(968,182)*	.50	.45
	FDC *(Oct. 24, 1953)*		1.00
	Inscription block of 4	2.00	

1953. DECLARATION OF HUMAN RIGHTS ISSUE The second commemorative stamp in the Human Rights series. Designed by Leon Helguera, Mexico. Engraved by Hubert Woyty-Wimmer, U.K. and A. B. Crossett. *Printed by Thomas de la Rue, U.K. Perforated 13.*

25, 26 *Hands and flame*

25		MNHVF	UseVF
3¢	blue *(1,456,928)*	.25	.20
	FDC *(Dec. 10, 1953)*		1.00
	Inscription block of 4	2.00	

26		MNHVF	UseVF
5¢	bright rose red *(983,831)*	1.25	.60
	FDC *(Dec. 10, 1953)*		1.00
	Inscription block of 4	3.00	

1954. FAO ISSUE Food and Agriculture Organization founded in 1945. Designed by Dirk van Gelder, Netherlands. Engraved by A. B. Crossett. *Printed by Thomas de la Rue, U.K. Perforated 13.*

27, 28 *Wheat*

27		MNHVF	UseVF
3¢	deep green & lemon *(1,250,000)*	.40	.30
	FDC *(Feb. 11, 1954)*		1.00
	Inscription block of 4	3.00	

28		MNHVF	UseVF
8¢	dark violet blue & lemon *(949,718)*	1.25	.75
	FDC *(Feb. 11, 1954)*		1.00
	Inscription block of 4	7.00	

1954. ILO ISSUE International Labor Organization founded in 1919. (8¢) inscribed OIT. Designed by José Renau, Mexico. Engraved by A. B. Crossett. *Printed by Thomas de la Rue, U.K. Perforated 12 1/2x13.*

29, 30 *Emblem*

29		MNHVF	UseVF
3¢	deep brown *(1,086,651)*	.25	.20
	FDC *(May 10, 1954)*		1.00
	Inscription block of 4	3.50	

30		MNHVF	UseVF
8¢	red mauve *(903,561)*	1.50	.75
	FDC *(May 10, 1954)*		1.00
	Inscription block of 4	8.50	

1954. U.N. DAY ISSUE The Palais des Nations in Geneva, Switzerland. Designed by Earl W. Purdie, U.S. Engraved by A. Lane and A. B. Crossett. *Printed by Thomas de la Rue, U.K. Perforated 14.*

31, 32 *Buildings*

31		MNHVF	UseVF
3¢	dark violet *(1,000,000)*	2.25	1.25
	FDC *(Oct. 25, 1954)*		1.00
	Inscription block of 4	10.00	

32		MNHVF	UseVF
8¢	rose red *(1,000,000)*	.30	.25
	FDC *(Oct. 25, 1954)*		1.00
	Inscription block of 4	3.00	

1954. DECLARATION OF HUMAN RIGHTS ISSUE The third commemorative stamp in the Human Rights series. Designed by Leonard Mitchell, New Zealand. Engraved by A. B. Crossett. *Printed by Thomas de la Rue, U.K. Perforated 14.*

33, 34 *Mother and child*

33		MNHVF	UseVF
3¢	**orange red** *(1,000,000)*	8.00	2.75
	FDC *(Dec. 10, 1954)*		1.00
	Inscription block of 4	45.00	

34		MNHVF	UseVF
8¢	**bronze green** *(1,000,000)*	.25	.20
	FDC *(Dec. 10, 1954)*		1.00
	Inscription block of 4	2.00	

1955. ICAO ISSUE Tenth anniversary of the International Civil Aviation Organization. Designed by Angel Medina, Uruguay. Engraved by E. Dickinson. *Printed by Waterlow & Sons, U.K. Perforated 13 1/2x14.*

35, 36 *Wing of Flight*

35		MNHVF	UseVF
3¢	**blue** *(1,000,000)*	2.75	1.25
	FDC *(Feb. 9, 1955)*		1.00
	Inscription block of 4	15.00	

36		MNHVF	UseVF
8¢	**rose carmine** *(1,000,000)*	1.50	.75
	FDC *(Feb. 9, 1955)*		1.00
	Inscription block of 4	5.50	

1955. UNESCO ISSUE Founded in 1946. United Nations Educational Scientific & Cultural Organization. Designed by George Hamori, Australia. Engraved by J. Keen. *Printed by Waterlow & Sons, U.K. Perforated 13 1/2x14.*

37, 38 *Organization emblem*

37		MNHVF	UseVF
3¢	**bright purple** *(1,000,000)*	.35	.30
	FDC *(May 11, 1955)*		1.00
	Inscription block of 4	1.50	

38		MNHVF	UseVF
8¢	**peacock blue** *(1,000,000)*	.45	.40
	FDC *(May 11, 1955)*		1.00
	Inscription block of 4	2.00	

39, 40, 41 *Open book*

39		MNHVF	UseVF
3¢	**purple lake** *(1,000,000)*	1.25	.75
	FDC *(Oct. 24, 1955)*		1.00
	Inscription block of 4	6.50	

40		MNHVF	UseVF
4¢	**slate green** *(1,000,000)*	.75	.50
	FDC *(Oct. 24, 1955)*		1.00
	Inscription block of 4	3.00	

41		MNHVF	UseVF
8¢	**slate black** *(1,000,000)*	.25	.20
	FDC *(Oct. 24, 1955)*		1.00
	Inscription block of 4	3.00	

1955. U.N. DAY SOUVENIR SHEET Tenth anniversary of U.N. Charter. Designed by Claude Bottiau, France. Engraved by J. Keen. *Printed by Waterlow & Sons, U.K. Sheet (108x88mm) of 3, imperforate, watermark 42, wavy lines, marginal inscription.*

42 *U.N. Day Souvenir Sheet with Nos. 39, 40 and 41*

42		MNHVF	UseVF
15¢	**Sheet of 3** *(250,000)*	110.00	50.00
	v. Reprint-retouched	110.00	50.00
	a. Single (3¢)	10.00	11.50
	b. Single (4¢)	10.00	11.50
	c. Single (8¢)	10.00	11.50
	FDC *(Oct. 24, 1955)*		65.00

1955. U.N. DAY ISSUE Tenth anniversary U.N. Charter; 1st phrase of preamble in English (3¢), Spanish (4¢), French (8¢). Designed by Claude Bottiau, France. Engraved by J. Keen. *Printed by Waterlow & Sons, U.K. Perforated 13 1/2x14, imperforate (Souvenir Sheet).*

1955. DECLARATION OF HUMAN RIGHTS ISSUE Fourth commemorative stamp in the Human Rights series. Designed by Hubert Woyty-Wimmer, U.K. Engraved by E. Dickinson. *Printed by Waterlow & Sons, U.K. Perforated 14x13 1/2.*

43, 44 *Flaming torch*

43		MNHVF	UseVF
3¢	**ultramarine** *(1,250,000)*	.30	.30
	FDC *(Dec. 9, 1955)*		1.00
	Inscription block of 4	1.25	

44		MNHVF	UseVF
8¢	**dull green** *(1,000,000)*	.65	.50
	FDC *(Dec. 9, 1955)*		1.00
	Inscription block of 4	2.00	

1956. ITU Issue International Telecommunications Union founded in 1865. (8¢) inscribed UIT. Designed by Hubert Woyty-Wimmer, U.K. Engraved by A. B. Crossett. *Printed by Thomas de la Rue, U.K. Perforated 14.*

45, 46 *Symbol of Communications*

45		MNHVF	UseVF
3¢	**slate blue** *(1,000,000)*	.40	.30
	FDC *(Feb. 17, 1956)*		1.00
	Inscription block of 4	1.50	

46		MNHVF	UseVF
8¢	**carmine red** *(1,000,000)*	.60	.45
	FDC *(Feb. 17, 1956)*		1.00
	Inscription block of 4	2.50	

1956. World Health Day Issue WHO was established in 1948. (3¢) inscribed WHO World Health Organization. (8¢) inscribed OMS Organization Mondiale de la Sante. Designed by Olav Mathiesen, Denmark. Engraved by A. B. Crossett. *Printed by Thomas de la Rue, U.K. Perforated 14.*

47, 48 *Caduceus Symbol of Medicine*

47		MNHVF	UseVF
3¢	**turquoise blue** *(1,250,000)*	.30	.25
	FDC *(April 6, 1956)*		1.00
	Inscription block of 4	1.25	

48		MNHVF	UseVF
8¢	**deep yellow brown** *(1,000,000)*	.45	.25
	FDC *(April 6, 1956)*		1.00
	Inscription block of 4	2.00	

1956. U.N. Day Issue General Assembly Building. Designed by Kurt Plowitz, U.S. *Printed by Thomas de la Rue, U.K. Engraved by A. B. Crossett. Perforated 14.*

49, 50 *General Assembly session*

49		MNHVF	UseVF
3¢	**deep gray blue** *(2,000,000)*	.20	.20
	FDC *(Oct. 24, 1956)*		1.00
	Inscription block of 4	.60	

50		MNHVF	UseVF
8¢	**dull bronze green** *(1,500,000)*	.30	.25
	FDC *(Oct. 24, 1956)*		1.00
	Inscription block of 4	1.25	

1956. Declaration of Human Rights Issue Fifth commemorative stamp in the Human Rights series. Designed by Rashid-ud-Din, Pakistan. Engraved by A. B. Crossett. *Printed by Thomas de la Rue, U.K. Perforated 14.*

51, 52 *Flame and globe*

51		MNHVF	UseVF
3¢	**deep rose lake** *(5,000,000)*	.20	.20
	FDC *(Dec. 9, 1956)*		1.00
	Inscription block of 4	.60	

52		MNHVF	UseVF
8¢	**deep blue** *(4,000,000)*	.30	.20
	FDC *(Dec. 9, 1956)*		1.00
	Inscription block of 4	1.25	

1957. World Meteorological Organization Issue The WMO is a U.N. agency which was founded in 1950. Designed by Alan Pollock, Canada. Engraved by Hubert Woyty-Wimmer. *Printed by Thomas de la Rue, U.K. Perforated 14.*

53, 54 *Weather balloon*

53		MNHVF	UseVF
3¢	**deep violet blue** *(5,000,000)*	.20	.20
	FDC *(Jan. 28, 1957)*		1.00
	Inscription block of 4	.60	

54		MNHVF	UseVF
8¢	**deep carmine** *(3,448,985)*	.25	.20

FDC *(Jan. 28, 1957)*   1.00
Inscription block of 4   1.00

1957. U.N. EMERGENCY FORCE ISSUE The UNEF was established in 1956 and subsequently served in the United Arab Republic and Gaza. Designed by Ole Hamann, Denmark. Engraved by A. B. Crossett. *Printed by Thomas de la Rue, U.K. Perforated 14x12 1/2.*

55, 56 UNEF badge

55		MNHVF	UseVF
3¢	**light blue** *(4,000,000)*	.20	.20
	FDC *(April 8, 1957)*		1.00
	Inscription block of 4	.60	

56		MNHVF	UseVF
8¢	**brown rose** *(3,000,000)*	.25	.20
	FDC *(April 8, 1957)*		1.00
	Inscription block of 4	1.00	

1957. U.N. EMERGENCY FORCE ISSUE Designed by Ole Hamann, Denmark. Engraved by A. B. Crossett. Re-engraved (April-May release); lighter shading around outer circle of design giving a halo effect; more space between figures of value and bottom inscription. *Printed by Thomas de la Rue, U.K. Perforated 14x12 1/2.*

57, 58 UNEF badge

57		MNHVF	UseVF
3¢	**light blue** *(2,736,206)*	.40	.25
	FDC *(April 30, 1957)*		1.00
	Inscription block of 4	1.50	

58		MNHVF	UseVF
8¢	**brown rose** *(1,000,000)*	.50	.30
	FDC *(May 10, 1957)*		1.00
	Inscription block of 4	2.00	

1957. U.N. DAY ISSUE The first issue to commemorate the U.N. Security Council. Designed by Rashid-ud-Din, Pakistan. Engraved by A. B. Crossett. *Printed by Thomas de la Rue, U.K. Perforated 12 1/2x13; 8¢: center inscribed in French.* The Security Council has responsibility of maintaining peace and security in world. It is composed of 11 members, 5 of which (China, France, United Kingdom, U.S. and U.S.S.R.) are permanent and the other 6 elected for 2 year periods by general assembly.

1957. AIRMAIL ISSUE Designed by Willi W. Wind, Israel. *Printed by Thomas de la Rue, U.K. Perforated 12 1/2x14.*

59 Globe and wing

59		MVF	UseVF
4¢	**brown carmine** *(5,000,000 printed)*	.20	.20
	FDC *(May 27, 1957)*		1.00
	Inscription block of 4	1.00	

60, 61 U.N. emblem shedding light on the globe

60		MNHVF	UseVF
3¢	**light orange brown** *(3,674,968)*	.25	.20
	FDC *(Oct. 24, 1957)*		1.00
	Inscription block of 4	.75	

61		MNHVF	UseVF
8¢	**dark blue green** *(2,885,938)*	.35	.20
	FDC *(Oct. 24, 1957)*		1.00
	Inscription block of 4	1.00	

1957. DECLARATION OF HUMAN RIGHTS ISSUE Sixth commemorative stamp in the Human Rights series. Designed by Olav Mathiesen, Denmark. Engraved by A. B. Crossett. *Printed by Thomas de la Rue & Co. Ltd., U.K. Perforated 14.*

62, 63 Flaming torch, symbolic of human rights and the endeavor to implement universal declaration of human rights

62		MNHVF	UseVF
3¢	**orange brown** *(3,368,405)*	.25	.20
	FDC *(Dec. 10, 1957)*		1.00
	Inscription block of 4	.75	

63		MNHVF	UseVF
8¢	**gray black** *(2,717,310)*	.35	.20
	FDC *(Dec. 10, 1957)*		1.00
	Inscription block of 4	1.00	

1958. INTERNATIONAL ATOMIC ENERGY AGENCY ISSUE The IAE agency was founded in 1957. Designed by Robert Perrot, France. Engraved by W. Hauck. *Printed by American Bank Note Co. Perforated 12. 8¢: inscribed in French.*

64, 65 U.N. emblem shedding light on atom, symbolizing peaceful uses of atomic energy

64		MNHVF	UseVF
3¢	**olive green** *(3,663,305)*	.20	.20
	FDC *(Feb. 10, 1958)*		1.00
	Inscription block of 4	.75	

65		MNHVF	UseVF
8¢	**Prussian blue** *(3,043,622)*	.25	.20
	FDC *(Feb. 10, 1958)*		1.00
	Inscription block of 4	1.00	

1958. CENTRAL HALL ISSUE Designed by Olav Mathiesen, Denmark. Engraved by W. Hauck. *Printed by American Bank Note Co. Perforated 12. 8¢: inscribed in French.*

66, 67 *Central Hall, Westminster, London, site of 1st part of 1st session of general assembly held in 1946*

66		MNHVF	UseVF
3¢	bright ultramarine *(3,353,716)*	.20	.20
	FDC *(April 14, 1958)*		1.00
	Inscription block of 4	.75	

67		MNHVF	UseVF
8¢	dull magenta *(2,836,747)*	.25	.20
	FDC *(April 14, 1958)*		1.00
	Inscription block of 4	1.00	

1958. U.N. SEAL ISSUE Designed by Herbert Sanborn, U.S. Engraved by C. Richardson and S. Ridler. *Intaglio by Bradbury, Wilkinson & Co., U.K. Perforated 13 1/2x14 (4¢), 13x14 (8¢).*

68, 69 *U.N. seal*

68		MNHVF	UseVF
4¢	red orange	.20	.20
	FDC *(Oct. 24, 1958)*		1.00
	Inscription block of 4	.80	

69		MNHVF	UseVF
8¢	blue	.25	.20
	FDC *(June 2, 1958)*		1.00
	Inscription block of 4	1.00	

1961. FLAGS ISSUE Designed by Herbert Sanborn, U.S. *Gravure by Helio Courvoisier, Switzerland. Perforated 11 1/2.*

99 *"To unite our strength," group of flags*

99		MNHVF	UseVF
30¢	multicolored	.60	.20
	FDC *(June 5, 1961)*		1.00
	Inscription block of 4	2.75	

1958. U.N. DAY ISSUE Economic and Social Council. Designed by Ole Hamann, Denmark. Engraved by E. MacAvoy and J. Bejcek. *Printed by American Bank Note Co. Perforated 12. 8¢ French inscribed in center, top and bottom inscribed reversed.*

70, 71 *Cogwheels*

70		MNHVF	UseVF
4¢	dark blue green *(2,556,784)*	.20	.20
	FDC *(Oct. 24, 1958)*		1.00
	Inscription block of 4	.25	

71		MNHVF	UseVF
8¢	red *(2,175,117)*	.25	.20
	FDC *(Oct. 24, 1958)*		1.00
	Inscription block of 4	1.00	

1958. DECLARATION OF HUMAN RIGHTS ISSUE Tenth anniversary. Seventh commemorative stamp in the Human Rights series. Designed by Leonard Mitchell, New Zealand. Engraved by W. Hauck. *Printed by American Bank Note Co. Perforated 12.*

72, 73 *Globe*

72		MNHVF	UseVF
4¢	green *(2,644,340)*	.20	.20
	FDC *(Dec. 10, 1958)*		1.00
	Inscription block of 4	.75	

73		MNHVF	UseVF
8¢	red brown *(2,216,838)*	.25	.20
	FDC *(Dec. 10, 1958)*		1.00
	Inscription block of 4	1.00	

1959. AIRMAIL ISSUE Designed by Olav Mathiesen, Denmark. Engraved by T. Pearson. *Printed by Waterlow & Sons, U.K. Perforated 12 1/2x13 1/2, 13 1/2x14 (7¢).*

74 *Globe and wing*

75 *Flag and plane*

74		MVF	UseVF
5¢	rose *(4,000,000 printed)*	.20	.20
	FDC *(Feb. 9, 1959)*		1.00
	Inscription block of 4	.75	

75		MVF	UseVF
7¢	bright blue *(4,000,000 printed)*	.30	.20
	FDC *(Feb. 9, 1959)*		1.00
	Inscription block of 4	1.25	

1959. GENERAL ASSEMBLY ISSUE Designed by Robert Perrot, France. Engraved by Yves P. J. Baril. *Printed by Canadian Bank Note Co. Perforated 12.*

76, 77 *Building in Flushing Meadows Park, N.Y., site of sessions of general assembly, 1946-50*

76		MNHVF	UseVF
4¢	rose magenta *(2,035,011)*	.20	.20
	FDC *(March 30, 1959)*		1.00
	Inscription block of 4	.75	

77		MNHVF	UseVF
8¢	turquoise green *(1,627,281)*	.25	.20
	FDC *(March 30, 1959)*		1.00
	Inscription block of 4	1.00	

1959. ECONOMIC COMMISSION FOR EUROPE ISSUE The ECE was established by the Economic and Social Council in 1947. Designed by Ole Hamann, Denmark. Engraved by D. J. Mitchell. *Printed by Canadian Bank Note Co. Perforated 12.*

78, 79 *Agriculture,* ear of wheat, *Industry,* factory chimneys, *Trade,* wheel

78		MNHVF	UseVF
4¢	blue *(1,743,502)*	.25	.20
	FDC *(May 18, 1959)*		1.00
	Inscription block of 4	1.00	

79		MNHVF	UseVF
8¢	orange red *(1,482,898)*	.35	.25
	FDC *(May 18, 1959)*		1.00
	Inscription block of 4	1.25	

1959. U.N. DAY ISSUE Trusteeship Council. Designed by Leon Helguera, Mexico. Engraved by Yves P. J. Baril. *Printed by Canadian Bank Note Co. Perforated 12.*

80, 81 The Age of Bronze, *by Auguste Rodin; depicted by Leon Helguera, Mexico*

80		MNHVF	UseVF
4¢	vermilion *(1,929,677)*	.25	.20
	FDC *(Oct. 23, 1959)*		1.00
	Inscription block of 4	1.00	

81		MNHVF	UseVF
8¢	bronze green *(1,587,647)*	.35	.25
	FDC *(Oct. 23, 1959)*		1.00
	Inscription block of 4	1.50	

1959. WORLD REFUGEE YEAR ISSUE The U.N. General Assembly on Dec. 5, 1958 adopted a resolution to promote a World Refugee

Year, dating from June 1959. The purpose was to urge people and encourage government and civic agencies to make contributions for the relief of refugees, proceeds to World Refugee fund. Designed by Olav Mathiesen, Denmark. Engraved by D. J. Mitchell. *Intaglio and offset by Canadian Bank Note Co. Perforated 12.*

82, 83 *Hands held protectively over a refugee*

82		MNHVF	UseVF
4¢	bistre & rose red *(2,168,963)*	.20	.20
	FDC *(Dec. 10, 1959)*		1.00
	Inscription block of 4	.75	

83		MNHVF	UseVF
8¢	bistre & light blue *(1,843,886)*	.30	.20
	FDC *(Dec. 10, 1959)*		1.00
	Inscription block of 4	1.00	

1960. CHAILLOT PALACE ISSUE Designed by Hubert Woyty-Wimmer, U.K. Engraved by A. Lane. *Printed by Thomas de la Rue, U.K. Perforated 14.*

84, 85 *Palais de Chaillot, Paris, site of General Assembly plenary meetings, first part of third session, 1948 and sixth session (1951)*

84		MNHVF	UseVF
4¢	red purple & blue *(2,276,678)*	.20	.20
	FDC *(Feb. 29, 1960)*		1.00
	Inscription block of 4	.75	

85		MNHVF	UseVF
8¢	gray green & red brown *(1,930,869)*	.25	.20
	FDC *(Feb. 29, 1960)*		1.00
	Inscription block of 4	1.25	

1960. ECAFE ISSUE U.N. Economic Commission for Asia and the Far East. Designed by Hubert Woyty-Wimmer, U.K.. *Gravure by Japanese Government Printing Office. Perforated 13x13 1/2.*

86, 87 *Steel beam with map of South Asia and Far East in background*

86		MNHVF	UseVF
4¢	multicolored *(2,195,945)*	.20	.20
	FDC *(April 11, 1960)*		1.00
	Inscription block of 4	.75	

87		MNHVF	UseVF
8¢	multicolored *(1,897,902)*	.25	.20
	FDC *(April 11, 1960)*		1.00
	Inscription block of 4	1.00	

1960. FIFTH WORLD FORESTRY CONGRESS ISSUE Designed by Ole Hamann, Denmark. *Gravure by Japanese Government Printing Office. Perforated 13 1/2.*

88, 89 *Symbolic tree*

88		MNHVF	UseVF
4¢	**multicolored** *(2,188,293)*	.20	.20
	FDC *(Aug. 29, 1960)*		1.00
	Inscription block of 4	.75	
	v. Pair, imperforate	—	

89		MNHVF	UseVF
8¢	**multicolored** *(1,837,778)*	.25	.20
	FDC *(Aug. 29, 1960)*		1.00
	Inscription block of 4	1.00	
	v. Pair, imperforate	—	

1960. U.N. 15TH ANNIVERSARY ISSUE Designed by Robert Perrot, France. Engraved by G. Gundersen. *Intaglio by British American Bank Note Co., Canada. Perforated 11.*

90, 91 *U.N. headquarters and preamble to U.N. Charter*

90		MNHVF	UseVF
4¢	**light blue** *(2,631,593)*	.20	.20
	FDC *(Oct. 24, 1960)*		1.00
	Inscription block of 4	.75	

91		MNHVF	UseVF
8¢	**dark gray** *(2,278,022)*	.25	.20
	FDC *(Oct. 24, 1960)*		1.00
	Inscription block of 4	1.00	

1960. U.N. 15TH ANNIVERSARY SOUVENIR SHEET Designed by Robert Perrot, France. Engraved by G. Gundersen. *Intaglio by British American Bank Note Co., Canada. Sheet (92x70mm) of 2.*

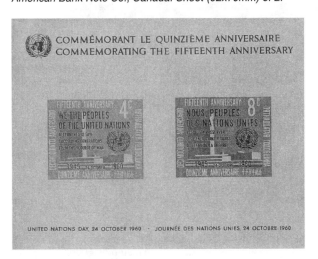

92 *Souvenir sheet with Nos. 90 and 91*

92		MNHVF	UseVF
12¢	**Sheet of 2** *(1,000,000)*	1.00	.60
	v. Small *v* in Anniversary	75.00	70.00
	a. Single (4¢)	.30	.20
	b. Single (8¢)	.30	.20
	FDC *(Oct. 24, 1960)*		1.25

1960. INTERNATIONAL BANK FOR RECONSTRUCTION & DEVELOPMENT ISSUE The IBRD agency was founded in 1945. Designed by Angel Medina, Uruguay. *Gravure by Japanese Government Printing Office. Perforated 13 1/2x13.*

93, 94 *Block and tackle*

93		MNHVF	UseVF
4¢	**multicolored** *(2,286,117)*	.20	.20
	FDC *(Dec. 9, 1960)*		1.00
	Inscription block of 4	.75	
	v. Pair, imperforate	1,000.00	

94		MNHVF	UseVF
8¢	**multicolored** *(1,882,019)*	.25	.20
	FDC *(Dec. 9, 1960)*		1.00
	Inscription block of 4	1.00	
	v. Pair, imperforate	1,000.00	

1961. INTERNATIONAL COURT OF JUSTICE ISSUE Adapted as a stamp by Kurt Plowitz, U.S., from an original design by Raphael, Italy. *Gravure by Japanese Government Printing Office. Perforated 13 1/2x13.*

95, 96 *Scales of Justice, detail from fresco by Raphael in one of the stanze (rooms), Vatican City*

95		MNHVF	UseVF
4¢	**lemon, orange brown & black** *(2,234,588)*	.20	.20
	FDC *(Feb. 13, 1961)*		1.00
	Inscription block of 4	.75	
	v. Pair, imperforate	1,000.00	500.00

96		MNHVF	UseVF
8¢	**lemon, yellow green & black** *(2,023,986)*	.25	.20
	FDC *(Feb. 13, 1961)*		1.00
	Inscription block of 4	1.00	
	v. Pair, imperforate	—	

1961. INTERNATIONAL MONETARY FUND ISSUE The IMF was founded in 1945. Designed by Roy E. Carlson, U.S. and Hordur Karlsson, Iceland. *Gravure by Japanese Government Printing Office. Perforated 13.*

97, 98 *Seal of fund and U.N. emblem*

97		MNHVF	UseVF
4¢	**turquoise blue** *(2,305,000)*	.20	.20
	FDC *(April 17, 1961)*		1.00
	Inscription block of 4	.75	
	v. Pair, imperforate	—	

98		MNHVF	UseVF
7¢	**brown red & lemon** *(2,147,201)*	.25	.20
	FDC *(April 17, 1961)*		1.00
	Inscription block of 4	1.00	

1961. FLAGS ISSUE Designed by Herbert Sanborn, U.S. *Gravure by Helio Courvoisier, Switzerland. Perforated 11 1/2.*

99 *"To unite our strength," group of flags*

99		MNHVF	UseVF
30¢	**multicolored**	.60	.20
	FDC *(June 5, 1961)*		1.00
	Inscription block of 4	2.75	

1961. ECLA ISSUE Economic Commission for Latin America. Designed by Robert Perrot, France. *Gravure by Japanese Government Printing Office. Perforated 13 1/2x13.*

100, 101 *Cogwheel and map of Latin America*

100		MNHVF	UseVF
4¢	**bright blue, olive yellow & red** *(2,037,912)*	.20	.20
	FDC *(Sept. 18, 1961)*		1.00
	Inscription block of 4	1.00	

101		MNHVF	UseVF
11¢	**blue green, orange red & purple** *(1,835,097)*	.40	.30
	FDC *(Sept. 18, 1961)*		1.00
	Inscription block of 4	2.50	

1961. ECA ISSUE Economic Commission for Africa. Designed by Robert Perrot, France. *Gravure by Helio Courvoisier, Switzerland. Perforated 11 1/2, granite paper.*

102, 103 *Africa House, headquarters, Addis Ababa, Ethiopia*

102		MNHVF	UseVF
4¢	**multicolored** *(2,044,842)*	.25	.20
	FDC *(Oct. 24, 1961)*		1.00
	Inscription block of 4	1.00	

103		MNHVF	UseVF
11¢	**multicolored** *(1,790,894)*	.40	.20
	FDC *(Oct. 24, 1961)*		1.00
	Inscription block of 4	1.50	

1961. UNICEF ISSUE Fifteenth anniversary U.N. Children's Emergency Fund. Designed by Minoru Hisano, Japan. *Gravure by Helio Courvoisier, Switzerland. Perforated 11 1/2.*

104-106 *Bird feeding her young*

104		MNHVF	UseVF
3¢	**multicolored** *(2,867,456)*	.20	.20
	FDC *(Dec. 4, 1961)*		1.00
	Inscription block of 4	.75	

105		MNHVF	UseVF
4¢	**multicolored** *(2,735,899)*	.20	.20
	FDC *(Dec. 4, 1961)*		1.00
	Inscription block of 4	1.00	

106		MNHVF	UseVF
13¢	**multicolored** *(1,951,715)*	.25	.20
	FDC *(Dec. 4, 1961)*		1.00
	Inscription block of 4	1.25	

1962. HOUSING AND COMMUNITY FACILITIES ISSUE Designed by Olav Mathiesen, Denmark. *Gravure by Harrison & Sons Ltd., U.K. Perforated 14 1/2x14.*

107, 108 *Family and settlement*

107		MNHVF	UseVF
4¢	**multicolored** *(2,204,190)*	.25	.20
	v. black omitted	600.00	
	v1. yellow omitted	400.00	
	v2. brown omitted	250.00	
	Inscription block of 4	1.00	
	FDC *(Feb. 28, 1962)*		1.00

108		MNHVF	UseVF
7¢	**multicolored** *(1,845,821)*	.50	.25
	v. red omitted	400.00	
	Inscription block of 4	1.00	
	FDC *(Feb. 28, 1962)*		1.00

1962. WORLD HEALTH ORGANIZATION ISSUE Malaria eradication. Designed by Rashid-ud-Din, Pakistan. *Gravure by Harrison & Sons Ltd., U.K. Perforated 14x14 1/2.*

109, 110 *WHO malaria campaign emblem*

109

		MNHVF	UseVF
4¢	**multicolored** *(2,047,000)*	.25	.20
	FDC *(March 30, 1962)*		1.00
	Inscription block of 4	1.00	

110

		MNHVF	UseVF
11¢	**multicolored** *(1,683,766)*	.40	.20
	FDC *(March 30, 1962)*		1.00
	Inscription block of 4	1.25	

1962. NEW REGULAR ISSUES *Gravure and intaglio (5¢).*

111 *"To Live Together in Peace," emblem over crossing banners, designed by Kurt Plowitz, U.S.; printed by Harrison & Sons Ltd., U.K.; perforated 14x14 1/2.*

111

		MNHVF	UseVF
1¢	**multicolored**	.20	.20
	FDC *(May 25, 1962)*		1.00
	Inscription block of 4	.75	

112 *U.N. flag, designed by Ole Hamann, Denmark; printed by Harrison & Sons Ltd., U.K.; perforated 14x14 1/2.*

112

		MNHVF	UseVF
3¢	**multicolored**	.20	.20
	FDC *(May 25, 1962)*		1.00
	Inscription block of 4	1.00	

113 *Two hands holding together letters "UN," designed by Renato Ferrini, Italy; engraved by Yves P. G. Baril and D. J. Mitchell, Canada; intaglio by Canadian Bank Note Co., Canada; perforated 12.*

113

		MNHVF	UseVF
5¢	**carmine**	.20	.20
	FDC *(May 25, 1962)*		1.00
	Inscription block of 4	1.00	

114 *U.N. emblem over world globe, designed by Olav Mathiesen, Denmark; gravure by Harrison & Sons Ltd., U.K.; perforated 12 1/2.*

114

		MNHVF	UseVF
11¢	**dark blue, light blue & gold**	.25	.20
	FDC *(May 25, 1962)*		1.00
	Inscription block of 4	1.25	

1962. MEMORIAL ISSUE Honored U.N. members who died on official missions; Dag Hammarskjold, U.N. Secretary General 1953-61, died on a peace mission Sept. 18, 1961; Count Folke Bernadotte, U.N. Mediator in Palestine, died Sept. 17, 1948. Designed by Ole Hamann, Denmark. *Gravure by Helio Courvoisier, Switzerland. Perforated 11 1/2x12, granite paper.*

115, 116 *U.N. building and flag at half mast*

115

		MNHVF	UseVF
5¢	**black & blue** *(2,195,707)*	.25	.20
	FDC *(Sept. 17, 1962)*		1.00
	Inscription block of 4	1.25	

116

		MNHVF	UseVF
15¢	**black, sage green & blue** *(1,155,047)*	.40	.30
	FDC *(Sept. 17, 1962)*		1.00
	Inscription block of 4	1.50	

1962. PEACE IN THE CONGO ISSUE Designed by George Hamori, Australia. *Gravure by Helio Courvoisier, Switzerland. Perforated 12x11 1/2, granite paper.*

117, 118 *Map showing location of Congo*

117

		MNHVF	UseVF
4¢	**multicolored** *(1,477,958)*	.25	.20
	FDC *(Oct. 24, 1962)*		1.00
	Inscription block of 4	1.25	

118

		MNHVF	UseVF
11¢	**multicolored** *(1,171,255)*	.40	.35
	FDC *(Oct. 24, 1962)*		1.00
	Inscription block of 4	1.50	

1962. PEACEFUL USES OF OUTER SPACE ISSUE Designed by Kurt Plowitz, U.S. Engraved by H. Cole. *Intaglio by Bradbury, Wilkinson & Co., U.K. Perforated 14x13 1/2.*

119, 120 *Palm frond and globe in universe*

119		MNHVF	UseVF
4¢	**blue** *(2,263,876)*	.25	.25
	FDC *(Dec. 3, 1962)*		1.00
	Inscription block of 4	1.00	

120		MNHVF	UseVF
11¢	**claret** *(1,681,584)*	.30	.25
	FDC *(Dec. 3, 1962)*		1.00
	Inscription block of 4	1.50	

1963. ECONOMIC, SCIENCE & TECHNOLOGY ISSUE Conference in Geneva, Feb. 4-20, 1963. Designed by Rashid-ud-Din, Pakistan. *Gravure by Helio Courvoisier, Switzerland. Perforated 11 1/2, granite paper.*

121, 122 Development decade emblem

121		MNHVF	UseVF
5¢	**multicolored** *(1,802,406)*	.25	.20
	FDC *(Feb. 4, 1963)*		1.00
	Inscription block of 4	1.00	

122		MNHVF	UseVF
11¢	**multicolored** *(1,530,190)*	.25	.20
	FDC *(Feb. 4, 1963)*		1.00
	Inscription block of 4	1.25	

1963. FREEDOM FROM HUNGER ISSUE World-wide campaign launched (1960) by the Food & Agriculture Organization (FAO) of the U.N. Designed by Ole Hamann, Denmark. *Gravure by Helio Courvoisier, Switzerland. Perforated 11 1/2, granite paper.*

123, 124 Stalks of wheat

123		MNHVF	UseVF
5¢	**red, green & yellow** *(1,666,178)*	.25	.20
	FDC *(March 22, 1963)*		1.00
	Inscription block of 4	1.00	

124		MNHVF	UseVF
11¢	**red, maroon & yellow** *(1,563,023)*	.25	.20
	FDC *(March 22, 1963)*		1.00
	Inscription block of 4	1.25	

1963. AIRMAIL ISSUE Designed by Claude Bottiau, France (6¢), George Hamori, Australia (8¢), Kurt Plowitz, U.S. (13¢). *Gravure by Helio Courvoisier, Switzerland. Perforated 11 1/2 (6¢ and 8¢), 12 1/2 (13¢), granite paper.*

125 Outer space

125		MVF	UseVF
6¢	**black, blue** *(4,000,000 printed)*	.20	.20
	FDC *(June 17, 1963)*		1.00

126 Triangular shapes

126		MVF	UseVF
8¢	**multicolored** *(4,000,000 printed)*	.25	.20
	FDC *(June 17, 1963)*		1.25

127 Stylized bird

127		MVF	UseVF
13¢	**multicolored** *(2,700,000 printed)*	.40	.20
	FDC *(June 17, 1963)*		1.50

1963. UNTEA ISSUE First anniversary U.N. Temporary Executive Authority. Designed by Henry Bencsath, U.S. *Gravure by Helio Courvoisier, Switzerland. Perforated 11 1/2, granite paper.*

128 Bridge over map of New Guinea. UNTEA administered former Netherlands New Guinea (West Irian) from Oct. 1, 1962 until May 1, 1963 when Indonesia assumed executive authority.

128		MNHVF	UseVF
25¢	**blue, green & gray** *(1,427,747)*	.75	.40
	FDC *(Oct. 1, 1963)*		1.00
	Inscription block of 4	2.75	

1963. U.N. GENERAL ASSEMBLY BUILDING ISSUE New York City. Designed by Kurt Plowitz, U.S. *Gravure by Japanese Government Printing Office. Perforated 13 1/2.*

129, 130 General Assembly building, New York City and flags

129		MNHVF	UseVF
5¢	**multicolored** *(2,208,008)*	.25	.20
	FDC *(Nov. 4, 1963)*		1.00
	Inscription block of 4	1.00	

130		MNHVF	UseVF
11¢	**multicolored** *(1,435,079)*	.25	.20
	FDC *(Nov. 4, 1963)*		1.00
	Inscription block of 4	1.25	

1963. DECLARATION OF HUMAN RIGHTS ISSUE The eighth commemorative stamp in the Human Rights series. 15th anniversary U.N.'s Human Rights Charter. Designed by Rashid-ud-Din, Pakistan. *Gravure by Japanese Government Printing Office. Perforated 13 1/2.*

131, 132 *Flame*

131		**MNHVF**	**UseVF**
5¢	**multicolored** *(1,892,539)*	.25	.20
	FDC *(Dec. 10, 1963)*		1.00
	Inscription block of 4	1.00	

132		**MNHVF**	**UseVF**
11¢	**multicolored** *(1,501,125)*	.30	.20
	FDC *(Dec. 10, 1963)*		1.00
	Inscription block of 4	1.25	

1964. IMCO ISSUE Inter-Governmental Maritime Consultative Organization was founded in 1958. Designed by Henry Bencsath, U.S. *Gravure by Helio Courvoisier, Switzerland. Perforated 11 1/2, granite paper.*

133, 134 *Emblem and ships*

133		**MNHVF**	**UseVF**
5¢	**multicolored** *(1,805,750)*	.25	.20
	FDC *(Jan. 13, 1964)*		1.00
	Inscription block of 4	1.00	

134		**MNHVF**	**UseVF**
11¢	**multicolored** *(1,583,848)*	.30	.20
	FDC *(Jan. 13, 1964)*		1.00
	Inscription block of 4	1.25	

1964. REGULAR STAMP ISSUE Designed by Hatim El Mekki, Tunisia. *Gravure by Helio Courvoisier, Switzerland. Perforated 11 1/2, granite paper.*

135 *Elongated globe with stylized dove of peace*

135		**MNHVF**	**UseVF**
50¢	**multicolored**	.75	.30
	FDC *(March 6, 1964)*		1.00
	Inscription block of 4	2.75	

1964. AIRMAIL ISSUE Designed by Ole Hamann, Denmark (15¢), George Hamori, Australia (25¢). *Gravure by Government Printing Office, Austria. Perforated 11 1/2x12 (15¢), 12x11 1/2 (25¢).*

136 *Symbol of flight*

136		**MVF**	**UseVF**
15¢	**multicolored** *(3,000,000 printed)*	.35	.20
	v. gray omitted	800.00	
	FDC *(May 1, 1964)*		1.00
	Inscription block of 4	1.75	

137 *Jet aircraft and letter*

137		**MVF**	**UseVF**
25¢	**multicolored** *(2,000,000 printed)*	.65	.25
	FDC *(May 1, 1964)*		1.50
	Inscription block of 4	3.00	
	v. Pair, imperforate	—	

1964. REGULAR POSTAGE ISSUE Designed by Ole Hamann, Denmark (2¢), George Hamori, Australia (7¢ & 10¢). *Gravure by Thomas de la Rue, U.K. (2¢), gravure by Helio Courvoisier, Switzerland (7¢, 10¢). Perforated 14 (2¢); perforated 11 1/2, (7¢, 10¢), granite paper.*

138 *World map projection in 3 sections*

138		**MNHVF**	**UseVF**
2¢	**multicolored**	.20	.20
	FDC *(May 29, 1964)*		1.00
	Inscription block of 4	1.50	
	v. Perforated 13x13 1/2 (1971)	.25	.20

139 *U.N. seal as bloom on plant*

139		**MNHVF**	**UseVF**
7¢	**multicolored**	.20	.20
	FDC *(May 29, 1964)*		1.00
	Inscription block of 4	1.00	

140 *Three united figures against world*

140		**MNHVF**	**UseVF**
10¢	**multicolored**	.20	.20
	FDC *(May 29, 1964)*		1.00
	Inscription block of 4	1.50	

1964. CONFERENCE ON TRADE & DEVELOPMENT ISSUE Held in Geneva March 23-June 15, 1964. Designed by Herbert Sanborn, U.S. and Ole Hamann, Denmark. *Gravure by Thomas de la Rue, U.K. Perforated 13.*

141, 142 *Arrows in two directions*

141

5¢	**black, red & yellow** *(2,400,000)*	MNHVF .25	UseVF .20
	FDC *(June 15, 1964)*		1.00
	Inscription block of 4	1.00	

142

11¢	**black, bistre & yellow** *(1,529,526)*	MNHVF .30	UseVF .20
	FDC *(June 15, 1964)*		1.00
	Inscription block of 4	1.25	

1964. NARCOTICS CONTROL ISSUE The 55th anniversary of the Shanghai Opium Commission. Designed by Kurt Plowitz, U.S. Engraved by A. C. Carswell. *Intaglio by Canadian Bank Note Co. Perforated 12.*

143, 144 *Hands reaching for opium poppy*

143

5¢	**red & black** *(1,508,999)*	MNHVF .30	UseVF .20
	FDC *(Sept. 21, 1964)*		1.00
	Inscription block of 4	1.25	

144

11¢	**green & black** *(1,340,691)*	MNHVF .45	UseVF .25
	FDC *(Sept. 21, 1964)*		1.00
	Inscription block of 4	1.50	

1964. CESSATION OF NUCLEAR TESTING ISSUE Designed by Ole Hamann, Denmark. *Intaglio and gravure by Artia, Prague, Czechoslovakia. Perforated 11 1/2.*

145 *Nuclear explosion*

145

5¢	**red brown & black** *(2,422,789)*	MNHVF .30	UseVF .20
	FDC *(Oct. 23, 1964)*		1.00
	Inscription block of 4	1.00	

1964. EDUCATION FOR PROGRESS ISSUE Designed by Kurt Plowitz, U.S. *Gravure by Helio Courvoisier, Switzerland. Perforated 12 1/2, granite paper.*

146-148 *Stylized student writing on blackboard*

146

4¢	**multicolored** *(2,375,181)*	MNHVF .20	UseVF .20
	FDC *(Dec. 7, 1964)*		1.00
	Inscription block of 4	.75	

147

5¢	**multicolored** *(2,496,877)*	MNHVF .20	UseVF .20
	FDC *(Dec. 7, 1964)*		1.00
	Inscription block of 4	1.00	

148

11¢	**multicolored** *(1,773,645)*	MNHVF .25	UseVF .20
	FDC *(Dec. 7, 1964)*		1.00
	Inscription block of 4	1.25	

1965. U.N. DEVELOPMENT FUND ISSUE Designed by Rashid-ud-Din, Pakistan. *Gravure by Japanese Government Printing Office. Perforated 13 1/2X13.*

149, 150 *Globe and key*

149

5¢	**multicolored** *(1,949,274)*	MNHVF .25	UseVF .20
	FDC *(Jan. 25, 1965)*		1.00
	Inscription block of 4	1.00	

150

11¢	**multicolored** *(1,690,908)*	MNHVF .25	UseVF .20
	FDC *(Jan. 25, 1965)*		1.00
	Inscription block of 4	1.25	
	v. black (U.N. emblem & key) omitted	—	

1965. PEACE-KEEPING FORCE IN CYPRUS ISSUE Designed by George Hamori, Australia. *Gravure by Helio Courvoisier, Switzerland. Perforated 11 1/2, granite paper.*

151, 152 *Stylized leaves and silhouette of Cyprus*

151

5¢	**multicolored** *(1,887,042)*	MNHVF .25	UseVF .20
	FDC *(March 4, 1965)*		1.00
	Inscription block of 4	1.00	

152

11¢	**multicolored** *(1,691,767)*	MNHVF .35	UseVF .20
	FDC *(March 4, 1965)*		1.00
	Inscription block of 4	1.00	

1965. INTERNATIONAL TELECOMMUNICATION UNION ISSUE Hundredth anniversary. Designed by Kurt Plowitz, U.S. *Gravure by Helio Courvoisier, Switzerland. Perforated 11 1/2, granite paper.*

153, 154 *Signals by semaphore and satellite*

153		**MNHVF**	**UseVF**
5¢	**multicolored** *(2,432,407)*	.20	.20
	FDC *(May 17, 1965)*		1.00
	Inscription block of 4	1.00	

154		**MNHVF**	**UseVF**
11¢	**multicolored** *(1,731,070)*	.25	.20
	FDC *(May 17, 1965)*		1.00
	Inscription block of 4	1.25	

1965. ICY ISSUE International Cooperation Year and 20th anniversary of U.N. Designed by Olav Mathiesen, Denmark. *Intaglio by Bradbury, Wilkinson & Co., U.K. Perforated 14x13 1/2.*

155, 156 *Outstretched hands and emblem of ICY*

155		**MNHVF**	**UseVF**
5¢	**dark blue** *(2,282,452)*	.25	.20
	FDC *(June 26, 1965)*		1.00
	Inscription block of 4	1.00	

156		**MNHVF**	**UseVF**
15¢	**magenta** *(1,993,562)*	.25	.20
	FDC *(June 26, 1965)*		1.00
	Inscription block of 4	1.25	

1965. ICY SOUVENIR SHEET International Cooperation Year and 20th anniversary of U.N. Designed by Olav Mathiesen, Denmark. *Intaglio by Bradbury, Wilkinson & Co., U.K. (92x70mm) sheet of 2, with Nos. 155 and 156. Perforated 14x13 1/2.*

157 *Souvenir sheet with Nos. 155 and 156*

157		**MNHVF**	**UseVF**
20¢	**Sheet of 2** *(1,928,366)*	.75	.60

a.	Single (5¢)	.25	.20
b.	Single (15¢)	.25	.20
	FDC *(June 26, 1965)*		1.75

1965. REGULAR POSTAGE ISSUE Designed by Kurt Plowitz, U.S. (1¢). *Gravure by Japanese Government Printing Office. Perforated 13 1/2x13.* (25¢) designed by Rashid-ud-Din, Pakistan. *Offset and embossed by German Government Printing Office, Berlin. Perforated 14.*

158 *"To Live Together in Peace with One Another"*

158		**MNHVF**	**UseVF**
1¢	**multicolored**	.20	.20
	FDC *(Sept. 20, 1965)*		1.00
	Inscription block of 4	1.00	

159 *U.N. Emblem*

159		**MNHVF**	**UseVF**
25¢	**light blue & dark blue**	.50	.40
	FDC *(Sept. 20, 1965)*		1.00
	Inscription block of 4	2.00	

1965. REGULAR POSTAGE ISSUE Designed by Olav Mathiesen, Denmark (15¢). Designed by Louis V. Pierre-Noel, Haiti (20¢). *Gravure by Government Printing Office, Austria. Perforated 14 (15¢), 12 (20¢).*

160 *Scroll of U.N. charter*

160		**MNHVF**	**UseVF**
15¢	**multicolored**	.30	.20
	FDC *(Oct. 25, 1965)*		1.00
	Inscription block of 4	1.00	

161 *Stylized U.N. emblem and building*

161		**MNHVF**	**UseVF**
20¢	**multicolored**	.35	.20
	v. yellow omitted	200.00	
	FDC *(Oct. 25, 1965)*		1.00
	Inscription block of 4	1.50	

1965. POPULATION TRENDS & DEVELOPMENT ISSUE World Population Conference held in Belgrade, Yugoslavia, in 1965. Designed by Olav Mathiesen, Denmark. *Gravure by Government Printing Office, Austria. Perforated 12.*

162-164 *World population expansion*

162		MNHVF	UseVF
4¢	multicolored *(1,966,033)*	.20	.20
	FDC *(Nov. 29, 1965)*		1.00
	Inscription block of 4	.75	

163		MNHVF	UseVF
5¢	multicolored *(2,298,731)*	.20	.20
	FDC *(Nov. 29, 1965)*		1.00
	Inscription block of 4	1.00	

164		MNHVF	UseVF
11¢	multicolored *(1,557,589)*	.25	.25
	FDC *(Nov. 29, 1965)*		1.00
	Inscription block of 4	1.25	

1966. FEDERATION OF U.N. ASSOCIATIONS ISSUE Designed by Olav Mathiesen, Denmark. *Gravure by Helio Courvoisier, Switzerland. Perforated 11 1/2, granite paper.*

165, 166 *Stylized world globe and flags*

165		MNHVF	UseVF
5¢	multicolored *(2,462,215)*	.20	.20
	FDC *(Jan. 31, 1966)*		1.00
	Inscription block of 4	1.00	

166		MNHVF	UseVF
15¢	multicolored *(1,643,661)*	.35	.25
	FDC *(Jan. 31, 1966)*		1.00
	Inscription block of 4	1.25	

1966. REGULAR POSTAGE ISSUE Designed by Ole Hamann, Denmark. *Gravure by Helio Courvoisier, Switzerland. Perforated 11 1/2, granite paper.*

167 *U.N. emblem within circles*

167		MNHVF	UseVF
$1.00	multicolored	1.50	1.00
	FDC *(March 25, 1966)*		1.75
	Inscription block of 4	6.00	

1966. WHO HEADQUARTERS ISSUE World Health Organization opened its new headquarters building in Geneva, Switzerland, in 1966. Designed by Rashid-ud-Din, Pakistan. *Gravure by Helio Courvoisier, Switzerland. Perforated 12 1/2x12, granite paper.*

168, 169 *WHO buildings, Geneva*

168		MNHVF	UseVF
5¢	multicolored *(2,079,893)*	.20	.20
	FDC *(May 26, 1966)*		1.00
	Inscription block of 4	1.00	

169		MNHVF	UseVF
11¢	multicolored *(1,879,879)*	.35	.20
	FDC *(May 26, 1966)*		1.00
	Inscription block of 4	1.50	

1966. COFFEE AGREEMENT ISSUE The International Coffee Agreement came into force on Dec. 27, 1963. Designed by Rashid-ud-Din, Pakistan. *Gravure by Japanese Government Printing Office. Perforated 13 1/2x13.*

170, 171 *Coffee tree branch and beans*

170		MNHVF	UseVF
5¢	multicolored *(2,020,308)*	.20	.20
	FDC *(Sept. 19, 1966)*		1.00
	Inscription block of 4	1.00	

171		MNHVF	UseVF
11¢	multicolored *(1,888,682)*	.35	.20
	FDC *(Sept. 19, 1966)*		1.00
	Inscription block of 4	1.50	

1966. MILITARY OBSERVERS ISSUE Designed by Ole Hamann, Denmark. *Gravure by Helio Courvoisier, Switzerland. Perforated 11 1/2, granite paper.*

172 *U.N. observer with binoculars*

172		MNHVF	UseVF
15¢	multicolored *(1,889,809)*	.50	.35
	FDC *(Oct. 24, 1966)*		1.00
	Inscription block of 4	1.75	

1966. UNICEF 20TH ANNIVERSARY ISSUE World's children in train cars. Designed by Kurt Plowitz, U.S. *Offset by Thomas de la Rue, U.K. Perforated 13x13 1/2.*

173-175 *Toy train and children*

173			**MNHVF**	**UseVF**
4¢	multicolored *(2,334,989)*		.20	.20
	FDC *(Nov. 28, 1966)*			1.00
	Inscription block of 4		.75	

174			**MNHVF**	**UseVF**
5¢	multicolored *(2,746,941)*		.20	.20
	FDC *(Nov. 28, 1966)*			1.00
	Inscription block of 4		1.00	
	v. yellow omitted		200.00	

175			**MNHVF**	**UseVF**
11¢	multicolored *(2,123,841)*		.40	.20
	FDC *(Nov. 28, 1966)*			1.00
	Inscription block of 4		1.50	
	v. Pair, imperforate		300.00	
	v1. blue (11¢ & Nations Unies) omitted		—	

1967. U.N. DEVELOPMENT PROGRAM ISSUE Designed by Olav Mathiesen, Denmark. *Gravure by Helio Courvoisier, Switzerland. Perforated 12 1/2, granite paper.*

176, 177 *Strong forearm over chart*

176			**MNHVF**	**UseVF**
5¢	multicolored *(2,204,679)*		.20	.20
	FDC *(Jan. 23, 1967)*			1.00
	Inscription block of 4		1.00	

177			**MNHVF**	**UseVF**
11¢	multicolored *(1,946,159)*		.35	.20
	FDC *(Jan. 23, 1967)*			1.00
	Inscription block of 4		1.25	

1967. REGULAR ISSUE Designed by Renato Ferrini, Italy. *Gravure by Helio Courvoisier, Switzerland. Perforated 11 1/2, granite paper.*

178 *Hands holding "UN" over globe*

178			**MNHVF**	**UseVF**
5¢	multicolored		.20	.20
	FDC *(Jan. 23, 1967)*			1.00
	Inscription block of 4		1.00	

1967. REGULAR ISSUE Designed by Jozsef Verbel, Hungary. *Gravure by Helio Courvoisier, Switzerland. Perforated 11 1/2, granite paper.*

179 *U.N. building against U.N. emblem*

179			**MNHVF**	**UseVF**
1-1/2¢	multicolored		.20	.20
	FDC *(March 17, 1967)*			1.00
	Inscription block of 4		.80	

1967. INDEPENDENCE OF NEW NATIONS ISSUE Designed by Rashid-ud-Din, Pakistan. *Gravure by Harrison & Sons Ltd., U.K. Perforated 14x14 1/2.*

180, 181 *Fireworks display*

180			**MNHVF**	**UseVF**
5¢	multicolored *(2,445,955)*		.20	.20
	FDC *(March 17, 1967)*			1.00
	Inscription block of 4		1.00	

181			**MNHVF**	**UseVF**
11¢	multicolored *(2,011,004)*		.30	.20
	FDC *(March 17, 1967)*			1.00
	Inscription block of 4		1.00	

Regular Issues

1967. EXPO 67 ISSUE Sold at the U.N. Exhibit at Montreal's EXPO 67, face values in Canadian currency, (4¢, 5¢, 10¢, 15¢), various designs after bas-relief by Ernest Cormier, Canada, donated by the Government of Canada to the U.N. in 1951; No.184 after photograph by Michael Drummond, Canada. *Intaglio (No.182, 183, 185 and 186) or offset (No.184) by British American Bank Note. Perforated 11.*

182, 183 *Peace, Justice*

182			**MNHVF**	**UseVF**
4¢	red & chestnut *(4,000,000 printed)*		.20	.20
	FDC *(April 28, 1967)*			1.00
	Inscription block of 4		.50	

183			**MNHVF**	**UseVF**
5¢	blue & chestnut *(4,000,000 printed)*		.25	.20
	FDC *(April 28, 1967)*			1.00
	Inscription block of 4		.60	

184 *U.N. Pavilion*

184			**MNHVF**	**UseVF**
8¢	multicolored *(3,000,000 printed)*		.40	.20
	FDC *(April 28, 1967)*			1.00
	Inscription block of 4		.75	

185, 186 *Fraternity, Truth*

191 *"Kiss of Peace"*

185		MNHVF	UseVF
10¢	sepia & chestnut *(3,000,000 printed)*	.25	.25
	FDC *(April 28, 1967)*		1.00
	Inscription block of 4	1.25	

186		MNHVF	UseVF
15¢	green & chestnut *(3,000,000 printed)*	.25	.25
	FDC *(April 28, 1967)*		1.00
	Inscription block of 4	2.00	

191		MNHVF	UseVF
6¢	multicolored *(3,178,656)*	.30	.20
	FDC *(Nov. 17, 1967)*		1.00
	Inscription block of 4	1.25	

Commemorative Issues

1967. TOURIST YEAR ISSUE Designed by David Dewhurst, U.S. *Offset by German Government Printing Office. Perforated 14.*

187, 188 *Luggage labels and tags*

187		MNHVF	UseVF
5¢	multicolored *(2,593,782)*	.20	.20
	FDC *(June 19, 1967)*		1.00
	Inscription block of 4	1.00	

188		MNHVF	UseVF
15¢	multicolored *(1,940,457)*	.30	.20
	FDC *(June 19, 1967)*		1.00
	Inscription block of 4	1.25	

1967. DISARMAMENT ISSUE Designed by Ole Hamann, Denmark. *Gravure by Heraclio Fournier, Spain. Perforated 14.*

189, 190 *Quotation from Isaiah*

189		MNHVF	UseVF
6¢	multicolored *(2,462,277)*	.20	.20
	FDC *(Oct. 24, 1967)*		1.00
	Inscription block of 4	1.00	

190		MNHVF	UseVF
13¢	multicolored *(2,055,541)*	.30	.20
	FDC *(Oct. 24, 1967)*		1.00
	Inscription block of 4	1.50	

1967. CHAGALL WINDOW ISSUE Adapted as a stamp by Ole Hamann, Denmark, from a design by Marc Chagall, France. *Offset by Joh. Enschedé and Sons, Netherlands. Perforated 12 1/2x13 1/2.*

1967. CHAGALL WINDOW SOUVENIR SHEET Adapted by Ole Hamann, Denmark, from a design by Marc Chagall, France. *(124x80mm) of 6 stamps denominated at 6¢ each. Rouletted 9. Offset by Joh. Enschedé and Sons, Netherlands.*

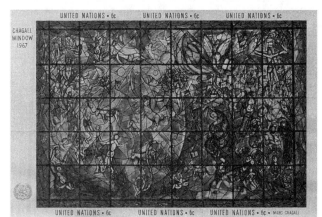

192 *Chagall Window Souvenir Sheet*

192		MNHVF	UseVF
36¢	multicolored *(3,178,656)*	1.20	.75
	top left	.20	.20
	top center	.20	.20
	top right	.20	.20
	bottom left	.20	.20
	bottom center	.20	.20
	bottom right	.20	.20
	FDC *(Nov. 17, 1967)*		1.25

1968. SECRETARIAT ISSUE Designed by Rashid-ud-Din, Pakistan. *Gravure by Helio Courvoisier, Switzerland. Perforated 11 1/2, granite paper.*

193, 194 *Globe and six circles*

193		MNHVF	UseVF
6¢	multicolored *(2,772,965)*	.25	.20
	FDC *(Jan. 16, 1968)*		1.00
	Inscription block of 4	1.00	

194		MNHVF	UseVF
13¢	multicolored *(2,461,992)*	.30	.20

FDC *(Jan. 16, 1968)* 1.00
Inscription block of 4 1.25

1968. U.N. ART ISSUE Adapted as a stamp by Ole Hamann, Denmark, from a statue design by Henrik Starcke, Denmark. *Gravure by Helio Courvoisier, Switzerland. Perforated 11 1/2, granite paper.*

195, 196 *Mankind's Search for Freedom and Happiness, teakwood carving by Henrik Starcke in Trusteeship Council chamber*

195		**MNHVF**	**UseVF**
6¢	**multicolored** *(2,537,320)*	.25	.35
	FDC *(March 1, 1968)*		1.00
	Inscription block of 4	1.00	

196		**MNHVF**	**UseVF**
75¢	**multicolored** *(2,300,000 printed)*	2.00	1.50
	FDC *(March 1, 1968)*		4.75
	Inscription block of 4	7.00	

1968. INDUSTRIAL DEVELOPMENT ORGANIZATION ISSUE Designed by Ole Hamann, Denmark. *Offset by Canadian Bank Note Co. Perforated 12.*

197, 198 *Factories and chart*

197		**MNHVF**	**UseVF**
6¢	**multicolored** *(2,439,656)*	.20	.20
	FDC *(April 18, 1968)*		1.00
	Inscription block of 4	.75	

198		**MNHVF**	**UseVF**
13¢	**multicolored** *(2,192,453)*	.35	.20
	FDC *(April 18, 1968)*		1.00
	Inscription block of 4	1.00	

1968. AIRMAIL ISSUE Designed by Ole Hamann, Denmark. *Offset by S. Setelipaino, Finland. Perforated 13 1/2.*

199 *Jet plane and U.N. emblem*

199		**MVF**	**UseVF**
20¢	**multicolored** *(3,000,000 printed)*	.60	.30
	FDC *(April 18, 1968)*		1.50

1968. U.N. HEADQUARTERS ISSUE Designed by Olav Mathiesen, Denmark. *Offset by Aspioti Elka-Chrome Mines Ltd., , Greece. Perforated 12 1/2.*

200 *U.N. building complex*

200		**MNHVF**	**UseVF**
6¢	**multicolored**	.25	.20
	FDC *(May 31, 1968)*		1.00
	Inscription block of 4	1.25	

1968. WORLD WEATHER WATCH ISSUE Publicized a program by the World Meteorological Organization to share weather forcasting with all nations. Designed by George A. Gundersen and George Fanais of British American Bank Note Co. Ltd., Canada. *Gravure by Japanese Government Printing Office. Perforated 13x13 1/2.*

201, 202 *Radarscope and globe*

201		**MNHVF**	**UseVF**
6¢	**multicolored** *(2,245,078)*	.25	.25
	FDC *(Sept. 19, 1968)*		1.00
	Inscription block of 4	1.00	

202		**MNHVF**	**UseVF**
20¢	**multicolored** *(2,069,966)*	.50	.35
	FDC *(Sept. 19, 1968)*		1.00
	Inscription block of 4	1.25	

1968. DECLARATION OF HUMAN RIGHTS ISSUE Twentieth anniversary of the adoption of the Universal Declaration of Human Rights. The ninth commemorative stamp in the Human Rights series. Designed by Robert Perrot, France. *Gravure and embossed by Harrison & Sons Ltd., U.K. Perforated 12 1/2.*

203, 204 *Symbolic flame*

203		**MNHVF**	**UseVF**
6¢	**blue & gold** *(2,394,235)*	.30	.25
	FDC *(Nov. 22, 1968)*		1.00
	Inscription block of 4	1.00	

204		**MNHVF**	**UseVF**
13¢	**carmine & gold** *(2,284,838)*	.40	.35
	FDC *(Nov. 22, 1968)*		1.00
	Inscription block of 4	1.50	

1969. INSTITUTE FOR TRAINING & RESEARCH ISSUE Designed by Olav Mathiesen, Denmark. *Offset by Japanese Government Printing Office. Perforated 13 1/2.*

205, 206 *Book and U.N. emblem*

205		MNHVF	UseVF
6¢	multicolored (2,436,559)	.25	.25
	FDC (Feb. 10, 1969)		1.00
	Inscription block of 4	1.00	

206		MNHVF	UseVF
13¢	multicolored (1,935,151)	.35	.25
	FDC (Feb. 10, 1969)		1.00
	Inscription block of 4	1.25	

1969. SANTIAGO ISSUE The U.N. offices in Santiago, Chile are the Headquarters of Economic Commission for Latin America and other agencies. Designed by Ole Hamann, Denmark. *Offset by German Government Printing Office, Berlin. Perforated 14.*

207, 208 *U.N. building in Santiago, Chile*

207		MNHVF	UseVF
6¢	light blue, blue & turquoise (2,543,992)	.25	.20
	FDC (March 14, 1969)		1.00
	Inscription block of 4	1.00	

208		MNHVF	UseVF
15¢	rose, maroon & buff (2,030,733)	.35	.25
	FDC (March 14, 1969)		1.00
	Inscription block of 4	1.25	

1969. REGULAR POSTAGE ISSUE Designed by Leszek Holdanowicz and Marek Freudenreich, Poland. *Gravure by Japanese Government Printing Office. Perforated 13 1/2.*

209 *U.N. emblem and initials*

209		MNHVF	UseVF
13¢	blue, black & gold	.30	.25
	FDC (March 14, 1969)		1.00
	Inscription block of 4	1.50	

1969. AIRMAIL ISSUE Designed by Olav Mathiesen, Denmark. *Gravure by S. Setelipaino, Finland. Perforated 13x13 1/2.*

210 *Wings and envelopes*

210		MVF	UseVF
10¢	multicolored (4,000,000 printed)	.30	.25
	FDC (April 21, 1969)		1.50
	Inscription block of 4	1.50	

1969. PEACE THROUGH LAW ISSUE Designed by Robert Perrot, France. *Gravure by Helio Courvoisier, Switzerland. Perforated 11 1/2, granite paper.*

211, 212 *Scales and U.N. emblem*

211		MNHVF	UseVF
6¢	multicolored (2,501,492)	.25	.20
	FDC (April 21, 1969)		1.00
	Inscription block of 4	.75	

212		MNHVF	UseVF
13¢	multicolored (1,966,994)	.55	.55
	FDC (April 21, 1969)		1.00
	Inscription block of 4	1.50	

1969. ILO ISSUE International Labor Organization. Designed by Nejat M. Gur, Turkey. *Gravure by Japanese Government Printing Office. Perforated 13.*

213, 214 *Men pushing cogwheel*

213		MNHVF	UseVF
6¢	multicolored (2,078,381)	.20	.20
	FDC (June 5, 1969)		1.00
	Inscription block of 4	1.00	

214		MNHVF	UseVF
20¢	multicolored (1,751,100)	.40	.30
	FDC (June 5, 1969)		1.00
	Inscription block of 4	1.25	

1969. TUNISIAN MOSAIC ART ISSUE Featured detail from bottom-center of third century mosaic found at Haidra, Tunisia. The complete mosaic of *The Four Seasons and the Genius of the Year* was donated to the U.N. by the Tunisian Republic. Adapted as a stamp by Olav Mathiesen, Denmark. *Gravure by Heraclio Fournier, Spain. Perforated 14.*

215 *Ostrich*

216 *Pheasant*

215		MNHVF	UseVF
6¢	**multicolored** *(2,280,702)*	.25	.20
	FDC *(Nov. 21, 1969)*		1.00
	Inscription block of 4	1.00	

216		MNHVF	UseVF
13¢	**multicolored** *(1,918,554)*	.35	.30
	FDC *(Nov. 21, 1969)*		1.00
	Inscription block of 4	1.25	

1970. JAPANESE PEACE BELL ISSUE Designed by Ole Hamann, Denmark. *Gravure by Japanese Government Printing Office. Perforated 13 1/2x13, multicolored, color of frame given below.*

217, 218 *Peace Bell presented to the U.N. by the U.N. Association of Japan. The bell, cast from contributed coins and other metals, is housed in Japanese structure of cypress wood.*

217		MNHVF	UseVF
6¢	**deep blue** *(2,604,253)*	.25	.25
	FDC *(March 13, 1970)*		1.00
	Inscription block of 4	1.25	

218		MNHVF	UseVF
25¢	**chocolate** *(2,090,185)*	.50	.40
	FDC *(March 13, 1970)*		1.00
	Inscription block of 4	2.00	

1970. MEKONG BASIN DEVELOPMENT ISSUE Designed by Ole Hamann, Denmark. *Gravure by Heraclio Fournier, Spain. Perforated 14, multicolored, color of frame given below.*

219, 220 *Map of Southeast Asia and power lines*

219		MNHVF	UseVF
6¢	**deep blue** *(2,207,309)*	.25	.25
	FDC *(March 13, 1970)*		1.00
	Inscription block of 4	1.00	

220		MNHVF	UseVF
13¢	**reddish purple** *(1,889,023)*	.50	.35
	FDC *(March 13, 1970)*		1.00
	Inscription block of 4	1.50	

1970. FIGHT CANCER ISSUE Tenth International Cancer Congress of International Union Against Cancer, Houston, Texas. Designed by Leonard Mitchell, New Zealand. *Offset by German Government Printing Office, Berlin. Perforated 14 1/2.*

221, 222 *Man wrestling with giant crab*

221		MNHVF	UseVF
6¢	**blue & black** *(2,157,742)*	.25	.20
	FDC *(May 22, 1970)*		1.00
	Inscription block of 4	1.00	

222		MNHVF	UseVF
13¢	**olive & black** *(1,824,714)*	.30	.25
	FDC *(May 22, 1970)*		1.00
	Inscription block of 4	1.50	

1970. U.N. 25TH ANNIVERSARY ISSUE No. 223-224 designed by Helio Courvoisier, Switzerland; No. 225 by Ole Hamann, Denmark. *Gravure by Helio Courvoisier, Switzerland. Perforated 11 1/2 (Nos. 223, 224), 12 1/2 (No. 225), granite paper.*

223, 224 *Olive branch*

223		MNHVF	UseVF
6¢	**multicolored** *(2,365,229)*	.25	.20
	FDC *(June 26, 1970)*		1.00
	Inscription block of 4	.75	

224		MNHVF	UseVF
13¢	**multicolored** *(1,861,613)*	.60	.50
	FDC *(June 26, 1970)*		1.00
	Inscription block of 4	1.25	

225 *U.N. emblem*

225		MNHVF	UseVF
25¢	**multicolored** *(1,844,669)*	.50	.25
	FDC *(June 26, 1970)*		1.00
	Inscription block of 4	2.25	

1970. U.N. 25TH ANNIVERSARY SOUVENIR SHEET *(95x78mm) of 3. Imperforate.*

226 *Souvenir sheet with Nos. 223, 224 and 225*

226		MNHVF	UseVF
44¢	Sheet of 3 *(1,923,639)*	1.50	1.00
	a. Single (6¢)	.25	.20
	b. Single (13¢)	.60	.50
	c. Single (25¢)	.50	.25
	FDC *(June 26, 1970)*		1.00

1970. PEACE, JUSTICE AND PROGRESS ISSUE Designed by Ole Hamann, Denmark. *Gravure by Japanese Government Printing Office. Perforated 13 1/2, multicolored, color of background given below.*

 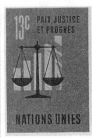

227, 228 *Scale, olive branch and graph*

227		MNHVF	UseVF
6¢	deep rose *(1,921,441)*	.30	.25
	FDC *(Nov. 20, 1970)*		1.00
	Inscription block of 4	1.25	

228		MNHVF	UseVF
13¢	blue *(1,663,669)*	.50	.35
	FDC *(Nov. 20, 1970)*		1.00
	Inscription block of 4	1.50	

1971. SEA-BED ISSUE Peaceful uses of sea-bed. Designed by Pentti Rahikainen, Finland. *Intaglio and Gravure by S. Setelipaino, Finland. Perforated 13.*

229 *Sea-bed and shoal of fish*

229		MNHVF	UseVF
6¢	multicolored *(2,354,179)*	.30	.20
	FDC *(Jan. 25, 1971)*		1.00
	Inscription block of 4	1.25	

1971. INTERNATIONAL SUPPORT FOR REFUGEES ISSUE Designed by Kaare K. Nygaard and Martin Weber, U.S. *Offset by Joh. Enschedé and Sons, Netherlands. Perorated 13x12 1/2.*

230, 231 Refugees, *bronze sculpture by Kaare K. Nygaard, U.S.*

230		MNHVF	UseVF
6¢	multicolored *(2,247,232)*	.25	.20
	FDC *(March 12, 1971)*		1.00
	Inscription block of 4	1.00	

231		MNHVF	UseVF
13¢	multicolored *(1,890,048)*	.25	.20
	FDC *(March 12, 1971)*		1.00
	Inscription block of 4	1.50	

1971. WORLD FOOD PROGRAM ISSUE Designed by Olav Mathiesen, Denmark. *Gravure by Heraclio Fournier, Spain. Perforated 14.*

232 *Sheaf of wheat and globe*

232		MNHVF	UseVF
13¢	multicolored *(1,968,542)*	.40	.25
	FDC *(April 13, 1971)*		1.00
	Inscription block of 4	1.75	

1971. UPU HEADQUARTERS ISSUE Universal Postal Union in Berne, Switzerland. Designed by Olav Mathiesen, Denmark. *Gravure by Helio Courvoisier, Switzerland. Perforated 11 1/2, granite paper.*

233 *Universal Postal Union headquarters, Bern, Switzerland*

233		MNHVF	UseVF
20¢	multicolored *(1,857,841)*	.50	.45
	FDC *(May 28, 1971)*		1.00
	Inscription block of 4	2.25	

1971. INTERNATIONAL RACE RELATIONS YEAR ISSUE (8¢) designed by Daniel Gonzague, France; (13¢) by Ole Hamann, Denmark. *Gravure by Japanese Government Printing Office. Perforated 13 1/2.*

234 *Four petals of a flower*

234		MNHVF	UseVF
8¢	**green & multicolored** *(2,324,349)*	.25	.20
	FDC *(Sept. 21, 1971)*		1.00
	Inscription block of 4	1.00	

235 *Three globes*

235		MNHVF	UseVF
13¢	**blue & multicolored** *(1,852,093)*	.50	.40
	FDC *(Sept. 21, 1971)*		1.00
	Inscription block of 4	1.50	

1971. REGULAR ISSUE Designed by Olav Mathiesen, Denmark (8¢), Robert Perrot, France (60¢). *Gravure by Heraclio Fournier, Spain (8¢), Japanese Government Printing Office (60¢). Perforated 13 1/2 (8¢), 13 (60¢).*

236 *U.N. New York building complex*

236		MNHVF	UseVF
8¢	**multicolored**	.25	.20
	FDC *(Oct. 22, 1971)*		1.00
	Inscription block of 4	1.00	

237 *Stylized flags*

237		MNHVF	UseVF
60¢	**multicolored**	1.10	.80
	FDC *(Oct. 22, 1971)*		1.00
	Inscription block of 4	5.00	

1971. INTERNATIONAL SCHOOL ISSUE Adapted by Ole Hamann, Denmark, from a painting by Pablo Picasso, Spain. *Gravure by Helio Courvoisier, Switzerland. Perforated 11 1/2, granite paper.*

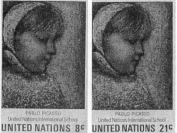

238, 239 *"Maia" by Pablo Picasso*

238		MNHVF	UseVF
8¢	**olive green & multicolored** *(2,668,214)*	.25	.20
	FDC *(Nov. 19, 1971)*		1.00
	Inscription block of 4	1.25	

239		MNHVF	UseVF
21¢	**blue & multicolored** *(2,040,754)*	.75	.60
	FDC *(Nov. 19, 1971)*		1.00
	Inscription block of 4	1.75	

1972. REGULAR POSTAGE ISSUE Designed by Olav Mathiesen, Denmark. *Offset by German Government Printing Office, Berlin. Perforated 13 1/2.*

240 *Letter changing hands*

240		MNHVF	UseVF
95¢	**multicolored**	2.50	1.75
	FDC *(Jan. 5, 1972)*		1.00
	Inscription block of 4	12.50	

1972. NON-PROLIFERATION OF NUCLEAR WEAPONS ISSUE Designed by Arnie Johnson, Norway. *Gravure by Heraclio Fournier, Spain. Perforated 13 1/2x14.*

241 *Nuclear explosion*

241		MNHVF	UseVF
8¢	**pink, black & blue** *(2,311,515)*	.40	.20
	FDC *(Feb. 14, 1972)*		1.00
	Inscription block of 4	1.00	

1972. WORLD HEALTH DAY ISSUE Basic design by Leonardo da Vinci, Italy, and adapted by George Hamori, Australia. *Intaglio and offset by S. Setelipaino, Finland. Perforated 13x13 1/2.*

242 *Proportions of Man, by Leonardo da Vinci*

242

			MNHVF	UseVF
15¢	**multicolored** *(1,788,962)*		.50	.35
	FDC *(April 7, 1972)*			1.00
	Inscription block of 4		1.75	

1972. AIRMAIL ISSUE Designs by Lyell L. Dolan, Australia (9¢), Arne Johnson, Norway (11¢), British American Bank Note Co., Canada (17¢), Asher Kalderon, Israel (21¢). *Offset by Japanese Government Printing Office (9¢), gravure by Heraclio Fournier, Spain (11¢, 17¢), gravure by S. Setelipaino, Finland. Perforated 13x13 1/2 (9¢), 14 (11¢), 13 1/2x14 (17¢), 13 1/2x13 (21¢).*

243 *Contempory flight*

243

			MVF	UseVF
9¢	**multicolored** *(3,000,000 printed)*		.30	.15
	FDC *(May 1, 1972)*			1.00
	Inscription block of 4		1.50	

244 *Birds in flight*

244

			MVF	UseVF
11¢	**multicolored** *(3,000,000 printed)*		.35	.20
	FDC *(May 1, 1972)*			1.00
	Inscription block of 4		1.25	

245 *Cloud formations*

245

			MVF	UseVF
17¢	**multicolored** *(3,000,000 printed)*		.55	.30
	FDC *(May 1, 1972)*			1.00
	Inscription block of 4		2.50	

246 *Aircraft and "UN" jetstream*

246

			MVF	UseVF
21¢	**multicolored** *(3,000,000 printed)*		.70	.35
	FDC *(May 1, 1972)*			1.00
	Inscription block of 4		3.00	

1972. HUMAN ENVIRONMENT ISSUE for U.N. Conference, Stockholm, Sweden, in June 1972. Designed by Robert Perrot, France. *Offset and embossed by Joh. Enschedé and Sons, Netherlands. Perforated 12 1/2x13 1/2, multicolored, color of background below.*

247, 248 *Human environment symbol*

247

			MNHVF	UseVF
8¢	**red** *(2,124,604)*		.25	.20
	FDC *(June 5, 1972)*			1.00
	Inscription block of 4		1.50	

248

			MNHVF	UseVF
15¢	**blue green** *(1,589,943)*		.50	.40
	FDC *(June 5, 1972)*			1.00
	Inscription block of 4		1.75	

1972. ECONOMIC COMMISSION FOR EUROPE ISSUE Designed by Angel Medina, Uruguay. *Offset by Japanese Government Printing Office. Perforated 13x13 1/2.*

249 *Petals of flower forming the word EUROPE*

249

			MNHVF	UseVF
21¢	**multicolored** *(1,748,675)*		.75	.50
	FDC *(Sept. 11, 1972)*			1.00
	Inscription block of 4		2.75	

1972. JOSÉ MARIA SERT MURAL ISSUE Designed by José Maria Sert, Spain, and adapted by Ole Hamann, Denmark. *Gravure by Helio Courvoisier, Switzerland. Perforated 12x12 1/2, granite paper.*

250, 251 *Five colossal figures*

250

			MNHVF	UseVF
8¢	**gold & brown** *(2,573,478)*		.25	.25
	FDC *(Nov. 17, 1972)*			1.00
	Inscription block of 4		1.50	

251

			MNHVF	UseVF
15¢	**gold, brown & dull green** *(1,768,432)*		.50	.35
	FDC *(Nov. 17, 1972)*			1.00
	Inscription block of 4		2.00	

1973. DISARMAMENT DECADE ISSUE Designed by Kurt Plowitz, U.S. *Offset by Ajans-Turk, Turkey. Perforated 13 1/2, multicolored, color of background given below.*

252, 253
Broken sword and olive branch

252		MNHVF	UseVF
8¢	blue *(2,272,716)*	.35	.30
	FDC *(March 9, 1973)*		1.00
	Inscription block of 4	1.50	

253		MNHVF	UseVF
15¢	bright purple *(1,643,712)*	.50	.35
	FDC *(March 9, 1973)*		1.00
	Inscription block of 4	2.00	

1973. DRUG ABUSE CONTROL ISSUE Designed by George Hamori, Australia. *Gravure by Heraclio Fournier, Spain. Perforated 13 1/2.*

254, 255 *Skull and plant*

254		MNHVF	UseVF
8¢	multicolored *(1,846,780)*	.35	.30
	FDC *(April 13, 1973)*		1.00
	Inscription block of 4	1.50	

255		MNHVF	UseVF
15¢	multicolored *(1,466,806)*	.50	.35
	FDC *(April 13, 1973)*		1.00
	Inscription block of 4	2.00	

1973. VOLUNTEERS PROGRAM ISSUE established on Jan. 1, 1971. Designed by Helio Courvoisier, Switzerland. *Gravure by Heraclio Fournier, Spain. Perforated 14, multicolored, color of frame given below.*

256, 257 *Honeycomb and symbols*

256		MNHVF	UseVF
8¢	brown *(1,868,176)*	.35	.30
	FDC *(May 25, 1973)*		1.00
	Inscription block of 4	1.75	

257		MNHVF	UseVF
21¢	gray *(1,530,114)*	.60	.40
	FDC *(May 25, 1973)*		1.00
	Inscription block of 4	2.25	

1973. NAMIBIA ISSUE The first issue in a series to draw attention to the desire of the Namibian people for independence and freedom from foreign occupation. Designed by George Hamori, Australia. *Gravure by Heraclio Fournier, Spain. Perforated 14, multicolored, color of background given below.*

258, 259
Outline map of Namibia

258		MNHVF	UseVF
8¢	green *(1,775,260)*	.30	.25
	FDC *(Oct. 1, 1973)*		1.00
	Inscription block of 4	1.50	

259		MNHVF	UseVF
15¢	magenta *(1,687,782)*	.50	.35
	FDC *(Oct. 1, 1973)*		1.00
	Inscription block of 4	2.00	

1973. DECLARATION OF HUMAN RIGHTS ISSUE Twenty-fifth anniversary of the proclamation, on Dec. 10, 1948 of the Universal Declaration of Human Rights. The tenth commemorative stamp in the Human Rights series. Designed by Alfredo Guerra, U.S. *Gravure by Japanese Government Printing Office. Perforated 13 1/2, multicolored, color of inscription given below.*

260, 261
Emblem, flame and globe

260		MNHVF	UseVF
8¢	dark carmine *(2,026,245)*	.30	.25
	FDC *(Nov. 16, 1973)*		1.00
	Inscription block of 4	1.50	

261		MNHVF	UseVF
21¢	blue green *(1,558,201)*	.50	.40
	FDC *(Nov. 16, 1973)*		1.00
	Inscription block of 4	2.00	

1974. ILO HEADQUARTERS ISSUE International Labor Organization. Commemorated the new headquarters building in Geneva, Switzerland laid in May 1970. Designed by Henry Bencsath, U.S. *Gravure by Heraclio Fournier, Spain. Perforated 14, multicolored, color of background given below.*

262, 263
International Labor Office, Geneva, built 1970-1974

262		MNHVF	UseVF
10¢	blue *(1,734,423)*	.50	.40
	FDC *(Jan. 11, 1974)*		1.00
	Inscription block of 4	2.00	

263		MNHVF	UseVF
21¢	green *(1,264,447)*	.75	.50
	FDC *(Jan. 11, 1974)*		1.00
	Inscription block of 4	2.50	

1974. UNIVERSAL POSTAL UNION ISSUE Celebrated the 100th anniversary of the UPU. Designed by Arne Johnson, Norway. *Offset by Ashton-Potter Ltd., Canada. Perforated 12 1/2.*

264 *Posthorn around globe and UPU emblem*

264		MNHVF	UseVF
10¢	**multicolored** *(2,104,919)*	.50	.25
	FDC *(March 22, 1974)*		1.00
	Inscription block of 4	1.75	

1974. BRAZILIAN PEACE MURAL ISSUE Designed by Candido Portinari, Brazil, and adapted by Ole Hamann, Denmark. *Gravure by Heraclio Fournier, Spain. Perforated 14.*

265, 266 Peace Mural, *by Candido Portinari, gift of Brazilian Government to U.N.*

265		MNHVF	UseVF
10¢	**multicolored & gold** *(1,769,342)*	.50	.25
	FDC *(May 6, 1974)*		1.00
	Inscription block of 4	2.00	

266		MNHVF	UseVF
18¢	**multicolored & blue** *(1,477,500)*	.75	.50
	FDC *(May 6, 1974)*		1.00
	Inscription block of 4	2.50	

1974. REGULAR ISSUE Designed by Negat Gur, Turkey (2¢), Olav Mathiesen, Denmark (10¢), Henry Bencsath, U.S. (18¢). *Gravure by Heraclio Fournier, Spain. Perforated 14x13 1/2 (2¢), 13 1/2x14 (10¢, 18¢).*

267 *Stylized dove*

267		MNHVF	UseVF
2¢	**deep blue & light blue**	.25	.20
	FDC *(June 10, 1974)*		1.00
	Inscription block of 4	1.00	

268 *U.N. building, north view*

268		MNHVF	UseVF
10¢	**multicolored**	.30	.25
	FDC *(June 10, 1974)*		1.00
	Inscription block of 4	1.50	

269 *Globe and U.N. emblem*

269		MNHVF	UseVF
18¢	**multicolored**	.50	.40
	FDC *(June 10, 1974)*		1.00
	Inscription block of 4	2.00	

1974. AIRMAIL ISSUE Designed by George Hamori, Australia (13¢), Shamir Bros. (18¢), Olav Mathiesen, Denmark (26¢). *Offset by S. Setelipaino, Finland. Perforated 13 1/2x13 (13¢, 26¢), 13x13 1/2 (18¢).*

270 *Plane, jetstream and globe*

270		MVF	UseVF
13¢	**multicolored** *(2,500,000 printed)*	.50	.25
	FDC *(Sept. 16, 1974)*		1.00

271 *Colored pathways from U.N. emblem*

271		MVF	UseVF
18¢	**multicolored** *(2,000,000 printed)*	.70	.35
	FDC *(Sept. 16, 1974)*		1.00

272 *Bird in flight and U.N. buildings*

272		MVF	UseVF
26¢	**multicolored** *(2,000,000 printed)*	1.00	.40
	FDC *(Sept. 16, 1974)*		1.00

1974. WORLD POPULATION YEAR ISSUE Designed by Henry Bencsath, U.S. *Gravure by Heraclio Fournier, Spain. Perforated 14.*

273, 274 *Babies reaching around globe*

273		MNHVF	UseVF
10¢	**multicolored & cobalt** *(1,762,595)*	.65	.50
	FDC *(Oct. 18, 1974)*		1.00
	Inscription block of 4	2.00	
274		MNHVF	UseVF
18¢	**multicolored & mauve** *(1,321,574)*	1.00	.75
	FDC *(Oct. 18, 1974)*		1.00
	Inscription block of 4	3.00	

1974. LAW OF THE SEA ISSUE Designed by Asher Kalderon, Israel. *Gravure by Heraclio Fournier, Spain. Perforated 14.*

275, 276 *Ship, fish and mineral bed*

275		MNHVF	UseVF
10¢	**multicolored, green & blue** *(1,621,328)*	.40	.30
	FDC *(Nov. 22, 1974)*		1.00
	Inscription block of 4	2.00	
276		MNHVF	UseVF
26¢	**multicolored, red & blue** *(1,293,084)*	.75	.50
	FDC *(Nov. 22, 1974)*		1.00
	Inscription block of 4	2.50	

1975. PEACEFUL USES OF OUTER SPACE ISSUE Designed by Henry Bencsath, U.S. *Offset by S. Setelipaino, Finland. Perforated 13 1/2x13.*

277, 278 *Satellite focused on earth's surface and activities benefiting from peaceful uses of outer space*

277		MNHVF	UseVF
10¢	**multicolored** *(1,681,115)*	.50	.30
	FDC *(March 14, 1975)*		1.00
	Inscription block of 4	2.00	
278		MNHVF	UseVF
26¢	**multicolored** *(1,463,130)*	1.00	.75
	FDC *(March 14, 1975)*		1.00
	Inscription block of 4	2.50	

1975. INTERNATIONAL WOMEN'S YEAR ISSUE Designed by Esther Kurti and Asher Kalderon, Israel. *Offset by The House of Questa, U.K. Perforated 15x14, multicolored, color of background given below.*

279, 280 *Men and women within circle*

279		MNHVF	UseVF
10¢	**deep blue** *(1,402,542)*	.40	.30

	FDC *(May 9, 1975)*		1.00
	Inscription block of 4	2.25	
280		MNHVF	UseVF
18¢	**blue green** *(1,182,321)*	.75	.50
	FDC *(May 9, 1975)*		1.00
	Inscription block of 4	2.75	

1975. U.N. 30TH ANNIVERSARY ISSUE Designed by Asher Kalderon, Israel. *Offset by Ashton-Potter Ltd., Canada. Perforated 13 1/2, multicolored, color of inscription given below.*

281, 282 *Numerals "XXX" in form of people supporting flag*

281		MNHVF	UseVF
10¢	**multicolored** *(1,904,545)*	.40	.30
	FDC *(June 26, 1975)*		1.00
	Inscription block of 4	2.00	
282		MNHVF	UseVF
26¢	**multicolored** *(1,547,766)*	1.00	.60
	FDC *(June 26, 1975)*		1.00
	Inscription block of 4	3.00	

1975. U.N. 30TH ANNIVERSARY SOUVENIR SHEET Designed by Olav Mathiesen, Denmark. *Souvenir sheet (92x70mm) of Nos. 281, 282, imperforate.*

283 *Souvenir sheet of Nos. 281 and 282*

283		MNHVF	UseVF
36¢	**Sheet of 2** *(1,196,578)*	1.50	1.00
	a. Single (10¢)	.40	.30
	b. Single (26¢)	1.00	.60
	FDC *(June 26, 1975)*		1.75

1975. NAMIBIA ISSUE Second set of stamps in the "Namibia" series. Designed by Henry Bencsath, U.S. *Gravure by Heraclio Fournier, Spain. Perforated 13 1/2.*

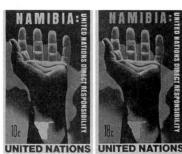

284, 285 *Map of Africa with Namibia shown in relief by cupped hand and forearm*

284		MNHVF	UseVF
10¢	multicolored *(1,354,374)*	.50	.30
	FDC *(Sept. 22, 1975)*		1.00
	Inscription block of 4	1.50	

285		MNHVF	UseVF
18¢	multicolored *(1,243,157)*	.75	.45
	FDC *(Sept. 22, 1975)*		1.00
	Inscription block of 4	2.50	

1975. PEACE-KEEPING OPERATIONS ISSUE Designed by Eeva Oivo, Finland. *Intaglio by S. Setelipaino, Finland. Perforated 12 1/2.*

286, 287 *Flower growing from barbed wire*

286		MNHVF	UseVF
13¢	blue *(1,628,039)*	.50	.35
	FDC *(Nov. 21, 1975)*		1.00
	Inscription block of 4	2.00	

287		MNHVF	UseVF
26¢	carmine *(1,195,580)*	1.00	.75
	FDC *(Nov. 21, 1975)*		1.00
	Inscription block of 4	2.75	

1976. REGULAR ISSUE Designed by Waldemar Andrejewski, Poland (3¢), Arnie Johnson, Norway (4¢), George Hamori, Australia (30¢), Arthur Congdon, U.S. (50¢). *Offset by Ashton-Potter Ltd., Canada. Perforated 13.*

288 *Flags forming dove*

288		MNHVF	UseVF
3¢	multicolored	.25	.20
	FDC *(Jan. 9, 1976)*		1.00
	Inscription block of 4	1.00	

289 *People of all races*

289		MNHVF	UseVF
4¢	multicolored	.25	.20
	FDC *(Jan. 9, 1976)*		1.00
	Inscription block of 4	1.00	

290 *United Nations flag*

290		MNHVF	UseVF
30¢	multicolored	.50	.20
	FDC *(Jan. 9, 1976)*		1.00
	Inscription block of 4	1.75	

291 *Dove and rainbow*

291		MNHVF	UseVF
50¢	multicolored	1.00	.40
	FDC *(Jan. 9, 1976)*		1.00
	Inscription block of 4	4.00	

1976. WFUNA ISSUE Thirtieth anniversary World Federation of U.N. Associations. Designed by George Hamori, Australia. *Gravure by Heraclio Fournier, Spain. Perforated 14, multicolored, color of inscription given below.*

292, 293 *Interlocking multicolored bands*

292		MNHVF	UseVF
13¢	carmine *(1,331,556)*	.40	.25
	FDC *(March 12, 1976)*		1.00
	Inscription block of 4	1.50	

293		MNHVF	UseVF
26¢	black *(1,050,145)*	.75	.75
	FDC *(March 12, 1976)*		1.00
	Inscription block of 4	2.50	

1976. CONFERENCE ON TRADE & DEVELOPMENT ISSUE Designed by Henry Bencsath, U.S. *Gravure by Helio Courvoisier, Switzerland. Perforated 11 1/2, granite paper, multicolored, color of background given below.*

294, 295 *Cargo, globe and graph*

294		MNHVF	UseVF
13¢	**reddish purple** *(1,317,900)*	.25	.20
	FDC *(April 23, 1976)*		1.00
	Inscription block of 4	1.50	

295		MNHVF	UseVF
31¢	**blue** *(1,216,959)*	.80	.75
	FDC *(April 23, 1976)*		1.00
	Inscription block of 4	2.75	

1976. CONFERENCE ON HUMAN SETTLEMENTS ISSUE Designed by Eliezer Weishoff, Israel. *Gravure by Heraclio Fournier, Spain. Perforated 14, multicolored, color of background given below.*

296, 297 *Globe encircled with houses*

296		MNHVF	UseVF
13¢	**brown purple** *(1,346,589)*	.35	.25
	FDC *(May 28, 1976)*		1.00
	Inscription block of 4	1.50	

297		MNHVF	UseVF
25¢	**dark green** *(1,057,924)*	.80	.75
	FDC *(May 28, 1976)*		1.00
	Inscription block of 4	2.75	

1976. POSTAL ADMINISTRATION 25TH ANNIVERSARY ISSUE Designed by Henry Bencsath, U.S. *Gravure by Helio Courvoisier, Switzerland. Perforated 11 1/2, granite paper, multicolored, color of background given below. Printed in sheets of 20 stamps.*

298, 299 *Stamps, magnifying glass and U.N. emblem*

298		MNHVF	UseVF
13¢	**blue** *(1,996,309)*	.25	.20
	FDC *(Oct. 8, 1976)*		1.00
	Inscription block of 4	2.00	

299		MNHVF	UseVF
31¢	**green** *(1,767,465)*	2.50	2.00
	FDC *(Oct. 8, 1976)*		1.00
	Inscription block of 4	7.00	

1976. WORLD FOOD COUNCIL ISSUE Designed by Eliezer Weishoff, Israel. *Offset by The House of Questa, U.K. Perforated 14 1/2x14.*

300 *Wheat and flags*

300		MNHVF	UseVF
13¢	**multicolored** *(1,515,573)*	.50	.30
	FDC *(Nov. 19, 1976)*		1.00
	Inscription block of 4	2.00	

1976. REGULAR ISSUE Designed by George Hamori, Australia. *Offset by The House of Questa, U.K. Perforated 14.*

301 *U.N. emblem*

301		MNHVF	UseVF
9¢	**multicolored**	.25	.20
	FDC *(Nov. 19, 1976)*		1.00
	Inscription block of 4	1.25	

Commemorative Issues

1977. WIPO ISSUE World Intellectual Property Organization founded in 1970. U.N. agency set up to help protect industrial inventions and designs and copyrights. Designed by Eliezer Weishoff, Israel. *Gravure by Heraclio Fournier, Spain. Perforated 14, multicolored, color of frame given below.*

302 *World Intellectual Property Organization headquarters, Geneva*

302		MNHVF	UseVF
13¢	**olive yellow** *(1,330,272)*	.30	.20
	FDC *(March 11, 1977)*		1.50
	Inscription block of 4	1.75	

303		MNHVF	UseVF
31¢	**turquoise green** *(1,115,406)*	.80	.75
	FDC *(March 11, 1977)*		1.50
	Inscription block of 4	2.50	

1977. WATER CONFERENCE ISSUE Held in Argentina in 1977 to discuss strategies to avoid a water crisis within the next few decades. Designed by Elio Tomei, Italy. *Gravure by Japanese Government Printing Office. Perforated 13, multicolored, color of background given below.*

304, 305 *Water drops falling into a funnel*

304		MNHVF	UseVF
13¢	**lemon** *(1,317,536)*	.30	.20
	FDC *(April 22, 1977)*		1.00
	Inscription block of 4	1.75	

305		MNHVF	UseVF
25¢	**orange red** *(1,077,424)*	.80	.75
	FDC *(April 22, 1977)*		1.00
	Inscription block of 4	2.50	

1977. SECURITY COUNCIL ISSUE The second issue to commemorate the U.N. Security Council. Designed by Witold Janowski and Marek Freudenreich, Poland. *Gravure by Heraclio Fournier, Spain. Perforated 13 1/2, multicolored, color of background given below.*

306, 307 *Severed burning fuse*

306		MNHVF	UseVF
13¢	**violet** *(1,700,000)*	.30	.20
	FDC *(May 27, 1977)*		1.00
	Inscription block of 4	1.75	

307		MNHVF	UseVF
31¢	**blue** *(1,137,195)*	.80	.75
	FDC *(May 27, 1977)*		1.00
	Inscription block of 4	2.50	

1977. AIRMAIL ISSUE Designed by Eliezer Weishoff, Israel (25¢); Alan L. Pollock, Canada (31¢). *Gravure by Heraclio Fournier, Spain. Perforated 13 1/2.*

308 *Winged airmail letter*

308		MVF	UseVF
25¢	**multicolored** *(2,000,000 printed)*	.50	.25
	FDC *(June 27, 1977)*		1.00
	Inscription block of 4	2.00	

309 *Globe and plane*

309		MVF	UseVF
31¢	**dark carmine** *(2,000,000 printed)*	.50	.30
	FDC *(June 27, 1977)*		1.00
	Inscription block of 4	2.00	

1977. COMBAT RACISM ISSUE Designed by Bruno K. Wiese, Germany. *Offset by S. Setelipaino, Finland. Perforated 13.*

310, 311 *Combat Racism*

310		MNHVF	UseVF
13¢	**black & lemon** *(1,195,739)*	.35	.25
	FDC *(Sept. 19, 1977)*		1.00
	Inscription block of 4	1.75	

311		MNHVF	UseVF
25¢	**black & red** *(1,074,639)*	.80	.75
	FDC *(Sept. 19, 1977)*		1.00
	Inscription block of 4	2.50	

1977. ATOMIC ENERGY ISSUE Peaceful use of atomic energy. Designed by Henry Bencsath, U.S. *Gravure by Heraclio Fournier, Spain. Perforated 14.*

312, 313 *Atom, industry and agriculture*

312		MNHVF	UseVF
13¢	**multicolored** *(1,316,473)*	.35	.25
	FDC *(Nov. 18, 1977)*		1.00
	Inscription block of 4	1.75	

313		MNHVF	UseVF
18¢	**multicolored** *(1,072,246)*	.80	.75
	FDC *(Nov. 18, 1977)*		1.00
	Inscription block of 4	2.50	

1978. REGULAR ISSUE Designed by Salahattin Kanidinc, U.S. (1¢), Elio Tomei, Italy (25¢), Paula Schmidt, Germany ($1). *Offset by The House of Questa, U.K. Perforated 14 1/2.*

314 *Preamble to U.N. charter*

Commemorative Issues 219

314		MNHVF	UseVF
1¢	**multicolored**	.25	.20
	FDC *(Jan. 27, 1978)*		1.00
	Inscription block of 4	1.00	

315 *"Live Together in Peace," flags tied together*

315		MNHVF	UseVF
25¢	**multicolored**	.50	.50
	FDC *(Jan. 27, 1978)*		1.00
	Inscription block of 4	4.00	

316 *Smiling people*

316		MNHVF	UseVF
$1.00	**multicolored**	1.75	1.25
	FDC *(Jan. 27, 1978)*		3.00
	Inscription block of 4	8.00	

1978. SMALLPOX ISSUE Global eradication of smallpox. Designed by Herbert Auchli, Switzerland. *Gravure by Helio Courvoisier, Switzerland. Perforated 11 1/2, granite paper.*

317, 318 *Smallpox virus*

317		MNHVF	UseVF
13¢	**pink** *(1,188,239)*	.35	.25
	FDC *(March 31, 1978)*		1.00
	Inscription block of 4	2.00	

318		MNHVF	UseVF
31¢	**blue** *(1,058,688)*	1.00	1.00
	FDC *(March 31, 1978)*		1.00
	Inscription block of 4	2.25	

1978. NAMIBIA ISSUE The third set in the Namibia series. Designed by Cafiero Tomei, Italy. *Gravure by Government Printing Office, Austria. Perforated 12.*

319, 320 *Open handcuff*

319		MNHVF	UseVF
13¢	**turquoise, red purple & black** *(1,203,079)*	.25	.20
	FDC *(May 5, 1978)*		1.00
	Inscription block of 4	2.00	

320		MNHVF	UseVF
18¢	**turquoise, blue & black** *(1,066,738)*	.75	.75
	FDC *(May 5, 1978)*		1.00
	Inscription block of 4	2.00	

1978. ICAO ISSUE International Civil Aviation Organization founded in 1947. Designed by Cemalettin Mutver, Turkey. *Gravure by Heraclio Fournier, Spain. Perforated 13 1/2, multicolored, color of background given below.*

321, 322 *Slogan in multicolored bands*

321		MNHVF	UseVF
13¢	**blue** *(1,295,617)*	.25	.25
	FDC *(June 12, 1978)*		1.00
	Inscription block of 4	2.00	

322		MNHVF	UseVF
25¢	**turquoise green** *(1,101,256)*	.85	.75
	FDC *(June 12, 1978)*		1.00
	Inscription block of 4	2.25	

1978. GENERAL ASSEMBLY ISSUE Designed by Jozsef Vertel, Hungary. *Gravure by Japanese Government Printing Office. Perforated 13 1/2.*

323, 324 *General Assembly Hall*

323		MNHVF	UseVF
13¢	**multicolored** *(1,093,005)*	.25	.25
	FDC *(Sept. 15, 1978)*		1.00
	Inscription block of 4	1.75	

324		MNHVF	UseVF
18¢	**multicolored** *(1,065,934)*	.75	.65
	FDC *(Sept. 15, 1978)*		1.00
	Inscription block of 4	2.50	

1978. TECHNICAL COOPERATION ISSUE First world conference on technical cooperation among developing countries was held in Buenos Aires, Argentina, in Sept. 1978. Designed by Shimeon Keter and David Pesach, Israel. *Gravure by Heraclio Fournier, Spain. Perforated 14, multicolored, color of background given below.*

325, 326 *Two hemispheres rotating in unison*

325		MNHVF	UseVF
13¢	**orange red** *(1,251,272)*	.50	.35

	FDC *(Nov. 17, 1978)*		1.00
	Inscription block of 4	2.00	

326		**MNHVF**	**UseVF**
31¢	**magenta** *(1,185,213)*	1.00	.75
	FDC *(Nov. 17, 1978)*		1.00
	Inscription block of 4	4.00	

1979. REGULAR ISSUE Designed by Raymon Muller, Germany (5¢), Alrun Fricke, Germany (14¢), Eliezer Weishoff, Israel (15¢), Y. S. Hahn, S. Korea (20¢). *Gravure by Heraclio Fournier, Spain. Perforated 14.*

327 *"To Practice Tolerance," branch of peace*

327		**MNHVF**	**UseVF**
5¢	**multicolored**	.30	.25
	FDC *(Jan. 19, 1979)*		1.00
	Inscription block of 4	1.00	

328 *"Faith in Fundamental Human Rights," trees*

328		**MNHVF**	**UseVF**
14¢	**multicolored**	.30	.25
	FDC *(Jan. 19, 1979)*		1.00
	Inscription block of 4	1.50	

329 *Globe and dove*

329		**MNHVF**	**UseVF**
15¢	**multicolored**	.35	.25
	FDC *(Jan. 19, 1979)*		1.00
	Inscription block of 4	1.75	

330 *"Peace, Justice and Security," globe and birds*

330		**MNHVF**	**UseVF**
20¢	**multicolored**	.60	.30
	FDC *(Jan. 19, 1979)*		1.00
	Inscription block of 4	2.50	

1979. UNDRO ISSUE U.N. Disaster Relief Organization began in March 1972. Designed by Gidon Sagi, Israel. *Gravure by Heraclio Fournier, Spain. Perforated 14, multicolored, color of frame given below.*

331, 332
Symbols of fire and flood

331		**MNHVF**	**UseVF**
15¢	**gray** *(1,448,600)*	.35	.30
	FDC *(March 9, 1979)*		1.00
	Inscription block of 4	2.00	

332		**MNHVF**	**UseVF**
20¢	**dark blue** *(1,126,295)*	.75	.60
	FDC *(March 9, 1979)*		1.00
	Inscription block of 4	2.75	

1979. INTERNATIONAL YEAR OF THE CHILD ISSUE Designed by Helena Matuszewska and Krystyna Tarkowska-Gruszecha, Poland. Border designed by Ruth Rasmussen, Denmark. *Gravure by Heraclio Fournier, Spain. Perforated 14, multicolored, color of frame given below. Printed in sheets of 20 stamps.*

333, 334
Child and IYC emblem

333		**MNHVF**	**UseVF**
15¢	**blue** *(2,290,329)*	.25	.30
	FDC *(May 4, 1979)*		1.00
	Inscription block of 4	1.25	

334		**MNHVF**	**UseVF**
31¢	**carmine** *(2,192,136)*	.50	.40
	FDC *(May 4, 1979)*		1.00
	Inscription block of 4	2.75	

1979. NAMIBIA ISSUE The fourth set in the Namibia series. Designed by Eliezer Weishoff, Israel. *Offset by Ashton-Potter, U.S. Perforated 13x13 1/2, multicolored, map color given below.*

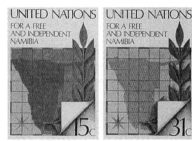

335, 336 *Map and olive branch*

335		**MNHVF**	**UseVF**
15¢	**brown** *(1,800,000)*	.25	.25
	FDC *(Oct. 5, 1979)*		1.00
	Inscription block of 4	1.75	

336		MNHVF	UseVF
31¢	lilac *(1,500,000)*	.50	.40
	FDC *(Oct. 5, 1979)*		1.50
	Inscription block of 4	2.00	

1979. INTERNATIONAL COURT OF JUSTICE ISSUE The court is located in the Hague, Netherlands. Designed by Henning Simon, Denmark. *Offset by S. Setelipaino, Finland. Perforated 13.*

337, 338 *Scales of Justice and sword*

337		MNHVF	UseVF
15¢	pale green, olive & black *(1,244,972)*	.30	.25
	FDC *(Nov. 9, 1979)*		1.00
	Inscription block of 4	1.25	

338		MNHVF	UseVF
20¢	pale blue, deep blue & black *(1,084,483)*	.50	.35
	FDC *(Nov. 9, 1979)*		1.00
	Inscription block of 4	2.25	

1980. NEW ECONOMIC ORDER ISSUE The General Assembly held a special session in 1980 to discuss the gap between developed and developing countries. Designed by Cemalettin Mutver, Turkey (15¢), and George Hamori, Australia (31¢). *Offset by The House of Questa, U.K. Perforated 14 1/2, multicolored.*

339 *Rising economic trend*

339		MNHVF	UseVF
15¢	multicolored *(1,163,801)*	.35	.30
	FDC *(Jan. 11, 1980)*		1.00
	Inscription block of 4	2.50	

340 *Key of flags*

340		MNHVF	UseVF
31¢	multicolored *(1,103,560)*	.45	.35
	FDC *(Jan. 11, 1980)*		1.25
	Inscription block of 4	3.50	

1980. U.N. DECADE FOR WOMEN'S ISSUE Designed by Susanne Rottenfusser, Germany. *Offset by The House of Questa, U.K. Perforated 14 1/2, multicolored, color of background given below.*

341, 342 *Women's year emblem*

341		MNHVF	UseVF
15¢	light gray *(1,409,350)*	.30	.25
	FDC *(March 7, 1980)*		1.00
	Inscription block of 4	1.50	

342		MNHVF	UseVF
20¢	light blue *(1,182,016)*	.35	.25
	FDC *(March 7, 1980)*		1.00
	Inscription block of 4	2.00	

1980. PEACE-KEEPING OPERATIONS ISSUE Commemorated the U.N. military observer missions and U.N. peace-keeping forces. Designed by Bruno K. Wiesey, Germany (15¢), James Gardiner, U.K. (31¢). *Offset by Joh. Enschedé and Sons, Netherlands. Perforated 14x13.*

343 *Helmet and U.N. seal;* 344 *Symbolic arrows*

343		MNHVF	UseVF
15¢	black & blue *(1,245,521)*	.30	.25
	FDC *(May 16, 1980)*		1.00
	Inscription block of 4	1.50	

344		MNHVF	UseVF
31¢	multicolored *(1,191,000)*	.45	.40
	FDC *(May 16, 1980)*		1.00
	Inscription block of 4	2.50	

1980. U.N. 35TH ANNIVERSARY ISSUE Designed by Cemalettin Mutver, Turkey (15¢), Mian Saeed, Pakistan (31¢). *Offset by Ashton-Potter Ltd., Canada. Perforated 13x13 1/2.*

345 "35"

345		MNHVF	UseVF
15¢	multicolored *(1,554,514)*	.30	.25
	FDC *(June 26, 1980)*		1.00
	Inscription block of 4	1.75	

346 *Globe and laurel leaves*

346		MNHVF	UseVF
31¢	**multicolored** *(1,389,606)*	.40	.30
	FDC *(June 26, 1980)*		1.00
	Inscription block of 4	2.00	

1980. U.N. 35TH ANNIVERSARY SOUVENIR SHEET Designed by Ole Hamann, Denmark. *Offset by Ashton-Potter Ltd., Canada. Sheet of 2 (92x73mm). Imperforate.*

347 *Souvenir sheet with Nos. 345 and 346*

347		MNHVF	UseVF
46¢	**Sheet of 2** *(1,215,505)*	1.00	1.00
	a. Single (15¢)	.20	
	b. Single (31¢)	.35	
	FDC *(June 26, 1980)*		1.00

1980. FLAG ISSUE This is the first group of sixteen Flag stamps showing the flags of Member States of the U.N. Designed by Ole Hamann, Denmark, and executed by Irving Konopiaty, U.S. *Gravure by Helio Courvoisier, Switzerland. Perforated 11 1/2, granite paper, multicolored. Printed in sheets of 16 showing 4 different flags, each in blocks of 4.*

348 *Yugoslavia*

348		MNHVF	UseVF
15¢	**multicolored** *(3,416,292)*	.30	.25
	FDC *(Sept. 26, 1980)*		1.00
	Inscription block of 4	1.00	

349 *France*

349		MNHVF	UseVF
15¢	**multicolored** *(3,416,292)*	.30	.25
	FDC *(Sept. 26, 1980)*		1.00
	Inscription block of 4	1.00	

350 *Venezuela*

350		MNHVF	UseVF
15¢	**multicolored** *(3,416,292)*	.30	.25
	FDC *(Sept. 26, 1980)*		1.00
	Inscription block of 4	1.00	

351 *El Salvador*

351		MNHVF	UseVF
15¢	**multicolored** *(3,416,292)*	.30	.25
	FDC *(Sept. 26, 1980)*		1.00
	Inscription block of 4	1.00	
	y. Se-tenant block of 4, Nos. 348-351	2.00	

352 *Guinea*

352		MNHVF	UseVF
15¢	**multicolored** *(3,442,633)*	.30	.25
	FDC *(Sept. 26, 1980)*		1.00
	Inscription block of 4	1.00	

353 *Suriname*

353		MNHVF	UseVF
15¢	**multicolored** *(3,442,633)*	.30	.25
	FDC *(Sept. 26, 1980)*		1.00
	Inscription block of 4	1.00	

354 *Bangladesh*

354		MNHVF	UseVF
15¢	**multicolored** *(3,442,633)*	.30	.25
	FDC *(Sept. 26, 1980)*		1.00
	Inscription block of 4	1.00	

355 *Mali*

355		MNHVF	UseVF
15¢	**multicolored** *(3,442,633)*	.30	.25
	FDC *(Sept. 26, 1980)*		1.00
	Inscription block of 4	1.00	
	y. Se-tenant block of 4, Nos. 352-355	2.00	

356 *Turkey*

356		MNHVF	UseVF
15¢	**multicolored** *(3,490,725)*	.30	.25
	FDC *(Sept. 26, 1980)*		1.00
	Inscription block of 4	1.00	

357 *Luxembourg*

357		MNHVF	UseVF
15¢	**multicolored** *(3,490,725)*	.30	.25
	FDC *(Sept. 26, 1980)*		1.00
	Inscription block of 4	1.00	

358 *Fiji*

358		MNHVF	UseVF
15¢	**multicolored** *(3,490,725)*	.30	.25
	FDC *(Sept. 26, 1980)*		1.00
	Inscription block of 4	1.00	

359 *Vietnam*

359		MNHVF	UseVF
15¢	**multicolored** *(3,490,725)*	.30	.25
	FDC *(Sept. 26, 1980)*		1.00
	Inscription block of 4	1.00	
	y. Se-tenant block of 4, Nos. 356-359	2.00	

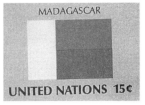

360 *Madagascar*

360		MNHVF	UseVF
15¢	**multicolored** *(3,442,497)*	.30	.25
	FDC *(Sept. 26, 1980)*		1.00
	Inscription block of 4	1.00	

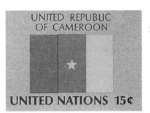

361 *Cameroon*

361		MNHVF	UseVF
15¢	**multicolored** *(3,442,497)*	.30	.25
	FDC *(Sept. 26, 1980)*		1.00
	Inscription block of 4	1.00	

362 *Rwanda*

362		MNHVF	UseVF
15¢	**multicolored** *(3,442,497)*	.30	.25
	FDC *(Sept. 26, 1980)*		1.00
	Inscription block of 4	1.00	

363 *Hungary*

363		MNHVF	UseVF
15¢	**multicolored** *(3,442,497)*	.30	.25
	FDC *(Sept. 26, 1980)*		1.00
	Inscription block of 4	1.00	
	y. Se-tenant block of 4, Nos. 360-363	2.00	

1980. ECONOMIC AND SOCIAL COUNCIL ISSUE Designed by Eliezer Weishoff, Israel (15¢); Dietmar Kowall, Germany (20¢). *Offset by Ashton-Potter Ltd., Canada. Perforated 13 1/2.*

364 *Bouquet of economic and social achievements*

364		MNHVF	UseVF
15¢	**multicolored** *(1,192,165)*	.25	.25
	FDC *(Nov. 21, 1980)*		1.00
	Inscription block of 4	2.00	

365 *Progress thru cooperation*

365		MNHVF	UseVF
20¢	**multicolored** *(1,011,382)*	1.00	.75
	FDC *(Nov. 21, 1980)*		1.00
	Inscription block of 4	2.75	

1981. RIGHTS OF PALESTINIAN PEOPLE ISSUE Designed by David Dewhurst, U.S. *Gravure by Helio Courvoisier, Switzerland. Perforated 11 1/2, granite paper.*

366 *Inalienable Rights of the Palestinian People*

366		MNHVF	UseVF
15¢	**multicolored** *(993,489)*	.50	.40
	FDC *(Jan. 30, 1981)*		1.00
	Inscription block of 4	2.00	

1981. YEAR OF DISABLED PERSONS ISSUE The General Assembly announced 1981 as "International Year of Disabled Persons." Designed by Sophia van Heeswijk, Germany (20¢), G. P. Vander Heyde, Australia (35¢). *Gravure by Heraclio Fournier, Spain. Perforated 14.*

367 *Jigsaw puzzle*

367		MNHVF	UseVF
20¢	**multicolored** *(1,218,371)*	.75	.50
	FDC *(March 6, 1981)*		1.00
	Inscription block of 4	3.00	

368 *International Year of Disabled Persons, geometric design*

368		MNHVF	UseVF
35¢	**black & orange** *(1,107,298)*	.85	.75
	FDC *(March 6, 1981)*		1.00
	Inscription block of 4	3.25	

1981. U.N. ART BULGARIAN MURAL ISSUE The Government of Bulgaria presented the U.N. with a replica of a 13th Century Bulgarian fresco inside Boyana Church near Sofia. Adapted as a stamp by Ole Hamann, Denmark, from an original design by an unknown artist from Bulgaria. *Gravure by Helio Courvoisier, Switzerland. Perforated 11 1/2, granite paper.*

369, 370 *Divislava and Sebastocrator Kaloyan, Bulgarian Mural, 1259, Boyana Church, Sofia*

369		MNHVF	UseVF
20¢	**multicolored** *(1,252,648)*	.40	.30
	FDC *(April 15, 1981)*		1.00
	Inscription block of 4	2.50	

370		MNHVF	UseVF
31¢	**multicolored** *(1,061,056)*	.70	.50
	FDC *(April 15, 1981)*		1.25
	Inscription block of 4	3.00	

1981. RENEWABLE ENERGY ISSUE Conference on New and Renewable Sources of Energy held in Nairobi, Kenya in August 1981. Designed by Ulrike Dreyer, Germany (20¢), Robert Perrot, France (40¢). *Offset by S. Setelipaino, Finland. Perforated 13.*

371, 372 *Symbols of renewable energy*

371		MNHVF	UseVF
20¢	**multicolored** *(1,132,877)*	.50	.45
	FDC *(May 29, 1981)*		1.00
	Inscription block of 4	2.75	

372		MNHVF	UseVF
40¢	**multicolored** *(1,158,319)*	1.00	1.00
	FDC *(May 29, 1981)*		1.25
	Inscription block of 4	4.00	

1981. FLAG ISSUE This is the second group of sixteen Flag stamps showing the flags of Member States of the U.N. Designed by Ole Hamann, Denmark, and executed by Irving Konopiaty, U.S. *Gravure by Helio Courvoisier, Switzerland. Granite paper. Issued in 4 panes of 16, each pane contains 4 blocks of four; se-tenant block of 4 designs centers each pane. Perforated 12.*

373 *United States*

373		MNHVF	UseVF
20¢	**multicolored** *(2,450,537)*	.40	.35
	FDC *(Sept. 25, 1981)*		1.00
	Inscription block of 4	2.00	

374 *Singapore*

374
20¢ **multicolored** *(2,450,537)*
FDC *(Sept. 25, 1981)*
Inscription block of 4

	MNHVF	UseVF
	.40	.35
		1.00
	2.00	

375 *Panama*

375
20¢ **multicolored** *(2,450,537)*
FDC *(Sept. 25, 1981)*
Inscription block of 4

	MNHVF	UseVF
	.40	.35
		1.00
	2.00	

376 *Costa Rica*

376
20¢ **multicolored** *(2,450,537)*
FDC *(Sept. 25, 1981)*
Inscription block of 4
y. Se-tenant block of 4, Nos. 373-376
y1. Miniature pane of 16

	MNHVF	UseVF
	.40	.35
		1.00
	2.00	
	3.00	
	10.00	

377 *Ukrainian SSR*

377
20¢ **multicolored** *(2,344,755)*
FDC *(Sept. 25, 1981)*
Inscription block of 4

	MNHVF	UseVF
	.40	.35
		1.00
	2.00	

378 *Kuwait*

378
20¢ **multicolored** *(2,344,755)*
FDC *(Sept. 25, 1981)*
Inscription block of 4

	MNHVF	UseVF
	.40	.35
		1.00
	2.00	

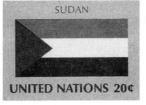

379 *Sudan*

379
20¢ **multicolored** *(2,344,755)*
FDC *(Sept. 25, 1981)*
Inscription block of 4

	MNHVF	UseVF
	.40	.35
		1.00
	2.00	

380 *Egypt*

380
20¢ **multicolored** *(2,344,755)*
FDC *(Sept. 25, 1981)*
Inscription block of 4
y. Se-tenant block of 4, Nos. 377-380
y1. Miniature pane of 16

	MNHVF	UseVF
	.40	.35
		1.00
	2.00	
	3.00	
	10.00	

381 *Djibouti*

381
20¢ **multicolored** *(2,342,224)*
FDC *(Sept. 25, 1981)*
Inscription block of 4

	MNHVF	UseVF
	.40	.35
		1.00
	2.00	

382 *Sri Lanka*

382
20¢ **multicolored** *(2,342,224)*
FDC *(Sept. 25, 1981)*
Inscription block of 4

	MNHVF	UseVF
	.40	.35
		1.00
	2.00	

383 *Bolivia*

383
20¢ **multicolored** *(2,342,224)*
FDC *(Sept. 25, 1981)*
Inscription block of 4

	MNHVF	UseVF
	.40	.35
		1.00
	2.00	

384 *Equatorial Guinea*

384		MNHVF	UseVF
20¢	multicolored *(2,342,224)*	.40	.35
	FDC *(Sept. 25, 1981)*		1.00
	Inscription block of 4	2.00	
	y. Se-tenant block of 4, Nos. 381-384	3.00	
	y1. Miniature pane of 16	10.00	

385 *Malta*

385		MNHVF	UseVF
20¢	multicolored *(2,360,297)*	.40	.35
	FDC *(Sept. 25, 1981)*		1.00
	Inscription block of 4	2.00	

386 *Czechoslovakia*

386		MNHVF	UseVF
20¢	multicolored *(2,360,297)*	.40	.35
	FDC *(Sept. 25, 1981)*		1.00
	Inscription block of 4	2.00	

387 *Thailand*

387		MNHVF	UseVF
20¢	multicolored *(2,360,297)*	.40	.35
	FDC *(Sept. 25, 1981)*		1.00
	Inscription block of 4	2.00	

388 *Trinidad and Tobago*

388		MNHVF	UseVF
20¢	multicolored *(2,360,297)*	.40	.35
	FDC *(Sept. 25, 1981)*		1.00
	Inscription block of 4	2.00	
	y. Se-tenant block of 4, Nos. 385-388	3.00	
	y1. Miniature pane of 16	10.00	

1981. U.N. 10TH ANNIVERSARY VOLUNTEERS PROGRAM ISSUE
Designed by Gabriele Nussgen, Germany (18¢), Angel Medina, Uruguay (28¢). *Offset by Walsall Security Printers, Ltd., U.K. Perforated 13.*

389 *Tree cross section;* 390 *"10" and development symbols*

389		MNHVF	UseVF
18¢	multicolored *(1,246,833)*	.50	.30
	FDC *(Nov. 13, 1981)*		1.00
	Inscription block of 4	2.75	

390		MNHVF	UseVF
28¢	multicolored *(1,282,868)*	1.00	.60
	FDC *(Nov. 13, 1981)*		1.00
	Inscription block of 4	3.50	

1982. RIGHTS AND PEACE ISSUE Designed by Rolf Christianson, Finland (17¢), George Hamori, Australia (28¢), Marek Kwiatkowski, Poland (40¢). *Printed by Helio Courvoisier, Switzerland. Perforated 11 1/2x12.*

391 *Respect for Human Rights*

391		MNHVF	UseVF
17¢	multicolored *(3,000,000 printed)*	.45	.40
	FDC *(Jan. 22, 1982)*		1.00
	Inscription block of 4	1.25	

392 *Independence of Colonial countries and peoples*

392		MNHVF	UseVF
28¢	multicolored *(3,000,000 printed)*	.75	.60
	FDC *(Jan. 22, 1982)*		1.00
	Inscription block of 4	3.00	

393 *Doves; Second Disarmament Decade*

393
		MNHVF	UseVF
40¢	**multicolored** *(3,400,000 printed)*	1.25	.75
	FDC *(Jan. 22, 1982)*		1.00
	Inscription block of 4	5.50	

1982. HUMAN ENVIRONMENT ISSUE Celebrated the 10th anniversary of the U.N. Environment Program to help coordinate sound environmental practices. Designed by Philine Hartert, Germany (20¢), Peer-Ulrich Bremer, Germany (40¢). *Offset by Joh. Enschedé and Sons, Netherlands. Perforated 13 1/2x13.*

394, 395 *Environment symbols*

394
		MNHVF	UseVF
20¢	**multicolored** *(1,017,117)*	.50	.40
	FDC *(March 19, 1982)*		1.00
	Inscription block of 4	3.50	

395
		MNHVF	UseVF
40¢	**multicolored** *(884,798)*	1.25	1.00
	FDC *(March 19, 1982)*		1.00
	Inscription block of 4	5.50	

1982. PEACEFUL USES OF OUTER SPACE ISSUE Designed by Wiktor C. Nerwinsk, Poland. *Offset by Joh. Enschedé and Sons, Netherlands. Perforated 13x13 1/2.*

396 *Laurel wreath, outer space*

396
		MNHVF	UseVF
20¢	**multicolored** *(1,083,426)*	1.00	.65
	FDC *(June 11, 1982)*		1.00
	Inscription block of 4	5.00	

1982. FLAG ISSUE This is the third group of sixteen Flag stamps showing the flags of Member States of the U.N. Designed by Ole Hamann, Denmark, and executed by Hamann; Irving Konopiaty, U.S.; and Thomas Lee, China. *Gravure by Helio Courvoisier, Switzerland. Issued in 4 panes of 16, each pane contains 4 blocks of four; a se-tenant block of 4 designs centers each pane. Perforated 12.*

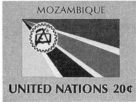

397 *Mozambique*

397
		MNHVF	UseVF
20¢	**multicolored** *(2,300,958)*	.40	.35
	FDC *(Sept. 23, 1982)*		1.00
	Inscription block of 4	2.00	

398 *Albania*

398
		MNHVF	UseVF
20¢	**multicolored** *(2,300,958)*	.40	.35
	FDC *(Sept. 23, 1982)*		1.00
	Inscription block of 4	2.00	

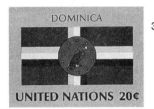

399 *Dominica*

399
		MNHVF	UseVF
20¢	**multicolored** *(2,300,958)*	.40	.35
	FDC *(Sept. 23, 1982)*		1.00
	Inscription block of 4	2.00	

400 *Solomon Islands*

400
		MNHVF	UseVF
20¢	**multicolored** *(2,300,958)*	.40	.35
	FDC *(Sept. 23, 1982)*		1.00
	Inscription block of 4	2.00	
	y. Se-tenant block of 4, Nos. 397-400	2.00	
	y1. Miniature pane of 16	10.00	

401 *Austria*

401
		MNHVF	UseVF
50¢	**multicolored** *(2,314,006)*	.40	.35
	FDC *(Sept. 23, 1982)*		1.00
	Inscription block of 4	2.00	

402 *Malaysia*

402
		MNHVF	UseVF
20¢	**multicolored** *(2,314,006)*	.40	.35
	FDC *(Sept. 23, 1982)*		1.00
	Inscription block of 4	2.00	

403 *Seychelles*

403		MNHVF	UseVF
20¢	multicolored *(2,314,006)*	.40	.35
	FDC *(Sept. 23, 1982)*		1.00
	Inscription block of 4	2.00	

404 *Ireland*

404		MNHVF	UseVF
20¢	multicolored *(2,314,006)*	.40	.35
	FDC *(Sept. 23, 1982)*		1.00
	Inscription block of 4	2.00	
	y. Se-tenant block of 4, Nos. 401-404	2.00	
	y1. Miniature pane of 16	10.00	

405 *Cape Verde*

405		MNHVF	UseVF
20¢	multicolored *(2,285,848)*	.40	.35
	FDC *(Sept. 23, 1982)*		1.00
	Inscription block of 4	2.00	

406 *Guyana*

406		MNHVF	UseVF
20¢	multicolored *(2,285,848)*	.40	.35
	FDC *(Sept. 23, 1982)*		1.00
	Inscription block of 4	2.00	

407 *Belgium*

407		MNHVF	UseVF
20¢	multicolored *(2,285,848)*	.40	.35
	FDC *(Sept. 23, 1982)*		1.00
	Inscription block of 4	2.00	

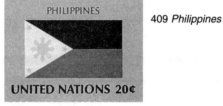

408 *Nigeria*

408		MNHVF	UseVF
20¢	multicolored *(2,285,848)*	.40	.35
	FDC *(Sept. 23, 1982)*		1.00
	Inscription block of 4	2.00	
	y. Se-tenant block of 4, Nos. 405-408	2.00	
	y1. Miniature pane of 16	10.00	

409 *Philippines*

409		MNHVF	UseVF
20¢	multicolored *(2,288,589)*	.40	.35
	FDC *(Sept. 23, 1982)*		1.00
	Inscription block of 4	2.00	

410 *Swaziland*

410		MNHVF	UseVF
20¢	multicolored *(2,288,589)*	.40	.35
	FDC *(Sept. 23, 1982)*		1.00
	Inscription block of 4	2.00	

411 *Nicaragua*

411		MNHVF	UseVF
20¢	multicolored *(2,288,589)*	.40	.35
	FDC *(Sept. 23, 1982)*		1.00
	Inscription block of 4	2.00	

412 *Burma*

412		MNHVF	UseVF
20¢	multicolored *(2,288,589)*	.40	.35
	FDC *(Sept. 23, 1982)*		1.00
	Inscription block of 4	2.00	
	y. Se-tenant block of 4, Nos. 409-412	2.00	
	y1. Miniature pane of 16	10.00	

1982. CONSERVATION AND PROTECTION OF NATURE ISSUE Designed by George Hamori, Australia. *Gravure by Heraclio Fournier, Spain. Perforated 14.*

413 *Leaf*

414 *Butterfly*

413
20¢   **multicolored** *(1,110,027)*   MNHVF .60   UseVF .40
FDC *(Nov. 19, 1982)*   1.00
Inscription block of 4   3.00

414
28¢   **multicolored** *(848,772)*   MNHVF .90   UseVF .65
FDC *(Nov. 19, 1982)*   1.00
Inscription block of 4   4.00

1983. WORLD COMMUNICATIONS YEAR ISSUE Designed by Hanns Lohrer, Germany (20¢), Lorena Berengo, Germany (40¢). *Offset by Walsall Security Printers Ltd., U.K. Perforated 13.*

415, 416 *U.N. seal, graphic design*

415
20¢   **multicolored** *(1,282,079)*   MNHVF .40   UseVF .40
FDC *(Jan. 28, 1983)*   1.00
Inscription block of 4   2.50

416
40¢   **multicolored** *(931,903)*   MNHVF 1.00   UseVF .80
FDC *(Jan. 28, 1983)*   1.00
Inscription block of 4   4.75

1983. SAFETY AT SEA ISSUE Designed by Jean-Marie Lenfant, Belgium (20¢), Ari Ron, Israel (37¢). *Offset by The House of Questa, U.K. Perforated 14 1/2.*

417, 418 *Stylized ship scenes*

417
20¢   **multicolored** *(1,252,456)*   MNHVF .50   UseVF .40
FDC *(March 18, 1983)*   1.00
Inscription block of 4   3.00

418
37¢   **multicolored** *(939,910)*   MNHVF 1.20   UseVF .80
FDC *(March 18, 1983)*   1.00
Inscription block of 4   4.75

1983. WORLD FOOD PROGRAM ISSUE Designed by Marek Kwiatkowski, Poland. Engraved by Sakae Yajima, Japan. *Intaglio by Japanese Government Printing Office. Perforated 13 1/2.*

419 *Hands presenting food bowl*

419
20¢   **rose lake** *(1,238,997)*   MNHVF .75   UseVF .65
FDC *(April 22, 1983)*   1.00
Inscription block of 4   3.50

1983. U.N. CONFERENCE ON TRADE AND DEVELOPMENT ISSUE Designed by Dietmar Braklow, Germany (20¢), Gabriele Genz, Germany (28¢). *Offset by Carl Uberreuter Druck and Verlag M. Salzer, Austria. Perforated 14.*

420, 421 *Symbols of commerce*

420
20¢   **multicolored** *(1,060,053)*   MNHVF .65   UseVF .50
FDC *(June 6, 1983)*   1.00
Inscription block of 4   3.50

421
28¢   **multicolored** *(948,981)*   MNHVF 1.25   UseVF 1.00
FDC *(June 6, 1983)*   1.00
Inscription block of 4   4.25

1983. FLAG ISSUE This is the fourth group of sixteen Flag stamps showing the flags of Member States of the U.N. Designed by Ole Hamann, Denmark, and executed by Hamann, Denmark; Irving Konopiaty, U.S.; and Thomas Lee, China. *Gravure by Helio Courvoisier, Switzerland. Panes of 16, perforated 12, granite paper.*

422 *United Kingdom*

422
20¢   **multicolored** *(2,490,599)*   MNHVF .50   UseVF .40
FDC *(Sept. 23, 1983)*   1.00
Inscription block of 4   2.00

423 *Barbados*

423		MNHVF	UseVF
20¢	**multicolored** *(2,490,599)*	.50	.40
	FDC *(Sept. 23, 1983)*		1.00
	Inscription block of 4	2.00	

424 Nepal

424		MNHVF	UseVF
20¢	**multicolored** *(2,490,599)*	.50	.40
	FDC *(Sept. 23, 1983)*		1.00
	Inscription block of 4	2.00	

425 Israel

425		MNHVF	UseVF
20¢	**multicolored** *(2,490,599)*	.50	.40
	FDC *(Sept. 23, 1983)*		1.00
	Inscription block of 4	2.00	
	y. Se-tenant block of 4, Nos. 422-425	1.65	
	y1. Miniature pane of 16	10.00	

426 China

426		MNHVF	UseVF
20¢	**multicolored** *(2,474,140)*	.50	.40
	FDC *(Sept. 23, 1983)*		1.00
	Inscription block of 4	2.00	

427 Peru

427		MNHVF	UseVF
20¢	**multicolored** *(2,474,140)*	.50	.40
	FDC *(Sept. 23, 1983)*		1.00
	Inscription block of 4	2.00	

428 Bulgaria

428		MNHVF	UseVF
20¢	**multicolored** *(2,474,140)*	.50	.40

	FDC *(Sept. 23, 1983)*		1.00
	Inscription block of 4	2.00	

429 Canada

429		MNHVF	UseVF
20¢	**multicolored** *(2,474,140)*	.50	.40
	FDC *(Sept. 23, 1983)*		1.00
	Inscription block of 4	2.00	
	y. Se-tenant block of 4, Nos. 426-429	1.65	
	y1. Miniature pane of 16	10.00	

430 Malawi

430		MNHVF	UseVF
20¢	**multicolored** *(2,483,010)*	.50	.40
	FDC *(Sept. 23, 1983)*		1.00
	Inscription block of 4	2.00	

431 Byelorussian SSR

431		MNHVF	UseVF
20¢	**multicolored** *(2,483,010)*	.50	.40
	FDC *(Sept. 23, 1983)*		1.00
	Inscription block of 4	2.00	

432 Jamaica

432		MNHVF	UseVF
20¢	**multicolored** *(2,483,010)*	.50	.40
	FDC *(Sept. 23, 1983)*		1.00
	Inscription block of 4	2.00	

433 Kenya

433		MNHVF	UseVF
20¢	**multicolored** *(2,483,010)*	.50	.40
	FDC *(Sept. 23, 1983)*		1.00
	Inscription block of 4	2.00	

y. Se-tenant block of 4, Nos. 430-433	1.65	
y1. Miniature pane of 16	10.00	

434 *Somalia*

434		MNHVF	UseVF
20¢	multicolored *(2,482,070)*	.50	.40
	FDC *(Sept. 23, 1983)*		1.00
	Inscription block of 4	2.00	

435 *Senegal*

435		MNHVF	UseVF
20¢	multicolored *(2,482,070)*	.50	.40
	FDC *(Sept. 23, 1983)*		1.00
	Inscription block of 4	2.00	

436 *Brazil*

436		MNHVF	UseVF
20¢	multicolored *(2,482,070)*	.50	.40
	FDC *(Sept. 23, 1983)*		1.00
	Inscription block of 4	2.00	

437 *Sweden*

437		MNHVF	UseVF
20¢	multicolored *(2,482,070)*	.50	.40
	FDC *(Sept. 23, 1983)*		1.00
	Inscription block of 4	2.00	
	y. Se-tenant block of 4, Nos. 434-437	1.65	
	y1. Miniature pane of 16	10.00	

1983. DECLARATION OF HUMAN RIGHTS ISSUE This is the eleventh commemorative stamp in the Human Rights series. On Dec. 10, 1948, the first world-wide proclamation and adoption of the Universal Declaration of Human Rights took place. Dec. 10 is recognized as Human Rights Day. Designed by Friedensreich Hundertwasser, Austria. Engraved by Wolfgang Seidel, Austria. *Gravure and intaglio by Government Printing Office, Austria. Perforated 13 1/2.*

438 Window Right, *abstract*

439 Treaty with Nature, *abstract*

438		MNHVF	UseVF
20¢	multicolored *(1,591,102)*	.50	.50
	FDC *(Dec. 9, 1983)*		1.00
	Inscription block of 4	3.50	

439		MNHVF	UseVF
40¢	multicolored *(1,566,789)*	1.00	1.25
	FDC *(Dec. 9, 1983)*		1.00
	Inscription block of 4	5.00	

1984. INTERNATIONAL CONFERENCE ON POPULATION ISSUE A conference in August 1984 in Mexico reviewed the global population programs since a previous conference 10 years earlier. Designed by Marina Langer-Rosa, Helmut Langer, Germany. *Offset by Bundesdruckerei, Germany. Perforated 14.*

440, 441 *Crowd of people*

440		MNHVF	UseVF
20¢	multicolored *(905,320)*	.40	.35
	FDC *(Feb. 3, 1984)*		1.00
	Inscription block of 4	2.50	

441		MNHVF	UseVF
40¢	multicolored *(717,084)*	1.25	1.00
	FDC *(Feb. 3, 1984)*		1.00
	Inscription block of 4	4.50	

1984. WORLD FOOD DAY ISSUE The Food and Agriculture Organization observes World Food Day every Oct. 16, its anniversary. Designed by Adth Vanooijen, Netherlands. *Offset by Walsall Security Printers, Ltd., U.K. Perforated 14 1/2.*

442 *Tractor;* 443 *Rice paddy workers*

442		MNHVF	UseVF
20¢	multicolored *(853,641)*	.40	.35
	FDC *(March 15, 1984)*		1.00
	Inscription block of 4	2.50	

443		MNHVF	UseVF
40¢	multicolored *(727,165)*	1.25	1.00
	FDC *(March 15, 1984)*		1.00
	Inscription block of 4	4.50	

1984. WORLD HERITAGE ISSUE First in a series. The World Heritage List was established in Nov. 1972 under terms of the Convention Concerning the Protection of the World Cultural and Natural Heritage. Designs adapted as stamps by Rocco J. Callari, U.S., and Thomas Lee, China. *Offset by Harrison and Sons Ltd., U.K. Perforated 14.*

444 *Grand Canyon, U.S., photo by Gaston Guarda, Chile;* 445 *Ancient City of Polonnaruwa, Sri Lanka, photo by Kate Bader, U.S.*

444		MNHVF	UseVF
20¢	multicolored *(814,316)*	.80	.40
	FDC *(April 18, 1984)*		1.00
	Inscription block of 4	2.50	

445		MNHVF	UseVF
50¢	multicolored *(579,136)*	1.25	1.25
	FDC *(April 18, 1984)*		1.00
	Inscription block of 4	6.00	

1984. FUTURE FOR REFUGEES ISSUE The office of the United Nations High Commissioner for Refugees was created in 1951. Designed by Hans Erni, Switzerland. *Gravure by Helio Courvoisier, Switzerland. Perforated 11 1/2.*

446, 447 *Women and children*

446		MNHVF	UseVF
20¢	multicolored *(956,743)*	.75	.50
	FDC *(May 29, 1984)*		1.00
	Inscription block of 4	2.25	

447		MNHVF	UseVF
50¢	multicolored *(729,036)*	1.25	1.00
	FDC *(May 29, 1984)*		1.00
	Inscription block of 4	6.00	

1984. FLAG ISSUE This is the fifth group of sixteen Flag stamps showing the flags of Member States of the U.N. Designed by Ole Hamann, Denmark, and executed by Rocco J. Callari, U.S.; Hamann; Irving Konopiaty, U.S.; and Thomas Lee, China. *Gravure by Helio Courvoisier, Switzerland. Pane of 16. Perforated 12.*

448 *Burundi*

448		MNHVF	UseVF
20¢	multicolored *(1,941,471)*	1.00	.75
	FDC *(Sept. 21, 1984)*		1.00
	Inscription block of 4	4.00	

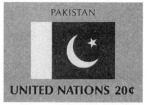

449 *Pakistan*

449		MNHVF	UseVF
20¢	multicolored *(1,941,471)*	1.00	.75
	FDC *(Sept. 21, 1984)*		1.00
	Inscription block of 4	4.00	

450 *Benin*

450		MNHVF	UseVF
20¢	multicolored *(1,941,471)*	1.00	.75
	FDC *(Sept. 21, 1984)*		1.00
	Inscription block of 4	4.00	

451 *Italy*

451		MNHVF	UseVF
20¢	multicolored *(1,941,471)*	1.00	.75
	FDC *(Sept. 21, 1984)*		1.00
	Inscription block of 4	4.00	
	y. Se-tenant block of 4, Nos. 448-451	6.00	1.00
	y1. Miniature pane of 16	7.50	

452 *Tanzania*

452		MNHVF	UseVF
20¢	multicolored *(1,969,051)*	1.00	.75
	FDC *(Sept. 21, 1984)*		1.00
	Inscription block of 4	4.00	

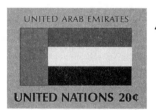

453 *United Arab Emirates*

453		MNHVF	UseVF
20¢	multicolored *(1,969,051)*	1.00	.75
	FDC *(Sept. 21, 1984)*		1.00
	Inscription block of 4	4.00	

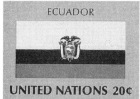

454 *Ecuador*

454
20¢ **multicolored** *(1,969,051)* MNHVF 1.00 UseVF .75
  FDC *(Sept. 21, 1984)* 1.00
  Inscription block of 4 4.00

455 *Bahamas*

455
20¢ **multicolored** *(1,969,051)* MNHVF 1.00 UseVF .75
  FDC *(Sept. 21, 1984)* 1.00
  Inscription block of 4 4.00
  y. Se-tenant block of 4, Nos. 452-455 6.00
  y1. Miniature pane of 16 7.50

456 *Poland*

456
20¢ **multicolored** *(2,001,091)* MNHVF 1.00 UseVF .75
  FDC *(Sept. 21, 1984)* 1.00
  Inscription block of 4 4.00

457 *Papua New Guinea*

457
20¢ **multicolored** *(2,001,091)* MNHVF 1.00 UseVF .75
  FDC *(Sept. 21, 1984)* 1.00
  Inscription block of 4 4.00

458 *Uruguay*

458
20¢ **multicolored** *(2,001,091)* MNHVF 1.00 UseVF .75
  FDC *(Sept. 21, 1984)* 1.00
  Inscription block of 4 4.00

459 *Chile*

459
20¢ **multicolored** *(2,001,091)* MNHVF 1.00 UseVF .75
  FDC *(Sept. 21, 1984)* 1.00
  Inscription block of 4 4.00
  y. Se-tenant block of 4, Nos. 456-459 6.00
  y1. Miniature pane of 16 7.50

460 *Paraguay*

460
20¢ **multicolored** *(1,969,875)* MNHVF 1.00 UseVF .75
  FDC *(Sept. 21, 1984)* 1.00
  Inscription block of 4 4.00

461 *Bhutan*

461
20¢ **multicolored** *(1,969,875)* MNHVF 1.00 UseVF .75
  FDC *(Sept. 21, 1984)* 1.00
  Inscription block of 4 4.00

462 *Central African Republic*

462
20¢ **multicolored** *(1,969,875)* MNHVF 1.00 UseVF .75
  FDC *(Sept. 21, 1984)* 1.00
  Inscription block of 4 4.00

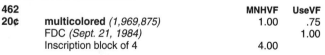

463 *Australia*

463
20¢ **multicolored** *(1,969,875)* MNHVF 1.00 UseVF .75
  FDC *(Sept. 21, 1984)* 1.00
  Inscription block of 4 4.00
  y. Se-tenant block of 4, Nos. 460-463 6.00
  y1. Miniature pane of 16 7.50

1984. INTERNATIONAL YOUTH YEAR ISSUE Designed by Raymon Müeller, Germany. *Offset by Waddingtons Ltd., U.K. Perforated 13 1/2.*

464, 465 *Abstract and line of people*

464		MNHVF	UseVF
20¢	multicolored *(884,692)*	.55	.45
	FDC *(Nov. 15, 1984)*		1.00
	Inscription block of 4	2.50	

465		MNHVF	UseVF
35¢	multicolored *(740,023)*	1.00	.65
	FDC *(Nov. 15, 1984)*		1.00
	Inscription block of 4	6.00	

1985. ILO TURIN CENTER ISSUE for the International Labor Organization training institution. Adapted from photographs by Rocco J. Callari, U.S. and Thomas Lee, China. *Intaglio by Japanese Government Printing Office. Perforated 13 1/2.*

466 *Turin Centre emblem*

466		MNHVF	UseVF
23¢	multicolored *(612,942)*	.75	.65
	FDC *(Feb. 1, 1985)*		1.00
	Inscription block of 4	3.50	

1985. U.N. UNIVERSITY ISSUE The UNU coordinates the work of scientists and scholars throughout the world. Designed by Moshe Pereg, Israel and Hinedi Geluda, Brazil. *Gravure by Helio Courvoisier, Switzerland. Perforated 13 1/2.*

467 *"UNU" and silhouettes*

467		MNHVF	UseVF
50¢	multicolored *(625,043)*	1.85	1.60
	FDC *(March 15, 1985)*		1.00
	Inscription block of 4	8.00	

1985. REGULAR ISSUE Designed by Fritz Henry Oerter, Germany (22¢), Rimondi Rino, Italy ($3). *Offset by Carl Ueberreuter Druck and Verlag M. Salzer, Austria. Perforated 14.*

468 *Drawing of people;* 469 *United Nations in six languages, paintbrush*

468		MNHVF	UseVF
22¢	multicolored *(2,000,000)*	.50	.35
	FDC *(May 10, 1985)*		1.00
	Inscription block of 4	3.00	

469		MNHVF	UseVF
$3	multicolored *(2,000,000)*	5.00	4.00
	FDC *(May 10, 1985)*		1.00
	Inscription block of 4	24.00	

1985. U.N. 40TH ANNIVERSARY ISSUE Featured paintings (details) by American artist Andrew Wyeth. Souvenir sheet designed by Rocco J. Callari, U.S. and Thomas Lee, China. *Gravure by Helio Courvoisier, Switzerland. Perforated 12x11 1/2.*

470 *Detail from* The Corner; 471 *Detail from* Alvaro Raking Hay

470		MNHVF	UseVF
22¢	multicolored *(944,960)*	.75	.45
	FDC *(June 26, 1985)*		1.00
	Inscription block of 4	3.00	

471		MNHVF	UseVF
45¢	multicolored *(680,079)*	1.50	1.50
	FDC *(June 26, 1985)*		1.00
	Inscription block of 4	7.00	

1985. U.N. 40TH ANNIVERSARY SOUVENIR SHEET Designed by Rocco J. Callari, U.S., and Thomas Lee, China. *Gravure by Helio Courvoisier, Switzerland. Imperforate.*

472 *Souvenir sheet with Nos. 470 and 471*

472		MNHVF	UseVF
67¢	Sheet of 2 *(506,004)*	2.50	2.25
	a. Single (22¢)	.75	
	b. Single (45¢)	1.75	
	FDC *(June 26, 1985)*		1.00

1985. FLAG ISSUE This is the sixth group of sixteen Flag stamps showing the flags of Member States of the U.N. Designed by Ole Hamann, Denmark, and executed by Rocco J. Callari, U.S.; Irving Kono-piaty, U.S.; and Thomas Lee, China. *Gravure by Helio Courvoisier, Switzerland. Perforated 12, granite paper.*

473 *Oman*

473			MNHVF	UseVF
22¢	multicolored *(1,215,533)*		1.00	.85
	FDC *(Sept. 20, 1985)*			1.00
	Inscription block of 4		4.00	

474 *Ghana*

474			MNHVF	UseVF
22¢	multicolored *(1,215,533)*		1.00	.85
	FDC *(Sept. 20, 1985)*			1.00
	Inscription block of 4		4.00	

475 *Sierra Leone*

475			MNHVF	UseVF
22¢	multicolored *(1,215,533)*		1.00	.85
	FDC *(Sept. 20, 1985)*			1.00
	Inscription block of 4		4.00	

476 *Finland*

476			MNHVF	UseVF
22¢	multicolored *(1,215,533)*		1.00	.85
	FDC *(Sept. 20, 1985)*			1.00
	Inscription block of 4		4.00	
	y. Se-tenant block of 4, Nos. 473-476		6.50	
	y1. Miniature pane of 16		8.00	

477 *Liberia*

477			MNHVF	UseVF
22¢	multicolored *(1,213,231)*		1.00	.85

		MNHVF	UseVF
FDC *(Sept. 20, 1985)*			1.00
Inscription block of 4		4.00	

478 *Mauritius*

478			MNHVF	UseVF
22¢	multicolored *(1,213,231)*		1.00	.85
	FDC *(Sept. 20, 1985)*			1.00
	Inscription block of 4		4.00	

479 *Chad*

479			MNHVF	UseVF
22¢	multicolored *(1,213,231)*		1.00	.85
	FDC *(Sept. 20, 1985)*			1.00
	Inscription block of 4		4.00	

480 *Dominican Republic*

480			MNHVF	UseVF
22¢	multicolored *(1,213,231)*		1.00	.85
	FDC *(Sept. 20, 1985)*			1.00
	Inscription block of 4		4.00	
	y. Se-tenant block of 4, Nos. 477-480		6.50	
	y1. Miniature pane of 16		8.00	

481 *Uganda*

481			MNHVF	UseVF
22¢	multicolored *(1,216,878)*		1.00	.85
	FDC *(Sept. 20, 1985)*			1.00
	Inscription block of 4		4.00	

482 *Sao Tome and Principe*

482			MNHVF	UseVF
22¢	multicolored *(1,216,878)*		1.00	.85
	FDC *(Sept. 20, 1985)*			1.00
	Inscription block of 4		4.00	

483 *Union of Soviet Socialist Republics*

483		MNHVF	UseVF
22¢	multicolored *(1,216,878)*	1.00	.85
	FDC *(Sept. 20, 1985)*		1.00
	Inscription block of 4	4.00	

484 *India*

484		MNHVF	UseVF
22¢	multicolored *(1,216,878)*	1.00	.85
	FDC *(Sept. 20, 1985)*		1.00
	Inscription block of 4	4.00	
	y. Se-tenant block of 4, Nos. 481-484	6.50	
	y1. Miniature pane of 16	8.00	

485 *Grenada*

485		MNHVF	UseVF
22¢	multicolored *(1,270,755)*	1.00	.85
	FDC *(Sept. 20, 1985)*		1.00
	Inscription block of 4	4.00	

486 *Federal Republic of Germany*

486		MNHVF	UseVF
22¢	multicolored *(1,270,755)*	1.00	.85
	FDC *(Sept. 20, 1985)*		1.00
	Inscription block of 4	4.00	

487 *Saudi Arabia*

487		MNHVF	UseVF
22¢	multicolored *(1,270,755)*	1.00	.85
	FDC *(Sept. 20, 1985)*		1.00
	Inscription block of 4	4.00	

488 *Mexico*

488		MNHVF	UseVF
22¢	multicolored *(1,270,755)*	1.00	.85
	FDC *(Sept. 20, 1985)*		1.00
	Inscription block of 4	4.00	
	y. Se-tenant block of 4, Nos. 485-488	6.50	
	y1. Miniature pane of 16	8.00	

1985. UNICEF CHILD SURVIVAL CAMPAIGN ISSUE Designed by Mel Harris, U.K. (22¢), Dipok Deyi, India (33¢). Engraved by Shoji Okamura, Japan (22¢); Hiroshi Sasaki, Japan (33¢). *Gravure and intaglio by the Japanese Government Printing Office. Perforated 13 1/2.*

489 *Asian Toddler*

490 *Breast-feeding*

489		MNHVF	UseVF
22¢	multicolored *(823,724)*	.50	.40
	FDC *(Nov. 22, 1985)*		1.00
	Inscription block of 4	2.75	

490		MNHVF	UseVF
33¢	multicolored *(632,753)*	1.25	1.25
	FDC *(Nov. 22, 1985)*		1.00
	Inscription block of 4	4.50	

1986. AFRICA IN CRISIS ISSUE Designed by Wosene Kosrof, Ethiopia. *Gravure by Helio Courvoisier, Switzerland. Perforated 11 1/2x12.*

491 *Abstract painting by Wosene Kosrof*

491		MNHVF	UseVF
22¢	multicolored *(708,169)*	.85	.75
	FDC *(Jan. 31. 1986)*		1.00
	Inscription block of 4	3.75	

1986. U.N. DEVELOPMENT PROGRAM ISSUE The program is a partnership of more than 170 countries and territories. Designed by Thomas Lee, China. *Gravure by the Japanese Government Printing Office. Perforated 13 1/2.*

492 *Dam;* 493 *Irrigation;* 494 *Hygiene;* 495 *Well*

492		MNHVF	UseVF
22¢	multicolored *(525,839)*	1.60	1.25

493		MNHVF	UseVF
22¢	multicolored *(525,839)*	1.60	1.25

494		MNHVF	UseVF
22¢	multicolored *(525,839)*	1.60	1.25

495		MNHVF	UseVF
22¢	multicolored *(525,839)*	1.60	1.25
	FDC *(March 14, 1986)* any single		1.00
	Inscription block of 4	12.00	
	y. Se-tenant block of 4	10.00	5.50
	FDC (block of 4)		6.00

1986. STAMP COLLECTING ISSUE Designed by Ingalill Axelsson, Sweden. Engraved by Czeslaw Slania, Sweden. *Intaglio by Swedish Post Office. Perforated 12 1/2.*

496 *Stamp of 1954 magnified;* 497 *Engraver*

496		MNHVF	UseVF
22¢	dark violet & bright blue *(825,782)*	.75	.60
	FDC *(May 22, 1986)*		1.00
	Inscription block of 4	3.00	

497		MNHVF	UseVF
44¢	brown & emerald green *(738,552)*	1.50	1.25
	FDC *(May 22, 1986)*		1.00
	Inscription block of 4	6.00	

1986. INTERNATIONAL YEAR OF PEACE ISSUE The U.N. General Assembly declared 1986 to be the International Year of Peace. Designed by Akira Iriguchi, Japan (22¢), Henryk Chylinski, Poland (33¢). *Gravure and embossed by the Japanese Government Printing Office. Perforated 13 1/2.*

498 *Birds in a tree;* 499 *"Peace" in seven languages*

498		MNHVF	UseVF
22¢	multicolored *(836,160)*	1.25	.75

	FDC *(June 20, 1986)*		1.00
	Inscription block of 4	5.50	

499		MNHVF	UseVF
33¢	multicolored *(663,882)*	2.75	1.75
	FDC *(June 20, 1986)*		1.00
	Inscription block of 4	11.00	

1986. FLAG ISSUE This is the seventh group of sixteen Flag stamps showing the flags of Member States of the U.N. Designed by Ole Hamann, Denmark, and executed by Rocco J. Callari, U.S.; Hamann; Irving Konopiaty, U.S.; Thomas Lee, China; and Robert Stein, U.S. *Gravure by Helio Courvoisier, Switzerland. Perforated 12.*

500 *Maldives*

500		MNHVF	UseVF
22¢	multicolored *(1,154,870)*	1.00	.85
	FDC *(Sept. 19, 1986)*		1.00
	Inscription block of 4	4.00	

501 *Ethiopia*

501		MNHVF	UseVF
22¢	multicolored *(1,154,870)*	1.00	.85
	FDC *(Sept. 19, 1986)*		1.00
	Inscription block of 4	4.00	

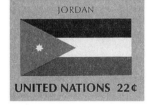

502 *Jordan*

502		MNHVF	UseVF
22¢	multicolored *(1,154,870)*	1.00	.85
	FDC *(Sept. 19, 1986)*		1.00
	Inscription block of 4	4.00	

503 *Zambia*

503		MNHVF	UseVF
22¢	multicolored *(1,154,870)*	1.00	.85
	FDC *(Sept. 19, 1986)*		1.00
	Inscription block of 4	4.00	
	y. Se-tenant block of 4, Nos. 500-503	6.50	
	y1. Miniature pane of 16	8.00	

504 *New Zealand*

504		MNHVF	UseVF
22¢	multicolored *(1,150,584)*	1.00	.85
	FDC *(Sept. 19, 1986)*		1.00
	Inscription block of 4	4.00	

505 *Lao Peoples Democratic Republic*

505		MNHVF	UseVF
22¢	multicolored *(1,150,584)*	1.00	.85
	FDC *(Sept. 19, 1986)*		1.00
	Inscription block of 4	4.00	

506 *Burkina Faso*

506		MNHVF	UseVF
22¢	multicolored *(1,150,584)*	1.00	.85
	FDC *(Sept. 19, 1986)*		1.00
	Inscription block of 4	4.00	

507 *Gambia*

507		MNHVF	UseVF
22¢	multicolored *(1,150,584)*	1.00	.85
	FDC *(Sept. 19, 1986)*		1.00
	Inscription block of 4	4.00	
	y. Se-tenant block of 4, Nos. 504-507	6.50	
	y1. Miniature pane of 16	8.00	

508 *Iceland*

508		MNHVF	UseVF
22¢	multicolored *(1,152,740)*	1.00	.85
	FDC *(Sept. 19, 1986)*		1.00
	Inscription block of 4	4.00	

509 *Antigua and Barbuda*

509		MNHVF	UseVF
22¢	multicolored *(1,152,740)*	1.00	.85
	FDC *(Sept. 19, 1986)*		1.00
	Inscription block of 4	4.00	

510 *Angola*

510		MNHVF	UseVF
22¢	multicolored *(1,152,740)*	1.00	.85
	FDC *(Sept. 19, 1986)*		1.00
	Inscription block of 4	4.00	

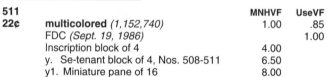

511 *Botswana*

511		MNHVF	UseVF
22¢	multicolored *(1,152,740)*	1.00	.85
	FDC *(Sept. 19, 1986)*		1.00
	Inscription block of 4	4.00	
	y. Se-tenant block of 4, Nos. 508-511	6.50	
	y1. Miniature pane of 16	8.00	

512 *Romania*

512		MNHVF	UseVF
22¢	multicolored *(1,150,412)*	1.00	.85
	FDC *(Sept. 19, 1986)*		1.00
	Inscription block of 4	4.00	

513 *Togo*

513		MNHVF	UseVF
22¢	multicolored *(1,150,412)*	1.00	.85
	FDC *(Sept. 19, 1986)*		1.00
	Inscription block of 4	4.00	

514 *Mauritania*

514		MNHVF	UseVF
22¢	multicolored *(1,150,412)*	1.00	.85
	FDC *(Sept. 19, 1986)*		1.00
	Inscription block of 4	4.00	

515 *Colombia*

515		MNHVF	UseVF
22¢	multicolored *(1,150,412)*	1.00	.85
	FDC *(Sept. 19, 1986)*		1.00
	Inscription block of 4	4.00	
	y. Se-tenant block of 4, Nos. 512-515	6.50	
	y1. Miniature pane of 16	8.00	

1986. WFUNA 40TH ANNIVERSARY SOUVENIR SHEET ISSUE World Federation of U.N. Associations. Format design by Rocco J. Callari, U.S. *Offset by Joh. Enschedé and Sons, Netherlands. Perforated 13x13 1/2.*

516a Mother Earth, *by Edna Hibel, U.S.;* 516b *Watercolor, by Salvadore Dali, Spain;* 516c New Dawn, *by Dong Kingman, U.S.;* 516d *Watercolor, by Chaim Gross, U.S.*

516		MNHVF	UseVF
$1.38	Sheet of 4 *(433,888)*	5.50	4.50
	a. Single (22¢)	.50	
	b. Single (33¢)	.80	
	c. Single (39¢)	.95	
	d. Single (44¢)	1.10	
	FDC *(Nov. 14, 1986)*		5.50

1987. TRYGVE LIE ISSUE Adapted as a stamp by Rocco J. Callari, U.S., from a portrait by Harald Dal, Norway. Engraved by Wolfgang Seidel, Austria. *Gravure and intaglio by the Government Printing Office, Austria. Perforated 13 1/2.*

517 *Trygve Lie (1896-1968), first U.N. secretary general, portrait by Harald Dal, Norway*

517		MNHVF	UseVF
22¢	multicolored *(596,440)*	1.40	1.00
	FDC *(Jan. 30, 1987)*		1.00
	Inscription block of 4	6.50	

1987. SHELTER FOR THE HOMELESS ISSUE The U.N. General Assembly declared 1987 to be the International Year of Shelter for the Homeless. Designed by Wladyslaw Brykczynski, Poland. *Offset by Joh. Enschedé and Sons, Netherlands. Perforated 13 1/2x12 1/2.*

518 *Blueprint;* 519 *Building hut*

518		MNHVF	UseVF
22¢	multicolored *(620,627)*	1.00	.75
	FDC *(March 13, 1987)*		1.00
	Inscription block of 4	3.00	
519		MNHVF	UseVF
44¢	multicolored *(538,096)*	1.75	1.25
	FDC *(March 13, 1987)*		1.00
	Inscription block of 4	9.00	

1987. FIGHT DRUG ABUSE ISSUE Designed by Susan Borgen and Noe Werrett, U.S. Illustrated by C.M. Dudash, U.S. *Offset by The House of Questa, U.K. Perforated 14 1/2x15.*

520 *Construction;* 521 *Education*

520		MNHVF	UseVF
22¢	multicolored *(674,563)*	.85	.75
	FDC *(June 12, 1987)*		1.00
	Inscription block of 4	3.00	
521		MNHVF	UseVF
33¢	multicolored *(643,153)*	1.75	1.00
	FDC *(June 12, 1987)*		1.00
	Inscription block of 4	9.00	

1987. FLAG ISSUE This is the eighth group of sixteen Flag stamps showing the flags of Member States of the U.N. Designed by Ole Hamann, Denmark, and executed by Rocco J. Callari, U.S.; Hamann; Irving Konopiaty, U.S.; Thomas Lee, China; and Robert Stein, U.S. *Gravure by Helio Courvoisier, Switzerland. Perforated 12, granite paper.*

522 *Comoros*

522		**MNHVF**	**UseVF**
22¢	**multicolored** *(1,235,828)*	1.00	.75
	FDC *(Sept. 18, 1987)*		1.00
	Inscription block of 4	4.00	

523 *Democratic Yemen*

523		**MNHVF**	**UseVF**
22¢	**multicolored** *(1,235,828)*	1.00	.75
	FDC *(Sept. 18, 1987)*		1.00
	Inscription block of 4	4.00	

524 *Mongolia*

524		**MNHVF**	**UseVF**
22¢	**multicolored** *(1,235,828)*	1.00	.75
	FDC *(Sept. 18, 1987)*		1.00
	Inscription block of 4	4.00	

525 *Vanuatu*

525		**MNHVF**	**UseVF**
22¢	**multicolored** *(1,235,828)*	1.00	.75
	FDC *(Sept. 18, 1987)*		1.00
	Inscription block of 4	4.00	
	y. Se-tenant block of 4, Nos. 522-525	6.50	
	y1. Miniature pane of 16	8.00	

526 *Japan*

526		**MNHVF**	**UseVF**
22¢	**multicolored** *(1,244,535)*	1.00	.75
	FDC *(Sept. 18, 1987)*		1.00
	Inscription block of 4	4.00	

527 *Gabon*

527		**MNHVF**	**UseVF**
22¢	**multicolored** *(1,244,534)*	1.00	.75
	FDC *(Sept. 18, 1987)*		1.00
	Inscription block of 4	4.00	

528 *Zimbabwe*

528		**MNHVF**	**UseVF**
22¢	**multicolored** *(1,244,534)*	1.00	.75
	FDC *(Sept. 18, 1987)*		1.00
	Inscription block of 4	4.00	

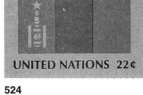

529 *Iraq*

529		**MNHVF**	**UseVF**
22¢	**multicolored** *(1,244,534)*	1.00	.75
	FDC *(Sept. 18, 1987)*		1.00
	Inscription block of 4	4.00	
	y. Se-tenant block of 4, Nos. 526-529	6.50	
	y1. Miniature pane of 16	8.00	

530 *Argentina*

530		**MNHVF**	**UseVF**
22¢	**multicolored** *(1,238,065)*	1.00	.75
	FDC *(Sept. 18, 1987)*		1.00
	Inscription block of 4	4.00	

531 *Congo*

531		**MNHVF**	**UseVF**
22¢	**multicolored** *(1,238,065)*	1.00	.75
	FDC *(Sept. 18, 1987)*		1.00
	Inscription block of 4	4.00	

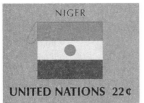

532 *Niger*

532
		MNHVF	UseVF
22¢	multicolored *(1,238,065)*	1.00	.75
	FDC *(Sept. 18, 1987)*		1.00
	Inscription block of 4	4.00	

533 *Saint Lucia*

533
		MNHVF	UseVF
22¢	multicolored *(1,238,065)*	1.00	.75
	FDC *(Sept. 18, 1987)*		1.00
	Inscription block of 4	4.00	
	y. Se-tenant block of 4, Nos. 530-533	6.50	
	y1. Miniature pane of 16	8.00	

534 *Bahrain*

534
		MNHVF	UseVF
22¢	multicolored *(1,239,323)*	1.00	.75
	FDC *(Sept. 18, 1987)*		1.00
	Inscription block of 4	4.00	

535 *Haiti*

535
		MNHVF	UseVF
22¢	multicolored *(1,239,323)*	1.00	.75
	FDC *(Sept. 18, 1987)*		1.00
	Inscription block of 4	4.00	

536 *Afghanistan*

536
		MNHVF	UseVF
22¢	multicolored *(1,239,323)*	1.00	.75
	FDC *(Sept. 18, 1987)*		1.00
	Inscription block of 4	4.00	

537 *Greece*

537
		MNHVF	UseVF
22¢	multicolored *(1,239,323)*	1.00	.75
	FDC *(Sept. 18, 1987)*		1.00
	Inscription block of 4	4.00	
	y. Se-tenant block of 4, Nos. 534-537	6.50	
	y1. Miniature pane of 16	8.00	

1987. U.N. Day Issue Designed by Elisabeth von Janota-Bzowski, Germany (22¢), Fritz Henry Oerter, Germany (39¢). Border designed by Rocco J. Callari, U.S. *Offset by The House of Questa, U.K. Perforated 14 1/2x15.*

538 *"U.N. Day" on U.N. building;* 539 *Line of dancers, U.N. emblem*

538
		MNHVF	UseVF
22¢	multicolored *(1,119,286)*	.80	.65
	FDC *(Oct. 23, 1987)*		1.00
	Inscription block of 4	3.25	

539
		MNHVF	UseVF
39¢	multicolored *(1,065,468)*	1.50	1.25
	FDC *(Oct. 23, 1987)*		1.00
	Inscription block of 4	5.00	

1987. Child Immunization Issue The goal of the World Health Organization and the United Nations Children's Fund was to immunize all children by 1990. Designed by Seymour Chwast, U.S. *Offset by The House of Questa, U.K. Perforated 15x14 1/2.*

540 *Measles*

541 *Tetanus*

540
		MNHVF	UseVF
22¢	multicolored *(660,495)*	1.25	.75
	FDC *(Nov. 20, 1987)*		1.00
	Inscription block of 4	6.00	

541
		MNHVF	UseVF
44¢	multicolored *(606,049)*	3.00	1.75
	FDC *(Nov. 20, 1987)*		1.00
	Inscription block of 4	13.50	

1988. IFAD Issue International Fund for Agricultural Development - World without hunger. Designed by Santiago Arolas, Switzerland. *Offset by CPE Australia Ltd. Perforated 13 1/2.*

 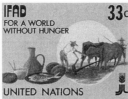

542 *Fishing;* 543 *Farming*

542		MNHVF	UseVF
22¢	**multicolored** *(392,649)*	1.00	.50
	FDC *(Jan. 29, 1988)*		1.00
	Inscription block of 4	5.50	

543		MNHVF	UseVF
33¢	**multicolored** *(475,185)*	1.75	1.25
	FDC *(Jan. 29, 1988)*		1.00
	Inscription block of 4	8.50	

1988. REGULAR ISSUE Designed by David Ben-Hador, Israel. *Gravure by Heraclio Fournier, Spain. Perforated 14.*

544 *"For a Better World," U.N. seal in tree cross section*

544		MNHVF	UseVF
3¢	**multicolored** *(3,000,000)*	.30	.25
	FDC *(Jan. 29, 1988)*		1.00
	Inscription block of 4	1.25	

Commemorative Issues

1988. FOREST ISSUE Designed by Braldt Bralds, Netherlands. *Offset by The House of Questa, U.K. Printed se-tenant in a continuous design. Perforated 14x15.*

545, 546 *Rain forest scene*

545		MNHVF	UseVF
25¢	**multicolored** *(647,360)*	2.50	1.50
	FDC *(March 18, 1988)*		4.50

546		MNHVF	UseVF
44¢	**multicolored** *(647,360)*	4.00	3.00
	FDC *(March 18, 1988)*		5.50
	Inscription block of 4	14.00	
	y. Se-tenant pair	7.00	6.00
	FDC (pair)		8.00

1988. INTERNATIONAL VOLUNTEER DAY ISSUE A U.N. General Assembly resolution calls for International Volunteer Day recognized annually on Dec. 5. Designed by James E. Tennison, U.S. *Offset by Joh. Enschedé and Sons, Netherlands. Perforated 13x14, 14x13.*

547 *Women in classroom*

548 *Vocational training*

547		MNHVF	UseVF
25¢	**multicolored** *(688,444)*	1.00	.50
	FDC *(May 6, 1988)*		1.00
	Inscription block of 4	4.00	

548		MNHVF	UseVF
50¢	**multicolored** *(447,784)*	1.50	1.25
	FDC *(May 6, 1988)*		1.00
	Inscription block of 4	8.50	

1988. HEALTH IN SPORTS ISSUE Designed by LeRoy Neiman, U.S. *Offset by Japanese Government Printing Office. Perforated 13 1/2x13, 13x13 1/2.*

549 *Cycling*
550 *Marathon*

549		MNHVF	UseVF
25¢	**multicolored** *(658,991)*	1.00	.50
	FDC *(June 17, 1988)*		1.00
	Inscription block of 4	5.00	

550		MNHVF	UseVF
38¢	**multicolored** *(420,421)*	2.00	1.50
	FDC *(June 17, 1988)*		1.00
	Inscription block of 4	8.50	

1988. FLAG ISSUE This is the ninth group of sixteen Flag stamps showing the flags of Member States of the U.N. Designed by Ole Hamann, Denmark, and executed by Rocco J. Callari, U.S.; Hamann; Irving Konopiaty, U.S.; Thomas Lee, China; and Robert Stein, U.S. *Gravure by Helio Courvoisier, Switzerland. Perforated 12, granite paper.*

551 *Spain*

551		MNHVF	UseVF
25¢	multicolored *(1,029,443)*	1.00	.65
	FDC *(Sept. 15, 1988)*		1.00
	Inscription block of 4	4.00	

552 *Saint Vincent and the Grenadines*

552		MNHVF	UseVF
25¢	multicolored *(1,029,443)*	1.00	.65
	FDC *(Sept. 15, 1988)*		1.00
	Inscription block of 4	4.00	

553 *Ivory Coast*

553		MNHVF	UseVF
25¢	multicolored *(1,029,443)*	1.00	.65
	FDC *(Sept. 15, 1988)*		1.00
	Inscription block of 4	4.00	

554 *Lebanon*

554		MNHVF	UseVF
25¢	multicolored *(1,029,443)*	1.00	.65
	FDC *(Sept. 15, 1988)*		1.00
	Inscription block of 4	4.00	
y.	Se-tenant block of 4, Nos. 551-554	6.00	1.00
y1.	Miniature pane of 16	8.00	

555 *Yemen*

555		MNHVF	UseVF
25¢	multicolored *(1,010,774)*	1.00	.65
	FDC *(Sept. 15, 1988)*		1.00
	Inscription block of 4	4.00	

556 *Cuba*

556		MNHVF	UseVF
25¢	multicolored *(1,010,774)*	1.00	.65

	FDC *(Sept. 15, 1988)*		1.00
	Inscription block of 4	4.00	

557 *Denmark*

557		MNHVF	UseVF
25¢	multicolored *(1,010,774)*	1.00	.65
	FDC *(Sept. 15, 1988)*		1.00
	Inscription block of 4	4.00	

558 *Libyan Arab Jamahiriya*

558		MNHVF	UseVF
25¢	multicolored *(1,010,774)*	1.00	.65
	FDC *(Sept. 15, 1988)*		1.00
	Inscription block of 4	4.00	
y.	Se-tenant block of 4, Nos. 555-558	6.00	
y1.	Miniature pane of 16	8.00	

559 *Qatar*

559		MNHVF	UseVF
25¢	multicolored *(1,016,941)*	1.00	.65
	FDC *(Sept. 15, 1988)*		1.00
	Inscription block of 4	4.00	

560 *Zaire*

560		MNHVF	UseVF
25¢	multicolored *(1,016,941)*	1.00	.65
	FDC *(Sept. 15, 1988)*		1.00
	Inscription block of 4	4.00	

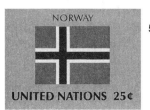

561 *Norway*

561		MNHVF	UseVF
25¢	multicolored *(1,016,941)*	1.00	.65
	FDC *(Sept. 15, 1988)*		1.00
	Inscription block of 4	4.00	

562 *German Democratic Republic*

562
25¢	multicolored (1,016,941)	MNHVF	UseVF
		1.00	.65
	FDC (Sept. 15, 1988)		1.00
	Inscription block of 4	4.00	
	y. Se-tenant block of 4, Nos. 559-562	6.00	
	y1. Miniature pane of 16	8.00	

563 *Iran*

563
25¢	multicolored (1,009,234)	MNHVF	UseVF
		1.00	.65
	FDC (Sept. 15, 1988)		1.00
	Inscription block of 4	4.00	

564 *Tunisia*

564
25¢	multicolored (1,009,234)	MNHVF	UseVF
		1.00	.65
	FDC (Sept. 15, 1988)		1.00
	Inscription block of 4	4.00	

565 *Samoa*

565
25¢	multicolored (1,009,234)	MNHVF	UseVF
		1.00	.65
	FDC (Sept. 15, 1988)		1.00
	Inscription block of 4	4.00	

566 *Belize*

566
25¢	multicolored (1,009,234)	MNHVF	UseVF
		1.00	.65
	FDC (Sept. 15, 1988)		1.00
	Inscription block of 4	4.00	
	y. Se-tenant block of 4, Nos. 563-566	6.00	
	y1. Miniature pane of 16	8.00	

1988. DECLARATION OF HUMAN RIGHTS ISSUE 40th anniversary. This is in the 12th stamp in the Human Rights series. Designed by Rocco J. Callari, U.S. *Gravure and intaglio by Helio Courvoisier, Switzerland. Perforated 12.*

567 *Symbolic flame*

567
25¢	multicolored (1,025,000 printed)	MNHVF	UseVF
		1.35	.75
	FDC (Dec. 9, 1988)		1.00
	Inscription block of 4	4.25	

1988. DECLARATION OF HUMAN RIGHTS SOUVENIR SHEET 40th anniversary. Designed by Rocco J. Callari, U.S. The $1.00 is a single strip souvenir sheet which includes the preamble to the human rights declaration in English. *Gravure and intaglio by Helio Courvoisier, Switzerland. Perforated 12.*

568 *Universal Declaration of Human Rights 1948-1988 with No. 567*

568
$1.00	Sheet of 1 (700,000 printed)	MNHVF	UseVF
		3.25	2.50
	a. Single ($1.00)	3.00	2.50
	FDC (Dec. 9, 1988)		3.00

1989. WORLD BANK ISSUE The World Bank is owned by the Governments of more than 151 nations. It provides development assistance. Designed by Saturnin Lumboy, Philippines. *Offset by Joh. Enschedé and Sons, Netherlands. Perforated 13x14.*

569 *Energy and nature*

570 *Agriculture*

569
25¢	multicolored (612,114)	MNHVF	UseVF
		1.50	.75

	FDC *(Jan. 27, 1989)*		1.00
	Inscription block of 4	5.00	
570		**MNHVF**	**UseVF**
45¢	**multicolored** *(528,184)*	2.00	1.25
	FDC *(Jan. 27, 1989)*		1.00
	Inscription block of 4	11.00	

1989. NOBEL PEACE PRIZE ISSUE Commemorated the awarding of the 1988 Nobel Peace Prize to the U.N. peace-keeping forces. Designed by Tom Bland, Australia. *Offset by CPE Australia, Ltd. Perforated 14x13 1/2.*

571 *U.N. soldier on watch*

571		**MNHVF**	**UseVF**
25¢	**multicolored** *(808,842)*	1.25	.75
	FDC *(March 17, 1989)*		1.00
	Inscription block of 4	5.75	

1989. REGULAR ISSUE Adapted as a stamp by Rocco J. Callari, U.S., from photo by Simon Nathan, U.S. *Offset by Joh. Enschedé and Sons, Netherlands. Perforated 14 1/2x14.*

572 *U.N. headquarters, New York*

572		**MNHVF**	**UseVF**
45¢	**multicolored** *(2,000,000)*	1.50	1.25
	FDC *(March 17, 1989)*		1.00
	Inscription block of 4	6.00	

1989. WORLD WEATHER WATCH ISSUE Honored a U.N. effort begun in 1963 to collect, analyze and distribute world weather data. Designed by Rocco J. Callari, U.S. and Robert Stein, U.S. *Offset by Joh. Enschedé and Sons, Netherlands. Perforated 13x14.*

573, 574 *Satellite photos: Storm off U.S. East Coast (25¢), typhoon in Pacific (36¢)*

573		**MNHVF**	**UseVF**
25¢	**multicolored** *(849,819)*	1.25	.65
	FDC *(April 21, 1989)*		1.00
	Inscription block of 4	5.50	
574		**MNHVF**	**UseVF**
36¢	**multicolored** *(826,547)*	2.50	1.50
	FDC *(April 21, 1989)*		1.00
	Inscription block of 4	11.00	

1989. 10TH ANNIVERSARY U.N. OFFICES IN VIENNA ISSUE The third secretariat location of the U.N. besides New York and Geneva. Designed by Paul Flora, Austria (25¢), Rudolf Hausner, Austria (90¢). Engraved by Wolfgang Seidel, Austria. *Gravure and intaglio (25¢), gravure (90¢) by Government Printing Office, Austria. Perforated 14.*

575 *Cartoon soldier*

576 *Flower*

575		**MNHVF**	**UseVF**
25¢	**multicolored** *(580,663)*	2.50	1.00
	FDC *(Aug. 23, 1989)*		1.00
	Inscription block of 4	9.00	
576		**MNHVF**	**UseVF**
90¢	**multicolored** *(505,776)*	6.00	2.00
	FDC *(Aug. 23, 1989)*		1.00
	Inscription block of 4	25.00	

1989. FLAG ISSUE This is the 10th group of 16 Flag stamps of 15 Member Nations and the U.N. flag itself. (The series resumed in 1997.) Designed by Ole Hamann, Denmark, and executed by Rocco J. Callari, U.S.; Hamann; Irving Konopiaty, U.S.; Thomas Lee, China; and Robert Stein, U.S. *Gravure by Helio Courvoisier, Switzerland. Perforated 12, granite paper.*

577 *Indonesia*

577		**MNHVF**	**UseVF**
25¢	**multicolored** *(959,076)*	1.00	.65
	FDC *(Sept. 22, 1989)*		1.00
	Inscription block of 4	4.00	

578 *Lesotho*

578		**MNHVF**	**UseVF**
25¢	**multicolored** *(959,076)*	1.00	.65
	FDC *(Sept. 22, 1989)*		1.00
	Inscription block of 4	4.00	

579 *Guatemala*

579		**MNHVF**	**UseVF**
25¢	**multicolored** *(959,076)*	1.00	.65

FDC *(Sept. 22, 1989)*		1.00
Inscription block of 4	4.00	

Inscription block of 4	4.00	
y. Se-tenant block of 4, Nos. 581-584	6.00	
y1. Miniature pane of 16	8.00	

585 *Honduras*

580 *Netherlands*

580

		MNHVF	UseVF
25¢	**multicolored** *(959,076)*	1.00	.65
	FDC *(Sept. 22, 1989)*		1.00
	Inscription block of 4	4.00	
	y. Se-tenant block of 4, Nos. 577-580	6.00	
	y1. Miniature pane of 16	8.00	

585

		MNHVF	UseVF
25¢	**multicolored** *(959,814)*	1.00	.65
	FDC *(Sept. 22, 1989)*		1.00
	Inscription block of 4	4.00	

581 *South Africa*

586 *Democratic Kampuchea*

581

		MNHVF	UseVF
25¢	**multicolored** *(960,502)*	1.00	.65
	FDC *(Sept. 22, 1989)*		1.00
	Inscription block of 4	4.00	

586

		MNHVF	UseVF
25¢	**multicolored** *(959,814)*	1.00	.65
	FDC *(Sept. 22, 1989)*		1.00
	Inscription block of 4	4.00	

582 *Portugal*

587 *Guinea-Bissau*

582

		MNHVF	UseVF
25¢	**multicolored** *(960,502)*	1.00	.65
	FDC *(Sept. 22, 1989)*		1.00
	Inscription block of 4	4.00	

587

		MNHVF	UseVF
25¢	**multicolored** *(959,814)*	1.00	.65
	FDC *(Sept. 22, 1989)*		1.00
	Inscription block of 4	4.00	

588 *Cyprus*

583 *Morocco*

583

		MNHVF	UseVF
25¢	**multicolored** *(960,502)*	1.00	.65
	FDC *(Sept. 22, 1989)*		1.00
	Inscription block of 4	4.00	

588

		MNHVF	UseVF
25¢	**multicolored** *(959,814)*	1.00	.65
	FDC *(Sept. 22, 1989)*		1.00
	Inscription block of 4	4.00	
	y. Se-tenant block of 4, Nos. 585-588	6.00	
	y1. Miniature pane of 16	8.00	

584 *Syrian Arab Republic*

589 *Algeria*

584

		MNHVF	UseVF
25¢	**multicolored** *(960,502)*	1.00	.65
	FDC *(Sept. 22, 1989)*		1.00

589

		MNHVF	UseVF
25¢	**multicolored** *(959,805)*	1.00	.65
	FDC *(Sept. 22, 1989)*		1.00
	Inscription block of 4	4.00	

590 *Brunei Darussalam*

590		**MNHVF**	**UseVF**
25¢	**multicolored** *(959,805)*	1.00	.65
	FDC *(Sept. 22, 1989)*		1.00
	Inscription block of 4	4.00	

591 *Saint Kitts and Nevis*

591		**MNHVF**	**UseVF**
25¢	**multicolored** *(959,805)*	1.00	.65
	FDC *(Sept. 22, 1989)*		1.00
	Inscription block of 4	4.00	

592 *United Nations*

592		**MNHVF**	**UseVF**
25¢	**multicolored** *(959,805)*	1.00	.65
	FDC *(Sept. 22, 1989)*		1.00
	Inscription block of 4	4.00	
	y. Se-tenant block of 4, Nos. 589-592	6.00	1.00
	y1. Miniature pane of 16	8.00	

1989. DECLARATION OF HUMAN RIGHTS ISSUE This 13th set in the Human Rights series depicts the first six articles of the Universal Declaration of Human Rights of 1948. Concept by Arleigh Gaines, U.S., designed by Rocco J. Callari, U.S., and Robert Stein, U.S. *Panes of 12 plus 12 se-tenant labels containing Articles 1 (25¢) or 2 (45¢), inscribed in English, French or German. Offset by Joh. Enschedé and Sons, Netherlands. Perforated 13 1/2.*

593 Table of Universal Brotherhood, *by José Clemente Orozco, Mexico*

593		**MNHVF**	**UseVF**
25¢	**multicolored** *(2,364,000)*	1.25	1.00

FDC *(Nov. 17, 1989)* 1.00
y. Strip of 3 plus 3 labels 5.00

594 Study for "Composition II," *by Vassily Kandinsky, France*

594		**MNHVF**	**UseVF**
45¢	**multicolored** *(2,364,000)*	2.00	1.25
	FDC *(Nov. 17, 1989)*		1.00
	y. Strip of 3 plus 3 labels	5.50	

1990. INTERNATIONAL TRADE CENTER ISSUE Designed by Richard Bernstein, U.S. *Offset by The House of Questa, U.K. Perforated 14 1/2x15.*

595 *Harbor scene*

595		**MNHVF**	**UseVF**
25¢	**multicolored** *(429,081)*	2.00	1.25
	FDC *(Feb. 2, 1990)*		1.00
	Inscription block of 4	8.75	

1990. FIGHT AIDS ISSUE Designed by Jacek Tofil, Poland (25¢), Fritz Henry Oerter, Germany (40¢). *Offset by Joh. Enschedé and Sons, Netherlands. Perforated 13 1/2x12 1/2.*

596 *AIDS;* 597 *Shadow over crowd*

596		**MNHVF**	**UseVF**
25¢	**multicolored** *(492,078)*	1.25	.55
	FDC *(March 16, 1990)*		1.00
	Inscription block of 4	4.50	
597		**MNHVF**	**UseVF**
40¢	**multicolored** *(394,149)*	2.00	1.25
	FDC *(March 16, 1990)*		1.00
	Inscription block of 4	8.50	

1990. MEDICINAL PLANTS ISSUE Illustration from *Curtis's Botanical Magazine* adapted as a stamp by Rocco J. Callari, U.S., and Robert Stein, U.S. *Gravure by Helio Courvoisier, Switzerland. Perforated 11 1/2, granite paper.*

598 *Catharanthus roseus*

599 *Panax quinquefolium*

598		MNHVF	UseVF
25¢	multicolored *(796,792)*	1.50	.50
	FDC *(May 4, 1990)*		1.00
	Inscription block of 4	5.50	

599		MNHVF	UseVF
90¢	multicolored *(605,617)*	2.75	2.50
	FDC *(May 4, 1990)*		1.00
	Inscription block of 4	12.00	

1990. U.N. 45TH ANNIVERSARY ISSUE Commemorated the signing of the U.N. Charter in 1945. Designed by Kris Geysen, Belgium (25¢), Nejat M. Gur, Turkey (45¢). *Offset by Joh. Enschedé and Sons, Netherlands. Perforated 14 1/2x13.*

600, 601 *Depictions of "45"*

600		MNHVF	UseVF
25¢	multicolored *(581,718)*	2.00	1.25
	FDC *(June 26, 1990)*		1.00
	Inscription block of 4	6.00	

601		MNHVF	UseVF
45¢	multicolored *(582,769)*	4.00	1.75
	FDC *(June 26, 1990)*		1.00
	Inscription block of 4	18.00	

1990. U.N. 45TH ANNIVERSARY SOUVENIR SHEET Commemorated the signing of the U.N. Charter in 1945. Designed by Robert Stein, U.S. *Offset by Joh. Enschedé and Sons, Netherlands. Perforated 14 1/2x13.*

602 *U.N. 45th Anniversary Souvenir sheet with Nos. 600 and 601*

602		MNHVF	UseVF
70¢	**Sheet of 2** *(315,946)*	10.50	9.00

a. Single (25¢)		2.00	1.25
b. Single (45¢)		4.00	1.75
c. Pair		6.50	
FDC *(June 26, 1990)*			8.00

1990. CRIME PREVENTION ISSUE Designed by Josef Ryzec, Czechoslovakia. *Gravure by Heraclio Fournier, Spain. Perforated 14.*

603 *Crimes of youth*

604 *Organized crime*

603		MNHVF	UseVF
25¢	multicolored *(533,089)*	1.50	1.25
	FDC *(Sept. 13, 1990)*		1.00
	Inscription block of 4	7.50	

604		MNHVF	UseVF
36¢	multicolored *(427,215)*	3.00	1.50
	FDC *(Sept. 13, 1990)*		1.00
	Inscription block of 4	13.00	

1990. DECLARATION OF HUMAN RIGHTS ISSUE This 14th set in the Human Rights series depicts Articles 7-12 of the Universal Declaration of Human Rights. Concept by Arleigh Gaines, U.S., designed by Rocco J. Callari, U.S. and Robert Stein, U.S. *Panes of 12 plus 12 se-tenant labels containing Articles 7 (25¢) or 8 (45¢) inscribed in English, French or German. Offset by Joh. Enschedé and Sons, Netherlands. Perforated 13 1/2.*

605 *Fragment from the Sarcophagus of Plotinus, Roman c. 270 A.D.*

605		MNHVF	UseVF
25¢	black, gray & tan *(2,502,000 printed)*	.75	.75
	FDC *(Nov. 16, 1990)*		1.00
	y. Strip of 3 plus 3 labels	3.25	

> Read the introduction to this catalog carefully. It contains much valuable information for all stamp collectors, and also makes the catalog easier for you to use.

606 Combined Chambers of the High Court of Appeal, *by Charles Paul Renouard, France*

606		MNHVF	UseVF
45¢	**black & brown** *(2,502,000 printed)*	2.00	1.00
	FDC *(Nov. 16, 1990)*		1.00
	y. Strip of 3 plus 3 labels	5.00	

1991. ECONOMIC COMMISSION FOR EUROPE ISSUE Designed by Carlos Ochagavia, Argentina. *Offset by Heraclio Fournier, Spain. Perforated 14.*

607 *Two storks;* 608 *Woodpecker, ibex;* 609 *Capercaille, plover;* 610 *Falcon, marmot*

607		MNHVF	UseVF
30¢	**multicolored** *(590,102)*	2.00	1.00
	FDC *(March 15, 1991)*		1.00

608		MNHVF	UseVF
30¢	**multicolored** *(590,102)*	2.00	1.00
	FDC *(March 15, 1991)*		1.00

609		MNHVF	UseVF
30¢	**multicolored** *(590,102)*	2.00	1.00
	FDC *(March 15, 1991)*		1.00

610		MNHVF	UseVF
30¢	**multicolored** *(590,102)*	2.00	1.00
	FDC *(March 15, 1991)*		1.00
	Inscription block of 4	9.00	
	y. Se-tenant block of 4	6.00	
	FDC (block)		6.00

1991. NAMIBIAN INDEPENDENCE ISSUE The 5th in the Namibia series. The African nation became independent March 21, 1990. Adapted by Rocco J. Callari, U.S., and Robert Stein, U.S., from photos by John Isaac, India. *Offset by Heraclio Fournier, Spain. Perforated 14.*

611 *Dunes, Namibia Desert;* 612 *Savanna*

611		MNHVF	UseVF
30¢	**multicolored** *(360,825)*	1.75	.60
	FDC *(May 10, 1991)*		1.00
	Inscription block of 4	7.00	

612		MNHVF	UseVF
50¢	**multicolored** *(415,648)*	2.25	1.25
	FDC *(May 10, 1991)*		1.00
	Inscription block of 4	10.00	

1991. REGULAR ISSUE Adapted as a stamp by Rocco J. Callari, U.S. and Robert Stein, U.S., from photo by Unmesh, U.S., engraved by Czeslaw Slania, Sweden. *Intaglio by Japanese Government Printing Office. Perforated 13 1/2.*

613 *U.N. building*

613		MNHVF	UseVF
$2	**dark blue** *(2,000,000)*	4.25	3.50
	FDC *(May 10, 1991)*		5.00
	Inscription block of 4	20.00	

1991. RIGHTS OF THE CHILD ISSUE Designed by Nicole Delia Legnani, U.S. (30¢), Alissa Duffy, U.S. (70¢). *Offset by The House of Questa, U.K. Perforated 14 1/2.*

614 *Children encircling globe;* 615 *Houses, rainbow*

614		MNHVF	UseVF
30¢	**multicolored** *(440,151)*	1.25	.50
	FDC *(June 14, 1991)*		1.00
	Inscription block of 4	5.75	

615		MNHVF	UseVF
70¢	**multicolored** *(447,803)*	2.75	1.50
	FDC *(June 14, 1991)*		1.00
	Inscription block of 4	13.00	

1991. REGULAR ISSUE Adapted as a stamp by Rocco J. Callari, U.S., from photo by Unmesh, U.S. For 30¢: *Offset by Joh. Enschedé and Sons, Netherlands, perforated 13 1/2; for 50¢:* Adapted as a stamp by Robert Stein, U.S., from photo by Andrea Brizzi, Italy, of painting *The Golden Rule,* by Norman Rockwell, U.S. *Gravure by Helio Courvoisier, Switzerland. Perforated 12x11 1/2.*

616 *U.N. flag*

616		MNHVF	UseVF
30¢	**multicolored** *(2,000,000)*	.75	.75
	FDC *(Sept. 11, 1991)*		1.00
	Inscription block of 4	6.00	

617 The Golden Rule, *by Norman Rockwell*

617		MNHVF	UseVF
50¢	**multicolored** *(2,000,000)*	2.00	1.25
	FDC *(Sept. 11, 1991)*		1.00
	Inscription block of 4	8.50	

1991. CHEMICAL WEAPONS BAN ISSUE Designed by Oscar Asboth, Austria (30¢), Michel Granger, France (90¢). *Offset by Heraclio Fournier, Spain. Perforated 13 1/2.*

618 *Skyline;* 619 *Hand on chemical drums*

618		MNHVF	UseVF
30¢	**multicolored** *(367,548)*	3.50	1.00
	FDC *(Sept. 11, 1991)*		1.00
	Inscription block of 4	10.00	

619		MNHVF	UseVF
90¢	**multicolored** *(346,161)*	4.00	2.50
	FDC *(Sept. 11, 1991)*		1.00
	Inscription block of 4	22.00	

1991. 40TH ANNIVERSARY U.N. POSTAL ADMINISTRATION ISSUE Designed by Rocco J. Callari, U.S., from the adaptation of 1951 1 cent stamp (No. 1) designed by O. C. Meronti, U.K. (30¢); adaptation of 1951 2 cent stamp (No. 3) designed by J. F. Doeve, Netherlands (40¢). *Offset by The House of Questa, U.K. Perforated 14x15.*

620 *Stamp on stamp: U.N. New York No. 1;* 621 *Stamp on stamp: U.N. New York No. 3*

620		MNHVF	UseVF
30¢	**multicolored** *(442,548)*	1.50	.75
	FDC *(Oct. 24, 1991)*		1.00
	Inscription block of 4	6.50	

621		MNHVF	UseVF
40¢	**multicolored** *(419,127)*	2.25	1.25
	FDC *(Oct. 24, 1991)*		1.00
	Inscription block of 4	12.00	

1991. DECLARATION OF HUMAN RIGHTS ISSUE This 15th set in the Human Rights series is the third group of six articles of the Universal Declaration of Human Rights. Concept by Arleigh Gaines, U.S., designed by Rocco J. Callari, U.S. and Robert Stein, U.S. *Panes of 12 plus 12 se-tenant labels containing Articles 13 (30¢) or 14 (50¢) inscribed in English, French or German. Offset by Joh. Enschedé and Sons, Netherlands. Perforated 13 1/2.*

622 The Last of England, *by Ford Madox Brown, U.K.*

622		MNHVF	UseVF
30¢	**multicolored** *(1,261,198)*	1.00	.75
	FDC *(Nov. 20, 1991)*		1.00
	y. Strip of 3 plus 3 labels	3.00	

623 The Emigration to the East, *by Titos Salas, Venezuela*

623		MNHVF	UseVF
50¢	**multicolored** *(1,255,077)*	2.00	1.25
	FDC *(Nov. 20, 1991)*		1.00
	y. Strip of 3 plus 3 labels	6.00	

1992. WORLD HERITAGE ISSUE Second in a World Heritage Series supporting the conservation of mankind's shared heritage. Adapted as a stamp by Robert Stein, U.S., from photographs by Georg Gerster, Switzerland. *Offset by Cartor, France. Perforated 13, size: 35x28mm.*

624
Uluru National Park, Australia;
625 *The Great Wall of China*

624		MNHVF	UseVF
30¢	**multicolored** *(337,717)*	1.00	1.00
	FDC *(Jan. 24, 1992)*		1.00
	Inscription block of 4	5.50	

625		MNHVF	UseVF
50¢	**multicolored** *(358,000)*	2.50	1.25
	FDC *(Jan. 24, 1992)*		1.00
	Inscription block of 4	10.00	

1992. CLEAN OCEAN ISSUE Designed paintings by Braldt Bralds, Netherlands. *Offset by The House of Questa, U.K. Pane of 12, perforated 14.*

626 *Ocean surface*

627 *Ocean bottom*

626		MNHVF	UseVF
29¢	**multicolored** *(983,126)*	1.00	.75
	FDC *(March 13, 1992)*		1.00

627		MNHVF	UseVF
29¢	**multicolored** *(983,126)*	1.00	.75
	FDC *(March 13, 1992)*		1.00
	Inscriptiion block of 4 - two each 626-627	5.25	
	y. Se-tenant pair (626-627)	1.50	1.40

Every entry in this catalog has been double-checked for accuracy, but mistakes may creep into any human endeavor, and we ask your assistance in eliminating them. Please call the attention of the editors to any errors in stamp descriptions found in this catalog.

1992. EARTH SUMMIT ISSUE Designed by Peter Max, U.S. *Gravure by Helio Courvoisier, Switzerland. Pane of 40, perforated 11 1/2.*

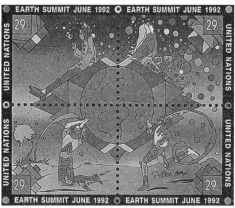

628 *Sitting figure facing left;*

629 *Sitting figure facing right;*

630 *Kneeling figure;*

631 *Running figure*

628		MNHVF	UseVF
29¢	**multicolored** *(806,268)*	1.00	.75
	FDC *(May 22, 1992)*		1.00

629		MNHVF	UseVF
29¢	**multicolored** *(806,268)*	1.00	.75
	FDC *(May 22, 1992)*		1.00

630		MNHVF	UseVF
29¢	**multicolored** *(806,268)*	1.00	.75
	FDC *(May 22, 1992)*		1.00

631		MNHVF	UseVF
29¢	**multicolored** *(806,268)*	1.00	.75
	FDC *(May 22, 1992)*		1.00
	Inscription block of 4	4.50	
	y. Se-tenant block of 4	3.00	2.75

1992. MISSION TO PLANET EARTH ISSUE Designed by Atilla Hejja, U.S., and sheet concept by Rocco J. Callari, U.S. *Gravure by Helio Courvoisier, Switzerland. Pane of 10, rouletted 8, granite paper.*

632 *Satellite over city;* 633 *Satellite over coast*

632		MNHVF	UseVF
29¢	**multicolored** *(643,647)*	4.50	4.00
	FDC *(Sept. 4, 1992)*		1.00

633		MNHVF	UseVF
29¢	**multicolored** *(643,647)*	7.00	5.00
	FDC *(Sept. 4, 1992)*		1.00
	Inscription block of 4	29.00	
	y. Se-tenant pair	18.50	1.25

1992. SCIENCE AND TECHNOLOGY DEVELOPMENT ISSUE Designed by Saul Mandel, U.S. *Offset by Unicover Corp., U.S. Perforated 14.*

634 *Winged man;* 635 *Alligator*

634		MNHVF	UseVF
29¢	multicolored *(453,365)*	.75	.75
	FDC *(Oct. 2, 1992)*		1.00
	Inscription block of 4	3.50	

635		MNHVF	UseVF
50¢	multicolored *(377,377)*	1.55	1.00
	FDC *(Oct. 2, 1992)*		1.00
	Inscription block of 4	6.50	

1992. U.N. UNIVERSITY BUILDING ISSUE Designed by Banks and Miles, U.S. (4¢, 40¢), Robert Stein, U.S. (29¢). *Offset by Cartor, France. Perforated 14, (4¢,40¢), 13 1/2x13 (29¢).*

636 *U.N. university building, Tokyo*

636		MNHVF	UseVF
4¢	multicolored *(1,500,000 printed)*	.20	.15
	FDC *(Oct. 2, 1992)*		1.00
	Inscription block of 4	1.25	

637 *U.N. headquarters*

637		MNHVF	UseVF
29¢	multicolored *(1,750,000 printed)*	.75	.50
	FDC *(Oct. 2, 1992)*		1.00
	Inscription block of 4	4.00	

638 *U.N. university building, Tokyo, side view*

638		MNHVF	UseVF
40¢	multicolored *(1,500,000 printed)*	1.25	1.00
	FDC *(Oct. 2, 1992)*		1.00
	Inscription block of 4	5.50	

Users of this Catalog are invited to write to us if they have information which they feel will supplement or correct any material contained herein. All such communications will be answered.

1992. DECLARATION OF HUMAN RIGHTS ISSUE This 16th set in the Human Rights series depicts the fourth group of six articles (19-25) of the Universal Declaration of Human Rights. Adapted as a stamp by Robert Stein, U.S. *Panes of 12 plus 12 se-tenant labels containing Articles 19 (29¢) or 20 (50¢), inscribed in English, French or German. Offset by Joh. Enschedé and Sons, Netherlands. Perforated 13 1/2.*

639 *Article 19,* Lady Writing a Letter With Her Maid, *by Johannes Vermeer, from The National Gallery of Ireland, Dublin.*

639		MNHVF	UseVF
29¢	multicolored *(1,184,531)*	1.25	1.00
	FDC *(Nov. 20, 1992)*		1.00
	y. Strip of 3 plus 3 labels	3.00	

640 *Article 20,* The Meeting, *by Ester Almqvist, from the National museum Stockholm, Sweden.*

640		MNHVF	UseVF
50¢	multicolored *(1,107,044)*	1.75	1.50
	FDC *(Nov. 20, 1992)*		1.00
	y. Strip of 3 plus 3 labels	6.00	

1993. AGING WITH DIGNITY ISSUE Designed by C. M. Dudash, U.S. *Offset by Cartor, France. Perforated 13.*

641 *Elderly man in crowd*

642 *Medical care for elderly man*

641		MNHVF	UseVF
29¢	multicolored *(336,933)*	2.00	1.00
	FDC *(Feb. 5, 1993)*		1.00
	Inscription block of 4	12.00	

642			MNHVF	UseVF
52¢	multicolored *(308,080)*		2.25	2.00
	FDC *(Feb. 5, 1993)*			1.00
	Inscription block of 4		12.00	

1993. ENDANGERED SPECIES ISSUE The first set of stamps in the Endangered Species series. Concept by Rocco J. Callari, U.S., and designs by Norman Adams, U.S. *Offset by Joh. Enschedé and Sons, Netherlands. Perforated 13x12 1/2.*

643 Queensland Hairy-nosed wombat; 644 Whooping crane; 645 Giant clam; 646 Giant sable antelope

643			MNHVF	UseVF
29¢	multicolored *(1,200,000 printed)*		1.00	.75
	FDC *(March 2, 1993)*			1.00

644			MNHVF	UseVF
29¢	multicolored *(1,200,000 printed)*		1.00	.75
	FDC *(March 2,1993)*			1.00

645			MNHVF	UseVF
29¢	multicolored *(1,200,000 printed)*		1.00	.75
	FDC *(March 2, 1993)*			1.00

646			MNHVF	UseVF
29¢	multicolored *(1,200,000 printed)*		1.00	.75
	FDC *(March 2, 1993)*			1.00
	Inscription block of 4		3.25	
	y. Se-tenant block of 4		3.25	2.50

1993. HEALTHY ENVIRONMENT ISSUE Designed by Milton Glaser, U.S. *Offset Leigh-Mardon Pty. Ltd., Australia. Perforated 15x14 1/2.*

647 Man; 648 Family

647			MNHVF	UseVF
29¢	multicolored *(430,463)*		1.50	.75
	FDC *(May 7, 1993)*			1.00
	Inscription block of 4		6.00	

648			MNHVF	UseVF
50¢	multicolored *(326,692)*		2.00	1.25
	FDC *(May 7, 1993)*			1.00
	Inscription block of 4		9.50	

1993. REGULAR ISSUE Adaptation of 13¢ Postal Card 1982 by Salahattin Kanidinc, U.S. *Offset by The House of Questa, U.K. Perforated 15x14.*

649 "United Nations" repeated

649			MNHVF	UseVF
5¢	multicolored *(1,500,000)*		.25	.20
	FDC *(May 7, 1993)*			1.00
	Inscription block of 4		1.25	

1993. DECLARATION OF HUMAN RIGHTS ISSUE This 17th set in the Human Rights series depicts the fifth of the six articles of the Universal Declaration of Human Rights. Concept by Arleigh Gaines, U.S., designed by Robert Stein, U.S. Panes of 12 plus 12 se-tenant labels containing Articles 25 (29¢) or 26 (35¢), inscribed in English. *Offset by Joh. Enschedé and Sons, Netherlands. Perforated 13 1/2.*

650 Article 25, Shocking Corn 1945, by Thomas Hart Benton, U.S., (1899-1975), collection Minnesota Museum of Art, Saint Paul.

650			MNHVF	UseVF
29¢	multicolored *(7,049,134)*		1.25	.75
	FDC *(June 11, 1993)*			1.00
	y. Strip of 3 plus 3 labels		3.50	

651 Article 26, The Library, 1960, by Jacob Lawrence, U.S., 1960 National Museum of American Art. Photo: Art Resource, New York.

651			MNHVF	UseVF
35¢	multicolored *(1,045,346)*		2.00	1.25
	FDC *(June 11, 1993)*			1.00
	y. Strip of 3 plus 3 labels		6.50	

1993. INTERNATIONAL PEACE DAY ISSUE The U.N. General Assembly declared in 1981 that the third Tuesday of September would be observed as the International Day of Peace. Designed by Hans Erni, Switzerland. Engraved by Pierre Schopfer, Switzerland. *Offset and intaglio by Swiss PTT, Switzerland. Rouletted 12 1/2.*

652-655 *Abstract design, four corners*

652		MNHVF	UseVF
29¢	blue & multicolored *(298,367)*	3.00	1.00
	FDC *(Sept. 21, 1993)*		1.00

653		MNHVF	UseVF
29¢	blue & multicolored *(298,367)*	3.00	1.00
	FDC *(Sept. 21, 1993)*		1.00

654		MNHVF	UseVF
29¢	blue & multicolored *(298,367)*	3.00	1.00
	FDC *(Sept. 21, 1993)*		1.00

655		MNHVF	UseVF
29¢	blue & multicolored *(298,367)*	3.00	1.00
	FDC *(Sept. 21, 1993)*		1.00
	Inscription block of 4	15.00	
	y. Se-tenant block of 4	12.00	7.00

1993. ENVIRONMENT CLIMATE ISSUE Designed paintings by Braldt Bralds, Netherlands. *Offset by The House of Questa, U.K. Perforated 14 1/2.*

656 *Chameleon;* 657 *Palm trees, top of funnel cloud;* 658 *Bottom of funnel cloud;* 659 *Bird of Paradise*

656		MNHVF	UseVF
29¢	multicolored *(383,434)*	1.25	.85
	FDC *(Oct. 19, 1993)*		1.00

657		MNHVF	UseVF
29¢	multicolored *(383,434)*	1.25	.85
	FDC *(Oct. 29, 1993)*		1.00

658		MNHVF	UseVF
29¢	multicolored *(383,434)*	1.25	.85
	FDC *(Oct. 29, 1993)*		1.00

659		MNHVF	UseVF
29¢	multicolored *(383,434)*	1.25	.85
	FDC *(Oct. 29, 1993)*		1.00
	Inscription block of 8	10.50	
	y. Se-tenant strip of 4	4.50	3.50

1994. YEAR OF THE FAMILY ISSUE The U.N. General Assembly proclaimed 1994 as the International Year of the Family. Designed by Rocco J. Callari, U.S., and computer graphics by Luis Sardá, Spain and John De Santis, U.S. *Offset by Cartor, France. Perforated 13.*

660, 661 *Figures silhouette*

660		MNHVF	UseVF
29¢	green & multicolored *(491,688)*	1.75	.75
	FDC *(Feb. 4, 1994)*		1.00
	Inscription block of 4	6.00	

661		MNHVF	UseVF
45¢	blue & multicolored *(331,250)*	3.00	1.50
	FDC *(Feb. 4, 1994)*		1.00
	Inscription block of 4	16.00	

1994. ENDANGERED SPECIES ISSUE The second set of stamps in the Endangered Species series. Concept by Rocco J. Callari, U.S., and designed by Kerrie Maddeford, Australia. *Offset by Joh. Enschedé and Sons, Netherlands. Perforated 12 1/2.*

662 *Chimpanzee;* 663 *St. Lucia Amazon;* 664 *American crocodile;* 665 *Dama gazelle*

662		MNHVF	UseVF
29¢	multicolored *(1,200,000 printed)*	1.00	.75
	FDC *(March 18, 1994)*		1.00

663		MNHVF	UseVF
29¢	multicolored *(1,200,000 printed)*	1.00	.75
	FDC *(March 18, 1994)*		1.00

664		MNHVF	UseVF
29¢	multicolored *(1,200,000 printed)*	1.00	.75
	FDC *(March 18, 1994)*		1.00

665		MNHVF	UseVF
29¢	multicolored *(1,200,000 printed)*	1.00	.75
	FDC *(March 18, 1994)*		1.00
	Inscription block of 4	4.50	
	y. Se-tenant block of 4	3.50	3.00

1994. PROTECTION FOR REFUGEES ISSUE Designed by Francoise Peyroux, U.S. *Offset by Leigh-Mardon Pty. Ltd., Australia. Perforated 14 1/2x15.*

666 *Hands clasped*

666		MNHVF	UseVF
50¢	multicolored *(316,051)*	2.25	1.50
	FDC *(April 29, 1994)*		1.00
	Inscription block of 4	9.00	

1994. REGULAR ISSUE Adapted as a stamp by Robert Stein, U.S. from a creation of the *"Dove of Peace"* from an unknown artist (10¢). Created by Halina Cieslinska-Brzeska, Poland from a drawing by Stainislaw Wysplanski, Poland, then adapted as a stamp by Robert Stein, U.S. (19¢). Adapted by Robert Stein, U.S. from a print *Mourning Owl* by Vanessa Isitt, Canada, engraved by Sverre Morken, Norway ($1). *(Nos. 667 and 668) offset by Cartor, France. (No. 669) intaglio and offset by Norges Banks Seddeltrykkeri, Norway. Perforated 13.*

667 *Dove of Peace*

667		MNHVF	UseVF
10¢	multicolored *(1,000,000)*	.20	.15
	FDC *(April 29, 1994)*		1.00
	Inscription block of 4	.75	

668 Sleeping Child, *by Stanislaw Wysplanski*

668		MNHVF	UseVF
19¢	multicolored *(1,000,000)*	.50	.45
	FDC *(April 29, 1994)*		1.00
	Inscription block of 4	3.00	

669 Mourning Owl, *by Vanessa Isitt*

669		MNHVF	UseVF
$1.00	red brown *(1,000,000)*	3.50	2.50
	FDC *(April 29, 1994)*		1.00
	Inscription block of 4	13.00	

1994. NATURAL DISASTER ISSUE The U.N. in 1989 designated the 1990s as the International Decade for Natural Disaster Reduction. De-

signed by Kenji Koga, Japan. *Offset by The House of Questa, U.K. Perforated 14x14 1/4.*

670 *North America;* 671 *Eurasia;* 672 *South America;* 673 *Australia*

670		MNHVF	UseVF
29¢	multicolored *(207,224)*	3.00	1.75
	FDC *(May 27, 1994)*		1.00

671		MNHVF	UseVF
29¢	multicolored *(207,224)*	3.00	1.75
	FDC *(May 27, 1994)*		1.00

672		MNHVF	UseVF
29¢	multicolored *(207,224)*	3.00	1.75
	FDC *(May 27, 1994)*		1.00

673		MNHVF	UseVF
29¢	multicolored *(207,224)*	3.00	1.75
	FDC *(May 27, 1994)*		1.00
	Inscription block of 4	12.50	
y.	Se-tenant block of 4	12.50	3.00

1994. POPULATION AND DEVELOPMENT ISSUE The International Conference on Population and Development believes that population should be at the core of all economic, social, political and environmental undertakings. A conference was held in Cairo, Egypt Sept. 5-13, 1994. Designed by Jerry Smath, U.S. *Offset by Joh. Enschedé and Sons, Netherlands. Perforated 13 1/4x13 1/2.*

674 *Children at play;* 675 *Family with possessions*

674		MNHVF	UseVF
29¢	multicolored *(373,661)*	1.25	1.00
	FDC *(Sept. 1, 1994)*		1.00
	Inscription block of 4	4.50	

675		MNHVF	UseVF
52¢	multicolored *(319,894)*	2.00	1.75
	FDC *(Sept. 1, 1994)*		1.00
	Inscription block of 4	10.00	

1994. UNCTAD 30TH ANNIVERSARY ISSUE The U.N. Conference on Trade and Development became a permanent intergovernmental body in 1964 in Geneva. UNCTAD's goal is to promote growth and development in countries. Designed by Luis Sardá, Spain. *Offset by Joh. Enschedé and Sons, Netherlands. Perforated 13 1/4x13 1/2.*

676 *Loose-looped ribbon;* 677 *Tight-looped ribbon*

676		MNHVF	UseVF
29¢	**multicolored** *(590,000 printed)*	1.25	1.00
	FDC *(Oct. 28, 1994)*		1.00
	Inscription block of 4	3.00	
677		**MNHVF**	**UseVF**
50¢	**multicolored** *(540,000 printed)*	1.50	1.25
	FDC *(Oct. 28, 1994)*		1.00
	Inscription block of 4	9.00	

1995. U.N. 50TH ANNIVERSARY ISSUE Celebrated the signing of the Charter of the United Nations, June 26, 1945. Designed by Rocco J. Callari, U.S. *Offset and intaglio by PTT, Switzerland. Perforated 13 1/2.*

678 *U.N. seal and "50"*

678		MNHVF	UseVF
32¢	**multicolored** *(938,644)*	1.75	1.25
	FDC *(Jan. 1, 1995)*		1.00
	Inscription block of 4	7.50	

1995. SOCIAL SUMMIT ISSUE The World Summit for Social Development met March 6-12, 1995, in Copenhagen, Denmark. Designed by Friedensreich Hunderwasser, Austria. Engraved by Wolfgang Seidel, Austria. *Gravure and intaglio by Government Printing Office, Austria. Perforated 13 1/2x14.*

679 *Drawings of people*

679		MNHVF	UseVF
50¢	**multicolored** *(495,388)*	1.50	1.25
	FDC *(Feb. 3, 1995)*		1.00
	Inscription block of 4	6.50	

1995. ENDANGERED SPECIES ISSUE This is the third set of stamps in the Endangered Species series. Concept by Rocco J. Callari, U.S. and designed by Chris Calle, U.S. *Offset by Joh. Enschedé and Sons, Netherlands. Perforated 13x12 1/2.*

680 *Giant armadillo;* 681 *American bald eagle;* 682 *Fijian/Tongin banded iguana;* 683 *Giant panda*

680		MNHVF	UseVF
32¢	**multicolored** *(756,000 printed)*	1.00	.75
	FDC *(March 24, 1995)*		1.00
681		**MNHVF**	**UseVF**
32¢	**multicolored** *(756,000 printed)*	1.00	.75
	FDC *(March 24, 1995)*		1.00
682		**MNHVF**	**UseVF**
32¢	**multicolored** *(756,000 printed)*	1.00	.75
	FDC *(March 23, 1995)*		1.00
683		**MNHVF**	**UseVF**
32¢	**multicolored** *(756,000 printed)*	1.00	.75
	FDC *(March 24, 1995)*		1.00
	Inscription block of 4	4.25	
	y. Se-tenant block of 4	3.75	3.00

1995. INTERNATIONAL YOUTH YEAR ISSUE Tenth anniversary. The U.N. General Assembly declared 1985 International Youth Year. Designed by Gottfried Kumpf, Austria. *Offset by The House of Questa, U.K. Perforated 14 1/2x14 3/4.*

684 *Seated child;* 685 *Children cycling*

684		MNHVF	UseVF
32¢	**multicolored** *(358,695)*	1.50	.75
	FDC *(May 26, 1995)*		1.00
	Inscription block of 4	5.00	
685		**MNHVF**	**UseVF**
55¢	**multicolored** *(288,424)*	2.00	1.50
	FDC *(May 26, 1995)*		1.00
	Inscription block of 4	9.50	

1995. U.N. 50TH ANNIVERSARY ISSUE The second issue in 1995 to commemorate the anniversary of the U.N., issued on the 50th anniversary date of the signing of the U.N. Charter. Designed by Paul and Chris Calle, U.S. Engraved by Inge Madlé, Netherlands. *Intaglio by Joh. Enschedé and Sons, Security Printing, Netherlands. Perforated 13 1/4x13 1/2.*

686 *Hand with pen*

687 *Veteran's War Memorial Opera House, San Francisco*

686			MNHVF	UseVF
32¢	**black** *(501,961)*		1.25	.75
	FDC *(June 26, 1995)*			1.00
	Inscription block of 4		5.50	

687			MNHVF	UseVF
50¢	**maroon** *(419,932)*		1.75	1.50
	FDC *(June 26, 1995)*			1.00
	Inscription block of 4		9.00	

1995. U.N. 50TH ANNIVERSARY SOUVENIR SHEET Designed by Paul and Chris Calle, U.S. *Offset and intaglio. Imperforate.*

688 *Designs from Nos. 686 and 687*

688			MNHVF	UseVF
82¢	**Sheet of 2** *(347,963)*		4.50	2.50
	a. Single (32¢)		1.25	1.00
	b. Single (50¢)		1.75	1.25
	FDC *(June 26, 1995)*			3.00

1995. WORLD CONFERENCE ON WOMEN ISSUE The fourth World Conference on Women was held Sept. 4-15, 1995, in Beijing, China. Designed by Ting Shao Kuang, China. *Gravure by Postage Stamp Printing House, MPT, both from the People's Republic of China. Perforated 12.*

689 *Mother and child;* 690 *Seated woman and cranes*

689			MNHVF	UseVF
32¢	**multicolored** *(561,847)*		1.25	.75
	FDC *(Sept. 5, 1995)*			1.00
	Inscription block of 4		5.00	

690			MNHVF	UseVF
40¢	**multicolored** *(499,850)*		2.00	1.25
	FDC *(Sept. 5, 1995)*			1.00
	Inscription block of 4		9.00	

Regular Issues

1995. U.N. HEADQUARTERS ISSUE Designed by John B. De Santis Jr., U.S. *Offset by The House of Questa, U.K, perforated 15.*

691 *U.N. headquarters*

691			MNHVF	UseVF
20¢	**multicolored** *(1,000,000 printed)*		.40	.20
	FDC *(Sept. 5, 1995)*			1.00
	Inscription block of 4		2.00	

Commemorative Issues

1995. U.N. PEOPLE, 50TH ANNIVERSARY ISSUE This was the third issue to commemorate the Charter of the U.N., which came into force Oct. 24, 1945. Designed by Ben Verkaaik, Netherlands; Rocco J. Callari and Robert Stein, U.S. designed the Prestige Booklet. *Offset by The House of Questa, U.K. Perforated 14.*

692-703 *People from coninuous design*

692			MNHVF	UseVF
32¢	**multicolored,** top left *(214,639)*		.75	.40

693			MNHVF	UseVF
32¢	**multicolored,** top right *(214,639)*		.75	.40

694			MNHVF	UseVF
32¢	**multicolored,** top center left *(214,639)*		.75	.40

695			MNHVF	UseVF
32¢	**multicolored,** top center right *(214,639)*		.75	.40

696			MNHVF	UseVF
32¢	**multicolored,** top lower left *(214,639)*		.75	.40

697			MNHVF	UseVF
32¢	**multicolored,** top lower right *(214,639)*		.75	.40

698		MNHVF	UseVF
32¢	**multicolored,** bottom left top*(214,639)*	.75	.40

699		MNHVF	UseVF
32¢	**multicolored,** bottom right top*(214,639)*	.75	.40

700		MNHVF	UseVF
32¢	**multicolored,** bottom center left *(214,639)*	.75	.40

701		MNHVF	UseVF
32¢	**multicolored,** bottom center right *(214,639)*	.75	.40

702		MNHVF	UseVF
32¢	**multicolored,** bottom lower left *(214,639)*	.75	.40

703		MNHVF	UseVF
32¢	**multicolored,** bottom lower right *(214,639)*	.75	.40
	FDC *(Oct. 24, 1995)* (sheetlet)		25.00
	y. Sheetlet of 12	10.00	
	n. Booklet of 12 *(85,256)*	12.00	
	FDC (booklet)		29.00

1996. WFUNA 50TH ANNIVERSARY ISSUE The initials stand for World Federation of United Nations Associations. Designed by Rudolf Mirer, Switzerland. *Offset by Joh. Enschedé and Sons, Netherlands. Perforated 13x13 1/2.*

704 *Faces in sun*

704		MNHVF	UseVF
32¢	**multicolored** *(580,000 printed)*	1.00	.60
	FDC *(Feb. 2, 1996)*		1.00
	Inscription block of 4	4.00	

1996. REGULAR ISSUE Adapted as a stamp by John B. De Santis, Jr., U.S. from a abstract mural by Fernand Léger, France. *Offset by The House of Questa, U.K. Perforated 14 1/2x15.*

705, 706
Abstract designs

705		MNHVF	UseVF
32¢	**multicolored** *(780,000)*	.75	.75
	FDC *(Feb. 2, 1996)*		1.00
	Inscription block of 4	4.50	

706		MNHVF	UseVF
60¢	**multicolored** *(680,000)*	2.00	1.50
	FDC *(Feb. 2, 1996)*		1.00
	Inscription block of 4	8.00	

1996. ENDANGERED SPECIES ISSUE This is the fourth set in the Endangered Species series. Designed by Diane Bruyninckx, Belgium, and concept and design by Rocco J. Callari, U.S. *Offset by Joh. Enschedé and Sons, Netherlands. Perforated 12 1/2.*

707 *Masdevallia veitchiana;* 708 *Saguaro cactus;* 709 *West Australian pitcher plant;* 710 *Encephalartos horridus*

707		MNHVF	UseVF
32¢	**multicolored** *(640,000 printed)*	.85	.65
	FDC *(March 14, 1996)*		1.00

708		MNHVF	UseVF
32¢	**multicolored** *(640,000 printed)*	.85	.65
	FDC *(March 14, 1996)*		1.00

709		MNHVF	UseVF
32¢	**multicolored** *(640,000 printed)*	.85	.65
	FDC *(March 14, 1996)*		1.00

710		MNHVF	UseVF
32¢	**multicolored** *(640,000 printed)*	.85	.65
	FDC *(March 14, 1996)*		1.00
	Inscription block of 4	3.75	
	y. Se-tenant block of 4	3.50	

1996. CITY SUMMIT (HABITAT II) ISSUE The second U.N. Conference on Human Settlements (Habitat II) was held in June 1996, in Istanbul, Turkey. Designed by Teresa Fasolino, U.S. *Offset by Joh. Enschedé and Sons, Netherlands. Perforated 14x13 1/2.*

711 *Deer;* 712 *Man, child;* 713 *Pathway;* 714 *Polynesian woman;* 715 *Bird*

711		MNHVF	UseVF
32¢	**multicolored** *(475,000 printed)*	1.00	.75
	FDC *(June 3, 1996)*		1.00

712		MNHVF	UseVF
32¢	**multicolored** *(475,000 printed)*	1.00	.75
	FDC *(June 3, 1996)*		1.00

713		MNHVF	UseVF
32¢	**multicolored** *(475,000 printed)*	1.00	.75
	FDC *(June 3, 1996)*		1.00

714		MNHVF	UseVF
32¢	**multicolored** *(475,000 printed)*	1.00	.75
	FDC *(June 3, 1996)*		1.00

715		MNHVF	UseVF
32¢	**multicolored** *(475,000 printed)*	1.00	.75
	FDC *(June 3, 1996)*		1.00
	Inscription block of 10	9.00	
	y. Se-tenant strip of 5	4.00	

1996. SPORT AND ENVIRONMENT ISSUE Commemorated the 100th anniversary of the Olympic Games. Designed by LeRoy Neiman, U.S. *Offset by The House of Questa, U.K. Perforated 14x14 1/2, 14 1/2x14.*

716 *Volleyball*

717 *Basketball*

716		MNHVF	UseVF
32¢	**multicolored** *(680,000 printed)*	1.00	.75
	FDC *(July 19, 1996)*		1.00
	Inscription block of 4	3.50	

717		MNHVF	UseVF
50¢	**multicolored** *(680,000 printed)*	1.50	1.25
	FDC *(July 19, 1996)*		1.00
	Inscription block of 4	7.50	

1996. SPORT AND ENVIRONMENT SOUVENIR SHEET ISSUE Commemorated the 100th anniversary of the modern Olympic Games. Designed by LeRoy Neiman, U.S. *Offset by The House of Questa, U.K. Imperforate.*

718 *Souvenir sheet with Nos. 716 and 717*

718		MNHVF	UseVF
82¢	**Sheet of 2** *(370,000 printed)*	2.25	1.75
	a. Single (32¢)	1.00	.75
	b. Single (50¢)	1.25	1.00
	FDC *(July 19, 1996)*		2.00

1996. PLEA FOR PEACE ISSUE The stamps drew attention to UNICEF's goal to reduce child mortality, disease and illiteracy. Designed by Peng Yue, China (32¢), Cao Chenyu, China (60¢). *Offset by The House of Questa, U.K. Perforated 14 1/2x15, 15x14 1/2.*

719 *Two doves;*

720 *Dove in flight*

719		MNHVF	UseVF
32¢	**multicolored** *(580,000 printed)*	.85	.75
	FDC *(Sept. 17, 1996)*		1.00
	Inscription block of 4	4.00	

720		MNHVF	UseVF
60¢	**multicolored** *(580,000 printed)*	1.75	1.50
	FDC *(Sept. 17, 1996)*		1.00
	Inscription block of 4	8.00	

1996. UNICEF 50TH ANNIVERSARY ISSUE Celebrated the 50th anniversary of UNICEF with depictions of fairy tales designed by The Walt Disney Co., U.S. *Offset by The House of Questa, U.K. Perforated 14 1/2x15.*

721 *Yeh-Shen, China; marginal text read "Right to Play" - Chinese Fairytale;* 722 *The Ugly Duckling; marginal text read "Right to Equality of Opportunity" homage to Hans Christian Andersen.*

721		MNHVF	UseVF
32¢	**multicolored** *(1,000,000 printed)*	.85	.75
	FDC *(Nov. 20, 1996)*		1.00
	Inscription block of 4	4.00	
	y. Pane of 8 plus label	10.00	

722		MNHVF	UseVF
60¢	**multicolored** *(1,000,00 printed)*	1.75	1.50
	FDC *(Nov. 20, 1996)*		1.00
	Inscription block of 4	8.00	
	y. Pane of 8 plus label	15.00	

1997. FLAG ISSUE This is the 11th group, eight Flag stamps, showing the flags of the Member States of the U.N. Concept by Ole Hamann, Denmark and designed by Oliver Corwin, U.S., and Robert Stein, U.S. *Gravure by Helio Courvoisier, Switzerland. Perforated 12, granite paper.*

723 *Tajikistan*

723		MNHVF	UseVF
32¢	**multicolored** *(940,000 printed)*	.75	.50
	FDC *(Feb. 12, 1997)*		1.00
	Inscription block of 4	2.50	

724 *Georgia*

724		MNHVF	UseVF
32¢	**multicolored** *(940,000 printed)*	.75	.50
	FDC *(Feb. 12, 1997)*		1.00
	Inscription block of 4	2.50	

725 *Armenia*

725		MNHVF	UseVF
32¢	multicolored *(940,000 printed)*	.75	.50
	FDC *(Feb. 12, 1997)*		1.00
	Inscription block of 4	2.50	

726 *Namibia*

726		MNHVF	UseVF
32¢	multicolored *(940,000 printed)*	.75	.50
	FDC *(Feb. 12, 1997)*		1.00
	Inscription block of 4	2.50	
	y. Se-tenant block of 4, Nos. 723-726	3.00	
	y1. Miniature pane of 16	12.00	

727 *Liechtenstein*

727		MNHVF	UseVF
32¢	multicolored *(940,000 printed)*	.75	.50
	FDC *(Feb. 12, 1997)*		1.00
	Inscription block of 4	2.50	

728 *Republic of Korea*

728		MNHVF	UseVF
32¢	multicolored *(940,000 printed)*	.75	.50
	FDC *(Feb. 12, 1997)*		1.00
	Inscription block of 4	2.50	

729 *Kazakstan*

729		MNHVF	UseVF
32¢	multicolored *(940,000 printed)*	.75	.50
	FDC *(Feb. 12, 1997)*		1.00
	Inscription block of 4	2.50	

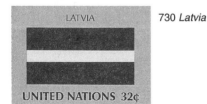

730 *Latvia*

730		MNHVF	UseVF
32¢	multicolored *(940,000 printed)*	.75	.50

	FDC *(Feb. 12, 1997)*		1.00
	Inscription block of 4	2.50	
	y. Se-tenant block of 4, Nos. 727-730	3.00	
	y1. Miniature pane of 16	12.00	

1997. REGULAR ISSUE Adapted as a stamp by Robert Stein, U.S. from a photo by Lois Conner, U.S. (8¢). Adapted as a stamp by Robert Stein, U.S. from a photo by Unmesh, U.S. (55¢). *Offset by The House of Questa, U.K. Perforated 14 1/2.*

731 *Cherry Blossoms, U.N. Headquarters, New York*

731		MNHVF	UseVF
8¢	multicolored	.25	.20
	FDC *(Feb. 12, 1997)*		1.00
	Inscription block of 4	2.50	

732 *Peace Rose*

732		MNHVF	UseVF
55¢	multicolored	1.25	.75
	FDC *(Feb. 12, 1997)*		1.00
	Inscription block of 4	5.00	

1997. ENDANGERED SPECIES ISSUE Fifth set in the Endangered Species series. Sheet concept and design by Rocco J. Callari, U.S. Designer Lori Anzalone, U.S. *Offset by Joh. Enschedé and Sons, Netherlands. Perforated 12 1/2.*

733 *African elephant;* 734 *Major Mitchell's cockatoo;*
735 *Black-footed ferret;* 736 *Cougar*

733		MNHVF	UseVF
32¢	multicolored *(532,000 printed)*	.75	.40
	FDC *(March 13, 1997)*		1.00

734		MNHVF	UseVF
32¢	multicolored *(532,000 printed)*	.75	.40
	FDC *(March 13, 1997)*		1.00

735		MNHVF	UseVF
32¢	multicolored *(532,000 printed)*	.75	.40
	FDC *(March 13, 1997)*		1.00

736		MNHVF	UseVF
32¢	multicolored *(532,000 printed)*	.75	.40
	FDC *(March 13, 1997)*		1.00
	Inscription block of 4, Nos. 733-736	4.00	

1997. EARTH SUMMIT ISSUE Fifth anniversary of the U.N. Conference on Environment and Development. The special session held in New York, June 1997, focused on development worldwide. Designed by Peter Max, U.S. *Gravure by Helio Courvoisier, Switzerland, granite paper, perforated 11 1/2.*

737 *Sailboat;*

738 *Three sailboats;*

739 *Two people watching sailboat, sun;*

740 *Person, sailboat*

737		MNHVF	UseVF
32¢	multicolored *(390,000 printed)*	.75	.30
	FDC *(May 30, 1997)*		1.00

738		MNHVF	UseVF
32¢	multicolored *(390,000 printed)*	.75	.30
	FDC *(May 30, 1997)*		1.00

739		MNHVF	UseVF
32¢	multicolored *(390,000 printed)*	.75	.30
	FDC *(May 30, 1997)*		1.00

740		MNHVF	UseVF
32¢	multicolored *(390,000 printed)*	.75	.30
	FDC *(May 30, 1997)*		1.00
	Inscription block of 4	4.00	
	y. Se-tenant block of 4, Nos. 737-740	2.60	1.20

1997. EARTH SUMMIT SOUVENIR SHEET ISSUE Designed by Peter Max, U.S. *Gravure by Helio Courvoisier, Switzerland. Perforated 11 1/2.*

741 *Fanciful Peter Max design*

741		MNHVF	UseVF
$1.00	multicolored *(345,000 printed)*	2.50	2.25
	FDC *(May 30, 1997)*		2.00

1997. EARTH SUMMIT SOUVENIR OVERPRINT ISSUE Designed by Peter Max, U.S. *(Overprinted Pacific 97). Gravure by Helio Courvoisier, Switzerland. Perforated 11 1/2.*

Minkus albums cover the globe. See your stamp dealer or hobby shop for a selection.

742 *Fanciful Peter Max design with overprint for Pacific '97*

742		MNHVF	UseVF
$1.00	multicolored *(170,000 printed)*	2.50	2.25
	FDC *(May 30, 1997)*		2.00

1997. TRANSPORTATION ISSUE The Economic Commission for Europe (ECE) and the Economic and Social Commission for Asia and the Pacific (ESCAP), celebrated their 50th anniversary in 1997. Designed by Michael Cockcroft, U.K. *Offset by The House of Questa, U.K. Perforated 14x14 1/2.*

743 *Clipper ship;* 744 *Paddle steamer;* 745 *Ocean liner;* 746 *Hovercraft;* 747 *Hydrofoil*

743		MNHVF	UseVF
32¢	multicolored *(316,000 printed)*	.75	.20
	FDC *(Aug. 29, 1997)*		1.00

744		MNHVF	UseVF
32¢	multicolored *(316,000 printed)*	.75	.30
	FDC *(Aug. 29, 1997)*		1.00

745		MNHVF	UseVF
32¢	multicolored *(316,000 printed)*	.75	.30
	FDC *(Aug. 29, 1997)*		1.00

746		MNHVF	UseVF
32¢	multicolored *(316,000 printed)*	.75	.30
	FDC *(Aug. 29, 1997)*		1.00

747		MNHVF	UseVF
32¢	multicolored *(316,000 printed)*	.75	.30
	FDC *(Aug. 29, 1997)*		10.00
	Inscription block of 10	6.00	
	y. Se-tenant strip of 5, Nos. 743-747	3.25	1.50
	FDC strip of 5		4.00

1997. TRIBUTE TO PHILATELY ISSUE Adapted by Robert Stein, U.S., the designs of the 1986 "Philately - The International Hobby," stamps designed by Ingalill Axelsson, Sweden. Engraved by Czeslaw Slania, Sweden. *Offset by Joh. Enschedé and Sons, Netherlands. Perforated 13 1/2x14.*

748, 749 *Tribute to Philately*

748		MNHVF	UseVF
32¢	**multicolored** *(485,000 printed)*	.75	.30
	FDC *(Oct. 14, 1997)*		2.00
	Inscription block of 4	3.25	
749		MNHVF	UseVF
50¢	**multicolored** *(405,000 printed)*	1.00	.40
	FDC *(Oct. 14, 1997)*		1.20
	Inscription block of 4	5.00	

1997. WORLD HERITAGE CONVENTION ISSUE Twenty-fifth anniversary. The first in a series of stamps and prestige booklet focusing on one specific World Heritage site or a group of World Heritage geographical locations. The third set of U.N. stamps illustrated World Heritage sites. Adapted by Robert Stein, U.S., from photographs by Guo Youmin, China. Computer graphics by Blake Tarpley, U.S. Two images of the Terracotta Warriors of the Qin Shi Huang Mausoleum in Mount Lishán, China. *Offset by the Government Printing Office, Austria. Perforated 13 1/2.*

750 *Kneeling warrior;*

751 *Group facing right*

750		MNHVF	UseVF
32¢	**multicolored** *(640,000 printed)*	1.00	.75
	FDC *(Nov. 19, 1997)*		1.00
	Inscription block of 4	3.50	
751		MNHVF	UseVF
60¢	**multicolored** *(560,000 printed)*	1.25	1.25
	FDC *(Nov. 19, 1997)*		1.00
	Inscription block of 4	6.00	

1997. WORLD HERITAGE CONVENTION SOUVENIR BOOKLET Twenty-fifth anniversary. Designed by Rorie Katz, U.S., and Robert Stein, U.S. *Includes 6 panes, one of each U.S., Vienna, Geneva design, with a block of 4 stamps of the same design revalued to an 8¢ denomination. One individual page 3 1/2x6 3/4. Offset by Government Printing Office, Austria. Perforated 13 1/2.*

751A *Kneeling warrior;* 751B *Warrior group facing right;* 751C *Head facing right;* 751D *Men standing;* 751E *Head facing left;* 751F *Warrior group facing forward*

751A		MNHVF	UseVF
8¢	**multicolored** *(305,000 printed)*	.50	.50
751B		MNHVF	UseVF
8¢	**multicolored** *(305,000 printed)*	.50	.50
751C		MNHVF	UseVF
8¢	**multicolored** *(305,000 printed)*	.50	.50

751D		MNHVF	UseVF
8¢	**multicolored** *(305,000 printed)*	.50	.50
751E		MNHVF	UseVF
8¢	**multicolored** *(305,000 printed)*	.50	.50
751F		MNHVF	UseVF
8¢	**multicolored** *(305,000 printed)*	.50	.50
	n. Booklet of 6 panes	6.00	

1998. FLAG SERIES ISSUE Twelfth group in the series of flags of U.N. Member Nations, which totals 176, including the U.N. flag itself. Concept by Ole Hamann, Denmark, and designed by Oliver Corwin, U.S., and Robert Stein, U.S. *Gravure by Helio Courvoisier, Switzerland. Perforated 12.*

752 *Micronesia*

752		MNHVF	UseVF
32¢	**multicolored** *(718,000 printed)*	.75	.50
	FDC *(Feb. 13, 1997)*		1.00
	Inscription block of 4	1.50	

753 *Slovakia*

753		MNHVF	UseVF
32¢	**multicolored** *(718,000 printed)*	.75	.50
	FDC *(Feb. 13, 1997)*		1.00
	Inscription block of 4	1.50	

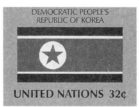

754 *Democratic People's Republic of Korea*

754		MNHVF	UseVF
32¢	**multicolored** *(718,000 printed)*	.75	.50
	FDC *(Feb. 13, 1997)*		1.00
	Inscription block of 4	1.50	

755 *Azerbaijan*

755		MNHVF	UseVF
32¢	**multicolored** *(718,000 printed)*	.75	.50
	FDC *(Feb. 13, 1997)*		1.00
	Inscription block of 4	1.50	
	y. Se-tenant block of 4, Nos. 752-755	2.25	
	y1. Miniature pane of 16	12.00	

756 *Uzbekistan*

756		MNHVF	UseVF
32¢	**multicolored** *(718,000 printed)*	.75	.50
	FDC *(Feb. 13, 1997)*		1.00
	Inscription block of 4	1.50	

757 *Monaco*

757		MNHVF	UseVF
32¢	**multicolored** *(718,000 printed)*	.75	.50
	FDC *(Feb. 13, 1997)*		1.00
	Inscription block of 4	1.50	

758 *Czech Republic*

758		MNHVF	UseVF
32¢	**multicolored** *(718,000 printed)*	.75	.50
	FDC *(Feb. 13, 1997)*		1.00
	Inscription block of 4	1.50	

759 *Estonia*

759		MNHVF	UseVF
32¢	**multicolored** *(718,000 printed)*	.75	.50
	FDC *(Feb. 13, 1997)*		1.00
	Inscription block of 4	1.50	
	y. Se-tenant block of 4, Nos. 756-759	2.50	
	y1. Miniature pane of 16	12.00	

1998. REGULAR ISSUE Designed by Zhang Le Lu, China (1¢), Robert Stein, U.S. (2¢), Gregory Halili, Philippines (21¢). *Offset by The House of Questa, U.K.*

760 *A childlike rendition of a boy with a white dove*

760		MNHVF	UseVF
1¢	**multicolored**	.30	.25
	FDC *(Feb. 13, 1998)*		1.00
	Inscription block of 4	1.50	

761 *Stylized birds in flight over plants*

761		MNHVF	UseVF
2¢	**multicolored**	.30	.25
	FDC *(Feb. 13, 1998)*		1.00
	Inscription block of 4	1.50	

762 *Stylized figures holding hands dance around the U.N. symbol*

762		MNHVF	UseVF
21¢	**multicolored**	.50	.25
	FDC *(Feb. 13, 1998)*		1.00
	Inscription block of 4	2.00	

1998. ENDANGERED SPECIES ISSUE A sixth set in a series to highlight the need for protection of endangered species throughtout the world. Concept by Rocco J. Callari, U.S., and designer Pat Medearis-Altman, New Zealand. *The 16 stamps on each sheetlet allow for four se-tenant blocks of four. Offset by Joh. Enschedé and Sons, Netherlands. Perforated 12 1/2x13 1/2.*

763 *Lesser Galago, Bush Baby of North-central Africa;* 764 *Hawaiian goose, native to the Hawaiian Islands;* 765 *Golden birdwing, a butterfly widespread in Asia;* 766 *Sun bear, found from India to Vietnam to Sumatra and Borneo*

763		MNHVF	UseVF
32¢	**multicolored** *(502,000 printed)*	.75	.25
	FDC *(March 13, 1998)*		1.00

764		MNHVF	UseVF
32¢	**multicolored** *(502,000 printed)*	.75	.25
	FDC *(March 13, 1998)*		1.00

765		MNHVF	UseVF
32¢	**multicolored** *(502,000 printed)*	.75	.25
	FDC *(March 13, 1998)*		1.00

766		MNHVF	UseVF
32¢	**multicolored** *(502,000 printed)*	.75	.25
	FDC *(March 13, 1998)*		1.00
	Inscription block of 4	3.50	
	y. Se-tenant block of 4	3.00	

1998. INTERNATIONAL YEAR OF THE OCEAN ISSUE A set to call attention to the importance of the oceans and their resources for life on Earth. The U.N. has declared 1998 as the International Year of the Ocean. Designed by Larry Taughter, U.S. *This sheetlet of 12, multicolored, 32¢ stamps depicts a temperate region. Offset by Joh. Enschedé and Sons, Netherlands. Perforated 13.*

767 *Various ocean life*

767		MNHVF	UseVF
32¢	**Pane of 12** *(280,000 printed)*	8.50	—
	a. Turtle	.40	.25
	b. Rays	.40	.25
	c. Fish	.40	.25
	d. Whale	.40	.25
	e. Manatee	.40	.25
	f. Grouper	.40	.25
	g. Dolphin fish and killer whale	.40	.25
	h. Sea horse and jellyfish	.40	.25
	i. Sea lion	.40	.25
	j. Octopus	.40	.25
	k. Submersible	.40	.25
	l. Sharks	.40	.25
	FDC *(May 20, 1998),* any single		1.00

1998. RAIN FORESTS ISSUE Commemorated the 50th anniversary of the World Health Organization. Designed by Rick Garcia, U.S. *Offset by Japanese Government Printing Office. Perforated 14.*

768 *A jaguar lies in the grass*

768		MNHVF	UseVF
32¢	**multicolored** *(570,000 printed)*	.75	.25
	FDC *(April 22, 1998)*		1.00

1998. RAIN FORESTS SOUVENIR SHEET ISSUE Using the same stamp design as No. 768, the jaguar on a $2 stamp lies in a setting that includes a butterfly and wading bird. Designed by Rick Garcia, U.S. *Offset by Japanese Government Printing Office. Perforated 14.*

769 *Jaguar in rain forest*

769		MNHVF	UseVF
$2	**multicolored** *(280,000 printed)*	4.00	2.00
	a. Single ($2)	3.75	1.75
	FDC *(April 22, 1998)*		1.00

1998. 50 YEARS OF U.N. PEACE-KEEPING ISSUE Commemorated the initiation in 1948 of a U.N. peacekeeping military force under U.N. control but under ultimate authority of the members' respective governments. Designed by Andrew Davidson, U.K. *Gravure by Helio Courvoisier, Switzerland. Perforated 12.*

770 *Soldier stands watch;* 771 *Two soldiers on armored vehicle*

770		MNHVF	UseVF
33¢	**multicolored** *(485,000 printed)*	.75	.25
	FDC *(Sept. 15, 1998)*		1.00
	Inscription block of 4	2.50	
771		MNHVF	UseVF
40¢	**multicolored** *(445,000 printed)*	.75	.25
	FDC *(Sept. 15, 1998)*		1.00
	Inscription block of 4	2.50	

1998. DECLARATION OF HUMAN RIGHTS ISSUE Noted the 50th anniversary of a document that called for a "common standard of achievement" for all people and nations.

772 *An abstract figure with a flag*

773 *Abstract walking pens*

772		MNHVF	UseVF
32¢	**multicolored** *(485,000 printed)*	.75	.25
	FDC *(Oct. 27, 1998)*		1.00
	Inscription block of 4	2.50	

773		MNHVF	UseVF
55¢	multicolored *(445,000 printed)*	.75	1.00
	FDC *(Oct. 27, 1998)*		1.00
	Inscription block of 4	3.00	

1998. SCHÖNBRUNN PALACE ISSUE Set celebrated a U.N. World Heritage Site in Vienna, Austria.

774 *The Gloriette*

774		MNHVF	UseVF
33¢	multicolored *(485,000 printed)*	.50	.25
	FDC *(Dec. 4, 1998)*		1.00
	Inscription block of 4	2.00	

775 *Detail from a wall painting on fabric by Johann Wenzle Bergl*

775		MNHVF	UseVF
60¢	multicolored *(445,000 printed)*	.85	.50
	FDC *(Dec. 4, 1998)*		1.00
	Inscription block of 4	3.50	

1998. SCHÖNBRUNN PALACE BOOKLET ISSUE The six designs in the U.N. World Hertiage Site issue are re-valued in a Prestige Booklet of 21 stamps.

776 *Palace and grounds, four 15¢ stamps;* 777 *Blue and white vase, three 11¢ stamps;* 778 *Detail from wall paintings, three 11¢ stamps;* 779 *Porcelain stove, three 11¢ stamps;* 780 *Great Palm House, four 15¢ stamps;* 781 *The Gloriette, four 15¢ stamps*

776		MNHVF	UseVF
15¢	multicolored *(110,000 printed)*	.50	.25
	n. Pane of 4	2.00	

777		MNHVF	UseVF
11¢	multicolored *(110,000 printed)*	.50	.25
	n. Pane of 4	1.50	

778		MNHVF	UseVF
11¢	multicolored *(110,000 printed)*	.50	.25
	n. Pane of 4	1.50	

779		MNHVF	UseVF
11¢	multicolored *(110,000 printed)*	.50	.25
	n. Pane of 4	1.50	

780		MNHVF	UseVF
15¢	multicolored *(110,000 printed)*	.50	.25
	n. Pane of 4	2.00	

781		MNHVF	UseVF
15¢	multicolored *(110,000 printed)*	.50	.25
	n. Pane of 4	2.00	
	n1. Full booklet of 6 panes	8.50	
	FDC *(Dec. 4, 1998)* (any pane)		1.50

1999. FLAG SERIES ISSUE Thirteenth group in the series of Flags of U.N. Member Nations, which total 176, including the U.N. flag itself. Concept by Ole Hamann, Denmark. Designed by Oliver Corwin, Robert Stein and Blake Tarpley, U.S. *Gravure by Helio Courvoisier, Switzerland. Perforated 11 3/4.*

782 *Lithuania;* 783 *San Marino;* 784 *Turkmenistan;* 785 *Marshall Islands*

782		MNHVF	UseVF
33¢	multicolored *(960,000 printed)*	.75	.50

783		MNHVF	UseVF
33¢	multicolored *(960,000 printed)*	.75	.50

784		MNHVF	UseVF
33¢	multicolored *(960,000 printed)*	.75	.50

785		MNHVF	UseVF
33¢	multicolored *(960,000 printed)*	.75	.50
	FDC *(Feb. 5, 1999)* (single)		1.00
	y. Inscription block of 4	3.00	
	y1. Pane of 16	12.00	
	y2. Block of Nos. 782-785	3.00	
	FDC (block)		4.00

786 *Moldova;* 787 *Krgyzstan;* 788 *Bosnia and Herzegovina;* 789 *Eritrea*

786		MNHVF	UseVF
33¢	multicolored *(960,000 printed)*	.75	.50

787		MNHVF	UseVF
33¢	multicolored *(960,000 printed)*	.75	.50

788		MNHVF	UseVF
33¢	multicolored *(960,000 printed)*	.75	.50

789		MNHVF	UseVF
33¢	multicolored *(960,000 printed)*	.75	.50
	FDC *(Feb. 5, 1999)* (single)		1.00
	y. Inscription block of 4	3.00	
	y1. Pane of 16	12.00	
	y2. Block of Nos. 786-789	3.00	
	FDC (block)		4.00

1999. REGULAR ISSUE For 33¢: Designed by Blake Tarpley, *offset by Joh. Enschedé and Sons, U.K., perforated 13 1/4x13 3/4. For $5:* Designed by Rorie Katz, *gravure and intaglio by Helio Courvoisier, Switzerland. Perforated 11 3/4.*

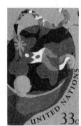

790 *Banner of flags around the globe*

790		MNHVF	UseVF
33¢	**multicolored**	.75	.50
	FDC *(Feb. 5, 1999)*		1.00
	Inscription block of 4	3.00	

791 *United Nations Rose*

791		MNHVF	UseVF
$5	**multicolored**	10.00	8.00
	FDC *(Feb. 5, 1999)*		15.00
	Inscription block of 4	40.00	

1999. WORLD HERITAGE - AUSTRALIA ISSUE The fifth in the U.N. World Heritage Sites Series. Designed by Passmore Design of Melbourne, Australia. *Offset by The House of Questa, U.K. Perforated 13.*

792 *The Willandra Lakes Region encompasses nearly 1 million acres of semi-arid country*

792		MNHVF	UseVF
33¢	**multicolored** *(480,000 printed)*	.75	.50
	FDC *(March 19, 1999)*		1.00
	Inscription block of 4	3.00	

793 *The Wet Tropics of Queensland cover more than 2.2 million acres of northeast Australia*

793		MNHVF	UseVF
60¢	**multicolored** *(440,000 printed)*	1.25	.75
	FDC *(March 19, 1999)*		2.00
	Inscription block of 4	3.00	

1999. WORLD HERITAGE AUSTRALIA BOOKLET The six designs in the U.N. Heritage Site series is re-valued in a *172x92mm Prestige booklet of 24 stamps, a block of 4 stamps in each design. Perforated 13.*

794 *Tasmania;* 795 *Uluru-Kata Tjuta;* 796 *Wet Tropics;* 797 *Kakadu;* 798 *Great Barrier Reef;* 799 *Willandra Lakes*

794		MNHVF	UseVF
5¢	**multicolored** *(97,000 printed)*	.25	.20
	FDC *(March 19, 1999)*		1.50
795		MNHVF	UseVF
15¢	**multicolored** *(97,000 printed)*	.50	.25
	FDC *(March 19, 1999)*		1.50
796		MNHVF	UseVF
5¢	**multicolored** *(97,000 printed)*	.25	.20
	FDC *(March 19, 1999)*		1.50
797		MNHVF	UseVF
15¢	**multicolored** *(97,000 printed)*	.50	.25
	FDC *(March 19, 1999)*		1.50
798		MNHVF	UseVF
5¢	**multicolored** *(97,000 printed)*	.25	.20
	FDC *(March 19, 1999)*		1.50
799		MNHVF	UseVF
15¢	**multicolored** *(97,000 printed)*	.50	.25
	FDC *(March 19, 1999)*		1.50
	n. Booklet of 24 stamps	5.00	

1999. ENDANGERED SPECIES ISSUE Seventh in a series to highlight the need for protection of endangered species throughout the world. Designed by Jimmy Wang, China. *Printed by Joh. Enschedé and Sons, Netherlands. Perforated 12 1/2x13 3/4.*

800 *Tiger;* 801 *Secretary Bird;* 802 *Green Tree Python;* 803 *Long-tailed Chinchilla*

800		MNHVF	UseVF
33¢	**multicolored** *(494,000 printed)*	.75	.25
	FDC *(April 22, 1999)*		1.50
801		MNHVF	UseVF
33¢	**multicolored** *(494,000 printed)*	.75	.25
	FDC *(April 22, 1999)*		1.50
802		MNHVF	UseVF
33¢	**multicolored** *(494,000 printed)*	.75	.25
	FDC *(April 22, 1999)*		1.50
803		MNHVF	UseVF
33¢	**multicolored** *(494,000 printed)*	.75	.25
	FDC *(April 22, 1999)*		1.50
	Inscription block of 4	2.50	

1999. UNISPACE III ISSUE An eerie moon forms a backdrop to a small space station and an exploration vehicle on a desolate planet in a pair of stamps to commemorate the third Conference on the Exploration and Peaceful uses of Outer Space in Vienna, Austria. Concept and pane design by Rocco J. Callari and Robert Stein, U.S. Designed by Attila Hejja, U.S. *Gravure by Helio Courvoisier, Switzerland. Rouletted.*

804 *Moon;* 805 *Rover vehicle*

804		MNHVF	UseVF
33¢	**multicolored** *(1,000,000 printed)*	.75	.25
805		MNHVF	UseVF
33¢	**multicolored** *(1,000,000 printed)*	.75	.25
	FDC *(July 7, 1999)* (pair)		2.00
	Inscription block of 4	2.50	

Commemorative Issues

1999. UNISPACE III SOUVENIR SHEET The full design of the se-tenant Nos. 804-805 are combined on a 90x75mm souvenir sheet and given a higher denomination. *Perforated 11 3/4.*

806 *Moon & Rover*

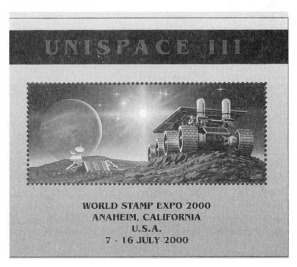

806y1 *Souvenir sheet, overprinted for World Stamp Expo 2000*

806		MNHVF	UseVF
$2	**multicolored** *(530,000 printed)*	4.00	2.00
	FDC *(July 7, 1999)*		5.00
	y. Mini sheetlet	4.00	2.00
	y1. Mini sheetlet overprinted for World Stamp Expo 2000	4.00	2.00
	FDC *(July 7, 2000)*		4.00

1999. UNIVERSAL POSTAL UNION 1874-1999 ISSUE Postal patrons in distinctive dress and means of carrying mail around the globe signify the impact of the Universal Postal Union over the last 125 years. Designed by Mark Hess, U.S. *Gravure by Helio Courvoisier, Switzerland. Perforated 11 1/2x11 3/4.*

807 *Denomination upper left;* 808 *Denomination upper right;* 809 *Denomination lower left;* 810 *Denomination lower right*

807		MNHVF	UseVF
33¢	**multicolored** *(1,512,000 printed)*	.75	.25
	FDC *(Aug. 23, 1999)*		1.50
808		MNHVF	UseVF
33¢	**multicolored** *(1,512,000 printed)*	.75	.25
	FDC *(Aug. 23, 1999)*		1.50
809		MNHVF	UseVF
33¢	**multicolored** *(1,512,000 printed)*	.75	.25
	FDC *(Aug. 23, 1999)*		1.50
810		MNHVF	UseVF
33¢	**multicolored** *(1,512,000 printed)*	.75	.25
	FDC *(Aug. 23, 1999)*		1.50
	Inscription block of 4	3.00	
	FDC *(Aug. 23, 1999)* (block)		4.00

1999. IN MEMORIAM ISSUE U.N. flags at half-staff honored those who have died in U.N. service for the cause of peace. Designed by Robert Stein, U.S. *Offset by Walsall Security Printers, Ltd., U.K. Sheet stamp perforated 14 1/2, souvenir sheet perforated 14.*

811 *Flags flying at half staff outside the U.N. headquarters in New York City*

Please read the introduction to this catalog carefully. It contains much valuable information for all stamp collectors, and also makes the catalog easier for you to use.

812 *SS with flags at half staff*

811		MNHVF	UseVF
33¢	**multicolored** *(550,000 printed)*	.75	.25
	FDC *(Sept. 21, 1999)*		1.00
	Inscription block of 4	3.00	

812		MNHVF	UseVF
$1.00	**multicolored** *(235,000 printed)*	2.00	.75
	FDC *(Sept. 21, 1999)*		3.00

1999. EDUCATION - KEYSTONE TO THE 21ST CENTURY ISSUE

Designed by Romero Britto, Brazil. *Offset by Osterreichische Staatsdruckerei. Perforated 13 3/4x13 1/2.*

813 *A wildly colored couple reads, hearts and globes in their lenses;*
814 *A happy heart flexes its muscles over an open book*

813		MNHVF	UseVF
33¢	**multicolored** *(430,000 printed)*	.75	.25
	FDC *(Nov. 18, 1999)*		1.00
	Inscription block of 4	3.00	

814		MNHVF	UseVF
60¢	**multicolored** *(430,000 printed)*	1.25	.50
	FDC *(Nov. 18, 1999)*		2.00
	Inscription block of 4	5.00	

Commemorative Issues

2000. INTERNATIONAL YEAR OF THANKSGIVING ISSUE

The United Nations proclaimed the year 2000 the International Year of Thanksgiving. Glory Window in the Chapel of Thanksgiving at Thanks-Giving Square in Dallas, Texas, designed by Gabrielle Loire of Chartres, France, for the Thanks-Giving Foundation. Stamps designed by Rorie Katz, U.S. *Offset by Cartor Security Printing, France, perforated 13.*

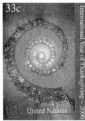

815 *Glory Window in the Chapel of Thanksgiving, Dallas, Texas*

815		MNHVF	UseVF
33¢	**multicolored** *(550,000 printed)*	.50	.20

	FDC *(Jan. 1, 2000)*			1.50
	Inscription block of 4		2.00	

2000. ENDANGERED SPECIES ISSUE

The eighth set in the Endangered Species series begun in 1993, designed by Suzanne Duranceau, Canada. *Printed by Joh. Enschéde and Sons, Netherlands, perforated 12 1/2 x 13 3/4, (1,960,000 stamps, 122,500 panes printed).*

816 *Brown Bear;*
817 *Black-bellied bustard;* 818
Chinese Crocodile Lizard; 819
Bonobo

816		MNHVF	UseVF
33¢	**multicolored**	.50	.20

817		MNHVF	UseVF
33¢	**multicolored**	.50	.20

818		MNHVF	UseVF
33¢	**multicolored**	.50	.20

819		MNHVF	UseVF
33¢	**multicolored**	.50	.20
	FDC *(April 6, 2000)*		1.50
	Inscription block of 4	2.00	
	y. Se-tenant block of 4	2.00	

2000. OUR WORLD ISSUE

A celebration of the new millennium, the stamps depict paintings submitted to a worldwide competition on the theme, "My Country in the Year 2000." Paintings adapted as stamps by Robert Stein, U.S. *Offset by Cartor Security Printing, France, perforated 13.*

820 Crawling Toward the Millennium *by Sam Yeates*

820		MNHVF	UseVF
33¢	**multicolored** *(400,000 printed)*	.50	.20
	FDC *(May 30, 2000)*		1.50
	Inscription block of 4	2.00	

821 Crossing *by Masakazu Takahata, Japan*

821		MNHVF	UseVF
60¢	**multicolored** *(360,000 printed)*	1.00	.50
	FDC *(May 30, 2000)*		2.50
	Inscription block of 4	4.00	

2000. 55TH ANNIVERSARY OF THE UNITED NATIONS ISSUE

Photographs documented the construction of the United Nations Headquarters complex in New York City, whose first occupation took place in 1950. Designed by Rorie Katz, U.S., based on U.N. photographs. *Offset by Cartor Security Printing, France, perforated 13.*

822 *Workers remove decorations during a 1956 remodeling of the General Assembly Hall*

822		MNHVF	UseVF
33¢	**blue** *(400,000 printed)*	.50	.20
	FDC *(July 7, 2000)*		1.50
	Inscription block of 4	2.00	

823 *A 1951 photo shows stages of construction of the low Conference Building, the Secretariat Building, and the steel structure of the General Assembly Hall*

823y *Mini-sheet of two stamps against a photo of workers cheering as a U.N. flag is unfurled atop the framework of the Secretariat Building*

823		MNHVF	UseVF
55¢	**blue** *(360,000 printed)*	1.00	.50
	FDC *(July 7, 2000)*		2.50
	Inscription block of 4	4.00	
	y. Sheetlet of 2	1.20	.90
	y1. Se-tenant pair #822-823	1.20	.90

2000. THE U.N. IN THE 21ST CENTURY ISSUE Intended to show the work of the United Nations in promoting respect for human rights, protection of the environment, economic development and reduction of poverty and disease. Designed by Wilson McLean, United Kingdom. *Offset by Government Printing Office, Austria, perforated 14, (274,000 panes printed).*

824y *The United Nations in the 21st century, wavy-haired woman at left*

824		MNHVF	UseVF
33¢	**multicolored**	.50	.20
	a. Rice paddy	.50	.20
	b. Loading vehicle	.50	.20
	c. Ballot	.50	.20
	d. Vaccination	.50	.20
	e Woman in shawl	.50	.20
	f. Building wall	.50	.20
	FDC *(Sept. 15, 2000)*		1.00
	y. Sheetlet of 6	3.00	1.50

2000. INTERNATIONAL FLAG OF PEACE ISSUE Students from around the world submitted designs for this stamp to reinforce the International Day of Peace. The stamp also includes the Olympic rings symbol. Designed by Mateja Prunk, age 12, the first Slovenian artist to have her work on a U.N. stamp. *Offset by the House of Questa, United Kingdom, perforated 14.*

825 *A friendly sun warms the Earth on the International Flag of Peace*

825		MNHVF	UseVF
33¢	**multicolored** *(400,000 printed)*	.50	.20
	FDC *(Sept. 15, 2000)*		1.50
	Inscription block of 4	2.00	

2000. WORLD HERITAGE - SPAIN ISSUE The sixth U.N. stamp issued to illustrate World Heritage sites and the fourth in a series of stamps and booklets to focus on sites in one geographical area. World Heritage sites have been designed to indicate places whose importance reach beyond geographical and political boundaries. Designed by Robert Stein, U.S. *Offset by The House of Questa, United Kingdom, perforated 14.*

826 *Medieval Granada exemplifies the Moorish tradition of lavish decoration;* 827 *Merida exhibits the well preserved artifacts of the town founded by the Romans in 25 B.C.*

826		MNHVF	UseVF
33¢	multicolored	.50	.20
	FDC *(Oct. 6, 2000)*		1.50
	Inscription block of 4	2.00	

827		MNHVF	UseVF
60¢	multicolored	1.10	.50
	FDC *(Oct. 6, 2000)*		2.50
	Inscription block of 4	4.40	

2000. WORLD HERITAGE - SPAIN PRESTIGE BOOKLET ISSUE Designs of the six stamps from the three U.N. offices are re-valued in low denominations in a descriptive booklet format. *Offset by The House of Questa, United Kingdom, perforated 14.*

828-833 *World Heritage - Spain Prestige Booklet*

828		MNHVF	UseVF
	multicolored	.50	.20

829		MNHVF	UseVF
	multicolored	.50	.20

830		MNHVF	UseVF
	multicolored	.50	.20

831		MNHVF	UseVF
	multicolored	.50	.20

832		MNHVF	UseVF
	multicolored	.50	.20

833		MNHVF	UseVF
	multicolored	.50	.20
	FDC *(Oct. 6, 2000)*		2.50
	n. Booklet of 6	1.10	.50

> Please read the introduction to this catalog carefully. It contains much valuable information for all stamp collectors, and also makes the catalog easier for you to use.

2000. RESPECT FOR REFUGEES ISSUE Called attention to the U.N. High Commissioner for Refugees, which noted its 50th anniversary in 2000. Designed by Yuri Gevorgian ("Yuroz"), U.S. *Offset by Joh. Enschéde Stamps Security Printers, Netherlands, perforated 12 3/4 x 13 1/4.*

834 *A doll lies on a crate in a group of refugees*

834		MNHVF	UseVF
33¢	multicolored *(540,000 printed)*	.50	.20
	FDC *(Nov. 9, 2000)*		1.50
	Inscription block of 4	2.00	

835 *The mini-sheet stamp image is taken from the far-right portion of a larger group of refugees*

835		MNHVF	UseVF
$1.00	multicolored *(225,000 printed)*	2.00	1.00
	FDC *(Nov. 9, 2000)*		2.00
	Sheetlet of 1	2.00	

Postal Cards

1952. POSTAL CARD ISSUE Designed by Leon Helguera, Mexico. Adaptation of 1 1/2¢ or 50¢ Definitives (Nos. 2 or 10) of 1951. *Printed by Dennison & Sons, U.S.*

PC1 *U.N. headquarters, U.N. seal*

PC1		MVF	UseVF
2¢	blue on buff *(899,415)*	.30	.20
	FDC *(July 18, 1952)*		1.50

1957. AIRMAIL POSTAL CARD ISSUE Designed by Willi W. Wind, Israel. Adaptation of 4¢ Airmail of 1957. *Printed by British American Bank Note Co., Ltd., Canada.*

PC2 *Globe and wing*

PC2		MVF	UseVF
4¢	light brown red *(1,750,000 printed)*	.40	.20
	FDC *(May 27, 1957)*		1.50

1958. POSTAL CARD ISSUE Designed by Leon Helguera, Mexico. Adaptation of 1 1/2¢ or 50¢ Definitives (Nos. 2 or 10) of 1951. *Printed by British American Bank Note Co., Ltd., Canada.*

PC3 *U.N. headquarters, U.N. seal*

PC3		MVF	UseVF
3¢	olive gray on buff *(575,000)*	.40	.20
	FDC *(Sept. 22, 1958)*		1.50

1959. AIRMAIL POSTAL CARD ISSUE Designed by Willi W. Wind, Israel. Adaptation of 4¢ Airmail of 1957 - 1¢ in wreath. *Overprinted with outlined "1" and "cent" within wreath by Eureka Specialty Printing Co., emblem in upper left corner. Original printing by British American Bank Note Co., Ltd., Canada.*

PC4 *Globe and wing, surcharged*

PC4		MVF	UseVF
1¢ on 4¢ light brown red *(1,119,000)*		.60	.20
	FDC *(June 5, 1959)*		40.00

1959. AIRMAIL POSTAL CARD ISSUE Designed by Willi W. Wind, Israel. Similar to No. PC2 but 5¢ denomination. *Printed by Eureka Specialty Printing Co., U.S.*

PC5 *Wing*

PC5		MVF	UseVF
5¢	carmine *(500,000)*	1.00	.20
	FDC *(Sept. 21, 1959)*		1.50

1963. POSTAL CARD ISSUE Designed by Ole Hamann, Denmark. Adaptation of 2¢ Definitive of 1964. *Offset by Eureka Specialty Printing Co., U.S.*

PC6 *Map*

PC6		MVF	UseVF
4¢	multicolored *(784,000)*	.40	.20
	FDC *(April 26, 1963)*		1.50

1963. AIRMAIL POSTAL CARD ISSUE Designed by Claude Bottiau, France. Adaptation of 6¢ Airmail of 1963. *Offset by Eureka Specialty Printing Co., U.S.*

PC7 *Outer space*

PC7		MVF	UseVF
6¢	black & blue *(350,000)*	1.00	.20
	FDC *(April 26, 1963)*		1.50

1966. AIRMAIL POSTAL CARD ISSUE Designed by Olav Mathiesen, Denmark. *Offset by Eureka-Carlisle Co., U.S.*

PC8 *Abstract space design*

PC8		MVF	UseVF
11¢	multicolored *(764,500)*	.60	.20
	FDC *(June 9, 1966)*		1.50
	2nd printing	.50	.20

1968. INTERNATIONAL AIRMAIL POSTAL CARD ISSUE Designed by Olav Mathiesen, Denmark. *Printed by Eureka-Carlisle Co., U.S.*

PC9 *Abstract space design*

PC9		MVF	UseVF
13¢	green & yellow *(829,000)*	.75	.20
	FDC *(May 31, 1968)*		1.50

1969. POST HORN POSTAL CARD ISSUE Designed by John Mason, Australia. *Offset by Canadian Bank Note Co., Canada.*

PC10 *Posthorn*

PC10		MVF	UseVF
5¢	blue & black *(500,000)*	.40	.20
	FDC *(Jan. 8, 1969)*		1.50

1969. WINGS POSTAL CARD ISSUE Designed by Lawrence Kurtz U.S. *Offset by Canadian Bank Note Co., Canada.*

PC11 *Abstract wing design*

PC11		MVF	UseVF
8¢	multicolored *(500,000)*	.80	.20
	FDC *(Jan. 8, 1969)*		1.50

1972. POSTAL CARD ISSUE Designed by Lyell Dolan, Australia. Adaptation of 9¢ Airmail 1972. *Printed by Japanese Government Printing Office.*

PC12 *Emblem and stylized wing*

PC12		MVF	UseVF
9¢	multicolored *(500,000)*	.60	.20
	FDC *(Oct. 16, 1972)*		1.50

1972. AIRMAIL POSTAL CARD ISSUE Designed by Lawrence Kurtz, U.S. Adaptation of 8¢ Airmail Postal Card (No. PC11) of 1969. *Offset by Japanese Government Printing Office.*

PC13 *Planes*

PC13		MVF	UseVF
15¢	multicolored *(500,000)*	.75	.20
	FDC *(Oct. 16, 1972)*		1.50

1973. POSTAL CARD ISSUE Designed by Asher Kalderon, Israel. *Printed by Japanese Government Printing Office.*

PC14 *"UN"*

PC14		MVF	UseVF
6¢	multicolored *(500,000)*	.40	.20
	FDC *(Jan. 12, 1973)*		1.50

1975. POSTAL CARD ISSUE Designed by Asher Kalderon, Israel. Similar to 6¢ Postal Card of 1973. *Offset by S. Setelipaino, Finland.*

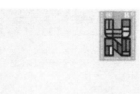

PC15 *"UN"*

PC15		MVF	UseVF
8¢	multicolored *(450,000)*	.65	.20
	FDC *(Jan. 10, 1975)*		1.50

1975. AIRMAIL POSTAL CARD ISSUE Designed by British American Bank Note Co., Canada, similar to 17¢ Airmail stamp of 1972 (11¢); and Shamir Bros., Israel, similar to 18¢ Airmail stamp of 1974 (18¢). *Offset by S. Setelipaino, Finland.*

PC16 *Clouds*

PC16		MVF	UseVF
11¢	multicolored *(250,000)*	.60	.20
	FDC *(Jan. 10, 1975)*		1.50

PC17 *Pathways radiating from U.N. emblem*

PC17		MVF	UseVF
18¢	multicolored *(250,000)*	.60	.20
	FDC *(Jan. 10, 1975)*		1.50

1977. U.N. EMBLEM POSTAL CARD ISSUE Designed by George Hamori, Australia. *Offset by S. Setelipaino, Finland.*

PC18 *U.N. emblem*

PC18		MVF	UseVF
9¢	multicolored *(350,000)*	.80	.20
	FDC *(June 27, 1977)*		1.50

1982. POSTAL CARD ISSUE Designed by Salahattin Kanidinc, U.S. *Printed by Helio Courvoisier, Switzerland.*

PC19 *Letter*

PC19		MVF	UseVF
13¢	multicolored *(350,000)*	2.00	.50
	FDC *(April 28, 1982)*		1.50

1982. AIRMAIL MAILMAN POSTAL CARD ISSUE Designed by Arieh Glaser, Israel. *Printed by Helio Courvoisier, Switzerland.*

PC20 *Flying mailman*

PC20		MVF	UseVF
28¢	**multicolored** *(350,000)*	2.00	.50
	FDC *(April 28, 1982)*		2.00

1989. POSTAL CARD SCENES ISSUE Adapted as Postal Cards by Thomas Lee, China. *Printed by Joh. Enschedé and Sons, Netherlands.*

PC21 *Spring flowers at U.N. headquarters, photograph by Lois Conner, U.S.*

PC21		MVF	UseVF
15¢	**multicolored** *(120,000)*	2.00	.50
	FDC *(March 17, 1989)*		4.00

PC22 *Cherry blossoms, U.N. gardens, photograph by John Isaac, India*

PC22		MVF	UseVF
15¢	**multicolored** *(120,000)*	2.00	.50
	FDC *(March 17, 1989)*		4.00

PC23 *Row of flags of member states at U.N. headquarters, photograph by Unmesh, U.S.*

PC23		MVF	UseVF
15¢	**multicolored** *(120,000)*	2.00	.50
	FDC *(March 17, 1989)*		4.00

PC24 *River view of U.N. headquarters, photograph by Unmesh, U.S.*

PC24		MVF	UseVF
15¢	**multicolored** *(120,000)*	2.00	.50
	FDC *(March 17, 1989)*		4.00

PC25 *U.N. General Assembly, photograph by U.N.*

PC25		MVF	UseVF
15¢	**multicolored** *(120,000)*	2.00	.50
	FDC *(March 17, 1989)*		4.00

PC26 *U.N. headquarters, photograph by Unmesh, U.S.*

PC26		MVF	UseVF
36¢	**multicolored** *(120,000)*	3.00	.50
	FDC *(March 17, 1989)*		4.25

PC27 *Row of flags of member states at U.N. headquarters, photograph by Unmesh, U.S.*

PC27		MVF	UseVF
36¢	**multicolored** *(120,000)*	3.00	.50
	FDC *(March 17, 1989)*		4.25

> Users of this Catalog are invited to write us if they have information which they feel will supplement or correct any material contained herein. All such communications will be answered.

PC28 *U.N. headquarters, evening, photograph by U.N.*

PC28
		MVF	UseVF
36¢	**multicolored** *(120,000)*	3.00	.50
	FDC *(March 17, 1989)*		4.25

PC29 *U.N. gardens, photograph by Lois Conner, U.S.*

PC29
		MVF	UseVF
36¢	**multicolored** *(120,000)*	3.00	.50
	FDC *(March 17, 1989)*		4.25

PC30 *U.N. Security Council, photograph by U.N.*

PC30
		MVF	UseVF
36¢	**multicolored** *(120,000)*	3.00	.50
	FDC *(March 17, 1989)*		4.25

1992. POSTAL CARD ISSUE Adaptation of $2.00 Definitive of 1991. Designed by Rocco J. Callari and Robert Stein, U.S., based on U.N. photograph by Unmesh, U.S.

PC31 *U.N. headquarters*

PC31
		MVF	UseVF
40¢	**multicolored** *(150,000)*	4.50	1.00
	FDC *(Sept. 4, 1992)*		1.50

1998. POSTAL CARD ISSUE Designed by Robert Stein, U.S. *Printed by Mercury-Walch Pty. Ltd., Australia.*

PC32 *U.N. rose garden, photograph by Unmesh, U.S.*

PC32
		MVF	UseVF
21¢	**multicolored** *(150,000)*	.55	.20
	FDC *(May 20, 1998)*		1.50

PC33 *U.N. headquarters on N.Y. skyline, photograph by Unmesh, U.S.*

PC33
		MVF	UseVF
50¢	**multicolored** *(150,000)*	1.25	.20
	FDC *(May 20, 1998)*		1.50

Postal Stationery

1952. AIR LETTER SHEET ISSUE Designed by Olav Mathiesen, Denmark. Adaptation of 15¢ and 25¢ Airmail stamps of 1951. *Printed by Dennison & Sons, U.S. Inscribed AIR LETTER; security paper tinted in light shade of color of stamp, white multi-lingual UNITED NATIONS in small letters repeated continuously over sheet, vertical outside, horizontal inside.*

E1 *Swallows and U.N. emblem*

E1
		MVF	UseVF
10¢	**Prussian blue,** *(187,000)* entire	35.00	20.00
	FDC *(Aug. 29, 1952)*		6.75

1953. ENVELOPE ISSUE Die design by American Bank Note Co., U.S. *Printed by International Envelope Corp., U.S.*

E2 *U.N. emblem, 3¢*

E2
		MVF	UseVF
3¢	**light blue on white,** entire, size 6 3/4x3 3/4 inches *(300,000)*	1.00	3.00
	a. entire, size 6 1/2x3 5/8 inches *(50,000)* *(June 16, 1958)*	1.20	10.00
	b. entire, size 9 1/2x4 1/8 inches *(205,000)*	1.00	3.00
	FDC *(Sept. 15, 1953)*		4.25

1954. AIR LETTER SHEET ISSUE Designed by Olav Mathiesen, Denmark. Adaptation of 15¢ and 25¢ Airmail stamps of 1951. *Printed by Dennison & Sons, U.S.*

E3 *Swallows and U.N. emblem*

E3		MVF	UseVF
10¢	**deep violet blue,** *(207,000)* entire	11.00	2.00
	FDC *(Sept. 14, 1954)*		75.00
	a. no border around stamp, *(148,800)*	9.00	30.00
	FDC *(Jan. 1958)*		20.00

1958. ENVELOPE ISSUE Die designed by American Bank Note Co., U.S. *Printed by International Envelope Corp., U.S.*

E4 *U.N. emblem, 4¢*

E4		MVF	UseVF
4¢	**ultramarine,** entire, size 6 1/2x3 5/8 inches *(500,000)*	.75	.25
	a. entire, size 9 1/2x4 1/8 inches *(500,000)*	.75	.25
	FDC *(Sept. 22, 1958)*		1.50

1960. AIRMAIL ENVELOPE ISSUE Designed by Olav Mathiesen, Denmark. Adaptation of 7¢ Airmail of 1959. *Printed and embossed by International Envelope Corp., U.S.; carmine and ultramarine lozenges at border; sold at 8¢.*

E5 *Flag and plane*

E5		MVF	UseVF
7¢	**ultramarine,** entire, size 6 1/2x3 5/8 inches *(300,000)*	2.25	.80
	FDC *(Sept. 21, 1960)*		1.75
	a. entire, size 9 1/2x4 1/8 inches *(250,000)*	6.00	8.00
	FDC *(Sept. 21, 1960)*		3.00

1960. AIR LETTER SHEET ISSUE Designed by Olav Mathiesen, Denmark. Adaptation of 7¢ Airmail stamp of 1959. *Printed by Thomas de la Rue, U.K. Emblem in upper left corner inscribed at bottom AIR LETTER-AEROGRAMME • PAR AVION; on security paper as No. E1.*

E6 *Flag and plane*

E6		MVF	UseVF
10¢	**ultramarine,** entire *(405,000)*	1.00	.20
	FDC *(Jan. 18, 1960)*		1.00

1961. AIR LETTER SHEET ISSUE Designed by Ole Hamann, Denmark. Adaptation of 10¢ Airmail stamp of 1951. *Printed by Thomas de la Rue, U.K. Emblem in upper left corner, inscribed at bottom AIR LETTER • AEROGRAMME • PAR AVION; on security paper as No. E1.*

E7 *Plane and bird*

E7		MVF	UseVF
11¢	**deep blue,** entire *(969,000)*	1.25	.20
	a. greenish background (1965)	1.50	.25
	FDC *(June 26, 1961)*		1.50
	FDC (greenish)		—

1963. ENVELOPE ISSUE Designed by Hatim El Mekki, Tunisia. Adaptation of 50¢ Definitive stamp of 1964. *Printed by U.S. Envelope Co.*

E8 *Dove of Peace atop elongated globe*

E8		MVF	UseVF
5¢	**multicolored,** entire, size 6 1/2x3 5/8 inches *(765,888)*	.50	.20
	a. entire, size 9 1/2x4 1/8 inches *(350,000)*	.50	.20
	FDC *(April 26, 1963)*		1.50

1963. AIRMAIL ENVELOPE ISSUE Designed by George Hamori, Australia. Adaptation of 8¢ Airmail stamp of 1963. *Printed by U.S. Envelope Co.*

E9 *U.N. emblem carried by image of wings, gold background*

E9		MVF	UseVF
8¢	**multicolored,** entire, size 6 1/2x3 5/8 inches *(630,000)*	.75	.20
	a. entire, size 9 1/2x4 1/8 inches *(250,000)*	.75	.20
	FDC *(April 26, 1963)*		1.50

1968. AIR LETTER SHEET ISSUE Designed by Robert Perrot, France. *Offset by S. Setelipaino, Finland.*

E10 *U.N. emblem and stylized airplane*

E10		MVF	UseVF
13¢	blue & light blue *(750,000)*	.50	.20
	FDC *(May 31, 1968)*		1.50

1969. ENVELOPE ISSUE Designed by Hatim El Mekki, Tunisia. Adaptation of 50¢ Definitive stamp of 1964. *Printed by S. Setelipaino, Finland.*

E11 *Dove of Peace on elongated globe*

E11		MVF	UseVF
6¢	multicolored, entire, size 6 1/2x3 5/8 inches *(500,000)*	.45	.20
	a. entire, size 9 1/2x4 1/8 inches *(350,000)*	.50	.20
	FDC *(Jan. 8, 1969)*		1.50

1969. AIRMAIL ENVELOPE ISSUE Designed by George Hamori, Australia. Adaptation of 8¢ Airmail stamp of 1963 and Envelope No. E9. *Printed by S. Setelipaino, Finland.*

E12 *U.N. emblem carried by image of wings, pink background*

E12		MVF	UseVF
10¢	multicolored, entire, size 6 1/2x3 5/8 inches *(500,000)*	.60	.20
	a. entire, size 9 1/2x4 1/8 inches *(250,000)*	.60	.20
	FDC *(Jan. 8, 1969)*		1.50

1972. AIR LETTER SHEET ISSUE Designed by Edmondo Calivis, Egypt. *Offset by Joh. Enschedé and Sons, Netherlands.*

E13 *"UN" as a contrail across globe*

E13		MVF	UseVF
15¢	deep blue & light blue *(500,000)*	.90	.20
	FDC *(Oct. 16, 1972)*		1.50

1973. ENVELOPE ISSUE Designed by Olav Mathiesen, Denmark. Adaptation of 6¢ Definitive stamp of 1968. *Offset by Eureka-Carlisle Co., U.S.*

E14 *U.N. headquarters building, New York*

E14		MVF	UseVF
8¢	multicolored, entire, size 6 1/2x3 5/8 inches *(350,000)*	.65	.20
	a. entire, size 9 1/2x4 1/8 inches *(350,000)*	.65	.20
	FDC *(Jan. 12, 1973)*		1.50

1973. AIRMAIL ENVELOPE ISSUE Designed by Arne Johnson, Norway. Adaptation of 11¢ Airmail stamp of 1972. *Offset by Eureka-Carlisle Co., U.S.*

E15 *Flock of birds*

E15		MVF	UseVF
11¢	multicolored, entire, size 6 1/2x3 5/8 inches *(350,000)*	.60	.20
	a. entire, size 9 1/2x4 1/8 inches *(350,000)*	.60	.20
	FDC *(Jan. 12, 1973)*		1.50

1975. ENVELOPE ISSUE Designed by Olav Mathiesen, Denmark. Adaptation of 10¢ Definitive stamp of 1974. *Offset by U.S. Envelope Co.*

E16 *U.N. headquarters building, New York*

E16		MVF	UseVF
10¢	multicolored, entire, size 6 1/2x3 5/8 inches *(295,000)*	.75	.20
	a. entire, size 9 1/2x4 1/8 inches *(252,500)*	.75	.20
	FDC *(Jan. 10, 1975)*		1.50

1975. AIRMAIL ENVELOPE ISSUE Designed by George Hamori, Australia. Adaptation of 13¢ Airmail stamp of 1974. *Gravure by U.S. Envelope Co.*

E17 *Globe and jet*

E17		MVF	UseVF
13¢	multicolored, entire, size 6 1/2x3 5/8 inches *(291,366)*	.75	.20

a. entire, size 9 1/2x4 1/8 inches *(264,173)*   .75   .20
FDC *(Jan. 10, 1975)*   1.50

1975. AIR LETTER SHEET ISSUE Designed by Olav Mathiesen, Denmark. Adaptation of 8¢ Definitive stamp of 1971. *Offset by Joh. Enschedé and Sons, Netherlands.*

E18 *U.N. headquarters building, New York*

E18		MVF	UseVF
18¢	**deep blue & light blue** *(400,000)*	1.00	.20
	FDC *(Jan. 10, 1975)*		1.50

1977. AIR LETTER SHEET ISSUE Designed by Angel Medina, Uruguay. *Offset by Joh. Enschedé and Sons, Netherlands.*

E19 *UN scribble*

E19		MVF	UseVF
22¢	**multicolored** *(400,000)*	1.00	.20
	FDC *(June 27, 1977)*		1.50

1982. AIR LETTER SHEET ISSUE Designed by Margaret-Ann Champion, U.S. *Offset by Joh. Enschedé and Sons, Netherlands.*

E20 *Folded paper airplane*

E20		MVF	UseVF
30¢	**gray** *(400,000)*	1.25	.70
	FDC *(April 28, 1982)*		3.25

1985. STAMPED ENVELOPE ISSUE Designed by George Hamori, Australia. *Offset by Carl Ueberreuter Druck and Verlag M. Salzer, Austria.*

E21 *Bouquet of colored strips*

E21		MVF	UseVF
22¢	**multicolored** *(247,800)*	9.00	.40
	FDC *(May 10, 1985)*		2.00

1987. AIR LETTER SHEET SURCHARGE ISSUE Designed by Margaret-Ann Champion, U.S. *Originally printed by Joh. Enschedé and Sons, Netherlands. 6¢ overprinted by U.N. in black below 30¢ indicium.*

E22 *Surcharge on paper airplane*

E22		MVF	UseVF
30¢ + 6¢	**black, green,** entire *(43,000)*	70.00	5.00
	FDC *(July 7, 1987)*		12.50

1989. STAMPED ENVELOPE ISSUE Designed by Rocco J. Callari, U.S. *Offset by Mercury-Walch, Australia.*

E23 *End-view drawing of U.N. headquarters*

E23		MVF	UseVF
25¢	**multicolored,** size 6 1/2x3 5/8 inches *(150,000)*	3.75	.20
	a. entire, size 9 1/2x4 1/8 inches *(200,000)*	3.75	.20
	FDC *(March 17, 1989)*		2.25

1989. AIR LETTER SHEET ISSUE Designed by Thomas Lee, China. *Offset by Mercury-Walch, Australia.*

E24 *Flat-view drawing of U.N. headquarters*

E24		MVF	UseVF
39¢	**multicolored,** entire *(350,000)*	5.50	.50
	FDC *(March 17, 1989)*		9.00

1991. AIR LETTER SHEET SURCHARGE ISSUE Designed by Thomas Lee, China. *Printed by United Nations. 6¢ overprinted by U.N. in black below 39¢ indicium on E24.*

E25 *Surcharge on drawing of U.N. headquarters*

E25		MVF	UseVF
39¢ + 6¢ multicolored, entire *(35,563)*		21.00	1.50
FDC *(Feb. 12, 1991)*			2.50

1991. STAMPED ENVELOPE SURCHARGE ISSUE Designed by Rocco J. Callari, U.S. *Originally printed by Mercury-Walch, Australia. 7¢ overprinted by U.N. in black below 25¢ indicium on E23.*

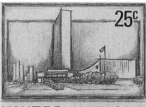

E26 *Surcharge on drawing of U.N. headquarters*

E26		MVF	UseVF
25¢ + 4¢ multicolored, entire, size 6 1/2x3 5/8 inches *(33,000)*		3.50	.25
a. entire, size 9 1/2x4 1/8 inches *(51,500)*		3.50	.25
FDC *(April 15, 1991)*			2.00

1992. AIR LETTER SHEET ISSUE Designed by Robert Stein, U.S., based on a concept by G. Calvi, Brazil. *Offset by Mercury-Walch Pty. Ltd., Australia.*

E27 *Winged hand with letter*

E27		MVF	UseVF
45¢ **multicolored,** entire *(185,000)*		4.25	.50
FDC *(Sept. 4, 1992)*			2.00

1991. STAMPED ENVELOPE SURCHARGE ISSUE Designed by Rocco J. Callari, U.S. *Originally printed by Mercury-Walch, Australia. 7¢ overprinted by U.N. in black below 25¢ indicium on E23.*

E28 *Surcharge on drawing of U.N. headquarters*

E28		MVF	UseVF
25¢ + 7¢ multicolored, entire, size 6 1/2x3 5/8 inches *(22,000)*		3.50	.20
a. entire, size 9 1/2x4 1/8 inches *(30,000)*		3.50	.20
FDC *(Jan. 20, 1995)*			6.00

1995. AIR LETTER SHEET SURCHARGE ISSUE Designed by Robert Stein, U.S., based on a concept by G. Calvi, Brazil. *Originally printed by Mercury-Walch, Australia. 5¢ overprinted by U.N. in black to left of 45¢ indicium on No. E27.*

E29 *Surcharge on winged hand with letter*

E29		MVF	UseVF
45¢ + 5¢ multicolored, entire *(32,656)*		7.00	1.00
FDC *(July 9, 1995)*			8.00

1997. STAMPED ENVELOPE ISSUE Featured the mural *Cripticandina* by Alfredo La Placa, Bolivia, presented to the U.N. in 1995. Adapted by Robert Stein, U.S., based on photographs by Andrea Brizzi, Italy. *Business size (E30) envelope indicium is larger than that on the personal size envelope (E30A).*

E30, E30A *Cripticandina*

E30		MVF	UseVF
32¢ **multicolored,** entire, size 9 1/2x4 1/8 inches *(80,000)*		2.00	.50
FDC *(Feb. 12, 1997)*			2.50

E30A
*Cripticandina
(smaller)*

E30A		MVF	UseVF
32¢	**multicolored,** entire, size 6 1/2x3 5/8	2.50	.50
	inches *(22,000)*		
	FDC *(Feb. 12, 1997)*		2.00

1997. AIR LETTER SHEET ISSUE Designed by Robert Stein, U.S. based on photographs by Unmesh, U.S. *Printed by Mercury-Walch Pty. Ltd., Australia.*

E31 *Cherry blossoms*

E31		MVF	UseVF
50¢	**multicolored,** entire	2.00	.25
	FDC *(March 13, 1997)*		5.00

1999. STAMPED ENVELOPE ISSUE *1¢ surcharge in black to left of indicium on 32¢ stamped envelope.* The indicia shows the abstract mural *Cripticandina* by Alfredo La Placa.

E32 *Cripticandina (business size)*

E32	MVF	UseVF
32¢ + 1¢ multicolored	2.00	.50
FDC *(Jan. 10, 1999)*		1.50

E33 *Cripticandina (smaller)*

E33	MVF	UseVF
32¢ + 1¢ multicolored	2.00	.50
FDC *(Jan. 10, 1999)*		1.50

1999. AIR LETTER SHEET ISSUE *10¢ surcharge in black to left of 50¢ indicium on air letter sheet E31 (1997).*

E34 *Cherry blossoms*

E34	MVF	UseVF
50¢ + 10¢ multicolored	2.50	.50
FDC *(June 1, 1999)*		2.00

Regular Issues

1969-1972. REGULAR ISSUES United Nations contemporary types value in Swiss francs.

1 *U.N. building against U.N. emblem, adaptation of 1 1/2¢ Definitive of 1967. Designed by Jozséf Vertel, Hungary. Similar to U.N. New York Minkus No. 179. Gravure by S. Setelipaino, Finland. Perforated 13 3/4.*

1

	MNHVF	UseVF
5¢ **multicolored** *(3,300,000 printed)*	.55	.50
FDC *(Oct. 4, 1969)*		1.00
v. green omitted	250.00	
Inscription block of 4	2.50	

2 *U.N. flag, adaptation of 3¢ Definitive of 1962. Designed by Ole Hamann, Denmark. Similar to U.N. New York Minkus No. 112. Gravure by Helio Courvoisier, Switzerland. Perforated 11 1/4x12 1/4.*

2

	MNHVF	UseVF
10¢ **multicolored** *(4,300,000 printed)*	.25	.20
FDC *(Oct. 4, 1969)*		1.00
Inscription block of 4	1.25	

3 *Three united figures against world, adaptation of 10¢ Definitive of 1964. Designed by George Hamori, Australia. Similar to U.N. New York Minkus No. 140. Gravure by Helio Courvoisier, Switzerland. Perforated 11 3/4.*

3

	MNHVF	UseVF
20¢ **multicolored** *(4,500,000 printed)*	.25	.20
FDC *(Oct. 4, 1969)*		1.00
Inscription block of 4	1.25	

4 *Palais des Nations. Designed by Ole Hamann, Denmark. Gravure by Helio Courvoisier, Switzerland. Perforated 11 3/4.*

4

	MNHVF	UseVF
30¢ **multicolored** *(3,000,000 printed)*	.30	.25
FDC *(Oct. 4, 1969)*		1.00
Inscription block of 4	1.50	

4A *Palais des Nations, Geneva, Switzerland. Designed by Ole Hamann, Denmark. Offset by Helio Courvoisier, Switzerland. Perforated 11 1/4x11 1/2.*

4A

	MNHVF	UseVF
40¢ **multicolored** *(3,500,000 printed)*	.60	.50
FDC *(Jan. 5, 1972)*		1.50
Inscription block of 4	3.00	

5 *Scroll of U.N. charter, adaptation of 15¢ Definitive of 1965. Designed by Olav Mathiesen, Denmark. Similar to U.N. New York Minkus No. 160. Gravure by Helio Courvoisier, Switzerland. Perforated 11 1/4x11 1/2.*

5

	MNHVF	UseVF
50¢ **multicolored** *(3,300,000 printed)*	.60	.50
FDC *(Oct. 4, 1969)*		1.00
Inscription block of 4	3.00	

6 *U.N. emblem over world globe, adaptation of 11¢ Definitive of 1962. Designed by Olav Mathiesen, Denmark. Similar to U.N. New York Minkus No. 114. Gravure by Helio Courvoisier, Switzerland. Perforated 11 3/4x11 1/2.*

6

	MNHVF	UseVF
60¢ **multicolored** *(3,300,000 printed)*	.60	.50
FDC *(April 17, 1970)*		1.00
Inscription block of 4	3.00	

7 *U.N. emblem and initials, adaptation of 13¢ Definitive of 1969. Designed by Leszak Holdanowicz and Marek Freudenreich, Poland. Similar to U.N. New York Minkus No. 209. Gravure by S. Setelipaino, Finland. Perforated 13x13 1/4.*

7

	MNHVF	UseVF
70¢ **multicolored** *(3,300,000 printed)*	.60	.50
FDC *(Sept. 22, 1970)*		1.00
Inscription block of 4	3.00	

8 *Symbol of flight, adaptation of 15¢ Airmail of 1964. Designed by Ole Hamann, Denmark. Similar to U.N. New York Minkus No. 36. Gravure by the Government Printing Office, Austria. Perforated 12.*

8

	MNHVF	UseVF
75¢ **multicolored** *(3,300,000 printed)*	.75	.60
FDC *(Oct. 4, 1969)*		1.00
Inscription block of 4	4.50	

9 *Stylized U.N. building and emblem, adaptation of 20¢ Definitive of 1965. Designed by Louis V. Pierre-Noel, Haiti. Similar to U.N. New York Minkus No. 161. Gravure by S. Setelipaino, Finland. Perforated 14.*

9

	MNHVF	UseVF
80¢ **multicolored** *(3,300,000 printed)*	.75	.60

FDC *(Sept. 22, 1970)* 1.00
Inscription block of 4 4.50

10 *"To unite our strength," adaptation of 30¢ Definitive of 1961. Designed by Herbert Sanborn, U.S. Similar to U.N. New York Minkus No. 99. Gravure by S. Setelipaino, Finland. Perforated 13 1/4x13.*

10		**MNHVF**	**UseVF**
90¢	**multicolored** *(3,300,000 printed)*	1.00	.75
	FDC *(Sept. 22, 1970)*		1.00
	Inscription block of 4	4.50	

11 *U.N. emblem, adaptation of 25¢ Definitive of 1965. Designed by Rashid-ud-Din, Pakistan. Similar to U.N. New York Minkus No. 159. Offset and embossed by Bundesdruckerei, Germany. Perforated 11 1/2.*

11		**MNHVF**	**UseVF**
1f	**multicolored** *(3,000,000 printed)*	1.25	1.00
	FDC *(Oct. 4, 1969)*		1.00
	Inscription block of 4	4.50	

12 *Elongated globe with stylized dove of peace, adaptation of 50¢ Definitive of 1964. Designed by Hatim El Mekki, Tunisia. Similar to U.N. New York Minkus No. 135. Gravure by S. Setelipaino, Finland. Perforated 12x11 3/4.*

12		**MNHVF**	**UseVF**
2f	**multicolored** *(3,000,000 printed)*	1.50	1.00
	FDC *(Sept. 22, 1970)*		1.00
	Inscription block of 4	4.50	

13 *Statue designed by Henrik Starke, Denmark, and adapted as a stamp by Ole Hamann, Denmark. Similar to U.N. New York Minkus No. 196. Gravure by Helio Courvoisier, Switzerland. Perforated 11 1/2.*

13		**MNHVF**	**UseVF**
3f	**multicolored** *(3,000,000 printed)*	2.00	1.50
	FDC *(Oct. 4, 1969)*		1.00
	Inscription block of 4	8.00	

14 *"Peace, Justice, Security" and U.N. emblem, adaptation of $1 Definitive of 1951. Designed by J. F. Doeve, Netherlands. Similar to U.N. New York Minkus No. 11. Intaglio by S. Setelipaino, Finland. Perforated 11 3/4.*

14		**MNHVF**	**UseVF**
10f	**multicolored** *(2,250,000 printed)*	7.50	6.00
	FDC *(April 17, 1970)*		1.00
	v. Pair, imperforate		
	Inscription block of 4	25.00	

Commemorative Issues

15
    not assigned

1971. SEA-BED ISSUE Peaceful uses of sea-bed. Designed by Pentti Rahikainen, Finland. Similar to U.N. New York Minkus No. 229 in changed colors and value in F.s. *Intaglio and gravure by S. Setelipaino, Finland. Perforated 13.*

16 *Sea-bed and shoal of fish*

16		**MNHVF**	**UseVF**
30¢	**multicolored** *(1,935,871)*	.35	.30
	FDC *(Jan. 25, 1971)*		1.00
	Inscription block of 4	1.25	

1971. INTERNATIONAL SUPPORT FOR REFUGEES ISSUE Designed by Kaare K. Nygaard and Martin Weber, U.S. Similar to U.N. New York Minkus Nos. 230 and 231. *Offset by Joh. Enschedé and Sons, Netherlands. Perforated 13x12 1/2.*

17 *Refugees, bronze sculpture, by Kaare K. Nygaard, U.S.*

17		**MNHVF**	**UseVF**
50¢	**multicolored** *(1,820,114)*	.35	.30
	FDC *(March 17, 1971)*		1.00
	Inscription block of 4	1.75	

1971. WORLD FOOD PROGRAM ISSUE Designed by Olav Mathiesen, Denmark. Similar to U.N. New York Minkus No. 232. *Gravure by Heraclio Fournier, Spain. Perforated 14.*

18 *Sheaf of wheat and globe*

18		**MNHVF**	**UseVF**
50¢	**multicolored** *(1,824,170)*	.50	.40
	FDC *(April 13, 1971)*		1.00
	Inscription block of 4	2.00	

1971. UPU HEADQUARTERS ISSUE Universal Postal Union in Berne, Switzerland. Designed by Olav Mathiesen, Denmark. Similar to U.N. New York Minkus No. 233. *Gravure by Helio Courvoisier, Switzerland. Perforated 11 1/2, granite paper.*

19 *Universal Postal Union headquarters, Bern, Switzerland*

19		MNHVF	UseVF
75¢	**multicolored** *(1,821,878)*	.75	.75
	FDC *(May 28, 1971)*		1.00
	Inscription block of 4	2.75	

1971. INTERNATIONAL RACE RELATIONS YEAR ISSUE (30¢) designed by Daniel Gonzague, France; (50¢) by Ole Hamann, Denmark. Similar to U.N. New York Minkus Nos. 234 and 235. *Gravure by Japanese Government Printing Office. Perforated 13 1/2.*

20 *Four petals of a flower*

20		MNHVF	UseVF
30¢	**multicolored** *(1,838,474)*	.30	.25
	FDC *(Sept. 21, 1971)*		1.00
	Inscription block of 4	1.50	

21 *Three globes*

21		MNHVF	UseVF
50¢	**multicolored** *(1,804,126)*	.40	.50
	FDC *(Sept. 21, 1971)*		1.00
	Inscription block of 4	2.00	

1971. INTERNATIONAL SCHOOL ISSUE Adapted by Ole Hamann, Denmark, from a painting by Pablo Picasso, Spain. Similar to U.N. New York Minkus Nos. 238 and 239. *Gravure by Helio Courvoisier, Switzerland. Perforated 11 1/2, granite paper.*

22 *"Maia" by Pablo Picasso*

22		MNHVF	UseVF
1.10f	**multicolored** *(1,467,993)*	1.25	1.00
	FDC *(Nov. 19, 1971)*		1.00
	Inscription block of 4	5.00	

1972. NON-PROLIFERATION OF NUCLEAR WEAPONS Designed by Arnie Johnson, Norway. Similar to New York Minkus No. 241. *Gravure by Heraclio Fournier, Spain. Perforated 13 1/2x14.*

23 *Nuclear explosion*

23		MNHVF	UseVF
40¢	**olive green black & carmine** *(1,567,305)*	.30	.30
	FDC *(Feb. 14, 1972)*		1.00
	Inscription block of 4	1.50	

1972. WORLD HEALTH DAY ISSUE Basic design by Leonardo da Vinci, Italy, and adapted by George Hamori, Australia. Similar to U.N. New York Minkus No. 242. *Intaglio and offset by S. Setelipaino, Finland. Perforated 13x13 1/2.*

24 *Proportions of Man, by Leonardo da Vinci*

24		MNHVF	UseVF
80¢	**multicolored** *(1,543,368)*	.50	.50
	FDC *(April 7, 1972)*		1.00
	Inscription block of 4	1.50	

1972. HUMAN ENVIRONMENT ISSUE for U.N. Conference, Stockholm, Sweden, in June 1972. Designed by Robert Perrot, France. Similar to U.N. New York Minkus Nos. 247 and 248; multicolored, color of background given below. *Offset and embossed by Joh. Enschedé and Sons, Netherlands. Perforated 12 1/2x13 1/2.*

25, 26 *Human environment symbol*

25		MNHVF	UseVF
40¢	**olive** *(1,594,089)*	.80	.25
	FDC *(June 5, 1972)*		1.00
	Inscription block of 4	1.50	

26		MNHVF	UseVF
80¢	**blue** *(1,568,009)*	1.40	1.25
	FDC *(June 5, 1972)*		1.00
	Inscription block of 4	3.50	

1972. ECONOMIC COMMISSION FOR EUROPE ISSUE Designed by Angel Medina, Uruguay. Similar to U.N. New York Minkus No. 249. *Offset by Japanese Government Printing Office. Perforated 13x13 1/2.*

27 *Petals of flower forming the word EUROPE*

27		MNHVF	UseVF
1.10f	**multicolored** *(1,604,082)*	1.50	1.50
	FDC *(Sept. 11, 1972)*		1.00
	Inscription block of 4	7.00	

1972. JOSÉ MARIA SERT MURAL ISSUE Designed by José Maria Sert, Spain, and adapted by Ole Hamann, Denmark. Similar to U.N. New York Minkus Nos. 250 and 251. *Gravure by Helio Courvoisier, Switzerland. Perforated 12x12 1/2, granite paper.*

28, 29 *Five colossal figures*

28		MNHVF	UseVF
40¢	**gold, brown & carmine** *(1,932,428)*	.60	.50
	FDC *(Nov. 17, 1972)*		1.00
	Inscription block of 4	3.00	
29		MNHVF	UseVF
80¢	**gold, brown & olive** *(1,759,600)*	1.00	.85
	FDC *(Nov. 17, 1972)*		1.00
	Inscription block of 4	4.00	

1973. DISARMAMENT DECADE ISSUE Designed by Kurt Plowitz, U.S. Similar to U.N. New York Minkus Nos. 252 and 253. *Offset by Ajans-Turk, Turkey. Perforated 13 1/2, multicolored, color of background given below.*

30, 31 *Broken sword and olive branch*

30		MNHVF	UseVF
60¢	**violet** *(1,586,845)*	.75	.70
	FDC *(March 9, 1973)*		1.00
	v. Imperforate	—	
	Inscription block of 4	3.25	
31		MNHVF	UseVF
1.10f	**olive** *(1,408,169)*	1.25	1.00
	FDC *(March 9, 1973)*		1.00
	v. Imperforate	—	
	Inscription block of 4	5.25	

1973. DRUG ABUSE CONTROL ISSUE Designed by George Hamori, Australia. Similar to U.N. New York Minkus Nos. 254 and 255. *Gravure by Heraclio Fournier, Spain. Perforated 13 1/2.*

32 *Skull and plant*

32		MNHVF	UseVF
60¢	**multicolored** *(1,481,432)*	.85	.75
	FDC *(April 13, 1973)*		1.00
	Inscription block of 4	3.25	

1973. VOLUNTEERS PROGRAM ISSUE established on Jan. 1, 1971. Designed by Helio Courvoisier, Switzerland. Similar to U.N. New York Minkus Nos. 256 and 257. *Gravure by Heraclio Fournier, Spain. Perforated 14, multicolored, color of frame given below.*

33 *Honeycomb and symbols*

33		MNHVF	UseVF
80¢	**olive** *(1,443,519)*	.85	.75
	FDC *(May 25, 1973)*		1.00
	Inscription block of 4	3.25	

1973. NAMIBIA ISSUE The first issue in a series to draw attention to the desire of the Namibian people for independence and freedom from foreign occupation. Designed by George Hamori, Australia. Similar to U.N. New York Minkus Nos. 258 and 259. *Gravure by Heraclio Fournier, Spain. Perforated 14, multicolored, color of background given below.*

34 *Outline map of Namibia*

34		MNHVF	UseVF
60¢	**red** *(1,673,898)*	.75	.60
	FDC *(Oct. 1, 1973)*		1.00
	Inscription block of 4	3.00	

1973. DECLARATION OF HUMAN RIGHTS ISSUE Twenty-fifth Anniversary of the proclamation, on Dec. 10, 1948 of the Universal Declaration of Human Rights. The tenth commemorative stamp in the Human Rights series. Designed by Alfredo Guerra, U.S. Similar to U.N. New York Minkus Nos. 260 and 261. *Gravure by Japanese Government Printing Office. Perforated 13 1/2, multicolored, color of inscription given below.*

35, 36 *Emblem, flame and globe*

35		MNHVF	UseVF
40¢	**deep blue** *(1,480,791)*	.50	.55
	FDC *(Nov. 16, 1973)*		1.00
	Inscription block of 4	2.50	

36		MNHVF	UseVF
80¢	**olive** *(1,343,349)*	.90	.75
	FDC *(Nov. 16, 1973)*		1.00
	Inscription block of 4	4.00	

1974. ILO HEADQUARTERS ISSUE International Labor Organization. Commemorated the new headquarters building in Geneva, Switzerland laid in May 1970. Designed by Henry Bencsath, U.S. Similar to U.N. New York Minkus Nos. 262 and 263. *Gravure by Heraclio Fournier, Spain. Perforated 14, multicolored, color of background given below.*

37, 38 *International Labor Office, Geneva, built 1970-1974*

37		MNHVF	UseVF
60¢	**violet** *(1,212,703)*	.55	.55
	FDC *(Jan. 11, 1974)*		1.00
	Inscription block of 4	3.00	

38		MNHVF	UseVF
80¢	**chocolate** *(1,229,851)*	1.10	1.00
	FDC *(Jan. 11, 1974)*		1.00
	Inscription block of 4	4.00	

1974. UNIVERSAL POSTAL UNION ISSUE Celebrated the 100th anniversary of the UPU. Designed by Arne Johnson, Norway. Similar to U.N. New York Minkus No. 264. *Offset by Ashton-Potter Ltd., Canada. Perforated 12 1/2.*

39, 40 *Posthorn around globe and UPU emblem*

39		MNHVF	UseVF
30¢	**multicolored** *(1,567,517)*	.60	.50
	FDC *(March 22, 1974)*		1.00
	Inscription block of 4	2.50	

40		MNHVF	UseVF
60¢	**multicolored** *(1,430,839)*	.90	.75
	FDC *(March 22, 1974)*		1.00
	Inscription block of 4	3.50	

1974. BRAZILIAN PEACE MURAL ISSUE Designed by Candido Portinari, Brazil, and adapted by Ole Hamann, Denmark. Similar to U.N. New York Minkus Nos. 265 and 266. *Gravure by Heraclio Fournier, Spain. Perforated 14.*

41, 42 *Peace Mural, by Candido Portinari, gift of Brazilian Government to U.N.*

41		MNHVF	UseVF
60¢	**red brown** *(1,202,357)*	.75	.75
	FDC *(May 6, 1974)*		1.00
	Inscription block of 4	3.00	

42		MNHVF	UseVF
1f	**green** *(1,230,045)*	1.10	1.00
	FDC *(May 6, 1974)*		1.00
	Inscription block of 4	3.75	

1974. WORLD POPULATION YEAR ISSUE Designed by Henry Bencsath, U.S. Similar to U.N. New York Minkus Nos. 273 and 274. *Gravure by Heraclio Fournier, Spain. Perforated 14.*

43, 44 *Babies reaching around globe*

43		MNHVF	UseVF
60¢	**blue green** *(1,292,954)*	1.00	.75
	FDC *(Oct. 18, 1974)*		1.00
	Inscription block of 4	2.50	

44		MNHVF	UseVF
80¢	**brown** *(1,221,288)*	1.25	1.10
	FDC *(Oct. 18. 1974)*		1.00
	Inscription block of 4	5.50	

1974. LAW OF THE SEA ISSUE Designed by Asher Kalderon, Israel. Similar to U.N. New York Minkus Nos. 275 and 276. *Gravure by Heraclio Fournier, Spain. Perforated 14.*

45 *Ship, fish and mineral bed*

45		MNHVF	UseVF
1.30f	**light bue & blue** *(1,266,270)*	1.40	1.25
	FDC *(Nov. 22, 1974)*		1.00
	Inscription block of 4	6.50	

1975. PEACEFUL USES OF OUTER SPACE ISSUE Designed by Henry Bencsath, U.S. Similar to U.N. New York Minkus Nos. 277 and 278. *Offset by S. Setelipaino, Finland. Perforated 13 1/2x13.*

46, 47 *Satellite focused on earth's surface and activities benefiting from peaceful uses of outer space*

46		MNHVF	UseVF
60¢	**multicolored** *(1,339,704)*	1.35	1.25
	FDC *(March 14, 1975)*		1.00
	Inscription block of 4	5.00	

47		MNHVF	UseVF
90¢	**multicolored** *(1,383,888)*	1.60	1.50
	FDC *(March 14, 1975)*		1.00
	Inscription block of 4	7.50	

1975. INTERNATIONAL WOMEN'S YEAR ISSUE Designed by Esther Kurti and Asher Kalderon, Israel. Similar to U.N. New York Minkus Nos. 279 and 280. *Offset by The House of Questa, U.K. Perforated 15x14, multicolored, color of background given below.*

48, 49 Men and women within circle

48		MNHVF	UseVF
60¢	**deep brown** *(1,176,080)*	.85	.75
	FDC *(May 9, 1975)*		1.00
	Inscription block of 4	3.50	

49		MNHVF	UseVF
90¢	**violet** *(1,167,863)*	1.25	1.25
	FDC *(May 9, 1975)*		1.00
	Inscription block of 4	5.00	

1975. U.N. 30TH ANNIVERSARY ISSUE Designed by Asher Kalderon, Israel. Similar to U.N. New York Minkus Nos. 281 and 282. *Offset by Ashton-Potter Ltd., Canada. Perforated 13 1/2, multicolored, color of inscription given below.*

50, 51 Numerals "XXX" in form of people supporting flag

50		MNHVF	UseVF
60¢	**green** *(1,442,075)*	.75	.60
	FDC *(June 26, 1975)*		1.00
	Inscription block of 4	3.00	

51		MNHVF	UseVF
90¢	**violet** *(1,612,411)*	1.00	1.25
	FDC *(June 26, 1975)*		1.00
	Inscription block of 4	4.50	

1975. U.N. 30TH ANNIVERSARY SOUVENIR SHEET Designed by Olav Mathiesen, Denmark. Similar to U.N. New York Minkus No. 283. *Souvenir sheet (92x70mm) of Nos. 50 and 51, imperforate.*

52 Souvenir sheet with Nos. 50 and 51

52		MNHVF	UseVF
1.50f	**Sheet of 2** *(1,210,148)*	1.25	1.25
	a. Single (60¢)	.75	.60
	b. Single (90¢)	1.00	1.25
	FDC *(June 26, 1975)*		1.25

1975. NAMIBIA ISSUE Second set of stamps in the "Namibia" series. Designed by Henry Bencsath, U.S. Similar to U.N. New York Minkus Nos. 284 and 285. *Gravure by Heraclio Fournier, Spain. Perforated 13 1/2.*

53, 54 Map of Africa with Namibia shown in relief by cupped hand and forearm

53		MNHVF	UseVF
50¢	**multicolored** *(1,261,019)*	.75	.60
	FDC *(Sept. 22, 1975)*		1.00
	Inscription block of 4	3.00	

54		MNHVF	UseVF
1.30f	**multicolored** *(1,241,990)*	1.25	1.00
	FDC *(Sept. 22, 1975)*		1.00
	Inscription block of 4	4.50	

1975. PEACE-KEEPING OPERATIONS ISSUE Designed by Eeva Oivo, Finland. Similar to U.N. New York Minkus Nos. 286 and 287. *Intaglio by S. Setelipaino, Finland. Perforated 12 1/2.*

55, 56 Flower growing from barbed wire

55		MNHVF	UseVF
60¢	**turquoise green** *(1,249,305)*	.60	.50
	FDC *(Nov. 21, 1975)*		1.00
	Inscription block of 4	3.00	

56		MNHVF	UseVF
70¢	**violet** *(1,249,935)*	1.25	1.00
	FDC *(Nov. 21, 1975)*		1.00
	Inscription block of 4	4.50	

1976. WFUNA ISSUE Thirtieth anniversary World Federation of U.N. Association. Designed by George Hamori, Australia. Similar to U.N. New York Minkus Nos. 292 and 293. *Gravure by Heraclio Fournier, Spain. Perforated 14, multicolored, color of inscription given below.*

57 Interlocking multicolored bands

57		**MNHVF**	**UseVF**
90¢	**multicolored** *(1,186,563)*	1.50	1.50
	FDC *(March 12, 1976)*		1.00
	Inscription block of 4	7.00	

1976. CONFERENCE ON TRADE & DEVELOPMENT ISSUE Designed by Henry Bencsath, U.S. (UNCTAD) similar to U.N. New York Minkus Nos. 294 and 295. *Gravure by Helio Courvoisier, Switzerland. Perforated 11 1/2, granite paper, multicolored, color of background given below.*

58 *Cargo, globe and graph*

58		**MNHVF**	**UseVF**
1.10f	**sepia** *(1,167,284)*	1.50	1.25
	FDC *(April 23, 1976)*		1.00
	Inscription block of 4	7.00	

1976. CONFERENCE ON HUMAN SETTLEMENTS ISSUE Designed by Eliezer Weishoff, Israel. Similar to U.N. New York Minkus Nos. 296 and 297. *Gravure by Heraclio Fournier, Spain. Perforated 14, multicolored, color of background given below.*

59, 50 *Globe encircled with houses*

59		**MNHVF**	**UseVF**
40¢	**dark blue** *(1,258,986)*	.75	.60
	FDC *(May 28, 1976)*		1.00
	Inscription block of 4	3.00	

60		**MNHVF**	**UseVF**
1.50f	**violet** *(1,110,507)*	1.25	1.00
	FDC *(May 28, 1976)*		1.00
	Inscription block of 4	4.25	

1976. POSTAL ADMINISTRATION 25TH ANNIVERSARY ISSUE Designed by Hector Viola, Argentina. *Gravure by Helio Courvoisier, Switzerland. Perforated 11 1/2, granite paper, multicolored, color of background given below.*

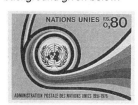

61, 62
Posthorn

61		**MNHVF**	**UseVF**
80¢	**tan** *(1,794,009)*	1.75	1.50
	FDC *(Oct. 8, 1976)*		1.00
	Inscription block of 4	8.00	

62		**MNHVF**	**UseVF**
1.10f	**turquoise** *(1,751,178)*	2.25	2.00
	FDC *(Oct. 8, 1976)*		1.00
	Inscription block of 4	10.50	

1976. WORLD FOOD COUNCIL ISSUE Designed by Eliezer Weishoff, Israel. Similar to U.N. New York Minkus No. 300. *Offset by The House of Questa, U.K. Perforated 14 1/2x14.*

63 *Wheat and flags*

63		**MNHVF**	**UseVF**
70¢	**multicolored** *(1,507,630)*	.85	.75
	FDC *(Nov. 19, 1976)*		1.00
	Inscription block of 4	4.00	

1977. WIPO ISSUE World Intellectual Property Organization founded in 1970. U.N. agency set up to help protect industrial inventions and designs and copyrights. Designed by Eliezer Weishoff, Israel. Similar to U.N. New York Minkus No. 302. *Gravure by Heraclio Fournier, Spain. Perforated 14, multicolored, color frame red.*

64 *World Intellectual Property Organization headquarters*

64		**MNHVF**	**UseVF**
80¢	**red** *(1,232,664)*	1.00	.90
	FDC *(March 11, 1977)*		1.00
	Inscription block of 4	4.50	

1977. WATER CONFERENCE ISSUE Held in Argentina in 1977 to discuss strategies to avoid a water crisis within the next few decades. Designed by Eliezer Weishoff, Israel. *Gravure by Japanese Government Printing Office. Perforated 13, multicolored, color of background given below.*

65, 66 *Water drop encompassing earth*

65		**MNHVF**	**UseVF**
80¢	**violet** *(1,146,650)*	.75	.75
	FDC *(April 22, 1977)*		1.00
	Inscription block of 4	3.00	

66		**MNHVF**	**UseVF**
1.10f	**deep carmine** *(1,138,236)*	1.25	1.10
	FDC *(April 22, 1977)*		1.00
	Inscription block of 4	6.00	

1977. SECURITY COUNCIL ISSUE The second issue to commemorate the U.N. Security Council. Designed by George Hamori, Australia. *Gravure by Heraclio Fournier, Spain. Perforated 13 1/2, multicolored, color of cupped hands given below.*

67, 68 *Cupped hands around U.N. emblem*

67		MNHVF	UseVF
80¢	black & blue *(1,096,030)*	1.00	.75
	FDC *(May 27, 1977)*		1.00
	Inscription block of 4	3.00	

68		MNHVF	UseVF
1.10f	black & emerald *(1,075,925)*	1.25	1.00
	FDC *(May 27, 1977)*		1.00
	Inscription block of 4	6.00	

1977. COMBAT RACISM ISSUE Designed by M. A. Munnawar, Pakistan. *Offset by S. Setelipaino, Finland. Perforated 13, multicolored, color of background given below.*

69, 70 *Multicolored strand from separate colors*

69		MNHVF	UseVF
40¢	light green *(1,218,834)*	.50	.50
	FDC *(Sept. 19, 1977)*		1.00
	Inscription block of 4	3.00	

70		MNHVF	UseVF
1.10f	cobalt *(1,138,250)*	1.00	1.00
	FDC *(Sept. 19, 1977)*		1.00
	Inscription block of 4	5.00	

1977. ATOMIC ENERGY ISSUE Designed by Witold Janowski and Marek Freudenreich, Poland. *Gravure by Heraclio Fournier, Spain. Perforated 14.*

71, 72 *Atom and olive branch*

71		MNHVF	UseVF
80¢	multicolored *(1,147,787)*	1.00	.75
	FDC *(Nov. 18, 1977)*		1.00
	Inscription block of 4	3.00	

72		MNHVF	UseVF
1.10f	multicolored *(1,121,209)*	1.40	1.25
	FDC *(Nov. 18, 1977)*		1.00
	Inscription block of 4	5.50	

1978. DEFINITIVE ISSUE. Designed by Masatoshi Hoiki, Japan. Offset by *The House of Questa*, U.K. Perforated 14.

73 *"Live Together in Peace" and tree of doves.*

73		MNHVF	UseVF
35¢	multicolored *(3,000,000 printed)*	.35	.35
	FDC *(Jan. 23, 1978)*		1.00
	Inscription block of 4	1.50	

1978. SMALLPOX ISSUE Global eradication of smallpox. Designed by Eliezer Weishoff, Israel. *Gravure by Helio Courvoisier, Switzerland. Perforated 11 1/2, granite paper, multicolored, color of background given below.*

74, 75 *Infected and disease-free globes*

74		MNHVF	UseVF
80¢	lemon *(1,116,044)*	.85	.80
	FDC *(March 31, 1978)*		1.00
	Inscription block of 4	4.00	

75		MNHVF	UseVF
1.10f	emerald *(1,109,946)*	1.25	1.10
	FDC *(March 31, 1978)*		1.00
	Inscription block of 4	5.00	

1978. NAMIBIA ISSUE The third set in the Namibia series. Designed by Cafiero Tomei, Italy. Similar to U.N. New York Minkus Nos. 319 and 320. *Gravure by Government Printing Office, Austria. Perforated 12.*

76 *Open handcuff*

76		MNHVF	UseVF
80¢	turquoise, yellow olive & black *(1,183,208)*	1.40	.75
	FDC *(May 5, 1978)*		1.00
	Inscription block of 4	6.50	

1978. ICAO ISSUE International Civil Aviation Organization founded in 1947. Designed by Tomas Savrda, U.S. *Gravure by Heraclio Fournier, Spain. Perforated 13 1/2, multicolored, color of background given below.*

77, 78 *Passing aircraft*

77			MNHVF	UseVF
70¢	**light brown** *(1,275,106)*		.75	.65
	FDC *(June 12, 1978)*			1.00
	Inscription block of 4		3.00	

78			MNHVF	UseVF
80¢	**light blue** *(1,144,339)*		1.20	1.00
	FDC *(June 12, 1978)*			1.00
	Inscription block of 4		5.00	

1978. GENERAL ASSEMBLY ISSUE Designed by Henry Bencsath, U.S. *Gravure by Japanese Government Printing Office. Perforated 13 1/2, multicolored, color of background given below.*

79, 80 *Flags and globe*

79			MNHVF	UseVF
70¢	**blue** *(1,204,441)*		.90	.75
	FDC *(Sept. 15, 1978)*			1.00
	Inscription block of 4		4.00	

80			MNHVF	UseVF
1.10f	**green** *(1,183,889)*		1.35	1.25
	FDC *(Sept. 15, 1978)*			1.00
	Inscription block of 4		6.50	

1978. TECHNICAL COOPERATION ISSUE First world conference among developing countries was held in Buenos Aires, Argentina, in Sept. 1978. Designed by Shimeon Keter and David Pesach, Israel. Similar to U.N. New York Minkus Nos. 325 and 326. *Gravure by Heraclio Fournier, Spain. Perforated 14, multicolored, color of background given below.*

81 *Two hemispheres rotating in unison*

81			MNHVF	UseVF
80¢	**violet** *(1,173,220)*		1.20	.90
	FDC *(Nov. 17, 1978)*			1.00
	Inscription block of 4		5.25	

1979. UNDRO ISSUE U.N. Disaster Relief Organization began in March 1972. Designed by Michael Klutmann, Germany. *Gravure by Heraclio Fournier, Spain. Perforated 14.*

82, 83 *Seismic waves*

82			MNHVF	UseVF
80¢	**multicolored** *(1,183,155)*		1.00	.75
	FDC *(March 9, 1979)*			1.00
	Inscription block of 4		4.00	

83			MNHVF	UseVF
1.50f	**multicolored** *(1,168,121)*		1.35	1.25
	FDC *(March 9, 1979)*			1.00
	Inscription block of 4		6.50	

1979. INTERNATIONAL YEAR OF THE CHILD ISSUE Designed by Arieh Glaser, Israel. Border designed by Bojana Spremo, Yugoslavia. *Gravure by Heraclio Fournier, Spain. Perforated 14, multicolored, color of IYC emblem given below.*

84, 85 *Children and rainbow*

84			MNHVF	UseVF
80¢	**black** *(2,251,623)*		3.50	3.50
	FDC *(May 4, 1979)*			1.00
	Inscription block of 4		6.00	

85			MNHVF	UseVF
1.10f	**light blue** *(2,220,463)*		5.75	5.75
	FDC *(May 4, 1979)*			1.00
	Inscription block of 4		12.50	

1979. NAMIBIA ISSUE The fourth set in the Namibia series. Designed by Eliezer Weishoff, Israel. Similar to U.N. New York Minkus Nos. 335 and 336. *Offset by Ashton-Potter, U.S. Perforated 13x13 1/2, multicolored, map color given below.*

86 *Map and olive branch*

86			MNHVF	UseVF
1.10f	**green** *(1,500,000 printed)*		1.65	1.65
	FDC *(Oct. 5, 1979)*			1.00
	Inscription block of 4		5.00	

1979. INTERNATIONAL COURT OF JUSTICE ISSUE The court is located in the Hague, Netherlands. Designed by Kyohei Maeno, Japan. *Offset by S. Setelipaino, Finland. Perforated 13, multicolored, color of background given below.*

87, 88 *Palace of Peace*

87			MNHVF	UseVF
80¢	**magenta** *(1,123,193)*		1.20	1.20
	FDC *(Nov. 9, 1979)*			1.00
	Inscription block of 4		3.75	

88			MNHVF	UseVF
1.10f	**blue** *(1,063,067)*		1.65	1.65
	FDC *(Nov. 9, 1979)*			1.00
	Inscription block of 4		7.00	

1980. NEW ECONOMIC ORDER ISSUE The General Assembly held a special session in 1980 to discuss the gap between developed and developing countries. Designed by George Hamori, Australia. Similar to U.N. New York Minkus No. 340. *Offset by The House of Questa, U.K. Perforated 14 1/2, multicolored.*

89 *Key of flags*

89			
80¢	**multicolored** *(1,315,918)*	MNHVF 1.20	UseVF 1.20
	FDC *(Jan. 11, 1980)*		1.00
	Inscription block of 4	4.00	

1980. U.N. DECADE FOR WOMEN'S ISSUE Designed by M. A. Munnawar, Pakistan. *Offset by The House of Questa, U.K. Perforated 14 1/2, multicolored, color of background given below.*

90, 91 *Women 's year emblem*

90			
40¢	**deep blue** *(1,265,221)*	MNHVF .60	UseVF .50
	FDC *(March 7, 1980)*		1.00
	Inscription block of 4	2.50	
91		MNHVF	UseVF
70¢	**maroon** *(1,240,375)*	.85	.75
	FDC *(March 7, 1980)*		1.00
	Inscription block of 4	3.75	

1980. PEACE-KEEPING OPERATIONS ISSUE Commemorated the U.N. military observer missions and U.N. peace-keeping forces. Designed by Bruno K. Wiesey, Germany. Similar to U.N. New York Minkus No. 343. *Offset by Joh. Enschedé and Sons, Netherlands. Perforated 14x13.*

92 *Helmet and U.N. emblem*

92			
1.10f	**blue & green** *(1,335,391)*	MNHVF 1.35	UseVF 1.20
	FDC *(May 16, 1980)*		1.25
	Inscription block of 4	6.25	

1980. U.N. 35TH ANNIVERSARY ISSUE No. 93 designed by Gidon Sagi, Israel. No. 94 similar to U.N. New York Minkus No. 345, designed by Cemalettin Mutver, Turkey. *Offset by Ashton-Potter Ltd., Canada. Perforated 13x13 1/2.*

93 *Dove and "35"*

93			
40¢	**multicolored** *(1,462,005)*	MNHVF .50	UseVF .65
	FDC *(June 26, 1980)*		1.00
	Inscription block of 4	3.50	

94 *"35"*

94			
70¢	**multicolored** *(1,444,639)*	MNHVF 1.00	UseVF .85
	FDC *(June 26, 1980)*		1.00
	Inscription block of 4	4.00	

1980. U.N. 35TH ANNIVERSARY SOUVENIR SHEET Designed by Ole Hamann, Denmark. *Offset by Ashton-Potter Ltd., Canada. Sheet of 2 (92x73mm). Imperforate.*

95 *Souvenir sheet with Nos. 93 and 94*

95			
1.10f	**Sheet of 2** *(1,235,200)*	MNHVF 1.25	UseVF 1.25
	a. Single (40¢)	.50	.65
	b. Single (70¢)	1.00	.85
	FDC *(June 26, 1980)*		1.50

1980. ECONOMIC AND SOCIAL COUNCIL ISSUE Type of U.N. New York Minkus No. 364, designed by Eliezer Weishoff, Israel (40¢); and new design by Angel Medina, Uruguay (70¢). *Offset by Ashton-Potter Ltd., Canada. Perforated 13 1/2.*

96 *Bouquet of economic and social achievements*

96			
40¢	**multicolored** *(986,435)*	MNHVF .60	UseVF .50
	FDC *(Nov. 21, 1980)*		1.00
	Inscription block of 4	3.00	

97 People and graph

97
70¢   **multicolored** *(1,016,462)*
FDC *(Nov. 21, 1980)*
Inscription block of 4

	MNHVF	UseVF
	.85	.75
		1.00
	4.00	

1981. RIGHTS OF PALESTINIAN PEOPLE ISSUE Designed by David Dewhurst, U.S. Similar to U.N. New York Minkus No. 366. *Gravure by Helio Courvoisier, Switzerland. Perforated 11 1/2, granite paper.*

98 Inalienable Rights of the Palestinian People

98
80¢   **multicolored** *(1,031,737)*
FDC *(Jan. 30, 1981)*
Inscription block of 4

	MNHVF	UseVF
	1.25	1.00
		1.00
	5.50	

1981. YEAR OF DISABLED PERSONS ISSUE The General Assembly announced 1981 as "International Year of Disabled Persons." Designed by G. P. Vander Heyde, Australia (40¢), similar to U.N. New York Minkus No. 368. No. 100 designed by Sophia van Heeswijk, Berlin, Germany. *Gravure by Heraclio Fournier, Spain. Perforated 14.*

99, 100 Geometric design, "Annee internationale des personnes handicapées"

99
40¢   **black & blue** *(1,057,909)*
FDC *(March 6, 1981)*
Inscription block of 4

	MNHVF	UseVF
	.85	.75
		1.00
	3.50	

100
1.50f   **black & scarlet** *(994,748)*
FDC *(March 6, 1981)*
Inscription block of 4

	MNHVF	UseVF
	1.25	1.00
		1.00
	4.75	

1981. U.N. ART BULGARIAN MURAL ISSUE The Government of Bulgaria presented the U.N. with a replica of a 13th Century Bulgarian fresco inside Boyana Church near Sofia. Adapted as a stamp by Ole Hamann, Denmark, from an original design by an unknown artist from Bulgaria. Similar to U.N. New York Minkus Nos. 369 and 370. *Gravure by Helio Courvoisier, Switzerland. Perforated 11 1/2, granite paper.*

101 Divislava and Sebastocrator Kaloyan, Bulgarian Mural, 1259, Boyana Church, Sofia

101
80¢   **multicolored** *(1,128,782)*
FDC *(April 15, 1981)*
Inscription block of 4

	MNHVF	UseVF
	1.35	1.10
		1.00
	6.25	

1981. RENEWABLE ENERGY ISSUE Conference on New and Renewable Sources of Energy held in Nairobi, Kenya in August 1981. Designed by Ulrike Dreyer, Germany. Similar to U.N. New York Minkus No. 371. *Offset by S. Setelipaino, Finland. Perforated 13.*

102 Symbol of renewable energy

102
1.10f   **multicolored** *(1,096,806)*
FDC *(May 29, 1981)*
Inscription block of 4

	MNHVF	UseVF
	1.35	1.25
		1.25
	6.50	

1981. U.N. 10TH ANNIVERSARY VOLUNTEERS PROGRAM ISSUE No. 103 similar to U.N. New York Minkus No. 389, designed by Gabriele Nussgen, Germany (40¢), Bernd Mirbach, Germany (70¢). *Offset by Walsall Security Printers Ltd., U.K. Perforated 13.*

103 Tree cross section; 104 Symbols of development

103
40¢   **multicolored** *(1,032,700)*
FDC *(Nov. 13, 1981)*
Inscription block of 4

	MNHVF	UseVF
	1.00	.75
		1.00
	4.00	

104
70¢   **multicolored** *(1,123,672)*
FDC *(Nov. 13, 1981)*
Inscription block of 4

	MNHVF	UseVF
	1.25	1.00
		1.00
	6.00	

1982. RIGHTS AND PEACE ISSUE Designed by Tomas Savrda, U.S. (30¢), Dietmar Kowall, Germany (1f). *Printed by Helio Courvoisier, Switzerland. Perforated 11 1/2x12.*

105 Woven design

106 "Flower" of flags

105
30¢   **multicolored** *(3,000,000 printed)*
FDC *(Jan. 22, 1982)*
Inscription block of 4

	MNHVF	UseVF
	.75	.60
		1.00
	3.00	

106
1f   **multicolored** *(3,000,000 printed)*
FDC *(Jan. 22, 1982)*
Inscription block of 4

	MNHVF	UseVF
	1.25	1.00
		1.00
	4.75	

1982. HUMAN ENVIRONMENT ISSUE Celebrated the 10th anniversary of U.N. Environment Program to help coordinate sound environment practices. Designed by Sybille Brunner, Germany (40¢); No. 108 similar to U.N. New York Minkus No. 394 designed by Philine Hartert,

Germany (1.20fr). *Offset by Joh. Enschedé and Sons, Netherlands. Perforated 13 1/2x13.*

107 *Leaf design*

108 *Hand with seedling*

107		MNHVF	UseVF
40¢	multicolored *(948,743)*	1.00	.75
	FDC *(March 19, 1982)*		1.00
	Inscription block of 4	4.50	

108		MNHVF	UseVF
1.20f	multicolored *(901,096)*	1.25	1.00
	FDC *(March 19, 1982)*		1.10
	Inscription block of 4	6.00	

1982. PEACEFUL USES OF OUTER SPACE ISSUE Exploration and peaceful uses of outer space. No. 109 similar to U.N. New York Minkus No. 396, designed by Wiktor C. Nerwinski, Poland (80¢) and George Hamori, Australia (1fr). *Offset by Joh. Enschedé and Sons, Netherlands. Perforated 13x13 1/2.*

109 *Laurel wreath, outer space;* 110 *Satellite and symbols of space technology*

109		MNHVF	UseVF
80¢	multicolored *(964,593)*	1.00	.75
	FDC *(June 11, 1982)*		1.00
	Inscription block of 4	4.50	

110		MNHVF	UseVF
1f	multicolored *(898,367)*	1.25	1.00
	FDC *(June 11, 1982)*		1.25
	Inscription block of 4	6.00	

1982. CONSERVATION AND PROTECTION OF NATURE ISSUE Designed by George Hamori, Australia. Similar in design to U.N. New York Minkus Nos. 413 and 414 but with different icons. *Gravure by Heraclio Fournier, Spain. Perforated 14.*

111 *Bird*

112 *Reptile*

111		MNHVF	UseVF
40¢	multicolored *(928,143)*	1.00	.75
	FDC *(Nov. 19, 1982)*		1.00
	Inscription block of 4	4.00	

112		MNHVF	UseVF
1.50f	multicolored *(847,173)*	1.75	1.50
	FDC *(Nov. 19, 1982)*		1.25
	Inscription block of 4	7.50	

1983. WORLD COMMUNICATIONS YEAR ISSUE Designed by Lorena Berengo, Germany. Similar to U.N. New York Minkus No. 416. *Offset by Walsall Security Printers, U.K. Perforated 13.*

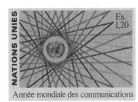

113 *U.N. seal, graphic design*

113		MNHVF	UseVF
1.20f	multicolored *(894,025)*	2.25	2.00
	FDC *(Jan. 28, 1983)*		1.25
	Inscription block of 4	6.00	

1983. SAFETY AT SEA ISSUE No. 114 similar to U.N. New York Minkus No. 417, designed by Jean Marie Lenfant, Belgium (40¢). No. 115 designed by Valentin Wurnitsch, Austria (80¢). *Offset by The House of Questa, U.K. Perforated 14 1/2.*

114 *Stylized ship scenes*

115 *Life preserver and radar screen*

114		MNHVF	UseVF
40¢	multicolored *(892,365)*	.75	.50
	FDC *(March 18, 1983)*		1.00
	Inscription block of 4	4.00	

115		MNHVF	UseVF
80¢	multicolored *(882,720)*	1.00	
	FDC *(March 18, 1983)*		1.00
	Inscription block of 4	5.75	

1983. WORLD FOOD PROGRAM ISSUE Designed by Mark Kwiatkowski, Poland. Engraved by Sakae Yajima, Japan. Similar to U.N. New York Minkus No. 419. *Intaglio by Japanese Government Printing Office. Perforated 13 1/2.*

116 *Hands presenting food bowl*

116		MNHVF	UseVF
1.50f	blue *(876,591)*	2.50	2.25
	FDC *(April 22, 1983)*		1.25
	Inscription block of 4	11.50	

1983. U.N. CONFERENCE ON TRADE AND DEVELOPMENT ISSUE No. 117 similar to U.N. New York Minkus No. 420, designed by Dietmar Braklow, (80¢). No. 118 designed by Wladyslaw Brykczynski, Poland (1.10f). *Offset by Carl Uberreuter Druck and Verlag M. Salzer, Austria. Perforated 14.*

117 *Symbols of Commerce*

118 *Flags on cargo box*

117		MNHVF	UseVF
80¢	**multicolored** *(902,495)*	.90	.75
	FDC *(June 6, 1983)*		1.00
	Inscription block of 4	4.00	

118		MNHVF	UseVF
1.10f	**multicolored** *(921,424)*	1.50	1.25
	FDC *(June 6, 1983)*		1.00
	Inscription block of 4	6.50	

1983. DECLARATION OF HUMAN RIGHTS ISSUE This is the eleventh commemorative stamp in the Human Rights series. On Dec. 10, 1948 the first world-wide proclamation and adoption of the Universal Declaration of Human Rights took place. Dec. 10 is recognized as Human Rights Day. Designed by Friedensreich Hundertwasser, Austria. Engraved by Wolfgang Seidel, Austria. *Gravure and intaglio by Government Printing Office, Austria. Perforated 13 1/2.*

119 Homo Humus Humanitas, *abstract;*

120 Right to Create, *abstract*

119		MNHVF	UseVF
40¢	**multicolored** *(1,770,921)*	1.00	.85
	FDC *(Dec. 9, 1983)*		1.25
	Inscription block of 4	5.00	

120		MNHVF	UseVF
1.20f	**multicolored** *(1,746,735)*	1.50	1.25
	FDC *(Dec. 9, 1983)*		1.25
	Inscription block of 4	6.50	

1984. INTERNATIONAL CONFERENCE ON POPULATION ISSUE A conference in August 1984 in Mexico, reviewed the global population programs since a previous conference 10 years earlier. Designed by Marina Langer-Rosa and Helmut Langer, Germany. *Offset by Bundesdruckerei, Germany. Perforated 14.*

121 *Crowded city*

121		MNHVF	UseVF
1.20f	**multicolored** *(776,879)*	2.00	1.75
	FDC *(Feb. 3, 1984)*		1.00
	Inscription block of 4	8.00	

1984. WORLD FOOD DAY ISSUE The Food and Agriculture Organization observes World Food Day every Oct. 16, its anniversary. Designed by Adth Vanooijen, Netherlands. *Offset by Walsall Security Printers, Ltd., U.K. Perforated 14 1/2.*

122 *Men fishing;* 123 *Women farm workers*

122		MNHVF	UseVF
50¢	**multicolored** *(744,506)*	.65	.60

	FDC *(March 15, 1984)*		1.00
	Inscription block of 4	3.00	

123		MNHVF	UseVF
80¢	**multicolored** *(784,047)*	1.25	1.00
	FDC *(March 15, 1984)*		1.00
	Inscription block of 4	5.50	

1984. WORLD HERITAGE ISSUE First in a series. The World Heritage List was established in Nov. 1972 under terms of the convention concerning the Protection of the World Cultural and Natural Heritage. Designs adapted as stamps by Rocco J. Callari, U.S., and Thomas Lee, China. *Offset by Harrison and Sons Ltd., U.K. Perforated 14.*

124 *Fort St. Angelo, Vittoriossa, Malta; photo by Alexis N. Vorontzoff, France;* 125 *Los Glaciares National Park, Argentina*

124		MNHVF	UseVF
50¢	**multicolored** *(763,627)*	1.00	1.00
	FDC *(April 18, 1984)*		1.00
	Inscription block of 4	4.00	

125		MNHVF	UseVF
70¢	**multicolored** *(784,489)*	1.50	1.25
	FDC *(April 18, 1984)*		1.00
	Inscription block of 4	7.50	

1984. FUTURE FOR REFUGEES ISSUE The office of the United Nations High Commissioner for Refugees was created in 1951. Designed by Hans Erni, Switzerland. *Gravure by Helio Courvoisier, Switzerland. Perforated 11 1/2.*

126 *Huddling couple*

127 *Figure with shawl*

126		MNHVF	UseVF
35¢	**multicolored** *(880,762)*	1.25	1.00
	FDC *(May 29, 1984)*		1.00
	Inscription block of 4	4.00	

127		MNHVF	UseVF
1.50f	**multicolored** *(829,895)*	1.50	1.25
	FDC *(May 29, 1984)*		1.00
	Inscription block of 4	7.50	

1984. INTERNATIONAL YOUTH YEAR ISSUE Designed by Eliezer Weishoff, Israel. *Offset by Waddingtons Ltd., U.K. Perforated 13 1/2.*

128 *Stylized people*

128		MNHVF	UseVF
1.20f	**multicolored** *(755,622)*	1.75	1.50
	FDC *(Nov. 15, 1984)*		1.25
	Inscription block of 4	8.00	

1985. ILO TURIN CENTER ISSUE for the International Labor Organization training institution. No. 129 similar to U.N. New York Minkus No. 466. Adapted from photographs by Rocco J. Callari, U.S. and Thomas Lee, China. (80¢) engraved by Mamoru Iwakuni and Hiroshi Ozaki, Japan; (1.20f) by Hiroshi Ozaki and Kohji Uematsu, both of Japan. *Intaglio by the Japanese Government Printing Office. Perforated 13 1/2.*

129 *Turin Centre emblem;* 130 *U Thant Pavilion*

129		MNHVF	UseVF
80¢	**multicolored** *(654,431)*	1.25	1.00
	FDC *(Feb. 1, 1985)*		1.00
	Inscription block of 4	4.50	
130		MNHVF	UseVF
1.20f	**multicolored** *(609,493)*	1.50	1.25
	FDC *(Feb. 1, 1985)*		1.00
	Inscription block of 4	6.50	

1985. U.N. UNIVERSITY ISSUE The UNU coordinates the work of scientists and scholars throughout the world. Designed by Moshe Pereg, Israel and Hinedi Geluda, Brazil. *Gravure by Helio Courvoisier, Switzerland. Perforated 13 1/2.*

131, 132 *"UNU" and silhouettes*

131		MNHVF	UseVF
50¢	**multicolored** *(625,087)*	1.25	1.00
	FDC *(March 15, 1985)*		1.00
	Inscription block of 4	4.50	
132		MNHVF	UseVF
80¢	**multicolored** *(712,674)*	1.50	1.25
	FDC *(March 15, 1985)*		1.25
	Inscription block of 4	6.50	

1985. REGULAR ISSUE. (20¢) adaptation of 28¢ Postal Card of 1982. Designed by Arieh Glaser, Israel. Similar to U.N. New York Minkus No. PC20. (1.20f) designed by Karol Sliwka, Poland. *Offset by Carl Ueberreuter Druck and Verlag M. Salzer, Austria. Perforated 14.*

133 Flying mail carrier, 134 Interlocking doves

133		MNHVF	UseVF
20¢	**multicolored** *(2,000,000 printed)*	.60	.40
	FDC *(May 10, 1985)*		1.00
	inscription block of 4	4.00	
134		MNHVF	UseVF
1.20f	**multicolored** *(2,000,000 printed)*	2.00	1.75
	FDC *(May 10, 1985)*		1.50
	inscription block of 4	8.00	

1985. U.N. 40TH ANNIVERSARY ISSUE Featured paintings (details) by American artist Andrew Wyeth. Similar to U.N. New York Minkus Nos. 470 and 471. *Gravure by Helio Courvoisier, Switzerland. Perforated 12x11 1/2.*

135 *Detail from* The Corner; 136 *Detail from* Alvaro Raking Hay

135		MNHVF	UseVF
50¢	**multicolored** *(764,924)*	.75	.65
	FDC *(June 26, 1985)*		1.00
	Inscription block of 4	4.00	
136		MNHVF	UseVF
70¢	**multicolored** *(779,074)*	1.35	1.20
	FDC *(June 26, 1985)*		1.25
	Inscription block of 4	5.50	

1985. U.N. 40TH ANNIVERSARY SOUVENIR SHEET Designed by Rocco J. Callari, U.S., and Thomas Lee, China. *Gravure by Helio Courvoisier, Switzerland. Imperforate.*

137 *Souvenir sheet with Nos. 135 and 136*

137		MNHVF	UseVF
1.20f	**Sheet of 2** *(498,041)*	3.00	2.50
	a. Single (50¢)	.75	.65
	b. Single (70¢)	1.35	1.20
	FDC *(June 26, 1985)*		1.00

Commemorative Issues

1985. UNICEF CHILD SURVIVAL CAMPAIGN ISSUE Designed by Mel Harris, U.K. (50¢); Adth Vanooijen, Netherlands (1.20f). Engraved by Sakae Yajima, Japan (50¢). *Gravure and intaglio by Japanese Government Printing Office. Perforated 13 1/2.*

138 *Three girls*

139 *Infant drinking*

138		MNHVF	UseVF
50¢	**multicolored** *(657,409)*	1.25	1.00
	FDC *(Nov. 22, 1985)*		1.00
	Inscription block of 4	4.50	

139		MNHVF	UseVF
1.20f	**multicolored** *(593,568)*	1.50	1.25
	FDC *(Nov. 22, 1985)*		1.25
	Inscription block of 4	8.50	

1986. AFRICA IN CRISIS ISSUE Designed by Alemayehou Gabremedhin, Ethiopia. *Gravure by Helio Courvoisier, Switzerland. Perforated 11 1/2x12.*

140 *Mother, hungry children*

140		MNHVF	UseVF
1.40f	**multicolored** *(590,576)*	2.25	1.75
	FDC *(Jan. 31, 1986)*		2.00
	Inscription block of 4	10.00	

1986. U.N. DEVELOPMENT PROGRAM ISSUE The program is a partnership of more than 170 countries and territories. Designed by Thomas Lee, China. *Gravure by Japanese Government Printing Office. Perforated 13 1/2.*

141 *Erosion control;*
142 *Logging;*
143 *Lumber transport;*
144 *Tree nursery*

141		MNHVF	UseVF
35¢	**multicolored** *(547,567)*	2.50	2.00
	FDC *(March 14, 1986)*		1.50

142		MNHVF	UseVF
35¢	**multicolored** *(547,567)*	2.50	2.00
	FDC *(March 14, 1986)*		1.50

143		MNHVF	UseVF
35¢	**multicolored** *(547,567)*	2.50	2.00
	FDC *(March 14, 1986)*		1.50

144		MNHVF	UseVF
35¢	**multicolored** *(547,567)*	2.50	2.00

	FDC *(March 14, 1986)*		1.50
	Inscription block of 4	10.00	
	y. Se-tenant block of 4	10.00	
	FDC block of 4		7.50

1986. DOVE AND SUN ISSUE Designed by Ramon Alcantara Rodriguez, Mexico. *Offset by The House of Questa Ltd., U.K. Perforated 15x14 1/2.*

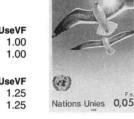

145 *Doves*

145		MNHVF	UseVF
5¢	**multicolored** *(2,000,000 printed)*	.30	.25
	FDC *(March 14, 1986)*		1.00
	Inscription block of 4	1.00	

1986. STAMP COLLECTING ISSUE Designed by Ingalill Axelsson, Sweden. Engraved by Czeslaw Slania, Sweden. *Intaglio by Swedish Post Office. Perforated 12 1/2.*

146 *Stamp of 1954 magnified;*   147 *U.N. stamps*

146		MNHVF	UseVF
50¢	**dark green & henna brown** *(722,015)*	1.00	.75
	FDC *(May 22, 1986)*		1.00
	Inscription block of 4	4.00	

147		MNHVF	UseVF
80¢	**dark green & yellow orange** *(750,945)*	2.25	1.00
	FDC *(May 22, 1986)*		1.00
	Inscription block of 4	7.50	

1986. INTERNATIONAL YEAR OF PEACE ISSUE The U.N. General Assembly declared 1986 to be the International Year of Peace. Designed by Renato Ferrini, Italy (45¢), Salahattin Kanidinc, U.S. (1.40f). *Gravure and embossed by the Japanese Government Printing Office. Perforated 13 1/2.*

148 *Stylized dove;*   149 *"Peace" in French*

148		MNHVF	UseVF
45¢	**multicolored** *(620,978)*	1.25	1.00
	FDC *(June 20, 1986)*		1.00
	Inscription block of 4	5.50	

149		MNHVF	UseVF
1.40f	**multicolored** *(559,658)*	2.00	1.50
	FDC *(June 20, 1986)*		1.50
	Inscription block of 4	10.00	

1986. WFUNA 40TH ANNIVERSARY SOUVENIR SHEET World Federation of U.N. Associations. Format design by Rocco J. Callari, U.S. *Offset by Joh. Enschedé and Sons, Netherlands. Perforated 13x13 1/2.*

150a Abstract, *by Benigno Gomez, Honduras;* 150b Abstract, *by Alexander Calder, U.S.;* 150c Abstract, *by Joan Miro, Spain;* 150d Sextet with Dove, *by Ole Hamann, Denmark*

150		MNHVF	UseVF
2f	**Sheet of 4** *(478,833)*	7.00	5.00
	a. Single (35¢), multicolored	.55	
	b. Single (45¢), multicolored	1.00	
	c. Single (50¢), multicolored	1.00	
	d. Single (70¢), multicolored	3.00	
	FDC *(Nov. 14, 1986)*		4.00

1987. TRYGVE LIE ISSUE Adapted as a stamp by Rocco J. Callari, U.S., from a portrait by Harald Dal, Norway. Engraved by Wolfgang Seidel, Austria. Similar to U.N. New York Minkus No. 517. *Gravure and intaglio by the Government Printing Office, Austria. Perforated 13 1/2.*

151 *Trygve Lie (1896-1968), first U.N. secretary general, portrait by Harald Dal, Norway*

151		MNHVF	UseVF
1.40f	**multicolored** *(516,605)*	2.25	2.00
	FDC *(Jan. 30, 1987)*		1.50
	Inscription block of 4	10.00	

1987. REGULAR ISSUE (90¢) designed by Georges Mathieu, France. *Gravure by Helio Courvoisier, Switzerland. Perforated 11 1/2 x 11 3/4.* (1.40f) adapted as a stamp by Rocco J. Callari, U.S., from a United Nations photograph. Engraved by Mitsuhiro Hizume, Japan. *Gravure and intaglio by the Japanese Government Printing Office. Perforated 13.*

152 *Abstract, by Georges Mathieu*

152		MNHVF	UseVF
90¢	**multicolored** *(1,600,000 printed)*	1.25	1.00
	FDC *(Jan. 30, 1987)*		1.00
	Inscription block of 4	6.50	

153 *Armillary Sphere, Palais des Nations*

153		MNHVF	UseVF
1.40f	**multicolored** *(1,600,000 printed)*	2.00	1.75
	FDC *(Jan. 30, 1987)*		1.00
	Inscription block of 4	7.50	

1987. SHELTER FOR THE HOMELESS ISSUE The U.N. General Assembly declared 1987 to be the International Year of Shelter for the Homeless. Designed by Wladyslaw Brykczynski, Poland. *Offset by Joh. Enschedé and Sons, Netherlands. Perforated 13 1/2x12 1/2.*

154 *Exterior construction;* 155 *Interior finishing*

154		MNHVF	UseVF
50¢	**multicolored** *(564,445)*	1.00	.85
	FDC *(March 13, 1987)*		1.00
	Inscription block of 4	4.50	
155		MNHVF	UseVF
90¢	**multicolored** *(526,646)*	1.50	1.25
	FDC *(March 13, 1987)*		1.00
	Inscription block of 4	8.00	

1987. FIGHT DRUG ABUSE ISSUE Designed by Susan Borgen and Noe Werrett, U.S. Illustrated by C. M. Dudash, U.S. *Offset by The House of Questa, U.K. Perforated 14.*

156 *Mother and child;* 157 *Workers in rice paddy*

156		MNHVF	UseVF
80¢	**multicolored** *(634,776)*	1.40	1.25
	FDC *(June 12, 1987)*		1.10
	Inscription block of 4	4.50	
157		MNHVF	UseVF
1.20f	**multicolored** *(609,475)*	1.75	1.50
	FDC *(June 12, 1987)*		1.50
	Inscription block of 4	6.50	

1987. U.N. DAY ISSUE Designed by Elisabeth von Janota-Bzowski, Germany (35¢); Fritz Henry Oerter, Germany (50¢). *Offset by The House of Questa, U.K. Perforated 14 1/2x15.*

158
People in boat; 159 Line of people, U.N. emblem

164 *Tiers of people*

158		MNHVF	UseVF
35¢	multicolored *(1,114,756)*	1.00	.75
	FDC *(Oct. 23, 1987)*		1.50
	Inscription block of 4	4.50	

159		MNHVF	UseVF
50¢	multicolored *(1,117,464)*	1.25	1.00
	FDC *(Oct. 23,1987)*		1.75
	Inscription block of 4	6.50	

164		MNHVF	UseVF
50¢	multicolored *(1,600,000 printed)*	1.25	1.00
	FDC *(Jan. 29, 1988)*		2.00
	Inscription block of 4	5.50	

1987. CHILD IMMUNIZATION ISSUE The goal of the World Health Organization and the United Nations Children's Fund was to immunize all children by 1990. Designed by Seymour Chwast, U.S. *Offset by The House of Questa, U.K. Perforated 15x14 1/2.*

1988. FOREST ISSUE Designed by Braldt Bralds, Netherlands. *Printed se-tenant in a continuous design. Offset by The House of Questa, U.K. Perforated 14x15.*

160, 161 *Innoculations for whooping cough and tuberculosis*

165, 166 *Northern pine forest scene*

160		MNHVF	UseVF
90¢	multicolored *(634,614)*	3.00	2.25
	FDC *(Nov. 20, 1987)*		1.00
	Inscription block of 4	10.00	

161		MNHVF	UseVF
1.70f	multicolored *(607,725)*	3.50	2.50
	FDC *(Nov. 20, 1987)*		1.25
	Inscription block of 4	17.50	

165		MNHVF	UseVF
50¢	multicolored *(728,569)*	2.00	1.50
	FDC *(March 18, 1988)*		4.50

166		MNHVF	UseVF
1.10f	multicolored *(728,569)*	5.00	4.50
	FDC *(March 18, 1988)*		6.00
	Inscription block of 4	14.00	
	y. Se-tenant pair	7.00	
	FDC (pair)		9.50

1988. IFAD ISSUE International Fund for Agricultural Development - World without hunger. Designed by Santiago Arolas, Switzerland. *Offset by CPE Australia Ltd. Perforated 13 1/2.*

1988. INTERNATIONAL VOLUNTEER DAY ISSUE A U.N. General Assembly resolution calls for International Volunteer Day recognized annually on Dec. 5. Designed by Christopher Magadini, U.S. *Offset by Joh. Enschedé and Sons, Netherlands. Perforated 13x14, 14x13.*

162 *Farm products; 163 Fruit*

167 *Agriculture workers; 168 Veterinary workers*

162		MNHVF	UseVF
35¢	multicolored *(524,817)*	1.00	.75
	FDC *(Jan. 29, 1988)*		1.00
	Inscription block of 4	4.50	

163		MNHVF	UseVF
1.40f	multicolored *(499,103)*	2.25	2.00
	FDC *(Jan. 29, 1988)*		1.50
	Inscription block of 4	12.00	

167		MNHVF	UseVF
80¢	multicolored *(612,166)*	1.50	1.25
	FDC *(May 6, 1988)*		1.75
	Inscription block of 4	7.00	

1988. REGULAR ISSUE Designed by Bjorn Wiinblad, Denmark. *Gravure by Heraclio Fournier, Spain. Perforated 14.*

168			MNHVF	UseVF
90¢	multicolored	(467,334)	2.00	1.50
	FDC	(May 6, 1988)		1.25
	Inscription block of 4		10.00	

1988. HEALTH IN SPORTS ISSUE Designed by LeRoy Neiman, U.S. *Offset by Japanese Government Printing Office. Perforated 13 1/2x13, 13x13 1/2.*

169 *Soccer;*

170 *Swimming*

169			MNHVF	UseVF
50¢	multicolored	(541,421)	1.50	1.25
	FDC	(June 17, 1988)		1.25
	Inscription block of 4		7.00	

170			MNHVF	UseVF
1.40f	multicolored	(475,445)	2.00	1.50
	FDC	(June 17, 1988)		1.25
	Inscription block of 4		11.00	

1988. DECLARATION OF HUMAN RIGHTS ISSUE Fortieth anniversary. This is in the 12th set of stamps in the Human Rights series. Designed by Rocco J. Callari, U.S. Similar to U.N. New York Minkus No. 567. *Gravure and intaglio by Helio Courvoisier, Switzerland. Perforated 12.*

171 *Symbolic flame*

171			MNHVF	UseVF
90¢	multicolored	(900,000 printed)	1.75	1.50
	FDC	(Dec. 9, 1988)		1.75
	Inscription block of 4		7.50	

1988. DECLARATION OF HUMAN RIGHTS SOUVENIR SHEET Fortieth anniversary. Designed by Rocco J. Callari, U.S. The 2f is a single strip souvenir sheet which includes the preamble to the human rights declaration in French. *Gravure and intaglio by Helio Courvoisier, Switzerland. Perforated 12.*

172 Universal Declaration of Human Rights 1948-1988 with No. 171

172			MNHVF	UseVF
2f	**Sheet of 1**	(700,000 printed)	4.00	3.50
	a. Single (2f)		3.00	3.00
	FDC	(Dec. 9, 1988)		3.50

1989. WORLD BANK ISSUE The World Bank is owned by the Governments of more than 151 nations. It provides development assistance. Designed by Saturnin Lumboy, Philippines. *Offset by Joh. Enschedé and Sons, Netherlands. Perforated 13x14.*

173 *Telecommunications*

174 *Industry*

173			MNHVF	UseVF
80¢	multicolored	(524,056)	1.75	1.50
	FDC	(Jan. 27, 1989)		1.50
	Inscription block of 4		7.50	

174			MNHVF	UseVF
1.40f	multicolored	(488,058)	3.00	2.50
	FDC	(Jan. 27, 1989)		2.35
	Inscription block of 4		15.00	

1989. NOBEL PEACE PRIZE ISSUE Commemorated the awarding of the 1988 Nobel Peace Prize to the U.N. peace-keeping forces. Designed by Tom Bland, Australia. Similar to U.N. New York Minkus No. 571. *Offset by CPE Australia Ltd. Perforated 14x13 1/2.*

175 *U.N. soldier on watch*

175			MNHVF	UseVF
90¢	multicolored	(684,566)	1.75	1.35
	FDC	(March 17, 1989)		2.00
	Inscription block of 4		8.00	

1989. WORLD WEATHER WATCH ISSUE Honored a U.N. effort begun in 1963 to collect, analyze and distribute world weather data. Designed by Rocco J. Callari, U.S. and Robert Stein, U.S. *Offset by Joh. Enschedé and Sons, Netherlands. Perforated 13x14.*

176 *Satellite photo: Artic air affecting Europe;*

177 *Satellite photo: Scandinavian temperatures*

176			MNHVF	UseVF
90¢	multicolored	(864,409)	1.50	1.25
	FDC	(April 21, 1989)		1.55
	Inscription block of 4		9.00	

177			MNHVF	UseVF
1.10f	multicolored	(853,556)	3.50	2.50
	FDC	(April 21, 1989)		1.80
	Inscription block of 4		13.50	

1989. 10TH ANNIVERSARY U.N. OFFICES IN VIENNA ISSUE The third secretariat location of the U.N. besides New York and Geneva. Designed by Anton Lehmden (50¢); Arik Brauer (2f). *Gravure (50¢), gravure and intaglio (2f) by Government Printing Office, Austria. Perforated 14.*

178 *Symbolic tree and birds;*

179 *Fanciful "10"*

178		MNHVF	UseVF
50¢	**multicolored** *(605,382)*	2.00	1.50
	FDC *(Aug. 23, 1989)*		1.25
	Inscription block of 4	10.00	

179		MNHVF	UseVF
2f	**multicolored** *(538,140)*	4.00	3.00
	FDC *(Aug. 23, 1989)*		2.60
	Inscription block of 4	17.50	

1989. DECLARATION OF HUMAN RIGHTS ISSUE The 13th set in the Human Rights series depicts the first six articles of the Universal Declaration of Human Rights of 1948. Concept by Arleigh Gaines, U.S., designed by Rocco J. Callari, U.S., and Robert Stein, U.S. Panes of 12 plus 12 se-tenant labels containing Articles 3 (35¢) or 4 (80¢) inscribed in English, French or German. *Offset by Joh. Enschedé and Sons, Netherlands. Perforated 13 1/2.*

180 Young Mother Sewing, *by Mary Cassatt, U.S.*

180		MNHVF	UseVF
35¢	**multicolored** *(2,502,000 printed)*	1.50	1.00
	FDC *(Nov. 17, 1989)*		1.25
	y. Strip of 3 plus 3 labels	4.50	

181 The Unknown Slave, *by Albert Mangones, Haiti*

181		MNHVF	UseVF
80¢	**multicolored** *(2,502,000 printed)*	2.50	1.25
	FDC *(Nov. 17, 1989)*		3.00
	y. Strip of 3 plus 3 labels	8.50	

1990. INTERNATIONAL TRADE CENTER ISSUE Designed by Richard Bernstein, U.S. Similar to U.N. New York Minkus No. 595. *Offset by The House of Questa, U.K. Perforated 14 1/2x15.*

182 *Harbor scene*

182		MNHVF	UseVF
1.50f	**multicolored** *(409,561)*	3.50	2.50
	FDC *(Feb. 2, 1990)*		3.50
		17.50	

1990. REGULAR ISSUE Designed by Guy Breniaux, France, lettering by Elizabeth A. White, U.S. *Gravure by Heraclio Fournier, Spain. Perforated 14x13 1/2.*

183 *Palais des Nations*

183		MNHVF	UseVF
5f	**multicolored** *(1,600,000 printed)*	7.00	6.00
	FDC *(Feb. 2, 1990)*		6.00
	Inscription block of 4	32.50	

1990. FIGHT AIDS ISSUE Designed by Jacek Tofil, Poland (50¢), and Lee Keun Moon, Korea (80¢). *Offset by Joh. Enschedé and Sons, Netherlands. Perforated 13 1/2x12 1/2.*

184 *"SIDA" (AIDS);*
185 *Leonardo Da Vinci figure drawing*

184		MNHVF	UseVF
50¢	**multicolored** *(480,625)*	1.75	1.25
	FDC *(March 16, 1990)*		1.25
	Inscription block of 4	8.00	

185		MNHVF	UseVF
80¢	**multicolored** *(602,721)*	2.50	2.00
	FDC *(March 16, 1990)*		1.50
	Inscription block of 4	12.00	

1990. MEDICINAL PLANTS ISSUE Illustrations from *Curtis's Botanical Magazine,* adapted as a stamp by Rocco J. Callari, U.S. and Robert Stein, U.S. *Gravure by Helio Courvoisier, Switzerland. Perforated 11 1/2, granite paper.*

186 *Plumeria rubra*

187 *Cincohona officinalis*

186		MNHVF	UseVF
90¢	**multicolored** *(625,522)*	2.00	1.75
	FDC *(May 4, 1990)*		1.40
	Inscription block of 4	8.00	

187		MNHVF	UseVF
1.40f	**multicolored** *(648,619)*	2.75	2.25
	FDC *(May 4, 1990)*		2.25
	Inscription block of 4	12.75	

1990. U.N. 45TH ANNIVERSARY ISSUE Commemorated the signing of the U.N. Charter in 1945. Designed by Ruth Schmidthammer, Germany (90¢), Michiel Mertens, Belgium (1.10f). *Offset by Joh. Enschedé and Sons, Netherlands. Perforated 14 1/2x13.*

188 "45" with symbols; 189 Silhouetted dove

188		MNHVF	UseVF
90¢	**multicolored** *(557,253)*	2.25	1.75
	FDC *(June 26, 1990)*		1.40
	Inscription block of 4	7.00	

189		MNHVF	UseVF
1.10f	**multicolored** *(519,635)*	3.00	2.50
	FDC *(June 26, 1990)*		1.75
	Inscription block of 4	10.00	

1990. U.N. 45TH ANNIVERSARY SOUVENIR SHEET Commemorated the signing of the U.N. Charter in 1945. Designed by Robert Stein, U.S. *Offset by Joh. Enschedé and Sons, Netherlands. Perforated 14 1/2x13.*

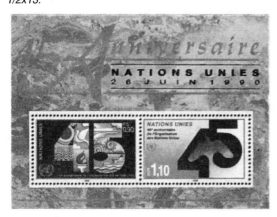

190 *U.N. 45th Anniversary Souvenir sheet with Nos. 188 and 189*

190		MNHVF	UseVF
2f	**Sheet of 2** *(401,027)*	8.50	5.75
	a. Single (90¢)	2.25	1.75
	b. Single (1.10f)	3.00	2.50
	c. Pair	5.50	
	FDC *(June 26, 1990)*		5.50

1990. CRIME PREVENTION ISSUE Designed by Josef Ryzec, Czechoslavakia. *Gravure by Heraclio Fournier, Spain. Perforated 14.*

191 *Official corruption*

192 *Environmental crime*

191		MNHVF	UseVF
50¢	**multicolored** *(494,876)*	2.25	1.75
	FDC *(Sept. 13, 1990)*		1.25
	Inscription block of 4	8.00	

192		MNHVF	UseVF
2f	**multicolored** *(417,033)*	3.75	3.25
	FDC *(Sept. 13, 1990)*		3.00
	Inscription block of 4	22.50	

1990. DECLARATION OF HUMAN RIGHTS ISSUE This 14th set in the Human Rights series depicts Articles 7-12 of the Universal Declaration of Human Rights. Concept by Arleigh Gaines, U.S., designed by Rocco J. Callari, U.S. and Robert Stein, U.S. *Panes of 12 plus 12 se-tenant labels containing Articles 9 (35¢) or 10 (90¢) inscribed in English, French or German. Offset by Joh. Enschedé and Sons, Netherlands. Perforated 13 1/2.*

193 The Prison Court-Yard, *by Vincent Van Gogh, Netherlands*

193		MNHVF	UseVF
35¢	**multicolored** *(2,502,000 printed)*	1.25	.75
	FDC *(Nov. 16, 1990)*		1.25
	y. Strip of 3 plus 3 labels	4.50	

194 Katho's Son Redeems the Evil Doer from Execution, *by Albrecht Durer, Germany*

194		MNHVF	UseVF
90¢	**black & brown** *(2,502,000 printed)*	2.25	1.25
	FDC *(Nov. 16, 1990)*		1.50
	y. Strip of 3 plus 3 labels	8.00	

1991. ECONOMIC COMMISSION FOR EUROPE ISSUE Designed by Carlos Ochagavia, Argentina. *Offset by Heraclio Fournier, Spain. Perforated 14.*

195 *Owl, gull;* 196 *Bittern, otter;* 197 *Swan, lizard;* 198 *Great crested grebe*

195		MNHVF	UseVF
90¢	**multicolored** *(643,143)*	2.00	1.50
	FDC *(March 15, 1991)*		2.00

196		MNHVF	UseVF
90¢	**multicolored** *(643,143)*	2.00	1.50
	FDC *(March 15, 1991)*		2.00

197		MNHVF	UseVF
90¢	**multicolored** *(643,143)*	2.00	1.50
	FDC *(March 15, 1991)*		2.00

198		MNHVF	UseVF
90¢	**multicolored** *(643,143)*	2.00	1.50
	FDC *(March 15, 1991)*		2.00
	Inscription block of 4	10.00	
	y. Se-tenant block of 4	8.00	
	FDC (block)		5.00

1991. NAMIBIAN INDEPENDENCE ISSUE The 5th in the Namibia series. The African nation became independent March 21, 1990. Adapted by Rocco J. Callari, U.S., and Robert Stein, U.S., from photos by John Isaac, India. *Offset by Heraclio Fournier, Spain. Perforated 14.*

199 *Mountains;* 200 *Baobab tree*

199		MNHVF	UseVF
70¢	**multicolored** *(328,014)*	2.50	2.25
	FDC *(May 10, 1991)*		1.65
	Inscription block of 4	8.00	

200		MNHVF	UseVF
90¢	**multicolored** *(395,362)*	3.00	2.50
	FDC *(May 10, 1991)*		2.00
		18.00	

1991. REGULAR ISSUE Designed by Ran Banda Mawilmada, Sri Lanka (80¢), Maurice Gouju, France (1.50f). *Offset by The House of Questa, U.K. Perforated 15x14 1/2 (80¢), perforated 14 (1.50f).*

201 *Colorful ballots;* 202 *U.N. emblem*

201		MNHVF	UseVF
80¢	**multicolored** *(1,600,000 printed)*	2.50	2.25
	FDC *(May 10, 1991)*		1.75
	Inscription block of 4	8.00	

202		MNHVF	UseVF
1.50f	**multicolored** *(1,600,000 printed)*	3.00	2.50
	FDC *(May 10, 1991)*		2.50
	Inscription block of 4	18.00	

Commemorative Issues

1991. RIGHTS OF THE CHILD ISSUE Designed by Ryuta Nakajima, Japan (80¢) and David Popper, Switzerland (1.10f). *Offset by The House of Questa, U.K. Perforated 14 1/2.*

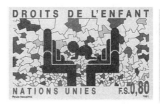 

203 *Hands holding infant;* 204 *Children, sun, flowers*

203		MNHVF	UseVF
80¢	**multicolored** *(469,962)*	2.50	2.25
	FDC *(June 14, 1991)*		1.75
	Inscription block of 4	8.00	

204		MNHVF	UseVF
1.10f	**multicolored** *(494,382)*	3.00	2.50
	FDC *(June 14, 1991)*		2.00
	Inscription block of 4	18.00	

1991. CHEMICAL WEAPONS BAN ISSUE Designed by Oscar Asboth, Austria (80¢), Michel Granger, France (1.40f). *Offset by Heraclio Fournier, Spain. Perforated 13 1/2.*

205 Skulls on canisters; 206 Hand holding back gas mask silhouette

205		MNHVF	UseVF
80¢	multicolored (345,658)	3.00	2.25
	FDC (Sept. 11, 1991)		1.75
	Inscription block of 4	11.00	

206		MNHVF	UseVF
1.40f	multicolored (366,076)	3.50	2.50
	FDC (Sept. 11, 1991)		2.50
	Inscription block of 4	20.00	

1991. 40TH ANNIVERSARY U.N. POSTAL ADMINISTRATION ISSUE
Designed by Rocco J. Callari, U.S. from adaptation of 1951 15¢ stamp designed by Ole Hamann, Denmark (50¢); adaptation of 1951 50¢ stamp designed by Leon Helguera, Mexico (1.60f). *Offset by The House of Questa, U.K. Perforated 14x15.*

207 Stamp on stamp: U.N. New York No. 7; 208 Stamp on stamp: U.N. New York No. 10

207		MNHVF	UseVF
50¢	multicolored (506,839)	2.25	2.00
	FDC (Oct. 24, 1991)		1.25
	Inscription block of 4	10.00	

208		MNHVF	UseVF
1.60f	multicolored (580,493)	3.00	2.25
	FDC (Oct. 24, 1991)		3.00
	Inscription block of 4	15.00	

1991. DECLARATION OF HUMAN RIGHTS ISSUE This 15th set in the Human Rights series is the third group of six articles of the Universal Declaration of Human Rights. Concept by Arleigh Gaines, U.S., designed by Rocco J. Callari, U.S. and Robert Stein, U.S. *Panes of 12 plus 12 se-tenant labels containing Articles 15 (50¢) or 16 (90¢) inscribed in English, French or German. Offset by Joh. Enschedé and Sons, Netherlands. Perforated 13 1/2.*

209 Early Morning in Ro... 1925, by Paul Klee, Germany

209		MNHVF	UseVF
50¢	multicolored (1,295,172)	1.50	1.00
	FDC (Nov. 20, 1991)		1.25
	y. Strip of 3 plus 3 labels	5.50	

210 The Marriage of Glovanni Arnolfini and Flovanna Cenami, *by Jan Van Eyck, Netherlands*

210		MNHVF	UseVF
90¢	multicolored (1,324,091)	2.25	1.50
	FDC (Nov. 20, 1991)		2.00
	y. Strip of 3 plus 3 labels	7.50	

1992. WORLD HERITAGE ISSUE Second in a World Heritage series supporting the conservation of mankind's shared heritage. Adapted as a stamp by Robert Stein, U.S. from photographs by Janet Wishnetsky, U.S. (50¢); Martin Western, U.K. (1.10f). *Offset by Cartor, France. Perforated 13, size 35x28mm.*

211 *Sagarmatha National Park, Nepal, photograph by Janet Wishnetsky, U.S.* 212 *Stonehenge, United Kingdom, photograph by Martin Western, U.K.*

211		MNHVF	UseVF
50¢	multicolored (468,647)	1.25	1.00
	FDC (Jan. 24, 1992)		1.25
	Inscription block of 4	5.00	

212		MNHVF	UseVF
1.10f	multicolored (369,345)	2.75	1.65
	FDC (Jan. 24, 1992)		2.25
	Inscription block of 4	11.00	

For a free Minkus product catalog write to Krause Publications, 700 E. State St., Iola, WI. 54990.

1992. REGULAR ISSUE Designed by Néstor José Martin, Argentina. *Printed by The House of Questa, U.K. Offset, pane of 50, perforated 15x14 1/2.*

213 *Cubist abstract of U.N. headquarters*

213		MNHVF	UseVF
3f	**multicolored** *(1,600,000 printed)*	5.50	4.25
	FDC *(Jan. 24, 1992)*		5.00
	Inscription block of 4	26.50	

1992. CLEAN OCEANS ISSUE Designed paintings by Braldt Bralds, Netherlands. *Offset by The House of Questa, U.K. Perforated 14.*

214 *Ocean surface*

215 *Ocean bottom*

214		MNHVF	UseVF
80¢	**multicolored** *(850,699)*	1.50	1.25
	FDC *(March 13, 1992)*		1.80

215		MNHVF	UseVF
80¢	**multicolored** *(850,699)*	1.50	1.25
	FDC *(March 13, 1992)*		1.80
	Inscription block of 4, 2 of each	9.50	
	y. Se-tenant block of 4	6.00	
	Pair, 1 each 214, 215	4.00	3.00

1992. EARTH SUMMIT ISSUE Designed by Peter Max, U.S. *Gravure by Helio Courvoisier, Switzerland. Pane of 40, perforated 11 1/2.*

216 *Rainbow and single face;*

217 *Two faces;*

218 *Two sailboats and "Peter Max";*

219 *Woman and flowers*

216		MNHVF	UseVF
75¢	**multicolored** *(826,543)*	1.75	1.50
	FDC *(May 22, 1992)*		2.00

217		MNHVF	UseVF
75¢	**multicolored** *(826,543)*	1.75	1.50
	FDC *(May 22, 1992)*		2.00

218		MNHVF	UseVF
75¢	**multicolored** *(826,543)*	1.75	1.50
	FDC *(May 22, 1992)*		2.00

219		MNHVF	UseVF
75¢	**multicolored** *(826,543)*	1.75	1.50
	FDC *(May 22, 1992)*		2.00
	Inscription block of 4	7.50	
	y. Se-tenant block of 4	7.00	
	FDC (block of 4)		5.00

1992. MISSION TO PLANET EARTH ISSUE Designed by Atilla Hejja, U.S. and sheet concept by Rocco J. Callari, U.S. *Gravure by Helio Courvoisier, Switzerland. Pane of 10, rouletted 8, granite paper.*

220 *Space station;* 221 *Probes of Jupiter*

220		MNHVF	UseVF
1.10f	**multicolored** *(668,241)*	4.00	3.00
	FDC *(Sept. 4, 1992)*		2.50

221		MNHVF	UseVF
1.10f	**multicolored** *(668,241)*	4.00	3.00
	FDC *(Sept. 4, 1992)*		2.50
	Inscription block of 2 each	20.00	
	y. Block of 4, Nos. 220 and 221	16.00	

1992. SCIENCE AND TECHNOLOGY DEVELOPMENT ISSUE Designed by Saul Mandel, U.S. *Offset by Unicover Corp., U.S. Perforated 14.*

222 *Drawing of doctor and nurse;* 223 *Student and computer*

222		MNHVF	UseVF
90¢	**multicolored** *(438,943)*	2.25	1.75
	FDC *(Oct. 2, 1992)*		2.00
	Inscription block of 4	12.00	

223		MNHVF	UseVF
1.60f	**multicolored** *(400,701)*	3.50	2.25
	FDC *(Oct. 2, 1992)*		2.50
	Inscription block of 4	15.00	

1992. DECLARATION OF HUMAN RIGHTS ISSUE This 16th set in the Human Rights series depicts the fourth group of six Articles (19-25) of the Universal Declaration of Human Rights. Adapted as a stamp by Robert Stein, U.S. *Panes of 12 plus 12 se-tenant labels containing Articles 21 (50¢) or 22 (90¢), inscribed in English, French or German. Offset by Joh. Enschedé and Sons, Netherlands. Perforated 13 1/2.*

224 The Oath of the Tennis Court, *by Jacques Louis David, France*

224		**MNHVF**	**UseVF**
50¢	**multicolored** *(4,201,788)*	1.50	1.00
	FDC *(Nov. 20, 1992)*		1.25
	y. Strip of 3 plus 3 labels	18.00	

225 Rocking Chair I, *by Henry Moore, U.K.*

225		**MNHVF**	**UseVF**
90¢	**multicolored** *(1,179,294)*	2.75	2.25
	FDC *(Nov. 20, 1992)*		2.00
	y. Strip of 3 plus 3 labels	8.00	

1993. AGING WITH DIGNITY ISSUE Designed by C. M. Dudash, U.S. *Offset by Cartor, France. Perforated 13.*

226 *Soccer coach*

227 *Man at computer*

226		**MNHVF**	**UseVF**
50¢	**multicolored** *(483,452)*	2.00	1.25
	FDC *(Feb. 5, 1993)*		1.00
	Inscription block of 4	10.00	
227		**MNHVF**	**UseVF**
1.60f	**multicolored** *(331,008)*	3.50	2.50
	FDC *(Feb. 5, 1993)*		2.75
	Inscription block of 4	17.50	

1993. ENDANGERED SPECIES ISSUE The first set of stamps in the Endangered Species series. Concept by Rocco J. Callari, U.S. and designs by Betina Ogden, Australia. *Offset by Joh. Enschedé and Sons, Netherlands. Perforated 13x12 1/2.*

228 *Gorilla;*

229 *Peregrine falcon;*

230 *Amazonian manatee;*

231 *Snow leopard*

228		**MNHVF**	**UseVF**
80¢	**multicolored** *(1,200,000 printed)*	1.75	1.50
	FDC *(March 3, 1993)*		1.80
229		**MNHVF**	**UseVF**
80¢	**multicolored** *(1,200,000 printed)*	1.75	1.50
	FDC *(March, 3, 1993)*		1.80
230		**MNHVF**	**UseVF**
80¢	**multicolored** *(1,200,000 printed)*	1.75	1.50
	FDC *(March, 3, 1993)*		1.80
231		**MNHVF**	**UseVF**
80¢	**multicolored** *(1,200,000 printed)*	1.75	1.50
	FDC *(March, 3, 1993)*		2.00
	Inscription block of 4	7.00	
	y. Se-tenant block of 4	7.00	

1993. HEALTHY ENVIRONMENT ISSUE Designed by Milton Glaser, U.S. *Offset Leigh-Mardon Pty. Ltd., Australia. Perforated 15x14 1/2.*

232 *Houses under tree;*
233 *Urban skyscrapers*

232		**MNHVF**	**UseVF**
60¢	**multicolored** *(456,304)*	2.50	1.25
	FDC *(May 7, 1993)*		1.25
	Inscription block of 4	10.00	
233		**MNHVF**	**UseVF**
1f	**multicolored** *(392,015)*	3.50	2.25
	FDC *(May 7, 1993)*		2.00
	Inscription block of 4	18.00	

Every entry in this catalog has been double-checked for accuracy, but mistakes may creep into any human endeavor, and we ask your assistance in eliminating them. Please call the attention of the editors to any errors in stamp descriptions found in this catalog.

1993. DECLARATION OF HUMAN RIGHTS ISSUE The 17th set in the Human Rights series depicts the fifth of the six articles of the Universal Declaration of Human Rights. Concept by Arleigh Gaines, U.S., designed by Robert Stein, U.S. Panes of 12 plus 12 se-tenant labels containing Article 27 (50¢) and 28 (90¢) inscribed in English, French or German. *Offset by Joh. Enschedé and Sons, Netherlands. Perforated 13 1/2.*

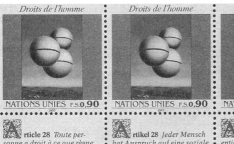

234 Three Musicians, *by Pablo Picasso*

234		MNHVF	UseVF
50¢	**multicolored** *(2,502,000 printed)*	1.50	2.50
	FDC *(June 11, 1993)*		1.25
	y. Strip of 3 plus 3 labels	1.50	

235
Voice of
Space,
*by René
Magritte,
Belgium*

235		MNHVF	UseVF
90¢	**multicolored** *(2,502,000 printed)*	3.00	2.50
	FDC *(June 11, 1993)*		2.00
	y. Strip of 3 plus 3 labels	8.00	

1993. INTERNATIONAL PEACE DAY ISSUE The U.N. General Assembly declared in 1981 that the third Tuesday of September would be observed as the International Day of Peace. Designed by Hans Erni, Switzerland. Engraved by Pierre Schopfer, Switzerland. *Offset and intaglio by PTT, Switzerland. Rouletted 12 1/2.*

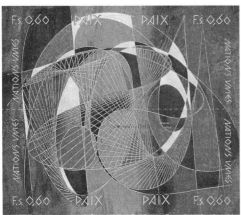

236-239
*Abstract design,
four corners*

236		MNHVF	UseVF
60¢	**purple & multicolored** *(357,760)*	2.50	1.50
	FDC *(Sept. 21, 1993)*		1.25

237		MNHVF	UseVF
60¢	**purple & multicolored** *(357,760)*	2.50	1.50
	FDC *(Sept. 21, 1993)*		1.25

238		MNHVF	UseVF
60¢	**purple & multicolored** *(357,760)*	2.50	1.50
	FDC *(Sept. 21, 1993)*		1.25

239		MNHVF	UseVF
60¢	**purple & multicolored** *(357,760)*	2.50	1.50
	FDC *(Sept. 21, 1993)*		1.25
	Inscription block of 4	12.00	
	y. Se-tenant block of 4	12.00	

1993. ENVIRONMENT CLIMATE ISSUE Designed paintings by Braldt Bralds, Netherlands. *Offset by The House of Questa, U.K. Perforated 14 1/2.*

240 *Polar bears;* 241 *Whale sounding;* 242 *Elephant seal;* 243 *Penguins*

240		MNHVF	UseVF
1.10f	**multicolored** *(391,593)*	2.50	1.50
	FDC *(Oct. 29, 1993)*		2.00

241		MNHVF	UseVF
1.10f	**multicolored** *(391,593)*	2.50	1.50
	FDC *(Oct. 29, 1993)*		2.00

242		MNHVF	UseVF
1.10f	**multicolored** *(391,593)*	2.50	1.50
	FDC *(Oct. 29, 1993)*		2.00

243		MNHVF	UseVF
1.10f	**multicolored** *(391,593)*	2.50	1.50
	FDC *(Oct. 29, 1993)*		2.00
	Inscription block of 8	22.50	
	y. Se-tenant strip of 4	10.00	

1994. YEAR OF THE FAMILY ISSUE The U.N. General Assembly proclaimed 1994 as the International Year of the Family. Designed by Rocco J. Callari, U.S., and computer graphics by Luis Sardá, Spain, and John De Santis, U.S. *Offset by Cartor, France. Perforated 13.*

244 *Teaching child to walk;*

245 *Women and child picking plants*

244		MNHVF	UseVF
80¢	**rose violet & multicolored** *(419,614)*	2.25	1.75
	FDC *(Feb. 4,1994)*		1.75
	Inscription block of 4	8.50	

245		MNHVF	UseVF
1f	**brown & multicolored** *(435,214)*	3.00	2.00
	FDC *(Feb. 4, 1994)*		2.00
	Inscription block of 4	15.00	

1994. ENDANGERED SPECIES ISSUE The second set of stamps in the Endangered Species series. Concept by Rocco J. Callari, U.S. and designed by Kerrie Maddeford, Australia. *Offset by Joh. Enschedé and Sons, Netherlands. Perforated 12 1/2.*

246 *Mexican prairie dog;* 247 *Jabiru;* 248 *Blue whale;* 249 *Golden lion tamarin*

251 *North America;* 252 *Eurasia;* 253 *South America;* 254 *Australia*

246		MNHVF	UseVF
80¢	multicolored *(1,200,000 printed)*	1.25	1.00
	FDC *(March 18, 1994)*		1.75

247		MNHVF	UseVF
80¢	multicolored *(1,200,000 printed)*	1.25	1.00
	FDC *(March 18, 1994)*		1.75

248		MNHVF	UseVF
80¢	multicolored *(1,200,000 printed)*	1.25	1.00
	FDC *(March 18, 1994)*		1.75

249		MNHVF	UseVF
80¢	multicolored *(1,200,000 printed)*	1.25	1.00
	FDC *(March 18, 1994)*		1.75
	Inscription block of 4	5.50	
	y. Se-tenant block of 4	5.00	

251		MNHVF	UseVF
60¢	multicolored *(175,870)*	2.00	1.00
	FDC *(May 27, 1994)*		1.50

252		MNHVF	UseVF
60¢	multicolored *(175,870)*	2.00	1.00
	FDC *(May 27, 1994)*		1.50

253		MNHVF	UseVF
60¢	multicolored *(175,870)*	2.00	1.00
	FDC *(May 27, 1994)*		1.50

254		MNHVF	UseVF
60¢	multicolored *(175,870)*	2.00	1.00
	FDC *(May 27, 1994)*		1.50
	Inscription block of 4	10.50	
	y. Se-tenant block of 4	9.00	

1994. PROTECTION FOR REFUGEES ISSUE Designed by Francoise Peyroux, U.S. *Offset by Leigh-Mardon Pty. Ltd. Perforated 14 1/2x15.*

 250 *Hand holding figure over cliffs*

250		MNHVF	UseVF
1.20f	multicolored *(306,160)*	4.25	2.00
	FDC *(April 29, 1994)*		2.50
	Inscription block of 4	20.00	

1994. POPULATION AND DEVELOPMENT ISSUE The International Conference on Population and Development believes that population should be at the core of all economic, social, political and environmental undertakings. A conference was held in Cairo, Egypt Sept. 5-13, 1994. Designed by Jerry Smath, U.S. *Offset by Joh. Enschedé and Sons, Netherlands. Perforated 13 1/4x13 1/2.*

255 *People at market;* 256 *People crossing bridge*

255		MNHVF	UseVF
60¢	multicolored *(395,208)*	1.25	1.00
	FDC *(Sept. 1, 1994)*		1.10
	Inscription block of 4	6.00	

256		MNHVF	UseVF
80¢	multicolored *(377,290)*	1.50	1.00
	FDC *(Sept. 1, 1994)*		1.10
	Inscription block of 4	6.00	

1994. NATURAL DISASTER ISSUE The U.N. in 1989 designated the 1990s as the International Decade for Natural Disaster Reduction. Designed by Kenji Koga, Japan. Similar to U.N. New York Minkus Nos. 670-673. *Offset by The House of Questa, U.K. Perforated 14x14 1/4.*

1994. REGULAR ISSUE Adapted as stamps by Rocco J. Callari, U.S., from photgraph by Nori Mahdi, U.S. for (1.80f); Carlos Da Silva, U.S. (60¢); and design by Oili Maki, Finland (80¢). *Offset by The House of Questa, U.K. Perforated 14.*

257-258
*Different
views of
Palais des
Nations;*
259
*Creation of
the World,
by Oili Maki*

257		MNHVF	UseVF
1.80f	multicolored *(1,075,000 printed)*	3.50	2.50
	FDC *(Sept. 1, 1994)*		2.75
	Inscription block of 4	18.00	

258		MNHVF	UseVF
60¢	multicolored *(1,075,000 printed)*	1.50	1.25
	FDC *(Sept. 1, 1994)*		1.25
	Inscription block of 4	8.00	

259		MNHVF	UseVF
80¢	multicolored *(1,075,000 printed)*	3.00	2.50
	FDC *(Sept. 1, 1994)*		1.75
	Inscription block of 4	13.50	

1994. UNCTAD 30TH ANNIVERSARY ISSUE The U.N. Conference on Trade and Development became a permanent intergovernmental body in 1964 in Geneva. UNCTAD's goal is to promote growth and development in countries. Designed by Luis Sardá, Spain. *Offset by Joh. Enschedé and Sons, Netherlands. Perforated 13 1/4x13 1/2.*

260-261
Map of world

260		MNHVF	UseVF
80¢	multicolored *(268,778)*	2.00	1.00
	FDC *(Oct. 28, 1994)*		1.75
	Inscription block of 4	10.00	

261		MNHVF	UseVF
1f	multicolored *(327,952)*	2.50	1.75
	FDC *(Oct. 28, 1994)*		2.00
	Inscription block of 4	12.50	
	v. gray-green omitted	—	

1995. U.N. 50TH ANNIVERSARY ISSUE Celebrated the signing of the Charter of the United Nations, June 26, 1945. Designed by Rocco J. Callari, U.S. Similar to U.N. New York Minkus No. 678. *Offset and intaglio by PTT, Switzerland. Perforated 13 1/2.*

262 U.N. seal and "50"

262		MNHVF	UseVF
80¢	multicolored *(823,837)*	2.25	2.00
	FDC *(Jan. 1, 1995)*		2.00
	Inscription block of 4	10.00	

1995. SOCIAL SUMMIT ISSUE The World Summit for Social Development met March 6-12, 1995, in Copenhagen, Denmark. Designed by Friedensreich Hunderwasser, Austria. Engraved by Wolfgang Seidel, Austria. *Gravure and intaglio by Government Printing Office, Austria. Perforated 13 1/2x14.*

263 *Drawings of people*

263		MNHVF	UseVF
1f	multicolored *(452,116)*	2.50	2.00
	FDC *(Feb. 3, 1995)*		2.00
	Inscription block of 4	11.50	

1995. ENDANGERED SPECIES ISSUE This is the third set of stamps in the Endangered Species series. Concept by Rocco J. Callari, U.S. and designed by Sibylie Erni, Switzerland. *Offset by Joh. Enschedé and Sons, Netherlands. Perforated 13x12 1/2.*

264 *Crowned lemur;* 265 *Giant Scops owl;* 266 *Zetek's frog;* 267 *Wood bison*

264		MNHVF	UseVF
80¢	multicolored *(730,000 printed)*	2.00	1.10
	FDC *(March 24, 1995)*		1.65

265		MNHVF	UseVF
80¢	multicolored *(730,000 printed)*	2.00	1.10
	FDC *(March 24, 1995)*		1.10

266		MNHVF	UseVF
80¢	multicolored *(730,000 printed)*	2.00	1.10
	FDC *(March 24, 1995)*		1.10

267		MNHVF	UseVF
80¢	multicolored *(730,000 printed)*	2.00	1.10
	FDC *(March 24, 1995)*		1.10
	Inscription block of 4	8.50	
	y. Se-tenant block of 4	8.00	

1995. INTERNATIONAL YOUTH YEAR ISSUE Tenth anniversary. The U.N. General Assembly declared 1985 International Youth Year. Designed by Gottfried Kumpf, Austria. *Offset by The House of Questa, U.K. Perforated 14 1/2x14 3/4.*

268 Farmer on tractor in fields; 269 Couple standing by field

268		MNHVF	UseVF
80¢	**multicolored** *(294,987)*	1.75	1.75
	FDC *(May 26, 1995)*		1.65
	Inscription block of 4	10.00	

269		MNHVF	UseVF
1f	**multicolored** *(264,823)*	2.25	2.25
	FDC *(May 26, 1995)*		1.75
	Inscription block of 4	12.50	

1995. U.N. 50TH ANNIVERSARY ISSUE The second issue in 1995 to commemorate the anniversary of the U.N., issued on the 50th anniversary date of the signing of the U.N. Charter. Designed by Paul and Chris Calle, U.S. Engraved by Inge Madlé, Netherlands. Similar to U.N. New York Minkus Nos. 686 and 687. *Intaglio by Joh. Enschedé and Sons, Security Printing, Netherlands. Perforated 13 1/4x13 1/2.*

270 Hand with pen; 271 Veterans' War Memorial Opera House, San Francisco

270		MNHVF	UseVF
60¢	**maroon** *(352,336)*	2.50	2.25
	FDC *(June 26, 1995)*		.90
	Inscription block of 4	10.00	

271		MNHVF	UseVF
1.80f	**green** *(377,391)*	3.75	3.00
	FDC *(June 26, 1995)*		3.00
	Inscription block of 4	20.00	

1995. U.N. 50TH ANNIVERSARY SOUVENIR SHEET Designed by Paul and Chris Calle, U.S. Similar to U.N. New York Minkus No. 688. *Offset and intaglio. Imperforate.*

272 U.N. 50th Anniversary Souvenir sheet with Nos. 270 and 271

272		MNHVF	UseVF
2.40f	**Sheet of 2** *(251,272)*	6.50	4.25
	a. Single (60¢)	2.50	1.25
	b. Single (1.80f)	3.75	2.50
	FDC *(June 26, 1995)*		4.00

1995. WORLD CONFERENCE ON WOMEN ISSUE The fourth World Conference on Women was held Sept. 4-5, 1995, in Beijing, China. Designed by Ting Shao Kuang, China. *Gravure by Postage Stamp Printing House, MPT, both from the People's Republic of China. Perforated 12.*

273 Black woman and flying cranes; 274 Women and dove

273		MNHVF	UseVF
60¢	**multicolored** *(343,336)*	1.50	.50
	FDC *(Sept. 5, 1995)*		1.25
	Inscription block of 4	6.50	

274		MNHVF	UseVF
1f	**multicolored** *(345,389)*	2.50	.85
	FDC *(Sept. 5, 1995)*		2.25
	Inscription block of 4	11.00	

1995. U.N. PEOPLE, 50TH ANNIVERSARY ISSUE This was the third issue to commemorate the Charter of the U.N., which came into force Oct. 24, 1945. Similar to U.N. New York Minkus Nos. 692-703. Designed by Ben Verkaaik, Netherlands. Rocco J. Callari, U.S. and Robert Stein, U.S. designed the Prestige Booklet. *Offset by The House of Questa, U.K. Perforated 14.*

275-286 People from continuous design

275		MNHVF	UseVF
30¢	**multicolored,** top left *(216,832)*	1.50	1.00

276		MNHVF	UseVF
30¢	**multicolored,** top right *(216,832)*	1.50	1.00

277		MNHVF	UseVF
30¢	**multicolored,** top center left *(216,832)*	1.50	1.00

278		MNHVF	UseVF
30¢	**multicolored,** top center right *(216,832)*	1.50	1.00

279		MNHVF	UseVF
30¢	**multicolored,** top lower left *(216,832)*	1.50	1.00

280		MNHVF	UseVF
30¢	**multicolored,** top lower right *(216,832)*	1.50	1.00

281		MNHVF	UseVF
30¢	**multicolored,** bottom top left *(216,832)*	1.50	1.00

282		MNHVF	UseVF
30¢	**multicolored,** bottom top right *(216,832)*	1.50	1.00

283		MNHVF	UseVF
30¢	**multicolored,** bottom center left *(216,832)*	1.50	1.00

284		MNHVF	UseVF
30¢	**multicolored,** bottom center right *(216,832)*	1.50	1.00

285		MNHVF	UseVF
30¢	**multicolored,** bottom left *(216,832)*	1.50	1.00

286		MNHVF	UseVF
30¢	**multicolored,** bottom right *(216,832)*	1.50	1.00
	FDC *(Oct. 24, 1995)* (sheetlet)		30.00
	y. Sheetlet of 12	20.00	
	n. Booklet of 12 *(74,151)*	22.00	
	FDC (booklet)		30.00

1996. WFUNA 50TH ANNIVERSARY ISSUE The initials stand for World Federation of United Nations Associations. Designed by Rudolf Mirer, Switzerland. *Offset by Joh. Enschedé and Sons, Netherlands. Perforated 13x13 1/2.*

287 *Boat above, fish below*

287		MNHVF	UseVF
80¢	**multicolored** *(550,000 printed)*	2.25	1.75
	FDC *(Feb. 2, 1996)*		2.00
	Inscription block of 4	10.50	

1996. REGULAR ISSUE Adapted as stamps by Rocco J. Callari, U.S., from a photograph by Laurent Bianco, Switzerland, for (40¢); and Catherine Charbonnier Casile, France, (70¢). *Offset by The House of Questa, U.K. Perforated 14.*

288 The Galloping Horse Treading on a Flying Swallow, *Chinese Bronzework, Eastern Han Dynasty (22-220 A.D.);* 289 *Palais des Nations, Geneva*

288		MNHVF	UseVF
40¢	**multicolored** *(1,125,000 printed)*	1.00	.50
	FDC *(Feb. 2, 1996)*		1.25
	Inscription block of 4	5.00	

289		MNHVF	UseVF
70¢	**multicolored** *(1,125,000 printed)*	1.75	1.25
	FDC *(Feb. 2, 1996)*		1.50
	Inscription block of 4	7.00	

1996. ENDANGERED SPECIES ISSUE This is the fourth set in the Endangered Species series. Designed by Diane Bruyninckx, Belgium and concept and design by Rocco J. Callari, U.S. *Offset by Joh. Enschedé and Sons, Netherlands. Perforated 12 1/2.*

290 *Paphiopedilum delenatii;*

291 *Pachypodium baronii;*

292 *Sternbergia lutea (winter daffodil)*

293 *Darlingtonia californico (Cobra lily)*

290		MNHVF	UseVF
80¢	**multicolored** *(680,000 printed)*	2.00	1.00
	FDC *(March 14, 1996)*		2.00

291		MNHVF	UseVF
80¢	**multicolored** *(680,000 printed)*	2.00	1.00
	FDC *(March 14, 1996)*		2.00

292		MNHVF	UseVF
80¢	**multicolored** *(680,000 printed)*	2.00	1.00
	FDC *(March 14, 1996)*		2.00

293		MNHVF	UseVF
80¢	**multicolored** *(680,000 printed)*	2.00	1.00
	FDC *(March 14, 1996)*		2.00
	Inscription block of 4	8.00	
	y. Se-tenant block of 4	8.00	

1996. CITY SUMMIT (HABITAT II) ISSUE The second U.N. Conference on Human Settlements (Habitat II) was held in June 1996, in Istanbul, Turkey. Designed by Teresa Fasolino, U.S. *Offset by Joh. Enschedé and Sons, Netherlands. Perforated 14x13 1/2.*

294 *Asian family;* 295 *Oriental garden;* 296 *Vendor;* 297 *Boys playing;* 298 *Couple under tree*

294		MNHVF	UseVF
70¢	**multicolored** *(420,000 printed)*	2.00	1.00
	FDC *(June 3, 1996)*		1.50

295		MNHVF	UseVF
70¢	**multicolored** *(420,000 printed)*	2.00	1.00
	FDC *(June 3, 1996)*		1.50

296		MNHVF	UseVF
70¢	**multicolored** *(420,000 printed)*	2.00	1.00
	FDC *(June 3, 1996)*		1.50

297		MNHVF	UseVF
70¢	**multicolored** *(420,000 printed)*	2.00	1.00
	FDC *(June 3, 1996)*		1.50

298		MNHVF	UseVF
70¢	**multicolored** *(420,000 printed)*	2.00	1.00
	FDC *(June 3, 1996)* (strip of 5)		6.75
	Inscription block of 10	22.50	
	y. Se-tenant strip of 5	10.00	

1996. SPORT AND ENVIRONMENT ISSUE Commemorated the 100th anniversary of the Olympic Games. Designed by LeRoy Neiman, U.S. *Offset by The House of Questa, U.K. Perforated 14x14 1/2, 14 1/2x14.*

299 *Cycling;*

300 *Sprinters*

299		MNHVF	UseVF
70¢	multicolored *(625,000 printed)*	2.00	1.50
	FDC *(July 19, 1996)*		1.50
	Inscription block of 4	9.00	

300		MNHVF	UseVF
1.10f	multicolored *(625,000 printed)*	2.75	2.50
	FDC *(July 19, 1996)*		2.25
	Inscription block of 4	13.50	

1996. SPORT AND ENVIRONMENT SOUVENIR SHEET Commemorated the 100th anniversary of the modern Olympic Games. Designed by LeRoy Neiman, U.S. *Offset by The House of Questa, U.K. Imperforate.*

301 *Souvenir sheet with Nos. 299 and 300*

301		MNHVF	UseVF
1.80f	**Sheet of 2** *(345,000 printed)*	5.00	4.00
	a. Single (70¢)	2.00	1.50
	b. Single (1.10f)	2.75	2.50

1996. PLEA FOR PEACE ISSUE The stamps drew attention to UNICEF's goal to reduce child mortality, disease and illiteracy. Designed by Chen Yu (90¢), Zhou Jing (1.10f), both of China. *Offset by The House of Questa, U.K. Perforated 15x14 1/2, 14 1/2x15.*

302 *Birds in tree;*

303 *Flowers bursting from rocket*

302		MNHVF	UseVF
90¢	multicolored *(550,000 printed)*	2.25	2.00
	FDC *(Sept. 17, 1996)*		2.00
	Inscription block of 4	9.00	

303		MNHVF	UseVF
1.10f	multicolored *(550,000 printed)*	3.00	2.50
	FDC *(Sept. 17, 1996)*		2.50
	Inscription block of 4	13.50	

1996. UNICEF 50TH ANNIVERSARY ISSUE Celebrated the 50th anniversary of UNICEF with depictions of fairy tales designed by The Walt Disney Co., U.S. *Offset by The House of Questa, U.K. Perforated 14 1/2x15.*

304 *The Sun and the Moon from South America; marginal text read "Right to a name and nationality - South American legend"*

305 *Ananse from Africa; marginal text read "Right to education - African story"*

304		MNHVF	UseVF
70¢	multicolored *(1,000,000 printed)*	2.25	2.00
	FDC *(Nov. 20, 1996)*		1.50
	y. Pane of 8 plus label	10.00	

305		MNHVF	UseVF
1.80f	multicolored *(1,000,000 printed)*	3.50	3.00
	FDC *(Nov. 20, 1996)*		3.00
	y. Pane of 8 plus label	27.50	

1997. REGULAR ISSUE Adapted as stamps by Robert Stein, U.S., from a photograph by Unmesh, U.S., for (10¢); and detail from a fresco by Massimo Campigli, Italy, (1.10f). *Offset by The House of Questa, U.K. Perforated 14 1/2. Size 35.96mmx25.73mm.*

306 *U.N. flag;*

307 *Palais des Nations Under Construction, by Massimo Campigli, Italy*

306		MNHVF	UseVF
10¢	multicolored *(600,000 printed)*	.25	.20
	FDC *(Feb. 12, 1997)*		1.25
	Inscription block of 4	2.00	

307		MNHVF	UseVF
1.10f	multicolored *(700,000 printed)*	2.50	1.75
	FDC *(Feb. 12, 1997)*		2.25
	Inscription block of 4	10.00	

1997. ENDANGERED SPECIES ISSUE Fifth set in the Endangered Species series. Sheet concept and design by Rocco J. Callari, U.S. Designer Daniela Costa, Italy. *Offset by Joh. Enschedé and Sons, Netherlands. Perforated 12 1/2.*

308 *Polar bear;*
309 *Blue-crowned pigeon;* 310 *Marine iguana;* 311 *Guanaco*

308		MNHVF	UseVF
80¢	multicolored *(620,000 printed)*	1.50	1.25

309		MNHVF	UseVF
80¢	multicolored *(620,000 printed)*	1.50	1.25

310		MNHVF	UseVF
80¢	multicolored *(620,000 printed)*	1.50	1.25

311		MNHVF	UseVF
80¢	multicolored *(620,000 printed)*	1.50	1.25

FDC *(March 13, 1997)*		5.00
Inscription block of 4	7.50	
y. Se-tenant block of 4	6.00	2.25

1997. EARTH SUMMIT ISSUE Fifth anniversary of the U.N. Conference on Environment and Development. The special session held in New York, June 1997, focused on development worldwide. Designed by Peter Max, U.S. *Gravure by Helio Courvoisier, Switzerland, granite paper. Perforated 11 1/2.*

312 *Figure flying;* 313 *Large face;* 314 *Boats and figure on hill;* 315 *Standing figure and trees*

312		MNHVF	UseVF
45¢	**multicolored** *(408,000 printed)*	1.00	1.25
	FDC *(May 30, 1997)*		2.20

313		MNHVF	UseVF
45¢	**multicolored** *(408,000 printed)*	1.00	1.25
	FDC *(May 30, 1997)*		2.20

314		MNHVF	UseVF
45¢	**multicolored** *(408,000 printed)*	1.00	1.25
	FDC *(May 30, 1997)*		2.20

315		MNHVF	UseVF
45¢	**multicolored** *(408,000 printed)*	1.00	1.25
	FDC *(May 30, 1997)*		2.20
	Inscription block of 4	4.00	
	y. Se-tenant block of 4	4.00	
	FDC (block of 4)		3.50

1997. EARTH SUMMIT SOUVENIR SHEET Designed by Peter Max, U.S. *Gravure by Helio Courvoisier, Switzerland. Perforated 11 1/2.*

316 *Earth Summit +5 Souvenir sheet with images on Nos. 312-315 as one stamp*

316		MNHVF	UseVF
1.10f	**multicolored** *(270,000 printed)*	2.00	2.00
	FDC *(May 30, 1997)*		2.50

1997. TRANSPORTATION ISSUE The Economic Commission for Europe (ECE) and the Economic and Social Commission for Asia and Pacific (ESCAP), celebrated their 50th anniversary in 1997. Designed by Michael Cockcroft, U.K. *Offset by The House of Questa, U.K. Perforated 14x14 1/2.*

317 *Zeplin, Fokker Trimotor;* 318 *Boeing 'Clipper,' Lockheed 'Constellation';* 319 *DeHavilland Comet;* 320 *Illyushin, Boeing jumbo jet;* 321 *Concorde*

317		MNHVF	UseVF
70¢	**multicolored** *(302,000 printed)*	1.25	1.50
	FDC *(Aug. 29, 1997)*		2.25

318		MNHVF	UseVF
70¢	**multicolored** *(302,000 printed)*	1.25	1.50
	FDC *(Aug. 29, 1997)*		2.25

319		MNHVF	UseVF
70¢	**multicolored** *(302,000 printed)*	1.25	1.50
	FDC *(Aug. 29, 1997)*		2.25

320		MNHVF	UseVF
70¢	**multicolored** *(302,000 printed)*	1.25	1.50
	FDC *(Aug. 29, 1997)*		2.25

321		MNHVF	UseVF
70¢	**multicolored** *(302,000 printed)*	1.25	1.50
	FDC *(Aug. 29, 1997)*		2.25
	y. Strip of 5	5.00	
	FDC (strip of 5)		5.00

1997. TRIBUTE TO PHILATELY ISSUE Adapted by Robert Stein, U.S., the designs of the 1986 "Philately - The International Hobby," stamps designed by Ingalill Axelsson, Sweden. Engraved by Czeslaw Slania, Sweden. *Offset by Joh. Enschedé and Sons, Netherlands. Perforated 13 1/2x14.*

322 *50¢ stamp of 1986 U.N. Geneva Minkus No. 146;* 323 *80¢ stamp of 1986 U.N. Geneva Minkus No. 147*

322		MNHVF	UseVF
70¢	**multicolored** *(400,000 printed)*	1.25	1.50
	FDC *(Oct. 14, 1997)*		2.25
	Inscription block of 4	3.50	

323		MNHVF	UseVF
1.10f	**multicolored** *(400,000 printed)*	1.25	1.50
	FDC *(Oct. 14, 1997)*		2.50
	Inscription block of 4	3.50	

1997. WORLD HERITAGE CONVENTION ISSUE Twenty-fifth anniversary. The first in a series of stamps and prestige booklet focusing on one specific World Heritage site or a group of World Heritage geographical locations. The third set of U.N. stamps illustrated World Heritage sites. Adapted by Robert Stein, U.S., from photographs by Guo Youmin, China. Computer graphics by Blake Tarpley, U.S. Two images of the Terracotta Warriors of the Qin Shi Huang Mausoleum in Mount Lishán, China. *Offset by the Government Printing Office, Austria. Perforated 13 1/2.*

324 *Warrior head;* 325 *Warrior group of 3*

324		MNHVF	UseVF
45¢	multicolored *(555,000 printed)*	1.00	1.25
	FDC *(Nov. 19, 1997)*		1.50
	Inscription block of 4	4.00	

325		MNHVF	UseVF
70¢	multicolored *(555,000 printed)*	1.25	1.50
	FDC *(Nov. 19, 1997)*		2.25
	Inscription block of 4	5.00	

1997. WORLD HERITAGE CONVENTION SOUVENIR BOOKLET Twenty-fifth anniversary. Designed by Rorie Katz, U.S., and Robert Stein, U.S. *Includes 6 panes, one of each U.S., Vienna, Geneva design, with a block of 4 stamps of the same design re-valued to an 10¢ denomination. One individual page, 3 1/2x6 3/4. Offset by the Government Printing Office, Austria. Perforated 13 1/2.*

325A *Kneeling warrior;* 325B *Warrior group facing right;* 325C *Head facing right;* 325D *Men standing;* 325E *Head facing left;* 325F *Warrior group facing forward*

325A		MNHVF	UseVF
10¢	multicolored *(283,000 printed)*	.50	.50
325B		MNHVF	UseVF
10¢	multicolored *(283,000 printed)*	.50	.50
325C		MNHVF	UseVF
10¢	multicolored *(283,000 printed)*	.50	.50
325D		MNHVF	UseVF
10¢	multicolored *(283,000 printed)*	.50	.50
325E		MNHVF	UseVF
10¢	multicolored *(283,000 printed)*	.50	.50
325F		MNHVF	UseVF
10¢	multicolored *(283,000 printed)*	.50	.50
	n. Booklet of 6 panes	6.00	

1998. REGULAR ISSUE Adapted as a stamp by Robert Stein, U.S., from a photograph credit to U.N. *Offset by The House of Questa, U.K. Perforated 14.*

 326 *Photo of flags outside the Palais des Nations in Geneva, Switzerland*

326		MNHVF	UseVF
2f	multicolored *(550,000 printed)*	1.25	1.00
	FDC *(Feb. 13, 1998)*		1.50
	Inscription block of 4	6.50	

1998. ENDANGERED SPECIES ISSUE A sixth set in a series to highlight the need for protection of endangered species throughout the world. Concept by Rocco J. Callari, U.S., and designer Pat Medearis-Altman, New Zealand. *The 16 stamps on each sheetlet allow for four se-tenant blocks of four. Offset by Joh. Enschedé and Sons, Netherlands. Perforated 12 1/2x13 1/2.*

 327 *Short-tailed Tibetan macaque, the largest in the macaque family;* 328 *Caribbean flamingo, the brightest of the flamingos;* 329 *Queen Alexandria's birdwing of Papua New Guinea;* 330 *Persian fallow deer, found only in a forest in western Iran*

327		MNHVF	UseVF
80¢	multicolored *(560,000 printed)*	1.00	.50
	FDC *(March 13, 1998)*		2.50
328		MNHVF	UseVF
80¢	multicolored *(560,000 printed)*	1.00	.50
	FDC *(March 13, 1998)*		2.50
329		MNHVF	UseVF
80¢	multicolored *(560,000 printed)*	1.00	.50
	FDC *(March 13, 1998)*		2.50
330		MNHVF	UseVF
80¢	multicolored *(560,000 printed)*	1.00	.50
	FDC *(March 13, 1998)*		2.50
	Inscription block of 4	4.00	
	y. Se-tenant block of 4	4.00	

Please read the introduction to this catalog carefully. It contains much valuable information for all stamp collectors, and also makes the catalog easier for you to use.

1998. INTERNATIONAL YEAR OF THE OCEAN ISSUE A set to call attention to the importance of the oceans and their resources for life on Earth. The U.N. has declared 1998 as the International Year of the Ocean. Designed by Jon Ellis, U.S. *This sheetlet of 12 multicolored, 45 centime stamps, depicts a polar region.*

331a *Walrus;* 331b *Polar bear;* 331c *Seal & penguins;* 331d *Diver under ice;* 331e *Sea lion;* 331f *Narwhal;* 331g *Shark;* 331h *Puffin & seal;* 331i *Fish & rocks;* 331j *Fish & jelly fish;* 331k *Swimming seal & penguin;* 331l *Feeding penguin & rocks*

331		MNHVF	UseVF
45¢	**multicolored,** pane of 20 *(270,000 printed)*	5.00	3.00
	a. Walrus	.75	.50
	b. Polar bear	.75	.50
	c. Seal & penguins	.75	.50
	d. Diver under ice	.75	.50
	e. Sea lion	.75	.50
	f. Narwhal	.75	.50
	g. Shark	.75	.50
	h. Puffin & seal	.75	.50
	i. Fish & rocks	.75	.50
	j. Fish & jelly fish	.75	.50
	k. Swimming seal & penguin	.75	.50
	l. Feeding penguin & rocks	.75	.50
	FDC *(May 20, 1998)* (pane)		18.00
	y. Pane of 12	18.00	

1998. RAIN FOREST ISSUE A mother urangutan and baby commemorate the 50th anniversary of the World Health Organization. *Offset by the Japanese Printing Office. Perforated 14.*

332 *A mother urangutan and baby*

332		MNHVF	UseVF
70¢	**multicolored** *(430,000 printed)*	1.00	.50
	FDC *(June 19, 1998)*		2.25

1998. RAIN FORESTS SOUVENIR SHEET Using the same stamp design as No. 332 against a rain forest background, the urangutan grasps a vine branch. *Offset by the Japanese Printing Office. Perforated 14.*

333 *A mother urangutan and baby within rain forest*

333		MNHVF	UseVF
3f	**multicolored** *(250,000 printed)*	3.00	2.50
	a. Single (70¢)	3.00	2.50
	FDC *(June 19, 1998)*		9.00

1998. 50 YEARS OF U.N. PEACE-KEEPING ISSUE Commemorated the initiation in 1948 of a U.N. peace-keeping military force under U.N. control but under ultimate authority of the members' respective governments. Designed by Andrew Davidson, U.K. *Gravure by Helio Courvoisier, Switzerland. Perforated 12.*

334 *A soldier comforting children;* 335 *Two soldiers hold children*

334		MNHVF	UseVF
70¢	**multicolored** *(400,000 printed)*	.75	.60
	FDC *(Sept. 15, 1998)*		1.50
	Inscription block of 4	3.00	

335		MNHVF	UseVF
90¢	**multicolored** *(390,000 printed)*	1.00	1.00
	FDC *(Sept. 15, 1998)*		1.50
	Inscription block of 4	3.50	

1998. DECLARATION OF HUAMN RIGHTS ISSUE Abstract birds swirl in the sky on a 90 centime stamp. Abstract, rainbow-colored birds fly from a hand on a 1.80 franc stamp.

336 *Abstract birds swirling in sky;*

337 *Abstract rainbow-colored birds flying from hand*

336		MNHVF	UseVF
90¢	**multicolored** *(535,000 printed)*	.75	.60
	FDC *(Oct. 27, 1998)*		1.50
	Inscription block of 4	2.50	

337		MNHVF	UseVF
1.80f	**multicolored** *(545,000 printed)*	1.00	1.00
	FDC *(Oct. 27, 1998)*		1.50
	Inscription block of 4	5.50	

1998. SCHÖNBRUNN PALACE ISSUE Set celebrated a U.N. World Heritage site in Vienna, Austria. The Great Palm House at the World Heritage Site is featured on a 70 centime stamp. A blue and white porcelain vase from the palace's Mirror Room is on a 1.10 franc stamp.

338 *The Great Palm House;* 339 *A blue and white porcelain vase*

338		MNHVF	UseVF
70¢	**multicolored** *(375,000 printed)*	.50	1.25
	FDC *(Dec. 4, 1998)*		1.50
	Inscription block of 4	1.75	

339		MNHVF	UseVF
1.10f	**multicolored** *(375,000 printed)*	.75	.25
	FDC *(Dec. 4, 1998)*		2.00
	Inscription block of 4	3.00	

1998. SCHÖNBRUNN PALACE BOOKLET ISSUE The six designs in the U.N. World Heritage Site issue are re-valued in a Prestige Booklet of 21 stamps.

340 *Palace & grounds;* 341 *Blue & white vase;* 342 *Detail from wall painting;* 343 *Porcelain stove;* 344 *Great Palm House;* 345 *The Gloriette*

340		MNHVF	UseVF
10¢	**multicolored** *(100,000 printed)*	.50	.25
	n. Pane of 4	1.00	

341		MNHVF	UseVF
30¢	**multicolored** *(100,000 printed)*	.50	.25
	n. Pane of 3	1.00	

342		MNHVF	UseVF
30¢	**multicolored** *(100,000 printed)*	.50	.25
	n. Pane of 3	1.00	

343		MNHVF	UseVF
30¢	**multicolored** *(100,000 printed)*	.50	.25
	n. Pane of 3	1.00	

344		MNHVF	UseVF
10¢	**multicolored** *(100,000 printed)*	.50	.25
	n. Pane of 4	1.00	

345		MNHVF	UseVF
10¢	**multicolored** *(100,000 printed)*	.50	.25
	n. Pane of 4	1.00	
	n1. Full booklet of 6 panes	3.50	
	FDC *(Dec. 4, 1998)* (any pane)		1.50

1999. REGULAR ISSUE Design and gravure by Helio Courvoisier, Switzerland. *Perforated 11 3/4.*

346 *Palais Wilson in Geneva, named for U.S. President Woodrow Wilson, who fostered the League of Nations. It is the headquarters of the office of the U.N. High Commissioner for Human Rights.*

346		MNHVF	UseVF
1.70f	**multicolored** *(600,000 printed)*	2.00	1.00
	FDC *(Feb. 5, 1999)*		2.00
	Inscription block of 4	8.00	

1999. WORLD HERITAGE - AUSTRALIA ISSUE The fifth in the U.N. World Heritage Sites Series. Designed by Passmore Design of Melbourne, Australia. *Offset by The House of Questa, U.K. Perforated 13.*

347 *Kakadu National Park teems with thousands of species of animal and bird life;* 348 *The Great Barrier Reef consists of corals that support a million species*

347		MNHVF	UseVF
90¢	**multicolored** *(420,000 printed)*	.75	.60
	FDC *(March 19, 1999)*		1.50
	Inscription block of 4	2.50	

348		MNHVF	UseVF
1.10f	**multicolored** *(420,000 printed)*	1.00	.60
	FDC *(March 19, 1999)*		2.00
	Inscription block of 4	3.00	

1999. WORLD HERITAGE AUSTRALIA BOOKLET The six designs in the U.N. Heritage Site issue are re-valued in a 172x92mm Prestige booklet of 24 stamps, a block of 4 stamps in each design. *Perforated 13.*

349 *Tasmania;* 350 *Uluru-Kata Tjuta;* 351 *Wet Tropics;* 352 *Kakadu;* 353 *Great Barrier Reef;* 354 *Willandra Lakes*

349		MNHVF	UseVF
10¢	**multicolored** *(90,000 printed)*	.50	.25
	FDC *(March 19, 1999)*		1.50

350		MNHVF	UseVF
20¢	**multicolored** *(90,000 printed)*	.50	.25
	FDC *(March 19, 1999)*		1.50

351		MNHVF	UseVF
10¢	**multicolored** *(90,000 printed)*	.50	.25
	FDC *(March 19, 1999)*		1.50

352		MNHVF	UseVF
20¢	**multicolored** *(90,000 printed)*	.50	.25
	FDC *(March 19, 1999)*		1.50

353		MNHVF	UseVF
10¢	**multicolored** *(90,000 printed)*	.50	.25
	FDC *(March 19, 1999)*		1.50

354		MNHVF	UseVF
20¢	**multicolored** *(90,000 printed)*	.50	.25
	FDC *(March 19, 1999)*		1.50
	Booklet of 24 stamps	12.00	

1999. ENDANGERED SPECIES ISSUE Seventh in a series to highlight the need for protection of endangered species throughout the world. Designed by Tim Barrall, New York. *Printed by Joh. Enschedé and Sons, Netherlands. Perforated 12 1/2x13 3/4.*

355 *Asiatic Wild Ass;* 356 *Hyacinth Macaw;* 357 *Jamaican Boa;* 358 *Bennetts' Tree-Kangaroo*

355		MNHVF	UseVF
90¢	**multicolored** *(488,000 printed)*	1.00	.60
	FDC *(April 22, 1999)*		1.50

356		MNHVF	UseVF
90¢	**multicolored** *(488,000 printed)*	1.00	.60
	FDC *(April 22, 1999)*		1.50

357		MNHVF	UseVF
90¢	**multicolored** *(488,000 printed)*	1.00	.60
	FDC *(April 22, 1999)*		1.50

358		MNHVF	UseVF
90¢	**multicolored** *(488,000 printed)*	1.00	.60
	FDC *(April 22, 1999)*		1.50
	Inscription block of 4	4.00	

1999. UNISPACE III ISSUE A large antenna dish and monitoring satellite help to make farming more precise and measure environmental factors. Designed by Attila Hejja, U.S. *Gravure by Helio Courvoisier, Switzerland. Rouletted.*

359 *Antenna, mountains;* 360 *City*

359		MNHVF	UseVF
45¢	**multicolored** *(925,000 printed)*	.75	.30
	FDC *(July 7, 1999)*		—

360		MNHVF	UseVF
45¢	**multicolored** *(925,000 printed)*	.75	.30
	FDC *(July 7, 1999)*		1.50
	Inscription block of 4	4.00	

1999. UNISPACE III SOUVENIR SHEET The full design of the se-tenant Nos. 359-360 are combined and given a higher denomination. *The souvenir sheet was also overprinted for Philexfrance. Perforated 11 3/4.*

361 *Antenna & city*

361		MNHVF	UseVF
2f	**multicolored** *(275,000 printed)*	1.25	.75
	FDC *(July 7, 1999)*		2.50
	y. Perforated in SS	3.00	
	vy. Overprinted for Philexfrance	3.00	

1999. UNIVERSAL POSTAL UNION 1874-1999 ISSUE Postal patrons in distinctive dress and means of carrying mail around the globe signify the impact of the Universal Postal Union over the last 125 years. Designed by Mark Hess, U.S. *Gravure by Helio Courvoisier, Switzerland. Perforated 11 1/2x11 3/4.*

362 *Denomination upper left;* 363 *Denomination upper right;* 364 *Denomination lower left;* 365 *Denomination lower right*

362		MNHVF	UseVF
70¢	multicolored	1.00	.50
	FDC (Aug. 23, 1999)		1.50

363		MNHVF	UseVF
70¢	multicolored	1.00	.50
	FDC (Aug. 23, 1999)		1.50

364		MNHVF	UseVF
70¢	multicolored	1.00	.50
	FDC (Aug. 23, 1999)		1.50

365		MNHVF	UseVF
70¢	multicolored	1.00	.50
	FDC (Aug. 23, 1999)		1.50
	Inscription block of 4	4.00	
	FDC (Aug. 23, 1999) (block)		4.00

1999. IN MEMORIAM ISSUE U.N. flags at half-staff honored those who have died in U.N. service for the cause of peace. Designed by Robert Stein, U.S. *Offset by Walsall Security Printers, Ltd., U.K. Sheet stamp perforated 14 1/2, souvenir sheet perforated 14.*

366 *Flags fly at half staff outside the Palace of Nations, Geneva;*

367 *Flags fly at half staff*

366		MNHVF	UseVF
1.10f	multicolored	.75	.50
	FDC (Sept. 21, 1999)		2.00
	Inscription block of 4	3.00	

367		MNHVF	UseVF
2f	multicolored	1.25	1.00
	FDC (Sept. 21, 1999)		2.00
	Inscription block of 4	3.00	

1999. EDUCATION - KEYSTONE TO THE 21ST CENTURY ISSUE Designed by Romero Britto, Brazil. *Offset by Osterreichische Staatsdruckerei. Perforated 13 3/4x13 1/2.*

368 *Two figures stand on a winged globe;* 369 *A fish and a bird flank the globe*

368		MNHVF	UseVF
90¢	multicolored	.75	.50
	FDC (Nov. 18, 1999)		1.50
	Inscription block of 4	3.00	

369		MNHVF	UseVF
1.80f	multicolored	1.00	1.00
	FDC (Nov. 18, 1999)		1.50
	Inscription block of 4	4.00	

Commemorative Issues

2000. INTERNATIONAL YEAR OF THANKSGIVING ISSUE The United Nations proclaimed the year 2000 the International Year of Thanksgiving. Glory Window in the Chapel of Thanksgiving at Thanks-Giving Square in Dallas, Texas, designed by Gabrielle Loire of Chartres, France, for the Thanks-Giving Foundation. Stamps designed by Rorie Katz, U.S. *Offset by Cartor Security Printing, France, perforated 13.*

370 Glory Window in the Chapel of Thanksgiving, *Dallas, Texas*

370		MNHVF	UseVF
90¢	multicolored (450,000 printed)	.50	.20
	FDC (Jan. 1, 2000)		1.50
	Inscription block of 4	2.00	

2000. ENDANGERED SPECIES ISSUE The eighth set in the Endangered Species series. Designed by Robert Hynes, U.S. *Printed by Joh. Enschéde and Sons, Netherlands, perforated 12 1/2 x 13 3/4, (1,952,000 stamps, 122,000 panes printed).*

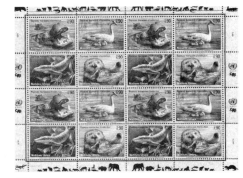

371 *Hippopotamus;* 372 *Coscoroba Swan of South America;* 373 *Emerald Monitor/Goanna of Papua New Guinea, Indonesia and Northern Australia;* 374 *Sea Otter*

371		MNHVF	UseVF
90¢	multicolored	.50	.20

372		MNHVF	UseVF
90¢	multicolored	.50	.20

373		MNHVF	UseVF
90¢	multicolored	.50	.20

374		MNHVF	UseVF
90¢	multicolored	.50	.20
	FDC (April 6, 2000)		1.50
	Inscription block of 4	2.00	
	y. Se-tenant block of 4	2.00	

2000. OUR WORLD ISSUE A celebration of the new millennium, the stamps depict paintings submitted to a worldwide competition on the theme, "My Country in the Year 2000." Paintings adapted as stamps by Robert Stein, U.S. *Offset by Cartor Security Printing, France, perforated 13.*

375 The Embrace, *by Rita Adaimy, Lebanon*

375		MNHVF	UseVF
90¢	**multicolored**	.50	.20
	FDC *(May 30, 2000)*		1.50
	Inscription block of 4	2.00	

376 Living Single, *by Richard Kimanthi, Kenya*

376		MNHVF	UseVF
1.10f	**multicolored**	1.00	.50
	FDC *(May 30, 2000)*		2.50
	Inscription block of 4	4.00	

2000. 55TH ANNIVERSARY OF THE UNITED NATIONS ISSUE Photographs documented the construction of the United Nations Headquarters complex in New York City, whose first occupation took place in 1950. Designed by Rorie Katz, U.S., based on U.N. photographs. *Offset by Cartor Security Printing, France, perforated 13.*

377 *The first U.N. secretary-general, Trgve Lie, and U.S. President Harry S Truman take part in a cornerstone-laying ceremony for the U.N. Headquarters, Oct. 24, 1949, United Nations Day*

377		MNHVF	UseVF
90¢	**multicolored** *(370,000 printed)*	.50	.20
	FDC *(July 7, 2000)*		1.50
	Inscription block of 4	2.00	

378 *A window cleaner works on the Secretariat Building while construction continues on the General Assembly Hall in a 1951 photo*

378y *Mini-sheet of two stamps against a photo of workers cheering as a U.N. flag is unfurled atop the framework of the Secretariat Building*

378		MNHVF	UseVF
1.40f	**multicolored** *(370,000 printed)*	1.00	.50
	FDC *(July 7, 2000)*		2.50
	Inscription block of 4	4.00	
	y. Sheetlet of 2 (235,000 printed)	1.50	.70
	y1. Se-tenant pair #377-378	1.50	.70

2000. THE U.N. IN THE 21ST CENTURY ISSUE Intended to show the work of the United Nations in promoting respect for human rights, protection of the environment, economic development and reduction of poverty and disease. Designed by Wilson McLean, United Kingdom. *Offset by Government Printing Office, Austria, perforated 14, (266,000 panes printed).*

379y *The United Nations in the 21st century, woman with yellow head wrap at left*

379		MNHVF	UseVF
50¢	**multicolored**	.75	.20
	a. Couple looking right	.75	.20
	b. Carrying bricks	.75	.20
	c. Soldier with binoculars	.75	.20
	d. Dam	.75	.20
	e. Man digging	.75	.20
	f. Man lifting	.75	.20
	FDC *(Sept. 15, 2000)*		1.50
	y. Sheetlet of 6	3.00	1.50

2000. WORLD HERITAGE - SPAIN ISSUE The sixth U.N. stamp issue to illustrate World Heritage sites and the fourth in a series of stamps and booklets to focus on sites in one geographical area. World Heritage sites have been designated to indicate places whose importance reach beyond geographical and political boundaries. Designed by Robert Stein, U.S. *Offset by The House of Questa, United Kingdom, perforated 14.*

380 *Cuenca, a fortified medieval city, was built by the Moors and is renowned for its hanging houses;* 381 *Toledo is the keeper of more than two millennia of history*

380		MNHVF	UseVF
1.00f	multicolored	.75	.50
	FDC *(Oct. 6, 2000)*		1.50
	Inscription block of 4	2.00	

381		MNHVF	UseVF
1.20f	multicolored	1.10	.50
	FDC *(Oct. 6, 2000)*		2.50
	Inscription block of 4	4.40	

2000. WORLD HERITAGE - SPAIN PRESTIGE BOOKLET ISSUE Designs of the six stamps from the three U.N. offices are re-valued in low denominations in a descriptive booklet format. Designed by Robert Stein, U.S. *Offset by The House of Questa, United Kingdom, perforated 14.*

382-387 World Heritage - Spain Prestige Booklet

382		MNHVF	UseVF
10¢	multicolored, Grenada	.50	.20

383		MNHVF	UseVF
10¢	multicolored, Cuenca	.50	.20

384		MNHVF	UseVF
10¢	multicolored, Segovia	.50	.20

385		MNHVF	UseVF
10¢	multicolored, Merida	.50	.20

386		MNHVF	UseVF
10¢	multicolored, Toledo	.50	.20

387		MNHVF	UseVF
10¢	multicolored, Barcelona	.50	.20
	FDC *(Oct. 6, 2000)*		1.50
	n. Booklet of 6	—	—

2000. RESPECT FOR REFUGEES ISSUE Called attention to the U.N. High Commissioner for Refugees, which noted its 50th anniversary in 2000. Designed by Yuri Gevorgian, U.S. *Offset by Joh. Enschéde and Sons, Netherlands, perforated 12 3/4 x 13 1/4.*

388 A father holds a cane in a group of refugees

388		MNHVF	UseVF
80¢	multicolored	.50	.20
	FDC *(Nov. 9, 2000)*		1.50
	Inscription block of 4	1.50	

389 the mini-sheet stamp image is taken from the central portion of a larger group of refugees

389		MNHVF	UseVF
1.80f	multicolored	2.00	1.00
	FDC *(Nov. 9, 2000)*		2.00
	y. Sheetlet of 1	2.00	

Air Letter Sheets

1969. AIR LETTER SHEET ISSUE Designed by Robert Perrot, France. Similar to U.N. New York Minkus No. E10. *Offset by S. Setelipaino, Finland.*

ALS1 U.N. emblem and stylized airplane

ALS1		MVF	UseVF
65¢	ultra & light blue *(350,000 printed)*	2.00	1.25
	FDC *(Oct. 4, 1969)*		1.05

Postal Cards

1969. POSTAL CARD ISSUE Designed by John Mason, Australia (20¢), similar to New York Minkus No. PC10; and Olav Mathiesen, Denmark (30¢), similar to U.N. New York Minkus Nos. PC8 and PC9. *Offset by Helio Courvoisier, Switzerland.*

PC1 Posthorn

PC1		MVF	UseVF
20¢	olive green & black, buff *(415,000 printed)*	.50	.20
	FDC *(Oct. 4, 1969)*		1.25

PC2 Abstract space design

PC2		MVF	UseVF
30¢	multicolored *(275,000 printed)*	.50	.15
	FDC *(Oct. 4, 1969)*		1.00

No. PC2 is not inscribed "Poste Aerienne" or "Air Mail."

1977. POSTAL CARD ISSUE Designed by Veronique Crombez, Belgium (40¢) and Lieve Baeten, Belgium (70¢); *offset by S. Setelipaino, Finland.*

A second printing of No. PC3 was made in 1984. It was released after the Swiss postal card rate had been increased to 50¢ so instructions were issued that all cards must have a 10¢ stamp affixed before being sold. A few were sold in New York without the added stamp. The card stock differs from the original printing.

PC3 *U.N. emblem*

PC3			MVF	UseVF
40¢	**multicolored** *(500,000 printed)*		.50	.15
	FDC *(June 27, 1977)*			1.00

PC4 *Interlocking ribbons*

PC4			MVF	UseVF
70¢	**multicolored** *(300,000 printed)*		.65	.20
	FDC *(June 27, 1977)*			1.00

1985. POSTAL CARD ISSUE Designed by George Hamori, Australia (50¢) and Ryszard Dudzicki, Poland (70¢). *Offset by Joh. Enschedé and Sons, Netherlands.*

PC5 *U.N. emblem;* PC6 *Abstract dove and rainbow*

PC5			MVF	UseVF
50¢	**multicolored** *(300,000 printed)*		3.00	.25
	FDC *(May 10, 1985)*			4.50
PC6			MVF	UseVF
70¢	**multicolored** *(300,000 printed)*		4.50	.55
	FDC *(May 10, 1985)*			4.50

1986. POSTAL CARD SURCHARGE ISSUE Revalued 70¢ (PC6). Designed by Ryszard Dudzicki, Poland. *Offset by Joh. Enschedé and Sons, Netherlands.*

PC7 *Abstract Dove of Peace and carmine surcharge*

PC7		MVF	UseVF
70¢ plus 10¢ multicolored *(90,500 printed)*		3.50	1.25
	FDC *(Jan. 2, 1986)*		13.00

1992. POSTAL CARD ISSUE Designed by Guy Breniaux, France, lettering by Elizabeth A. White, U.S. Adaptation of Geneva 5f Definitive of 1990 No. 183. *Offset by Mercury-Walch Pty. Ltd., Australia.*

PC8 *Palais des Nations*

PC8			MVF	UseVF
90¢	**multicolored** *(150,000 printed)*		1.75	.60
	FDC *(Sept. 4, 1992)*			4.00

1993. POSTAL CARD ISSUE PC9 revalued 50¢ (PC5). Designed by George Hamori, Australia. *Offset by Joh. Enschedé and Sons, Netherlands.*

PC10 photograph of Palais des Nations, Geneva. *Printed by Leigh Mardon Pty. Limited, Australia.*

PC9 *U.N. emblem and carmine surcharge*

PC9		MVF	UseVF
50¢ plus 10¢ multicolored *(47,000 printed)*		1.50	.40
	FDC *(May 7, 1993)*		19.00

PC10 *Palais des Nations and reflections*

PC10			MVF	UseVF
80¢	**multicolored** *(200,000 printed)*		3.00	.50
	FDC *(May 7, 1993)*			6.50

1996. POSTAL CARD ISSUE PC11 revalued 50¢ (PC5). Designed by George Hamori, Australia. *Offset by Joh. Enschedé and Sons, Netherlands.*

PC12 revalued 80¢ (PC10). Photograph of Palais des Nations, Geneva. *Printed by Leigh Mardon Pty. Limited, Australia.*

PC11 *U.N. emblem with carmine surcharge*

PC11		MVF	UseVF
50¢ plus 20¢ multicolored *(10,500 printed)*		1.10	.55
	FDC *(March 22, 1996)*		1.50

PC12 *Palais des Nations with carmine surcharge*

PC12		**MVF**	**UseVF**
80¢ plus 30¢ multicolored *(10,500 printed)*		1.75	.85
FDC *(March 22, 1996)*			1.50

1998. POSTAL CARD ISSUE 70¢ designed by Robert Stein, U.S., based on a photograph by Fabrice Piraud, France. 1.10f also designed by Robert Stein, U.S., based on a photograph credited to U.N. *Printed by Mercury-Walch Pty. Ltd., Australia.*

PC13 *Assembly Hall at U.N. headquarters, Geneva, photo by Fabrice Piraud, France*

PC13		**MVF**	**UseVF**
70¢	**multicolored** *(80,000 printed)*	1.10	.55
	FDC *(March 20, 1998)*		1.50

PC14 *Palais des Nations and lawn*

PC14		**MVF**	**UseVF**
1.10f	**multicolored** *(80,000 printed)*	1.75	.85
	FDC *(March 20, 1998)*		1.50

Regular Issues

1979. REGULAR ISSUES *Gravure by Helio Courvoisier, Switzerland. Perforated 11 3/4x11 1/2.*

1 *Tree of doves, adaptation of Geneva Definitive of 1978. Designed by Masatoshi Hioki, Japan.*

1		**MNHVF**	**UseVF**
50g	**multicolored** *(3,500,000 printed)*	.20	.20
	FDC *(Aug. 24, 1979)*		1.00
	Inscription block of 4	.50	

2 *U.N. flag, adaptation of 3¢ New York Definitive of 1962 and Geneva Definitive of 1969. Designed by Ole Hamann, Denmark.*

2		**MNHVF**	**UseVF**
1s	**multicolored** *(3,500,000 printed)*	.20	.20
	FDC *(Aug. 24, 1979)*		1.00
	Inscription block of 4	.50	

3 *Donaupark, Vienna, designed by Henryk Chylinski, Poland.*

3		**MNHVF**	**UseVF**
4s	**multicolored** *(3,500,000 printed)*	.25	.25
	FDC *(Aug. 24, 1979)*		1.00
	Inscription block of 4	1.00	

4 *Birds in flight, adaptation of 11¢ New York Airmail of 1972. Designed by Arne Johnson, Norway.*

4		**MNHVF**	**UseVF**
5s	**multicolored** *(3,500,000 printed)*	.40	.35
	FDC *(Aug. 24, 1979)*		1.00
	Inscription block of 4	1.50	

5 *Donaupark, Vienna, designed by Jozsef Vertel, Hungary.*

5		**MNHVF**	**UseVF**
6s	**multicolored** *(4,500,000 printed)*	.40	.35
	FDC *(Aug. 24, 1979)*		1.25
	Inscription block of 4	1.60	

6 *Collecton of flags, adaptation of 30¢ New York Definitive of 1961 and Geneva 90¢ Definitive of 1970. Designed by Herbert Sanborn, U.S.*

6		**MNHVF**	**UseVF**
10s	**multicolored** *(3,500,000 printed)*	.50	.45
	FDC *(Aug. 24, 1979)*		2.00
	Inscription block of 4	3.00	

1980. REGULAR ISSUE Adaptation of 3¢ New York Definitive of 1976. Designed by Waldemar Andrejewski, Poland. *Offset by Bundesdruckerei, Germany. Perforated 14.*

7 *Flags forming dove*

7		**MNHVF**	**UseVF**
2.50s	**multicolored** *(3,500,000 printed)*	.75	.50
	FDC *(Jan. 11, 1980)*		1.00
	Inscription block of 4	2.75	

Commemorative Issues

1980. NEW ECONOMIC ORDER ISSUE The General Assembly held a special session in 1980 to discuss the gap between developed and developing countries. Designed by Cemalettin Mutver, Turkey. Similar to U.N. New York Minkus No. 339. *Offset by The House of Questa, U.K. Perforated 14 1/2.*

8 *Graph of rising economic trends*

8		**MNHVF**	**UseVF**
4s	**multicolored** *(1,418,418)*	1.00	.80
	FDC *(Jan. 11, 1980)*		1.00
	Inscription block of 4		
	top portion	30.00	
	bottom portion	14.00	

1980. U.N. DECADE FOR WOMEN'S ISSUE Designed by Gunnar Janssen, Germany. *Offset by The House of Questa, U.K. Perforated 14 1/2, multicolored frame given below.*

9, 10 *Women's year emblem*

9		MNHVF	UseVF
4s	deep green *(1,569,080)*	.75	.50
	FDC *(March 7, 1980)*		1.00
	Inscription block of 4	3.00	

10		MNHVF	UseVF
6s	deep bistre *(1,556,016)*	1.50	1.25
	FDC *(March 7, 1980)*		1.00
	Inscription block of 4	6.00	

1980. PEACE-KEEPING OPERATIONS ISSUE Designed by James Gardiner, U.K. Similar to U.N. New York Minkus No. 344. *Offset by Joh. Enschedé and Sons, Netherlands. Perforated 14.*

11 *Symbolic arrows*

11		MNHVF	UseVF
6s	multicolored *(1,719,852)*	1.00	.80
	FDC *(May 16, 1980)*		1.00
	Inscription block of 4	4.00	

1980. U.N. 35TH ANNIVERSARY ISSUE Designed by Gidon Sagi, Israel (4s); and Mian Saeed, Pakistan (6s). Similar to Geneva No. 93 (4s); and similar to U.N. New York Minkus No. 346 (6s). *Offset by Ashton-Potter. Perforated 13x13 1/2.*

12 *Dove and "35"*

12		MNHVF	UseVF
4s	gray & carmine *(1,626,582)*	.75	.60
	FDC *(June 26, 1980)*		1.00
	Inscription block of 4	2.50	

13 *Globe and laurel leaves*

13		MNHVF	UseVF
6s	multicolored *(1,625,400)*	1.00	.80
	FDC *(June 26, 1980)*		1.00
	Inscription block of 4	4.50	

1980. U.N. 35TH ANNIVERSARY SOUVENIR SHEET Designed by Ole Hamann, Denmark. *Offset by Ashton-Potter Ltd., Canada. Sheet of 2 (92x73mm), imperforate.*

14 *Souvenir sheet with Nos. 12 and 13*

14		MNHVF	UseVF
10s	Sheet of 2 *(1,675,191)*	1.00	1.00
	a. Single (4s)		
	b. Single (6s)		
	FDC *(June 26, 1980)*		1.00

1980. ECONOMIC AND SOCIAL COUNCIL ISSUE 4s designed by Dietmar Kowall, Germany, similar to U.N. New York Minkus No. 365. 6s new design by Angel Medina, Uruguay, similar to Geneva No. 97. *Offset by Ashton-Potter Ltd., Canada. Perforated 13 1/2.*

15 *Progress through cooperation*

15		MNHVF	UseVF
4s	multicolored *(1,811,218)*	.75	.70
	FDC *(Nov. 21, 1980)*		1.00
	Inscription block of 4	3.00	

16 *People and graph*

16		MNHVF	UseVF
6s	multicolored *(1,878,805)*	1.00	.80
	FDC *(Nov. 21, 1980)*		1.00
	Inscription block of 4	5.00	

1981. RIGHTS OF PALESTINIAN PEOPLE ISSUE Designed by David Dewhurst, U.S. Similar to U.N. New York Minkus No. 366. *Gravure by Helio Courvoisier, Switzerland. Perforated 11 1/2, granite paper.*

17 *Inalienable Rights of the Palestinian People*

17		MNHVF	UseVF
4s	multicolored *(1,673,310)*	.75	.65
	FDC *(Jan. 30, 1981)*		1.00
	Inscription block of 4	3.50	

1981. YEAR OF DISABLED PERSONS ISSUE The General Assembly announced 1981 as "International Year of Disabled Persons." Designed by Sophia van Heeswijk, Germany. No. 18 similar to U.N. New York Minkus No. 367. No. 19 similar to Geneva No. 100. *Gravure by Heraclio Fournier, Spain. Perforated 14.*

18 *Jigsaw puzzle pieces;*

19 *Woven thread and U.N. emblem*

18		MNHVF	UseVF
4s	multicolored *(1,508,719)*	.75	.60
	FDC *(March 6, 1981)*		1.00
	Inscription block of 4	3.00	

19		MNHVF	UseVF
6s	black & orange *(1,569,385)*	1.00	.70
	FDC *(March 6, 1981)*		1.00
	Inscription block of 4	4.00	

1981. U.N. ART BULGARIAN MURAL ISSUE The Government of Bulgaria presented the U.N. with a replica of a 13th century Bulgarian fresco inside Boyana Church near Sofia. Adapted as a stamp by Ole Hamann, Denmark, from an original design by an unknown artist from Bulgaria. Similar to U.N. New York Minkus No. 369 and 370. *Gravure by Helio Courvoisier, Switzerland. Perforated 11 1/2, granite paper.*

20 *Divislava and Sebastocrator Kaloyan, Bulgarian Mural, 1259, Boyana Church, Sofia*

20		MNHVF	UseVF
6s	multicolored *(1,643,527)*	1.25	1.00
	FDC *(April 15, 1981)*		1.00
	Inscription block of 4	6.00	

1981. RENEWABLE ENERGY ISSUE Conference on New and Renewable Sources of Energy held in Nairobi, Kenya in August 1981. Designed by Robert Perrot, France. Similar to U.N. New York Minkus No. 372. *Offset by S. Setelipaino, Finland. Perforated 13.*

21 *Stylized letter "E"*

21		MNHVF	UseVF
7.50s	multicolored *(1,611,130 printed)*	1.30	1.25
	FDC *(May 29, 1981)*		1.00
	Inscription block of 4	5.50	

1981. U.N. 10TH ANNIVERSARY VOLUNTEERS PROGRAM ISSUE No. 22 designed by Angel Medina, Uruguay, similar to U.N. New York Minkus No. 390. No. 23 designed by Bernd Mirbach, Germany, similar to Geneva No. 104. *Offset by Walsall Security Printers, Ltd., U.K. Perforated 13.*

22 *"10" and development symbols;* 23 *Symbols of development*

22		MNHVF	UseVF
5s	multicolored *(1,582,780 printed)*	.75	.70
	FDC *(Nov. 13, 1981)*		1.00
	Inscription block of 4	4.00	

23		MNHVF	UseVF
7s	multicolored *(1,516,139)*	1.75	1.50
	FDC *(Nov. 13, 1981)*		1.00
	Inscription block of 4	6.50	

1982. BETTER WORLD ISSUE Designed by Eliezer Weishoff, Israel. *Gravure by Helio Courvoisier, Switzerland. Perforated 11 1/2x12.*

24 *"...für eine bessere Welt" (For a Better World)*

24		MNHVF	UseVF
3s	multicolored *(3,300,000 printed)*	.40	.20
	FDC *(Jan. 22, 1982)*		1.00
	Inscription block of 4	2.00	

1982. HUMAN ENVIRONMENT ISSUE Celebrated the 10th anniversary of the U.N. Environment Program to help coordinate sound environmental practices. No. 25 designed by Peer-Ulrich Bremer, Germany, similar to U.N. New York Minkus No. 395. No. 26 designed by Sybille Brunner, Germany, similar to Geneva No. 107. *Offset by Joh. Enschedé and Sons, Netherlands. Perforated 13 1/2x13.*

25 *Environment symbols;*

26 *Leaf design*

25		MNHVF	UseVF
5s	multicolored *(1,312,765)*	1.00	.90
	FDC *(March 19, 1982)*		1.00
	Inscription block of 4	4.25	

26		MNHVF	UseVF
7s	multicolored *(1,357,513)*	1.25	1.00
	FDC *(March 19, 1982)*		1.00
	Inscription block of 4	6.00	

1982. PEACEFUL USES OF OUTER SPACE ISSUE Exploration and peaceful uses of outer space. Designed by George Hamori, Australia. Similar to Geneva No. 110. *Offset by Joh. Enschedé and Sons, Netherlands. Perforated 13x13 1/2.*

27 *Satellite and symbols of space technology*

27		MNHVF	UseVF
5s	**multicolored** *(2,100,000 printed)*	1.25	1.00
	FDC *(June 11, 1982)*		1.75
	inscription block of 4	5.00	

1982. CONSERVATION AND PROTECTION OF NATURE ISSUE Designed by George Hamori, Australia. *Gravure by Heraclio Fournier, Spain. Perforated 14.*

28 *Fish*

29 *Rhinoceros*

28		MNHVF	UseVF
5s	**multicolored** *(1,202,694)*	1.00	.75
	FDC *(Nov. 19, 1982)*		1.00
	Inscription block of 4	3.50	
29		MNHVF	UseVF
7s	**multicolored** *(1,194,403)*	1.50	1.25
	FDC *(Nov. 19, 1982)*		1.00
	Inscription block of 4	5.50	

1983. WORLD COMMUNICATIONS YEAR ISSUE Designed by Hanns Lohrer, Germany. Similar to U.N. New York Minkus No. 415. *Offset by Walsall Security Printers Ltd., U.K. Perforated 13.*

30 *U.N. seal, graphic design*

30		MNHVF	UseVF
4s	**multicolored** *(1,517,443)*	.85	.75
	FDC *(Jan. 28, 1983)*		1.40
	Inscription block of 4	3.50	

1983. SAFETY AT SEA ISSUE No. 31 designed by Valentin Wurnitsch, Austria, similar to Geneva No. 115. No. 32 designed by Ari Ron, Israel, similar to U.N. New York Minkus No. 418. *Offset by The House of Questa, U.K. Perforated 14 1/2.*

31 *Life preserver and radar screen;*

32 *Stylized ship scene*

31		MNHVF	UseVF
4s	**multicolored** *(1,506,052)*	.90	.75
	FDC *(March 18, 1983)*		1.00
	inscription block of 4	3.00	
32		MNHVF	UseVF
6s	**multicolored** *(1,527,990)*	1.25	1.00
	FDC *(March 18, 1983)*		1.00
	inscription block of 4	5.00	

1983. WORLD FOOD PROGRAM ISSUE Designed by Marek Kwiatkowski, Poland. Engraved by Sakae Yajima, Japan. Similar to U.N. New York Minkus No. 419 and Geneva No. 116. *Intaglio by Japanese Government Printing Office. Perforated 13 1/2.*

33, 34 *Hands presenting food bowl*

33		MNHVF	UseVF
5s	**green** *(1,419,237)*	.90	.75
	FDC *(April 22, 1983)*		1.00
	Inscription block of 4	3.00	
34		MNHVF	UseVF
7s	**brown** *(1,454,227)*	1.25	1.00
	FDC *(April 22, 1983)*		1.00
	Inscription block of 4	5.00	

1983. U.N. CONFERENCE ON TRADE AND DEVELOPMENT ISSUE No. 35 designed by Wladyslaw Brykczynski, Poland, similar to Geneva No. 118. No. 36 designed by Gabriele Genz, Germany, similar to U.N. New York Minkus No. 421. *Offset by Carl Uberreuter Druck and Verlag M. Salzer, Austria. Perforated 14.*

35 *Flags on cargo box;*

36 *Symbols of commerce*

35		MNHVF	UseVF
4s	**multicolored** *(1,544,973)*	.85	.75
	FDC *(June 6, 1983)*		1.00
	Inscription block of 4	3.00	
36		MNHVF	UseVF
8.50s	**multicolored** *(1,423,172)*	1.25	1.00
	FDC *(June 6, 1983)*		1.00
	Inscription block of 4	5.00	

1983. DECLARATION OF HUMAN RIGHTS ISSUE This is the eleventh commemorative stamp in the Human Rights series. On Dec. 10, 1948 the first world-wide proclamation and adoption of the Universal Declaration of Human Rights took place. Dec. 10 is recognized as Human Rights Day. Designed by Friedensreich Hundertwasser, Austria. Engraved by Wolfgang Seidel, Austria. *Gravure and intaglio by Government Printing Office, Austria. Perforated 13 1/2.*

37 The Second Skin, *abstract;*

38 The Right to Dream, *abstract*

37		MNHVF	UseVF
5s	multicolored *(2,163,419)*	.85	.75
	FDC *(Dec. 9, 1983)*		1.00
	Inscription block of 4	3.00	

38		MNHVF	UseVF
7s	multicolored *(2,163,542)*	1.25	1.00
	FDC *(Dec. 9, 1983)*		1.25
	Inscription block of 4	5.00	

1984. INTERNATIONAL CONFERENCE ON POPULATION ISSUE A conference in August 1984 in Mexico, reviewed the global population programs since a previous conference 10 years earlier. Designed by Marina Langer-Rosa and Helmut Langer, Germany. *Offset by Bundesdruckerei, Germany. Perforated 14.*

39 *Crowded market*

39		MNHVF	UseVF
7s	multicolored *(1,135,791)*	1.25	1.00
	FDC *(Feb. 3, 1984)*		1.50
	Inscription block of 4	5.25	

1984. WORLD FOOD DAY ISSUE The Food and Agriculture Organization observes World Food Day every Oct. 16, its anniversary. Designed by Adth Vanooijen, Netherlands. *Offset by Walsall Security Printers, Ltd., U.K. Perforated 14 1/2.*

40 *Irrigation ditches;* 41 *Harvesting crops*

40		MNHVF	UseVF
4.50s	multicolored *(994,106)*	.85	.75
	FDC *(March 15, 1984)*		1.00
	Inscription block of 4	3.50	

41		MNHVF	UseVF
6s	multicolored *(1,027,115)*	1.25	1.00
	FDC *(March 15, 1984)*		1.00
	Inscription block of 4	5.50	

1984. WORLD HERITAGE ISSUE First in a series. The World Heritage List was established in Nov. 1972 under terms of the convention

concerning the Protection of the World Cultural and Natural Heritage. Designs adapted as stamps by Rocco J. Callari, U.S., and Thomas Lee, China. *Offset by Harrison and Sons Ltd., U.K. Perforated 14.*

42 *Zebras in Serengeti National Park, Tanzania, photo by Bernard Pierre Wolff, U.S.;* 43 *Ancient Town of Shibam, Yemen, photo by unknown artist of Yemen*

42		MNHVF	UseVF
3.50s	multicolored *(957,518)*	1.00	.75
	FDC *(April 18, 1984)*		1.25
	Inscription block of 4	3.50	

43		MNHVF	UseVF
15s	multicolored *(928,794)*	2.00	1.75
	FDC *(April 18, 1984)*		1.75
	Inscription block of 4	8.00	

1984. FUTURE FOR REFUGEES ISSUE The office of the United Nations High Commissioner for Refugees was created in 1951. Designed by Hans Erni, Switzerland. *Gravure by Helio Courvoisier, Switzerland. Perforated 11 1/2.*

44 *Adult and child;*

45 *Woman*

44		MNHVF	UseVF
4.50s	multicolored *(1,086,393)*	1.00	.75
	FDC *(May 29, 1984)*		1.25
	Inscription block of 4	4.50	

45		MNHVF	UseVF
8.50s	multicolored *(1,109,865)*	2.25	1.75
	FDC *(May 29, 1984)*		1.75
	Inscription block of 4	8.50	

1984. INTERNATIONAL YOUTH YEAR ISSUE Designed by Ruel A. Mayo, Philippines. *Offset by Waddingtons Ltd., U.K. Perforated 13 1/2.*

46, 47 *Stylized figures*

46		MNHVF	UseVF
3.50s	multicolored *(1,178,833)*	1.00	.75
	FDC *(Nov. 15, 1984)*		1.25
	Inscription block of 4	3.00	

47			MNHVF	UseVF
6.50s	multicolored (1,109,337)		1.50	1.25
	FDC (Nov. 15, 1984)			1.50
	Inscription block of 4		6.00	

1985. ILO TURIN CENTER ISSUE for the International Labor Organization training institution. Similar to U.N. New York Minkus No. 130. Adapted from photographs by Rocco J. Callari, U.S., and Thomas Lee, China. Engraved by Hiroshi Sasaki and Kohji Uematsu, Japan. *Intaglio by the Japanese Government Printing Office. Perforated 13 1/2.*

 48 *U Thant Pavilion*

48			MNHVF	UseVF
7.50s	multicolored (948,317)		1.40	1.25
	FDC (Feb. 1, 1985)			1.75
	Inscription block of 4		6.00	

1985. U.N. UNIVERSITY ISSUE The UNU coordinates the work of scientists and scholars throughout the world. Designed by Moshe Pereg, Israel, and Hinedi Geluda, Brazil. *Gravure by Helio Courvoisier, Switzerland. Perforated 13 1/2.*

 49 *"UNU" and silhouettes of rural scene, lab researcher*

49			MNHVF	UseVF
8.50s	multicolored (863,673)		1.75	1.50
	FDC (March 15, 1985)			1.75
	Inscription block of 4		7.50	

1985. REGULAR ISSUE Designed by Ran Banda Mawilmada, Sri Lanka (4.50s), Sophia Van Heeswijk, Germany (15s). *Offset by Carl Ueberreuter Druck and Verlag M. Salzer, Austria. Perforated 14.*

  50 *Laurel-leaf boat;*

51 *People under an umbrella*

50			MNHVF	UseVF
4.50s	multicolored (2,000,000 printed)		.55	.40
	FDC (May 10, 1985)			1.00
	Inscription block of 4		2.00	
51			MNHVF	UseVF
15s	multicolored (2,500,000 printed)		3.00	2.50
	FDC (May 10, 1985)			2.50
	Inscription block of 4		12.00	

1985. U.N. 40TH ANNIVERSARY ISSUE Featured paintings (details) by American artist Andrew Wyeth, U.S. Similar to U.N. New York Minkus Nos. 470 and 471 and Geneva Nos. 135 and 136. *Gravure by Helio Courvoisier, Switzerland. Perforated 12x11 1/2.*

52 *Detail from* The Corner; 53 *Detail from* Alvaro Raking Hay

52			MNHVF	UseVF
6.50s	multicolored (984,820)		1.25	1.00
	FDC (June 26, 1985)			1.25
	Inscription block of 4		5.00	
53			MNHVF	UseVF
8.50s	multicolored (914,347)		3.00	2.25
	FDC (June 26, 1985)			1.75
	Inscription block of 4		12.50	

1985. U.N. 40TH ANNIVERSARY SOUVENIR SHEET Designed by Rocco J. Callari, U.S., and Thomas Lee, China. *Gravure by Helio Courvoisier, Switzerland. Gravure by Helio Courvoisier, Switzerland. Imperforate.*

54 *Souvenir sheet with Nos. 52 and 53*

54			MNHVF	UseVF
15s	Sheet of 2 (676,648)		4.50	4.50
	a. Single (6.50s)		1.25	1.00
	b. Single (8.50s)		2.00	1.50
	FDC (June 26, 1985)			3.50

1985. UNICEF CHILD SURVIVAL CAMPAIGN ISSUE Designed by Mel Harris, U.K. (4s), Vreni Wyss-Fischer, Switzerland (6s). Engraved by Masao Orihara, Japan (4s). *Gravure and intaglio by Japanese Government Printing Office. Perforated 13 1/2.*

55 *Spoonfeeding children;*

56 *Mother hugging infant*

55		MNHVF	UseVF
4s	multicolored *(889,918)*	1.75	1.00
	FDC *(Nov. 22, 1985)*		1.50
	Inscription block of 4	6.00	

56		MNHVF	UseVF
6s	multicolored *(852,958)*	2.25	1.75
	FDC *(Nov. 22, 1985)*		1.50
	Inscription block of 4	10.00	

1986. AFRICA IN CRISIS ISSUE Designed by Tesfaye Tessema, Ethiopia. *Gravure by Helio Courvoisier, Switzerland. Perforated 11 1/2x12.*

57 *Abstract, "Afrika in Not"*

57		MNHVF	UseVF
8s	multicolored *(809,854)*	1.35	1.25
	FDC *(Jan. 31, 1986)*		1.50
	Inscription block of 4	6.50	

1986. U.N. DEVELOPMENT PROGRAM ISSUE The program is a partnership of more than 170 countries and territories. Designed by Thomas Lee, China. *Gravure by Japanese Government Printing Office. Perforated 13 1/2.*

58 *Developing crop strains;* 59 *Animal husbandry;* 60 *Technical instruction;* 61 *Nutrition education*

58		MNHVF	UseVF
4.50s	multicolored *(730,691)*	2.00	1.00
	FDC *(March 14, 1986)*		1.25

59		MNHVF	UseVF
4.50s	multicolored *(730,792)*	2.00	1.00
	FDC *(March 14, 1986)*		1.25

60		MNHVF	UseVF
4.50s	multicolored *(730,691)*	2.00	1.00
	FDC *(March 14, 1986)*		1.25

61		MNHVF	UseVF
4.50s	multicolored *(730,691)*	2.00	1.00
	FDC *(March 14, 1986)* any single		1.25
	Inscription block of 4	8.00	
	y. Se-tenant block of 4	8.00	
	FDC (block of 4)		2.75

1986. STAMP COLLECTING ISSUE Designed by Ingalill Axelsson, Sweden. Engraved by Czeslaw Slania, Sweden. (3.50s) similar to

U.N. Geneva Minkus No. 147, (6.50s) similar to New York No. 497. *Intaglio by Swedish Post Office. Perforated 12 1/2.*

62 *U.N. stamps;* 63 *Engraver*

62		MNHVF	UseVF
3.50s	dark ultra & dark brown *(874,119)*	1.00	.60
	FDC *(May 22, 1986)*		1.50
	Inscription block of 4	4.00	

63		MNHVF	UseVF
6.50s	indigo blue and burnt rose *(877,284)*	1.50	1.25
	FDC *(May 22, 1986)*		1.50
	Inscription block of 4	5.50	

1986. INTERNATIONAL PEACE YEAR ISSUE The U.N. General Assembly declared 1986 to be the International Year of Peace. Designed by Milo Schor, Israel (5s), Mohammad Sardar, Pakistan (6s). *Gravure and offset by the Japanese Government Printing Office. Perforated 12 1/2.*

64 *Olive branch an rainbow;* 65 *Doves in a circle*

64		MNHVF	UseVF
5s	multicolored *(914,699)*	1.25	1.00
	FDC *(June 20, 1986)*		1.50
	Inscription block of 4	5.00	

65		MNHVF	UseVF
6s	multicolored *(818,386)*	1.50	1.25
	FDC *(June 20, 1986)*		1.50
	Inscription block of 4	8.00	

1986. WFUNA 40TH ANNIVERSARY SOUVENIR SHEET World Federation of U.N. Associations. Format design by Rocco J. Callari, U.S. *Offset by Joh. Enschedé and Sons, Netherlands. Perforated 13x13 1/2.*

66a *White Stallion, by Elisabeth von Janota-Bzowski, Germany;* 66b *Surrealistic landscape, by Ernst Fuchs, Austria;* 66c *Geometric abstract, by Victor Vasarely, France;* 66d *Mythological abstract, by Wolfgang Hutter, Austria*

66			MNHVF	UseVF
22s	**Sheet of 4** *(668,264)*		6.50	6.00
	a. Single (4s)		1.00	
	b. Single (5s)		1.25	
	c. Single (6s)		1.50	
	d. Single (7s)		1.75	
	FDC *(Nov. 14, 1986)*			6.00

1987. TRYGVE LIE ISSUE Adapted as a stamp by Rocco J. Callari, U.S., from a portrait by Harald Dal, Norway. Engraved by Wolfgang Seidel, Austria. Similar to U.N. New York Minkus No. 517, and Geneva No. 151. *Gravure and intaglio by the Government Printing Office, Austria. Perforated 13 1/2.*

67 *Trygve Lie (1896-1968), first U.N. secretary general, portrait by Harald Dal, Norway*

67		MNHVF	UseVF
8s	**multicolored** *(778,010)*	1.40	1.25
	FDC *(Jan. 30, 1987)*		2.00
	Inscription block of 4	6.50	

1987. SHELTER FOR THE HOMELESS ISSUE The U.N. General Assembly declared 1987 to be the International Year of Shelter for the Homeless. Designed by Wladyslaw Brykczynski, Poland. *Offset by Joh. Enschedé and Sons, Netherlands. Perforated 13 1/2x12 1/2.*

68 *Family and village;* 69 *Family at doorway*

68		MNHVF	UseVF
4s	**multicolored** *(704,922)*	1.25	2.00
	FDC *(March 13, 1987)*		1.25
	Inscription block of 4	5.50	

69		MNHVF	UseVF
9.50s	**multicolored** *(671,200)*	1.75	1.40
	FDC *(March 13, 1987)*		1.75
	Inscription block of 4	8.00	

1987. FIGHT DRUG ABUSE ISSUE Designed by Susan Borgen and Noe Werrett, U.S. Illustrated by C. M. Dudash, U.S. *Offset by The House of Questa, U.K. Perforated 14 1/2x15.*

70 *Youths playing soccer;* 71 *Family group*

70		MNHVF	UseVF
5s	**multicolored** *(869,875)*	1.25	1.00
	FDC *(June 12, 1987)*		1.50
	Inscription block of 4	5.00	

71		MNHVF	UseVF
8s	**multicolored** *(797,889)*	1.50	1.25
	FDC *(June 12, 1987)*		1.75
	Inscription block of 4	6.50	

1987. REGULAR ISSUE Designed by Henry Bencsath, U.S. (2s), and Eliezer Weishoff, Israel (17s). *Offset by The House of Questa, U.K. Perforated 14 1/2 x 15.*

72 *Vienna International Centre;* 73 *Doves and*

laurel branch encircling globe

72		MNHVF	UseVF
2s	**multicolored** *(2,000,000)*	.75	.50
	FDC *(June 12, 1987)*		1.50
	Inscription block of 4	3.00	

73		MNHVF	UseVF
17s	**multicolored** *(2,000,000)*	2.00	2.00
	FDC *(June 12, 1987)*		2.50
	Inscription block of 4	10.50	

1987. U.N. DAY ISSUE Designed by Elisabeth von Janota-Bzowski, Germany (5s), Fritz Henry Oerter, Germany (6s). *Offset by The House of Questa, U.K. Perforated 14 1/2x15.*

74 *Danciny against skyline;* 75 *Dancing in line, U.N. emblem*

74		MNHVF	UseVF
5s	**multicolored** *(1,575,731 sold)*	1.50	1.25
	FDC *(Oct. 23, 1987)*		1.40
	Inscription block of 4	6.00	

75		MNHVF	UseVF
6s	**multicolored** *(1,540,523 sold)*	1.75	1.50
	FDC *(Oct. 23, 1987)*		1.75
	Inscription block of 4	7.50	

1987. CHILD IMMUNIZATION ISSUE The goal of the World Health Organization and the United Nations Children's Fund was to immunize all children by 1990. Designed by Seymour Chwast, U.S. *Offset by The House of Questa, U.K. Perforated 15x14 1/2.*

76 *Polio immunization;*

77 *Diphtheria immunization*

76		MNHVF	UseVF
4s	multicolored *(793,716)*	1.50	1.25
	FDC *(Nov. 20, 1987)*		1.50
	Inscription block of 4	7.50	

77		MNHVF	UseVF
9.50s	multicolored *(769,288)*	2.50	2.00
	FDC *(Nov. 20, 1987)*		2.00
	Inscription block of 4	12.00	

1988. IFAD ISSUE International Fund for Agricultural Development - World without hunger. Designed by Santiago Arolas, Switzerland. *Offset by CPE Australia Ltd. Perforated 13 1/2.*

78 *Woman picking crop;* 79 *Processing vegetables*

78		MNHVF	UseVF
4s	multicolored *(697,307)*	1.25	1.00
	FDC *(Jan. 29, 1988)*		1.25
	Inscription block of 4	6.00	

79		MNHVF	UseVF
6s	multicolored *(701,521)*	1.75	1.50
	FDC *(Jan. 29, 1988)*		1.75
	Inscription block of 4	7.50	

1988. FOREST ISSUE Designed by Braldt Bralds, Netherlands. *Offset by The House of Questa, U.K. Printed se-tenant in a continuous design. Perforated 14x15.*

80,81 *Autumn deciduous forest scene*

80		MNHVF	UseVF
4s	multicolored *(990,607)*	3.50	3.00
	FDC *(March 18, 1988)*		3.25

81		MNHVF	UseVF
5s	multicolored *(990,607)*	4.50	5.00
	FDC *(March 18, 1988)*		5.50
	Inscription block of 4	16.00	
	y. Se-tenant pair	8.00	
	FDC (pair)		8.00

1988. INTERNATIONAL VOLUNTEER DAY ISSUE A U.N. General Assembly resolution calls for International Volunteer Day recognized an-

nually on Dec. 5. Designed by James E. Tennison, U.S. *Offset by Joh. Enschedé and Sons, Netherlands. Perforated 13x14, 14x13.*

82 *Blood pressure check;*

83 *Construction assistance*

82		MNHVF	UseVF
6s	multicolored *(701,167)*	1.50	1.25
	FDC *(May 6, 1988)*		1.40
	Inscription block of 4	7.50	

83		MNHVF	UseVF
7.50s	multicolored *(638,240)*	2.00	1.50
	FDC *(May 6, 1988)*		1.65
	Inscription block of 4	10.00	

1988. HEALTH IN SPORTS ISSUE Designed by LeRoy Neiman, U.S. *Offset by Japanese Government Printing Office. Perforated 13 1/2x13, 13x13 1/2.*

84 *Skiing;*

85 *Tennis*

84		MNHVF	UseVF
6s	multicolored *(668,902)*	1.75	1.50
	FDC *(June 17, 1988)*		1.75
	Inscription block of 4	8.00	

85		MNHVF	UseVF
8s	multicolored *(647,915)*	2.00	1.75
	FDC *(June 17, 1988)*		2.00
	Inscription block of 4	11.50	

1988. DECLARATION OF HUMAN RIGHTS ISSUE Fortieth anniversary. This is in the 12th set of stamps in the Human Rights series. Designed by Rocco J. Callari, U.S. Similar to U.N. New York Minkus No. 567 and Geneva No. 171. *Gravure and intaglio by Helio Courvoisier, Switzerland. Perforated 12.*

86 *Symbolic flame*

86		MNHVF	UseVF
5s	multicolored *(1,275,000 printed)*	1.00	.75
	FDC *(Dec. 9, 1988)*		1.50
	Inscription block of 4	4.00	

1988. DECLARATION OF HUMAN RIGHTS SOUVENIR SHEET Fortieth anniversary. Designed by Rocco J. Callari, U.S. The 11s is a single strip souvenir sheet which includes the preamble to the human rights declaration in German. *Gravure and intaglio by Helio Courvoisier, Switzerland. Perforated 12.*

87 *Universal Declaration of Human Rights 1948-1988 with No. 86*

87		MNHVF	UseVF
11s	**Sheet of 1** *(1,000,000 printed)*	2.75	2.50
	a. Single (5s)	2.00	1.00
	FDC *(Dec. 9, 1988)*		2.50

1989. WORLD BANK ISSUE The World Bank is owned by the Government of more than 151 nations. It provides development assistance. Designed by Saturnin Lumboy, Philippines. *Offset by Joh. Enschedé and Sons, Netherlands. Perforated 13x14.*

88 *Transportation;*

89 *Health care, education*

88		MNHVF	UseVF
5.50s	**multicolored** *(682,124)*	1.75	1.25
	FDC *(Jan. 27, 1989)*		1.50
	Inscription block of 4	10.00	

89		MNHVF	UseVF
8s	**multicolored** *(628,649)*	3.25	2.00
	FDC *(Jan. 27, 1989)*		2.00
	Inscription block of 4	13.00	

1989. NOBEL PEACE PRIZE ISSUE Commemorated the awarding of the 1988 Nobel Peace Prize to the U.N. peace-keeping forces. Designed by Tom Bland, Australia. Similar to U.N. New York Minkus No. 571 and Geneva No. 175. *Offset by CPE Australia, Ltd. Perforated 14x13 1/2.*

 90 *U.N. soldier on watch*

90		MNHVF	UseVF
6s	**multicolored** *(912,731)*	1.50	1.40
	FDC *(March 17, 1989)*		1.75
	Inscription block of 4	7.00	

1989. WORLD WEATHER WATCH ISSUE Honored a U.N. effort begun in 1963 to collect, analyze and distribute world weather data. Designed by Rocco J. Callari, U.S., and Robert Stein, U.S. *Offset by Joh. Enschedé and Sons, Netherlands. Perforated 13x14.*

91 *Satellite photo: Mediterranean cyclone affects weather over Alps;*

92 *Satellite photo: Forcast of rain in Japan*

91		MNHVF	UseVF
4s	**multicolored** *(948,680)*	2.50	1.00
	FDC *(April 21, 1989)*		1.40
	Inscription block of 4	7.50	

92		MNHVF	UseVF
9.50s	**multicolored** *(880,138)*	3.25	2.50
	FDC *(April 21, 1989)*		2.00
	Inscription block of 4	20.00	

1989. 10TH ANNIVERSARY U.N. OFFICES IN VIENNA ISSUE The third secretariat location of the U.N. besides New York and Geneva. Designed by Gottfried Kumpf, Austria (5s), André Heller, Austria (7.50s). Engraved by Wolfgang Seidel, Austria (5s). *Gravure and intaglio (5s), gravure (7.50s) by Government Printing Office, Austria. Perforated 14.*

93 *Figure under sun;*

94 *Abstract with moon and heart*

93		MNHVF	UseVF
5s	**multicolored** *(958,339)*	3.50	2.00
	FDC *(Aug. 23, 1989)*		1.25
	Inscription block of 4	15.00	

94		MNHVF	UseVF
7.50s	**multicolored** *(785,517)*	5.50	3.00
	FDC *(Aug. 23, 1989)*		1.50
	Inscription block of 4	25.00	

1989. DECLARATION OF HUMAN RIGHTS ISSUE This 13th set in the Human Rights series depicts the first six articles of the Universal Declaration of Human Rights of 1948. Concept by Arleigh Gaines, U.S., designed by Rocco J. Callari, U.S., and Robert Stein, U.S. *Panes of 12 plus 12 se-tenant labels containing Articles 5 (4s) or 6 (6s), inscribed in English, French or German. Offset by Joh. Enschedé and Sons, Netherlands. Perforated 13 1/2.*

95 The Prisoners, *by Kathe Kollwitz, Germany*

Article 5 *Nul ne sera soumis à la torture, ni à des peines ou traitements cruels, inhumains ou dégradants.*

95		MNHVF	UseVF
4s	multicolored *(2,502,000 printed)*	2.50	1.50
	FDC *(Nov. 17, 1989)*		2.00
	y. Strip of 3 plus 3 labels	6.50	

96 Justice, *by Raphael, Italy*

Article 6 *Chacun a le droit à la reconnaissance en tous lieux de sa personnalité juridique.*

96		MNHVF	UseVF
6s	multicolored *(2,502,000 printed)*	2.50	2.00
	FDC *(Nov. 17, 1989)*		2.00
	y. Strip of 3 plus 3 labels	8.00	

1990. INTERNATIONAL TRADE CENTER ISSUE Designed by Richard Bernstein, U.S. Similar to U.N. New York Minkus No. 595 and Geneva No. 182. *Offset by The House of Questa, U.K. Perforated 14 1/2x15.*

97 *Harbor scene*

97		MNHVF	UseVF
12s	multicolored *(559,556)*	2.50	2.25
	FDC *(Feb. 2, 1990)*		3.00
	inscription block of 4	12.50	

1990. REGULAR ISSUE Designed by Kurt Regschek, Austria. *Offset by National Postage Stamps and Fiduciary Printing Works, France. Perforated 13.*

98 *Vienna International Centre*

98		MNHVF	UseVF
1.50s	multicolored *(2,000,000)*	.60	.50
	FDC *(Feb. 2, 1990)*		2.50
	Inscription block of 4	2.25	

1990. FIGHT AIDS ISSUE Designed by Jacek Tofil, Poland (5s), Orlando Pelaez, Colombia (11s). Offset by Joh. Enschedé and Sons, Netherlands. Perforated 13 1/2x12 1/2.

90 *AIDS;* 100 *People fighting blob*

99		MNHVF	UseVF
5s	multicolored *(623,155)*	2.25	1.25
	FDC *(March 16, 1990)*		1.25
	Inscription block of 4	8.00	

100		MNHVF	UseVF
11s	multicolored *(588,742)*	3.00	2.50
	FDC *(March 16, 1990)*		2.50
	Inscription block of 4	17.50	

1990. MEDICINAL PLANTS ISSUE Illustration from *Curtis's Botanical Magazine* adapted as a stamp by Rocco J. Callari, U.S., and Robert Stein, U.S. *Gravure by Helio Courvoisier, Switzerland. Perforated 11 1/2, granite paper.*

101 *Bixa orellana;*

102 *Momordica charantia*

101		MNHVF	UseVF
4.50s	multicolored *(709,840)*	1.50	1.00
	FDC *(May 4, 1990)*		1.25
	Inscription block of 4	7.50	

102		MNHVF	UseVF
9.50s	multicolored *(732,883)*	3.50	2.50
	FDC *(May 4, 1990)*		2.00
	Inscription block of 4	15.00	

1990. U.N. 45TH ANNIVERSARY ISSUE Commemorated the signing of the U.N. Charter in 1945. Designed by Talib Nauman, Pakistan (7s), Marleen Bosmans, Belgium (9s). *Offset by Joh. Enschedé and Sons, Netherlands. Perforated 14 1/2x13.*

103, 104 *Depictions of "45"*

103		MNHVF	UseVF
7s	**multicolored** *(604,878)*	1.50	1.25
	FDC *(June 26, 1990)*		1.50
	Inscription block of 4	10.00	

104		MNHVF	UseVF
9s	**multicolored** *(550,902)*	3.50	2.50
	FDC *(June 26, 1990)*		2.50
	Inscription block of 4	15.00	

1990. U.N. 45TH ANNIVERSARY SOUVENIR SHEET Commemorated the signing of the U.N. Charter in 1945. Designed by Robert Stein, U.S. *Offset by Joh. Enschedé and Sons, Netherlands. Perforated 14 1/2x13.*

105 *U.N. 45th Anniversary Souvenir sheet with Nos. 103 and 104*

105		MNHVF	UseVF
16s	**Sheet of 2** *(423,370)*	7.50	5.50
	a. Single (7s)	1.50	1.25
	b. Single (9s)	3.50	2.50
	c. Pair	5.50	
	FDC *(June 26, 1990)*		4.00

1990. CRIME PREVENTION ISSUE Designed by Josef Ryzec, Czechoslovakia. *Gravure by Heraclio Fournier, Spain. Perforated 14.*

106 *Domestic violence;* 107 *Crimes against cultural heritage*

106		MNHVF	UseVF
6s	**multicolored** *(661,810)*	1.75	1.50
	FDC *(Sept. 13, 1990)*		1.50
	Inscription block of 4	8.00	

107		MNHVF	UseVF
8s	**multicolored** *(607,940)*	3.00	2.75
	FDC *(Sept. 13, 1990)*		2.25
	Inscription block of 4	17.50	

1990. DECLARATION OF HUMAN RIGHTS ISSUE This 14th set in the Human Rights series depicts Articles 11-12 of the Universal Declaration of Human Rights. Concept by Arleigh Gaines, U.S., designed by Rocco J. Callari, U.S., and Roberts Stein, U.S. *Panes of 12 plus 12 se-tenant labels containing Articles 11 (4.50s) or 12 (7s) inscribed in English, French or German. Offset by Joh. Enschedé and Sons, Netherlands. Perforated 13.*

108 Before the Judge, 1886, *by Sándor Bihari, Hungary*

108		MNHVF	UseVF
4.50s	**multicolored** *(2,502,000 printed)*	2.00	1.50
	FDC *(Nov. 16, 1990)*		1.50
	y. Strip of 3 plus 3 labels	7.00	

109 Young Man Greeted by a Woman Writing a Poem, *by Suzuki Harunobu, Japan*

109		MNHVF	UseVF
7s	**multicolored** *(2,502,000 printed)*	2.75	2.00
	FDC *(Nov. 16, 1990)*		2.00
	y. Strip of 3 plus 3 labels	10.00	

Every entry in this catalog has been double-checked for accuracy, but mistakes may creep into any human endeavor, and we ask your assistance in eliminating them. Please call the attention of the editors to any errors in stamp descriptions found in this catalog.

1991. ECONOMIC COMMISSION FOR EUROPE ISSUE Designed by Carlos Ochagavia, Argentina. *Offset by Heraclio Fournier, Spain. Perforated 14.*

110 *Weasel, hoopoe;* 111 *Warbler, swans;* 112 *Badgers, squirrel;* 113 *Fish*

110		MNHVF	UseVF
5s	multicolored *(727,436)*	1.75	1.25
	FDC *(March 15, 1991)*		1.25

111		MNHVF	UseVF
5s	multicolored *(727,436)*	1.75	1.25
	FDC *(March 15, 1991)*		1.25

112		MNHVF	UseVF
5s	multicolored *(727,436)*	1.75	1.25
	FDC *(March 15, 1991)*		1.25

113		MNHVF	UseVF
5s	multicolored *(727,436)*	1.75	1.25
	FDC *(March 15, 1991)*		1.25
	Inscription block of 4	7.00	
	y. Se-tenant block of 4	8.00	
	FDC (block)		6.00

1991. NAMIBIAN INDEPENDENCE ISSUE The 5th in the Namibia series. The African nation became independent March 21, 1990. Adapted by Rocco J. Callari, U.S., and Robert Stein, U.S., from photos by John Isaac, India. *Offset by Heraclio Fournier, Spain.*

114 *Mountains;* 115 *Dune, Namib Desert*

114		MNHVF	UseVF
6s	multicolored *(531,789)*	2.00	1.50
	FDC *(May 10, 1991)*		2.00
	Inscription block of 4	10.00	

115		MNHVF	UseVF
9.50s	multicolored *(503,735)*	4.00	3.00
	FDC *(May 10, 1991)*		3.00
	Inscription block of 4	18.50	

1991. REGULAR ISSUE Designed by Marina Langer-Rosa, Germany. *Offset by The House of Questa, U.K.* Perforated 14.

116 *Peoples of the world in a circle*

116		MNHVF	UseVF
20s	multicolored *(1,750,000)*	4.00	3.00

FDC *(May 10, 1991)*			4.00
Inscription block of 4		15.00	

1991. RIGHTS OF THE CHILD ISSUE Designed by Anna Harmer, Austria (7s), Emiko Takegawa, Japan (9s). *Offset by The House of Questa U.K.* Perforated 14 1/2.

117 *Stick-figures drawing;* 118 *Child with heart*

117		MNHVF	UseVF
7s	multicolored *(645,145)*	2.50	1.75
	FDC *(June 14, 1991)*		1.75
	Inscription block of 4	13.00	

118		MNHVF	UseVF
9s	multicolored *(568,214)*	3.00	2.25
	FDC *(June 14, 1991)*		2.25
	Inscription block of 4	15.50	

1991. CHEMICAL WEAPONS BAN ISSUE Designed by Oscar Asboth, Austria (5s), Michel Granger, France (10s). *Offset by Heraclio Fournier, Spain.* Perforated 13 1/2.

119 *Red skull and landscape;* 120 *Pushing back gloom*

119		MNHVF	UseVF
5s	multicolored *(469,454)*	2.25	1.75
	FDC *(Sept. 11, 1991)*		1.75
	Inscription block of 4	11.50	

120		MNHVF	UseVF
10s	multicolored *(525,704)*	3.50	2.50
	FDC *(Sept. 11, 1991)*		2.50
	Inscription block of 4	17.50	

1991. 40TH ANNIVERSARY U.N. POSTAL ADMINISTRATION ISSUE Designed by Rocco J. Callari, U.S., from the adaptation of 1951 20¢ stamp designed by Hubert Woyty-Wimmer, U.K. (5s); adaptation of 1951 5¢ stamp designed by S. L. Hartz, Netherlands. *Offset by The House of Questa, U.K.* Perforated 14x15.

121 *Stamp on stamp: U.N. New York No. 8;* 122 *Stamp on stamp: U.N. New York No. 5*

121		MNHVF	UseVF
5s	UN New York No. 8 *(564,450)*	1.75	1.50
	FDC *(Oct. 24, 1991)*		1.40
	Inscription block of 4	6.50	

122		MNHVF	UseVF
8s	UN New York No. 5 *(609,830)*	2.50	2.25
	FDC *(Oct. 24, 1991)*		2.10
	Inscription block of 4	12.50	

1991. DECLARATION OF HUMAN RIGHTS ISSUE This 15th set in the Human Rights series is the third group of six articles of the Universal Declaration of Human Rights. Concept by Arleigh Gaines, U.S., designed by Rocco J. Callari, U.S., and Robert Stein, U.S. *Panes of 12 plus 12 se-tenant labels containing Articles 17 (4.50s) or 18 (7s) inscribed in English, French or German. Offset by Joh. Enschedé and Sons, Netherlands. Perforated 13 1/2.*

123 *Ancient Mexican pottery*

123		MNHVF	UseVF
4.50s	**black & brown** *(1,717,097)*	2.25	1.25
	FDC *(Nov. 20, 1991)*		1.75
	y. Strip of 3 plus 3 labels	6.50	

124 Windows 1912, *by Robert Delaunay, France*

124		MNHVF	UseVF
7s	**multicolored** *(1,717,738)*	3.25	2.00
	FDC *(Nov. 20, 1991)*		2.25
	y. Strip of 3 plus 3 labels	12.50	

1992. WORLD HERITAGE ISSUE Second in a World Heritage series supporting the conservation of mankind's shared heritage. Adapted as a stamp by Robert Stein, U.S. from photographs by Adam Tanner, U.S. (5s), Hartman-Dewitt, U.S. (9s). *Offset by Cartor, France. Perforated 13, size 35x28mm.*

125 *Iguacú National Park, Brazil, photograph by Adam Tanner, U.S.;*
126 *Abu Simbel, Egypt, photograph by Hartman-Dewitt, U.S.*

125		MNHVF	UseVF
5s	**multicolored** *(586,738)*	2.25	1.75
	FDC *(Jan. 24, 1992)*		1.50
	Inscription block of 4	10.50	

126		MNHVF	UseVF
9s	**multicolored** *(476,965)*	3.25	3.00
	FDC *(Jan.24, 1992)*		2.75
	Inscription block of 4	15.00	

1992. CLEAN OCEANS ISSUE Designed paintings by Braldt Bralds, Netherlands. *Offset by The House of Questa, U.K. Perforated 14.*

127 *Ocean surface;*

128 *Ocean bottom*

127		MNHVF	UseVF
7s	**multicolored** *(1,121,870)*	1.75	.75
	FDC *(March 13, 1992)*		2.00

128		MNHVF	UseVF
7s	**multicolored** *(1,121,870)*	1.75	1.75
	FDC *(March 13, 1992)*		2.00
	Inscription block of 4, 2 of each	6.25	
	y. Se-tenant block of 4	6.25	
	Pair, 1 each 127, 128	3.00	2.50

1992. EARTH SUMMIT ISSUE Designed by Peter Max, U.S. *Gravure by Helio Courvoisier, Switzerland. Pane of 40, perforated 11 1/2.*

129 *Man in space;*

130 *Sun;*

131 *Man Fishing;*

132 *Sailboat*

129		MNHVF	UseVF
5.50s	**multicolored** *(784,197)*	2.00	1.25
	FDC *(May 22, 1992)*		1.50

130		MNHVF	UseVF
5.50s	**multicolored** *(784,197)*	2.00	1.25
	FDC *(May 22, 1992)*		1.50

131		MNHVF	UseVF
5.50s	**multicolored** *(784,197)*	2.00	1.25
	FDC *(May 22, 1992)*		1.50

132		MNHVF	UseVF
5.50s	**multicolored** *(784,197)*	2.00	1.25
	FDC *(May 22, 1992)*		1.50
	Inscription block of 4	8.00	
	y. Se-tenant block of 4	8.00	4.25
	FDC (block of 4)		4.95

1992. MISSION TO PLANT EARTH ISSUE Designed by Atilla Hejja, U.S. and sheet concept by Rocco J. Callari, U.S. *Gravure by Helio Courvoisier, Switzerland. Pane of 10, rouletted 8, granite paper.*

133 *Satellite and mouth;* 134 *Satellite and ear*

133		MNHVF	UseVF
10s	**multicolored** *(881,716)*	3.00	2.75
	FDC *(Sept. 4, 1992)*		2.50

134		MNHVF	UseVF
10s	**multicolored** *(881,716)*	3.00	2.75
	FDC *(Sept. 4, 1992)*		2.50
	Inscription block of 4	12.00	
	y. Se-tenant pair	6.00	5.00

1992. SCIENCE AND TECHNOLOGY DEVELOPMENT ISSUE Designed by Saul Mandel, U.S. *Offset by Unicover Corp., U.S. Perforated 14.*

135 *Woman advancing from computer screen;* 136 *Flowers growing from green thumb*

135		MNHVF	UseVF
5.50s	**multicolored** *(482,830)*	1.75	1.25
	FDC *(Oct. 2, 1992)*		1.75
	Inscription block of 4	7.50	

136		MNHVF	UseVF
7s	**multicolored** *(500,517)*	2.00	1.75
	FDC *(Oct. 2, 1992)*		2.00
	Inscription block of 4	12.00	

1992. REGULAR ISSUE Designed by Gundi Groh, Austria (5.50s), Rocco J. Callari, U.S. (7s). *Offset by Walsall Security Printers, Ltd., U.K. Perforated 13.*

137 *Woman with rose, birds and butterfly;* 138 *Vienna International Centre*

137		MNHVF	UseVF
5.50s	**multicolored** *(2,100,000)*	1.75	1.00
	FDC *(Oct. 2, 1992)*		1.25
	Inscription block of 4	6.50	

138		MNHVF	UseVF
7s	**multicolored** *(2,100,000)*	2.00	1.75
	FDC *(Oct. 2, 1992)*		2.00
	Inscription block of 4	8.00	

1992. DECLARATION OF HUMAN RIGHTS ISSUE This 16th set in the Human Rights series depicts the fourth group of six Articles (19-25) of the Universal Declaration of Human Rights. Adapted as a stamp by Robert Stein, U.S. *Panes of 12 plus 12 se-tenant labels containing Articles 23 (6s) or 24 (10s) inscribed in English, French or German. Offset by Joh. Enschedé and Sons, Netherlands. Perforated 13 1/2.*

139 Les Constructeurs, *by Fernand Léger, France*

139		MNHVF	UseVF
6s	**multicolored** *(1,536,516)*	2.50	1.75
	FDC *(Nov. 20, 1992)*		1.50
	y. Strip of 3 plus 3 labels	6.50	

140 Sunday Afternoon on the Island of La Grande Jatte, 1884-86, *by Georges Seurat, France*

140		MNHVF	UseVF
10s	**multicolored** *(1,527,861)*	3.50	2.00
	FDC *(Nov. 20, 1992)*		2.35
	y. Strip of 3 plus 3 labels	12.50	

1993. AGING WITH DIGNITY ISSUE Designed by C. M. Dudash, U.S. *Offset by Cartor, France. Perforated 13.*

141 *Family gardening with older couple;*

142 *Older woman teaching*

141		MNHVF	UseVF
5.50s	**multicolored** *(428,886)*	1.75	1.25
	FDC *(Feb. 5, 1993)*		1.75
	Inscription block of 4	7.50	

142		MNHVF	UseVF
7s	**multicolored** *(459,471)*	2.50	2.25
	FDC *(Feb. 5, 1992)*		2.00
	Inscription block of 4	12.50	

1993. ENDANGERED SPECIES ISSUE The first set of stamps in the Endangered species series. Concept by Rocco J. Callari, U.S. and designs by Steve Brennan, U.S. *Offset by Joh. Enschedé and Sons, Netherlands. Perforated 13x12 1/2.*

143 *Equus grevyi (Grevy's zebra);* 144 *Spheniscus humboldti (Humboldt's penguins);* 145 *Varanus griseus (Desert monitor);* 146 *Canis lupus (Grey wolf)*

143		MNHVF	UseVF
7s	**multicolored** *(1,200,000 printed)*	1.75	1.35
	FDC *(March 3, 1993)*		1.25

144		MNHVF	UseVF
7s	**multicolored** *(1,200,000 printed)*	1.75	1.35
	FDC *(March 3, 1993)*		1.25

145		MNHVF	UseVF
7s	**multicolored** *(1,200,000 printed)*	1.75	1.35
	FDC *(March 3, 1993)*		1.25

146		MNHVF	UseVF
7s	**multicolored** *(1,200,000 printed)*	1.75	1.35
	FDC *(March 3, 1993)*		1.25
	Inscription block of 4	8.50	
	y. Se-tenant block of 4	7.00	6.00

1993. HEALTHY ENVIRONMENT ISSUE Designed by Milton Glaser, U.S. *Offset Leigh-Mardon Pty. Ltd., Australia. Perforated 15x14 1/2.*

147 *Wave in ocean;* 148 *Globe*

147		MNHVF	UseVF
6s	**multicolored** *(517,433)*	2.25	1.50
	FDC *(May 7, 1993)*		1.50
	Inscription block of 4	10.00	

148		MNHVF	UseVF
10s	**multicolored** *(453,123)*	3.50	2.00
	FDC *(May 7, 1993)*		2.25
	Inscription block of 4	15.00	

1993. REGULAR ISSUE Adaptation of 40¢ New York Definitive stamp of 1982 by Marek Kwiatkowski, Poland. *Gravure by Helio Courvoisier, Switzerland. Perforated 11 1/2x11 3/4.*

149 *Doves and globe*

149		MNHVF	UseVF
13s	**multicolored** *(1,500,000)*	3.00	2.50
	FDC *(May 7, 1993)*		2.50
	Inscription block of 4	12.00	

1993. DECLARATION OF HUMAN RIGHTS ISSUE The 17th set in the Human Rights series depicts the fifth of the six articles of the Universal Declaration of Human Rights. Concept by Arleigh Gaines, U.S., designed by Robert Stein, U.S. *Panes of 12 plus 12 se-tenant labels containing Article 29 (5s) or 30 (6s) inscribed in English, French or German. Offset by Joh. Enschedé and Sons, Netherlands. Perforated 13 1/2.*

150 *Article 29,* Lower Austrian Pheasants' Wedding, 1843, *by Ferdinand G. Waldmuller, Austria,* 151 *Article 30,* Outback, *by Sally Morgan, Australia*

150		MNHVF	UseVF
5s	**multicolored** *(2,502,000 printed)*	3.00	1.50
	FDC *(June 11, 1993)*		1.40
	y. Strip of 3 plus 3 labels	9.00	

151		MNHVF	UseVF
6s	**multicolored** *(2,502,000 printed)*	3.00	1.75
	FDC *(June 11, 1993)*		1.50
	y. Strip of 3 plus 3 labels	11.00	

1993. INTERNATIONAL PEACE DAY ISSUE The U.N. General Assembly declared in 1981 that the third Tuesday of September would be observed as the International Day of Peace. Designed by Hans Erni, Switzerland. Engraved by Pierre Schopfer, Switzerland. *Offset and intaglio by PTT, Switzerland. Rouletted 12 1/2.*

152-155 *Abstract design, four corners*

152		MNHVF	UseVF
5.50s	green & multicolored *(445,699)*	3.00	1.75
	FDC *(Sept. 21, 1993)*		2.25
153		MNHVF	UseVF
5.50s	green & multicolored *(445,699)*	3.00	1.75
	FDC *(Sept. 21, 1993)*		2.25
154		MNHVF	UseVF
5.50s	green & multicolored *(445,699)*	3.00	1.75
	FDC *(Sept. 21, 1993)*		2.25
155		MNHVF	UseVF
5.50s	green & multicolored *(445,699)*	3.00	1.75
	FDC *(Sept. 21, 1993)*		2.25
	Inscription block of 4	16.00	
	y. Se-tenant block of 4	14.00	13.00

1993. ENVIRONMENT CLIMATE ISSUE Designed paintings by Braldt Bralds, Netherlands. *Offset by The House of Questa, U.K. Perforated 14 1/2.*

156 *Monkeys;* 157 *Bluebird, factory pollution, volcano;* 158 *Volcano, nuclear plant, tree stumps;* 159 *Owl, cactus, tree stumps*

156		MNHVF	UseVF
7s	multicolored *(484,517)*	2.00	1.25
	FDC *(Oct. 29, 1993)*		1.00
157		MNHVF	UseVF
7s	multicolored *(484,517)*	2.00	1.25
	FDC *(Oct. 29, 1993)*		1.00
158		MNHVF	UseVF
7s	multicolored *(484,517)*	2.00	1.25
	FDC *(Oct. 29, 1993)*		1.00
159		MNHVF	UseVF
7s	multicolored *(484,517)*	2.00	1.25
	FDC *(Oct. 29, 1993)*		1.00
	Inscription block of 8	20.00	
	y. Se-tenant strip of 4	9.00	

1994. YEAR OF THE FAMILY ISSUE The U.N. General Assembly proclaimed 1994 as the International Year of the Family. Designed by Rocco J. Callari, U.S., and computer graphics by Luis Sardá, Spain and John De Santis, U.S. *Offset by Cartor, France. Perforated 13.*

160 *Family holding hands;*

161 *Family tending garden*

160		MNHVF	UseVF
5.50s	blue green & multicolored *(528,325)*	2.00	1.25
	FDC *(Feb. 4, 1994)*		1.75
	Inscription block of 4	10.00	
161		MNHVF	UseVF
8s	red & multicolored *(462,847)*	3.00	1.50
	FDC *(Feb. 4, 1994)*		2.25
	Inscription block of 4	14.00	

1994. ENDANGERED SPECIES ISSUE The second set of stamps in the Endangered Species series. Concept by Rocco J. Callari, U.S. and designed by Paul Margocsy, Australia. *Offset by Joh. Enschedé and Sons, Netherlands. Perforated 12 1/2.*

162 *Ocelot;* 163 *White-breasted silver-eye;* 164 *Mediterranean monk seal;* 165 *Asian elephant*

162		MNHVF	UseVF
7s	multicolored *(1,200,000 printed)*	2.00	1.25
	FDC *(March 18, 1994)*		1.75
163		MNHVF	UseVF
7s	multicolored *(1,200,000 printed)*	2.00	1.25
	FDC *(March 18, 1994)*		1.75
164		MNHVF	UseVF
7s	multicolored *(1,200,000 printed)*	2.00	1.25
	FDC *(March 18, 1994)*		1.75
165		MNHVF	UseVF
7s	multicolored *(1,200,000 printed)*	2.00	1.25
	FDC *(March 18, 1994)*		1.75
	Inscription block of 4	7.00	5.50
	y. Se-tenant block of 4	9.00	

1994. PROTECTION FOR REFUGEES ISSUE Designed by Francoise Peyroux, U.S. *Offset by Leigh-Mardon Pty. Ltd. Perforated 14 1/2x15.*

166 *Hands saving refugees from cliff*

166		MNHVF	UseVF
12s	**multicolored** *(420,002)*	4.00	3.00
	FDC *(April 29, 1994)*		3.00
	Inscription block of 4	20.00	

1994. REGULAR ISSUE Adapted as a vertical stamp from horizontal 50g stamp of 1979, designed by Masatoshi Hioki, Japan (50g); adapted from 5¢ Geneva stamp of 1986, designed by Ramon Alcantara Rodriguez, Mexico (4s); adapted from 15¢ New York stamp of 1979, designed by Eliezer Weishoff, Israel. *Offset by Cartor, France. Perforated 13.*

167 *Tree of birds;* 168 *Doves fly over U.N. seal;* 169 *Dove of Peace, globe;*

167		MNHVF	UseVF
50g	**multicolored** *(1,450,000)*	.25	.20
	FDC *(April 29, 1994)*		1.25
	Inscription block of 4	.50	

168		MNHVF	UseVF
4s	**multicolored** *(1,150,000)*	.80	.75
	FDC *(April 29, 1994)*		1.25
	Inscription block of 4	4.00	

169		MNHVF	UseVF
30s	**multicolored** *(560,000)*	6.00	5.00
	FDC *(April 29, 1994)*		5.00
	Inscription block of 4	25.00	

1994. NATURAL DISASTER ISSUE The U.N. in 1989 designated the 1990s as the International Decade for Natural Disaster Reduction. Designed by Kenji Koga, Japan. Similar to U.N. New York Minkus No. 670-673 and Geneva 251-254. *Offset by The House of Questa, U.K. Perforated 14x14 1/4.*

170 *North America;* 171 *Eurasia;* 172 *South America;* 173 *Australia*

170		MNHVF	UseVF
6s	**multicolored** *(690,000 printed)*	3.00	2.00
	FDC *(May 24, 1994)*		2.00

171		MNHVF	UseVF
6s	**multicolored** *(690,000 printed)*	3.00	2.00
	FDC *(May 24, 1994)*		2.00

172		MNHVF	UseVF
6s	**multicolored** *(690,000 printed)*	3.00	2.00
	FDC *(May 24, 1994)*		2.00

173		MNHVF	UseVF
6s	**multicolored** *(690,000 printed)*	3.00	2.00
	FDC *(May 24, 1994)*		2.00
	Inscription block of 4	13.00	
	y. Se-tenant block of 4	11.50	7.50

1994. PROTECTION AND DEVELOPMENT ISSUE The International Conference on Population and Development believes that population should be at the core of all economic, social, political and environmental undertakings. A conference was held in Cairo, Egypt Sept. 5-13, 1994. Designed by Jerry Smath, U.S. *Offset by Joh. Enschedé and Sons, Netherlands. Perforated 13 1/4x13 1/2.*

174 *Women in occupations;* 175 *Family in the tropics*

174		MNHVF	UseVF
5.50s	**multicolored** *(455,989)*	2.25	1.25
	FDC *(Sept. 1, 1994)*		1.25
	Inscription block of 4	10.00	

175		MNHVF	UseVF
7s	**multicolored** *(438,535)*	3.00	2.25
	FDC *(Sept. 1, 1994)*		1.75
	Inscription block of 4	15.00	

1994. UNCTAD 30TH ANNIVERSARY ISSUE The U.N. conference on Trade and Development became a permanent intergovernmental body in 1964 in Geneva. UNCTAD's goal is to promote growth and development in countries. Designed by Luis Sardá, Spain. *Offset by Joh. Enschedé and Sons, Netherlands. Perforated 13 1/4x13 1/2.*

176 *Map of World with colors spraying from center;* 177 *Colored star over map of the world*

176		MNHVF	UseVF
6s	**multicolored** *(427,948)*	2.25	1.75
	FDC *(Oct. 28, 1994)*		1.25
	Inscription block of 4	8.50	

177		MNHVF	UseVF
7s	**multicolored** *(367,275)*	3.00	2.25
	FDC *(Oct. 28, 1994)*		1.75
	Inscription block of 4	15.00	

1995. U.N. 50TH ANNIVERSARY ISSUE Celebrated the signing of the Charter of the United Nations, June 26, 1945. Designed by Rocco J. Callari, U.S. Emblem design by Joan Rainford, UNICEF. Similar to U.N. New York Minkus No. 678 and Geneva No. 268. *Offset by PTT, Switzerland. Perforated 13 1/2.*

178		MNHVF	UseVF
7s	multicolored *(742,052)*	2.50	2.00
	FDC *(Jan. 1, 1995)*		2.50
	Inscription block of 4	12.50	

1995. SOCIAL SUMMIT ISSUE The World Summit for Social Development met March 6-12, 1995 in Copenhagen, Denmark. Designed by Friedensreich Hunderwasser, Austria. Engraved by Wolfgang Seidel, Austria. *Gravure and intaglio by Government Printing Office, Austria. Perforated 13 1/2x14.*

179 *Drawing of beings*

179		MNHVF	UseVF
14s	multicolored *(595,554)*	3.75	3.25
	FDC *(Feb. 3, 1995)*		3.75
	Inscription block of 4	18.50	

1995. ENDANGERED SPECIES ISSUE This is the third set of stamps in the Endangered Species series. Concept by Rocco J. Callari, U.S. and designed by Salvatore Catalano, U.S. *Offset by Joh. Enschedé and Sons, Netherlands. Perforated 13x13 1/2.*

180 *Black rhinocerus;* 181 *Golden conure;* 182 *Douc langur;* 183 *Arabian oryx*

180		MNHVF	UseVF
7s	multicolored *(938,000 printed)*	2.00	1.75
	FDC *(March 24, 1995)*		1.50

181		MNHVF	UseVF
7s	multicolored *(938,000 printed)*	2.00	1.75
	FDC *(March 24, 1995)*		1.50

182		MNHVF	UseVF
7s	multicolored *(938,000 printed)*	2.00	1.75
	FDC *(March 24, 1995)*		1.50

183		MNHVF	UseVF
7s	multicolored *(938,000 printed)*	2.00	1.75
	FDC *(March 24, 1995)*		1.50
	Inscription block of 4	8.50	
	y. Se-tenant block of 4	7.00	

1995. INTERNATIONAL YOUTH YEAR ISSUE Tenth anniversary. The U.N. General Assembly declared 1985 International Youth Year. Designed by Gottfried Kumpf, Austria. *Offset by The House of Questa, U.K. Perforated 14 1/2x14 3/4.*

184 *Winter village scene;* 185 *Teepees*

184		MNHVF	UseVF
6s	multicolored *(437,462)*	3.00	2.00
	FDC *(May 26, 1995)*		1.25
	Inscription block of 4	12.50	

185		MNHVF	UseVF
7s	multicolored *(409,449)*	3.25	2.25
	FDC *(May 26,1995)*		2.00
	Inscription block of 4	15.50	

1995. U.N. 50TH ANNIVERSARY ISSUE The second issue in 1995 to commemorate the anniversary of the U.N., issued on the 50th anniversary date of the signing of the U.N. Charter. Designed by Paul and Chris Calle, U.S. Engraved by Inge Madlé, Netherlands. (7s) similar to U.N. New York Minkus No. 686 and Geneva No. 270; (10s) U.N. New York Minkus No. 687 and Geneva No. 271. *Intaglio by Joh. Enschedé and Sons, Security Printing, Netherlands. Perforated 13 1/4x13 1/2.*

186 *Hand with pen;* 187 *Veteran's War Memorial Opera House, San Francisco*

186		MNHVF	UseVF
7s	green *(433,922)*	3.25	2.50
	FDC *(June 26, 1995)*		2.00
	Inscription block of 4	10.00	

187		MNHVF	UseVF
10s	black *(471,198)*	3.75	3.50
	FDC *(June 26, 1995)*		1.75
	inscription block of 4	20.00	

1995. U.N. ANNIVERSARY SOUVENIR SHEET Designed by Paul and Chris Calle, U.S. Similar to U.N. New York Minkus No. 688 and Geneva No. 272. *Offset and intaglio. Imperforate.*

188 *Designs from Nos. 186 and 187*

188		MNHVF	UseVF
	Sheet of 2 *(367,773)*	10.00	6.75
	a. Single (7s)	2.00	1.00
	b. Single (10s)	2.00	1.00
	FDC *(June 26, 1995)*		5.00

1995. WORLD CONFERENCE ON WOMEN ISSUE The fourth World Conference on Women was held Sept. 4-15, 1995, in Beijing, China. Designed by Ting Shao Kuang, China. *Gravure by Postage Stamp Printing House, MPT, both from the People's Republic of China. Perforated 12.*

189 *Women within tropical forest;*
190 *Woman reading beside water with swans*

189		MNHVF	UseVF
5.50s	**multicolored** *(549,951)*	2.25	1.50
	FDC *(Sept. 5, 1995)*		1.25
	Inscription block of 4	10.00	
190		MNHVF	UseVF
6s	**multicolored** *(556,569)*	2.75	1.75
	FDC *(Sept. 5, 1995)*		1.25
	Inscription block of 4	14.00	

1995. U.N. PEOPLE, 50TH ANNIVERSARY ISSUE This was the third issue to commemorate the Charter of the U.N., which came into force Oct. 24, 1945. Similar to U.N. New York Minkus Nos. 692-703 and Geneva Nos. 275-286. Designed by Ben Verkaaik, Netherlands. Rocco J. Callari, U.S. and Robert Stein, U.S. designed the Prestige Booklet. *Offset by The House of Questa, U.K. Perforated 14.*

191-202 *People from continuous design*

191		MNHVF	UseVF
3s	**multicolored,** top left *(280,528)*	.85	

192		MNHVF	UseVF
3s	**multicolored,** top right *(280,528)*	2.75	1.75
	FDC *(Sept. 5, 1995)*		1.25
	inscription block of 4	14.00	
193		MNHVF	UseVF
3s	**multicolored,** top right *(280,528)*	.85	
194		MNHVF	UseVF
3s	**multicolored,** top center left *(280,528)*	.85	
195		MNHVF	UseVF
3s	**multicolored,** top center right *(280,528)*	.85	
196		MNHVF	UseVF
3s	**multicolored,** top lower left *(280,528)*	.85	
197		MNHVF	UseVF
3s	**multicolored,** top lower right *(280,528)*	.85	
198		MNHVF	UseVF
3s	**multicolored,** bottom left top *(280,528)*	.85	
199		MNHVF	UseVF
3s	**multicolored,** bottom right top *(280,528)*	.85	
200		MNHVF	UseVF
3s	**multicolored,** bottom center left *(280,528)*	.85	
201		MNHVF	UseVF
3s	**multicolored,** bottom center right *(280,528)*	.85	

1995. U.N. PEOPLE, 50TH ANNIVERSARY ISSUE This was the third issue to commemorate the Charter of the U.N., which came into force Oct. 24, 1945. Designed by Ben Verkaaik, Netherlands; Rocco J. Callari and Robert Stein, U.S. designed the Prestige Booklet. *Offset by The House of Questa, U.K. Perforated 14.*

202		MNHVF	UseVF
3s	**multicolored,** bottom left	.85	.85
	FDC *(Oct. 24, 1995) (sheetlet)*		40.00
	Sheetlet of 12	15.00	
	Booklet of 12 (95,449)	15.00	
	FDC (booklet)		42.00

1996. WFUNA 50TH ANNIVERSARY ISSUE The initials stand for World Federation of United Nations Associations. Designed by Rudolf Mirer, Switzerland. *Offset by Joh. Enschedé and Sons, Netherlands. Perforated 13x13 1/2.*

203 *Figure holding dove*

203		MNHVF	UseVF
7s	**multicolored** *(655,000 printed)*	2.00	1.50
	FDC *(Feb. 2, 1996)*		2.00
	Inscription block of 4	10.00	

1996. REGULAR ISSUE Designed as stamps by Robert Stein, U.S., from a photograph of U.N. flag by Unmesh, U.N. (1s) and artwork *Oil on Linen* by Karl Korab, Austria, photo by Christian Marzinger, Austria (10s). *Offset by The House of Questa, U.K. Perforated 14.*

204 *U.N. flag;*

205 Oil on Linen *abstract*

204		MNHVF	UseVF
1s	**multicolored** *(1,180,000)*	.25	.20
	FDC *(Feb. 2, 1996)*		1.25
	Inscription block of 4	1.00	

205		MNHVF	UseVF
10s	**multicolored** *(880,000)*	2.50	1.50
	FDC *(Feb. 2, 1996)*		2.75
	Inscription block of 4	11.00	

1996. ENDANGERED SPECIES ISSUE This is the fourth set in the Endangered Species series. Designed by Diane Bruyninckx, Belgium, and concept and design by Rocco J. Callari, U.S. *Offset by Joh. Enschedé and Sons, Netherlands. Perforated 12 1/2.*

206 Lady's slipper orchid; 207 Aztekium ritteri; 208 Euphorbia cremersii; 209 Dracula bella

206		MNHVF	UseVF
7s	**multicolored** *(846,000 printed)*	1.75	1.50
	FDC *(March 14, 1996)*		2.00

207		MNHVF	UseVF
7s	**multicolored** *(846,000 printed)*	1.75	1.50
	FDC *(March 14, 1996)*		2.00

208		MNHVF	UseVF
7s	**multicolored** *(846,000 printed)*	1.75	1.50
	FDC *(March 14, 1996)*		2.00

209		MNHVF	UseVF
7s	**multicolored** *(846,000 printed)*	1.75	1.50
	FDC *(March 14, 1996)*		2.00
	Inscription block of 4	8.50	
	y. Se-tenant block of 4	6.00	

1996. CITY SUMMIT (HABITAT II) ISSUE The second U.N. Conference on Human Settlements (Habitat II) was held in June 1996, in Istanbul, Turkey. Designed by Teresa Fasolino, U.S. *Offset by Joh. Enschedé and Sons, Netherlands. Perforated 14x13 1/2.*

210 Arab family with fruit; 211 Women beside stream; 212 Woman with bundle on head; 213 Woman attending grain; 214 Elephant within native village

210		MNHVF	UseVF
6s	**multicolored** *(500,000 printed)*	2.25	2.00
	FDC *(June 3, 1996)*		1.50

211		MNHVF	UseVF
6s	**multicolored** *(500,000 printed)*	2.25	2.00
	FDC *(June 3, 1996)*		1.50

212		MNHVF	UseVF
6s	**multicolored** *(500,000 printed)*	2.25	2.00
	FDC *(June 3, 1996)*		1.50

213		MNHVF	UseVF
6s	**multicolored** *(500,000 printed)*	2.25	2.00
	FDC *(June 3, 1996)*		1.50

214		MNHVF	UseVF
6s	**multicolored** *(500,000 printed)*	2.25	2.00
	FDC *(June 3, 1996)*		1.50
	Inscription block of 10	25.00	
	y. Se-tenant strip of 5	9.00	

1996. SPORT AND ENVIRONMENT ISSUE Commemorated the 100th anniversary of the Olympic Games. Designed by LeRoy Neiman, U.S. *Offset by The House of Questa, U.K. Perforated 14x14 1/2, 14 1/2x14.*

215 Man on parallel bars;

216 Man jumping hurdle

215		MNHVF	UseVF
6s	**multicolored** *(730,000 printed)*	1.75	1.50
	FDC *(July 19, 1996)*		1.50
	Inscription block of 4	6.50	

216		MNHVF	UseVF
7s	**multicolored** *(730,000 printed)*	2.00	1.75
	FDC *(July 19, 1996)*		1.50
	Inscription block of 4	10.00	

1996. SPORT AND ENVIRONMENT SOUVENIR SHEET Commemorated the 100th anniversary of the modern Olympic Games. Designed by LeRoy Neiman, U.S. *Offset by The House of Questa, U.K. Imperforated.*

217 Souvenir sheet with Nos. 215 and 216

217		MNHVF	UseVF
	Sheet of 2 *(500,000 printed)*	3.25	2.75
	a. Single (6s)	—	—
	b. Single (7s)	—	—
	FDC *(July 19, 1996)*	—	—

1996. PLEA FOR PEACE ISSUE The stamps drew attention to UNICEF's goal to reduce child mortality, disease and illiteracy. Designed by Du Keqing (7s), Xu Kangdeng (10s) both from China. *Offset by The House of Questa, U.K. Perforated 14 1/2x15, 15x14 1/2.*

218 *Dove and butterflies;*

219 *Stylized dove*

218		MNHVF	UseVF
7s	**multicolored** *(655,000 printed)*	2.75	
	FDC *(Sept. 17, 1996)*		1.50
	Inscription block of 4	10.00	
219		**MNHVF**	**UseVF**
10s	**multicolored** *(655,000 printed)*	2.75	
	FDC *(Sept. 17, 1996)*		3.75
	Inscription block of 4	13.50	

1996. UNICEF 50TH ANNIVERSARY ISSUE Celebrated the 50th anniversary of UNICEF with depictions of fairy tales designed by The Walt Disney Co., U.S. *Offset by The House of Questa, U.K. Perforated 14 1/2x15.*

220 *Hansel and Gretel;*

221 *How Maui Stole Fire from the Gods*

220		MNHVF	UseVF
5.50s	**multicolored** *(1,160,000 printed)*	1.25	1.25
	FDC *(Nov. 20, 1996)*		1.50
	Inscription block of 4	5.00	
	y. Pane of 8 plus label	10.00	
221		**MNHVF**	**UseVF**
8s	**multicolored** *(1,160,000 printed)*	2.00	1.75
	FDC *(Nov. 20, 1996)*		1.50
	Inscription block of 4	10.00	
	y. Pane of 8 plus label	20.00	

1997. REGULAR ISSUE Adapted as a stamp by Robert Stein, U.S. from artist Sagenji Yoshida, Japan. *Offset by The House of Questa, U.K. Perforated 14 1/2.*

222-223 *Details from "Hoo-o Raigi" (Phoenixes Flying Down), artist Sagenji Yoshida, Japan*

222		MNHVF	UseVF
5s	**multicolored** *(750,000 printed)*	1.00	.50
	FDC *(Feb. 12, 1997)*		1.50
	Inscription block of 4	3.50	
223		**MNHVF**	**UseVF**
6s	**multicolored** *(1,050,000 printed)*	1.00	.50
	FDC *(Feb. 12, 1997)*		1.50
	Inscription block of 4	4.50	

1997. ENDANGERED SPECIES ISSUE Fifth set in the Endangered Species series. Sheet concept and design by Rocco J. Callari, U.S. Designer Robert Goldstrom, U.S. *Offset by Joh. Enschedé and Sons, Netherlands. Perforated 12 1/2.*

224 *Barbary macaque;* 225 *Blue crane;* 226 *Przewalski's wild horse;* 227 *Giant anteater*

224		MNHVF	UseVF
7s	**multicolored** *(710,000 printed)*	2.00	1.75
	FDC *(March 13, 1997)*		1.50
225		**MNHVF**	**UseVF**
7s	**multicolored** *(710,000 printed)*	2.00	1.75
	FDC *(March 13, 1997)*		1.50
226		**MNHVF**	**UseVF**
7s	**multicolored** *(710,000 printed)*	2.00	1.75
	FDC *(March 13, 1997)*		1.50
227		**MNHVF**	**UseVF**
7s	**multicolored** *(710,000 printed)*	2.00	1.75
	FDC *(March 13, 1997)*		1.50
	y. Inscription block of 4, Nos. 224-227	7.00	
	y1. Pane of 16	30.00	

1997. EARTH SUMMIT ISSUE Fifth anniversary of the U.N. Conference on Environment and Development. The special session held in New York, June 1997, focused on development worldwide. Designed by Peter Max, U.S. *Gravure by Helio Courvoisier, Switzerland, granite paper, perforated 11 1/2.*

228 *Man and two trees;* 229 *Rainbow and tree;* 230 *Tree (lower left);* 231 *Tree (lower right);*

228		MNHVF	UseVF
3.50s	**multicolored** *(510,000 printed)*	1.00	1.25
	FDC *(May 30, 1997)*		1.00
229		**MNHVF**	**UseVF**
3.50s	**multicolored** *(510,000 printed)*	1.00	1.25
	FDC *(May 30, 1997)*		1.00
230		**MNHVF**	**UseVF**
3.50s	**multicolored** *(510,000 printed)*	1.00	1.25
	FDC *(May 30, 1997)*		1.00
231		**MNHVF**	**UseVF**
3.50s	**multicolored** *(510,000 printed)*	1.00	1.25
	FDC *(May 30, 1997)*		1.00
	Inscription block of 4	3.25	
	Se-tenant block of 4	—	
	FDC (block of 4)		—

1997. EARTH SUMMIT SOUVENIR SHEET Designed by Peter Max, U.S. *Gravure by Helio Courvoisier, Switzerland. Perforated 11 1/2.*

232 Earth Summit +5 with Souvenir sheet with images on Nos. 228-231 as one stamp

232		MNHVF	UseVF
11s	multicolored *(405,000 printed)*	4.50	3.50
	FDC *(May 30, 1997)*	—	

1997. TRANSPORTATION ISSUE The Economic Commission for Europe (ECE) and the Economic and Social Commission for Asia and the Pacific (ESCAP), celebrated their 50th anniversary in 1997. Designed by Michael Cockcroft, U.K. *Offset by The House of Questa, U.K. Perforated 14x14 1/2.*

233 Steam engine and automobile; 234 Steam engine and cable car; 235 Double decker bus; 236 Diesel locomotive and truck; 237 High-speed train and automobile

233		MNHVF	UseVF
7s	multicolored *(376,000 printed)*	1.25	1.50
	FDC *(Aug 29, 1997)*	—	
234		MNHVF	UseVF
7s	multicolored *(376,000 printed)*	1.25	1.50
	FDC *(Aug. 29, 1997)*	—	
235		MNHVF	UseVF
7s	multicolored *(376,000 printed)*	1.25	1.50
	FDC *(Aug. 29, 1997)*	—	
236		MNHVF	UseVF
7s	multicolored *(376,000 printed)*	1.25	1.50
	FDC *(Aug. 29, 1997)*	—	
237		MNHVF	UseVF
7s	multicolored *(376,000 printed)*	1.25	1.50
	FDC *(Aug. 29, 1997)*	—	
	Inscription block of 10	—	
	y. Se-tenant strip of 5, Nos. 233-237	—	—
	FDC strip of 5	—	

1997. TRIBUTE TO PHILATELY ISSUE Adapted by Robert Stein, U.S., the designs of the 1986 "Philately - The International Hobby," stamps designed by Ingalill Axelsson, Sweden. Engraved by Czeslaw Slania, Sweden. *Offset by Joh. Enschedé and Sons, Netherlands. Perforated 13 1/2x14.*

238, 239
Tribute to Philately

238		MNHVF	UseVF
6.50s	multicolored *(515,000 printed)*	1.25	1.50
	FDC *(Oct 14, 1997)*	—	—
	Inscription block of 4	—	
239		MNHVF	UseVF
7s	multicolored *(515,000 printed)*	1.25	1.50
	FDC *(Oct. 14, 1997)*	—	—
	Inscription block of 4	—	

1997. WORLD HERITAGE CONVENTION ISSUE Twenty-fifth anniversary. The first in a series of stamps and prestige booklet focusing on one specific World Heritage site or a group of World Heritage geographical locations. The third set of U.N. stamps illustrated World Heritage sites. Adapted by Robert Stein, U.S., from photographs by Guo Youmin, China. Computer graphics by Blake Tarpley, U.S. Two images of the Terracotta Warriors of the Qin Shi Huang Mausoleum in Mount Lishán, China. *Offset by the Government Printing Office, Austria. Perforated 13 1/2.*

240 *Warrior head;* 241 *Kneeling warrior*

240		MNHVF	UseVF
3s	multicolored *(750,000 printed)*	1.00	1.25
	FDC *(Nov. 19, 1997)*		1.50
	Inscription block of 4	4.00	
241		MNHVF	UseVF
6s	multicolored *(750,000 printed)*	1.25	1.50
	FDC *(Nov. 19, 1997)*		1.50
	Inscription block of 4	5.00	

1997. WORLD HERITAGE CONVENTION SOUVENIR BOOKLET Twenty-fifth anniversary. Designed by Rorie Katz, U.S., and Robert Stein, U.S. Includes 6 panes, one of each U.S., Vienna, Geneva design, with a block of 4 stamps of the same design re-valued to a 1s denomination. One individual page, 3 1/2x6 3/4. *Offset by the Government Printing Office, Austria. Perforated 13 1/2.*

241A *Kneeling warrior;* 241B *Warrior group facing right;* 241C *Head facing right;* 241D *Men standing;* 241E *Head facing left;* 241F *Warrior group facing forward*

241A		MNHVF	UseVF
1s	multicolored *(311,000 printed)*	.50	.50

241B		MNHVF	UseVF
1s	multicolored *(311,000 printed)*	.50	.50

241C		MNHVF	UseVF
1s	multicolored *(311,000 printed)*	.50	.50

241D		MNHVF	UseVF
1s	multicolored *(311,000 printed)*	.50	.50

241E		MNHVF	UseVF
1s	multicolored *(311,000 printed)*	.50	.50

241F		MNHVF	UseVF
1s	multicolored *(311,000 printed)*	.50	.50

241C		MNHVF	UseVF
1s	multicolored *(311,000 printed)*	.50	.50
	n. Booklet of 6 panes	6.00	

1998. REGULAR ISSUE Designed by Robert Stein, U.S., from photo by Heinz Pfeifer, Austria of a Peace Bell donated to the U.N. by two Japanese groups (6.50s); and photo by Pigneter, Austria, of elevated train passing the Vienna International Center. *Offset by The House of Questa, U.K. Perforated 14.*

242 *Peace Bell;*

243 *Elevated Train passing the Vienna International Center*

242		MNHVF	UseVF
6.50s	multicolored *(670,000 printed)*	.70	.50
	FDC *(Feb. 13, 1998)*		1.50
	Inscription block of 4	4.50	

243		MNHVF	UseVF
9s	multicolored *(770,000 printed)*	1.50	.70
	FDC *(Feb. 13, 1998)*		1.75
	Inscription block of 4	6.00	

Commemorative Issues

1998. ENDANGERED SPECIES ISSUE A sixth set in a series to highlight the need for protection of endangered species throughout the world. Concept by Rocco J. Callari, U.S., designer Robert Hynes, U.S. *The 16 se-tenant stamps on each sheetlet allow four blocks of four stamps. Offset by Joh. Enschedé and Sons, Netherlands. Perforated 12 1/2x13 1/2.*

244 *Green turtle, the largest of the hard-shelled marine turtles that live in the open seas;* 245 *Burrowing owl, which lives in the Americas in animal burrows and is active in daylight;* 246 *Rajah Brooke's birdwing,* Malaysia's national butterfly; 247 *Lesser panda, found in Nepal and Bhutan to China*

244		MNHVF	UseVF
7s	multicolored *(620,000 printed)*	.70	.50
	FDC *(March 13, 1998)*		1.00

245		MNHVF	UseVF
7s	multicolored *(620,000 printed)*	.75	.50
	FDC *(March 13, 1998)*		1.00

246		MNHVF	UseVF
7s	multicolored *(620,000 printed)*	.75	.50
	FDC *(March 13, 1998)*		1.00

247		MNHVF	UseVF
7s	multicolored *(620,000 printed)*	.75	.50
	FDC *(March 13, 1998)*		1.00
	Inscription block of 4	—	
	y. Se-tenant block of 4	3.00	

1998. INTERNATIONAL YEAR OF THE OCEAN ISSUE A set to call attention to the importance of the oceans and their resources for life on Earth. The U.N. has declared 1998 as the International Year of the Ocean. Designed by Yvan Lee, China. *This sheelet of 12, 3.50 schilling stamps depicts a tropical region. Offset by Joh. Enschedé and Sons, Netherlands. Perforated 13.*

248a *Shark;* 248b *Diver connected to submersible;* 248c *Diver & porpoises;* 248d *Diver w/air tanks;* 248e *Sea lions;* 248f *Diver & submersible w/lights;* 248g *Black & white angelfish;* 248h *Diver & habitat;* 248i *Sea turtle;* 248j *Orange & white angelfish;* 248k *Blue fish, three lobes of starfish;* 248l *Yellow-nosed angelfish*

248		MNHVF	UseVF
3.50s	multicolored, pane of 12 *(345,000 printed)*	5.00	3.00
	a. Shark	.75	.50
	b. Diver connected to submersible	.75	.50
	c. Diver & porpoises	.75	.50
	d. Diver w/air tanks	.75	.50
	e. Sea lions	.75	.50
	f. Diver & submersible w/lights	.75	.50
	g. Black & white angelfish	.75	.50
	h. Diver & habitat	.75	.50
	i. Sea turtle	.75	.50
	j. Orange & white angelfish	.75	.50
	k. Blue fish, three lobes of starfish	.75	.50
	l. Yellow-nosed angelfish	.75	.50
	FDC (any single)		1.00

1998. RAIN FOREST ISSUE An ocelot peers out of foliage in a 6.50 schilling stamp commemorating the 50th anniversary of the World Health Organization. Designed by Rick Garcia, U.S. *Offset by the Japanese Printing Office. Perforated 14.*

249 Ocelot

249		MNHVF	UseVF
6.50s	**multicolored** *(590,000 printed)*	.75	.60
	FDC *(June 19, 1998)*		1.00

1998. RAIN FOREST SOUVENIR SHEET The design of the 22 schilling stamp is the same as 249, but the fanciful landscape includes birds, flowers, and a waterfall. Designed by Rick Garcia, U.S. *Offset by the Japanese Printing Office. Perforated 14.*

250 Ocelot within a fanciful landscape including birds, flowers, and a waterfall

250		MNHVF	UseVF
22s	**multicolored** *(340,000 printed)*	2.50	2.00
	a. Single (6.50s)	—	—
	FDC *(June 19, 1998)*		—

1998. 50 YEARS OF U.N. PEACE-KEEPING ISSUE Commemorated the initiaion in 1948 of a U.N. peace-keeping military force under U.N. control but under ultimate authority of the members' respective governments. Designed by Andrew Davidson, U.K. *Gravure by Helio Courvoisier, Switzerland. Perforated 12.*

251 A soldier hands rations to a group of grateful refugees; 252 U.N. monitors ensure an orderly voting process

251		MNHVF	UseVF
4s	**multicolored** *(555,000 printed)*	.75	.60
	FDC *(Sept. 15, 1998)*		1.50
	Inscription block of 4	3.00	

252		MNHVF	UseVF
7.50s	**multicolored** *(545,000 printed)*	1.00	1.00
	FDC *(Sept. 15, 1998)*		1.50
	Inscription block of 4	3.50	

1998. UNIVERSAL DECLARATION OF HUMAN RIGHTS ISSUE Designed by Jean-Michel Falon, Belgium. Ideas seem to sprout from a pot-like human head on one abstract stamp; figures ride gears on the other. *Printed by Cartor Security Printing, France. Perforated 13.*

253 Stylized person;

254 Gears

253		MNHVF	UseVF
4.50s	**multicolored** *(535,000 printed)*	.75	.60
	FDC *(Oct. 27, 1998)*		1.50
	Inscription block of 4	2.50	

254		MNHVF	UseVF
7s	**multicolored** *(545,000 printed)*	1.00	1.00
	FDC *(Oct. 27, 1998)*		1.50
	Inscription block of 4	5.50	

1998. SCHÖNBRUNN PALACE ISSUE Vienna's World Heritage Site. An exterior view of the World Heritage Site is featured on one stamp; a white and gilt porcelain stove from the Bedchamber of the palace is featured on the other. Designed by Robert Stein, U.S based on photographs. *Offset by The House of Questa, U.K. Pane of 20, perforated 14.*

255 Exterior view of the Schönbrunn Palace;
256 Porcelain stove

255		MNHVF	UseVF
3.50s	**multicolored** *(615,000 printed)*	.50	1.25
	FDC *(Dec. 4, 1998)*		1.50
	Inscription block of 4	1.75	

256		MNHVF	UseVF
7s	**multicolored** *(615,000 printed)*	.75	.25
	FDC *(Dec. 4, 1998)*		2.00
	Inscription block of 4	3.00	

> Every entry in this catalog has been double-checked for accuracy, but mistakes may creep into any human endeavor, and we ask your assistance in eliminating them. Please call the attention of the editors to any errors in stamp descriptions found in this catalog.

1998. SCHÖNBRUNN PALACE BOOKLET ISSUE The six designs in the U.N. World Heritage Site issue are re-valued in a Prestige Booklet of 21 stamps.

264 *Uluru-Kata Tjuta National Park;* 265 *The Tasmanian Wilderness*

257 *Palace & grounds, four 2 schillings stamps;* 258 *Blue & white vase, three 1 schilling stamps;* 259 *Detail from wall painting, three 1 schilling stamps;* 260 *Porcelain stove, three 1 schilling stamps;* 261 *Great Palm House, four 2 schillings stamps;* 262 *The Gloriette, four 2 schillings stamps*

257		MNHVF	UseVF
2s	multicolored *(158,000 printed)*	.50	.25
	n. Pane of 4, 2 schillings stamps	1.00	

258		MNHVF	UseVF
1s	multicolored *(158,000 printed)*	.50	.25
	n. Pane of 3, 1 schilling stamps	1.00	

259		MNHVF	UseVF
1s	multicolored *(158,000 printed)*	.50	.25
	n. Pane of 3, 1 schilling stamps	1.00	

260		MNHVF	UseVF
1s	multicolored *(158,000 printed)*	.50	.25
	n. Pane of 3, 1 schilling stamps	1.00	

261		MNHVF	UseVF
2s	multicolored *(158,000 printed)*	.50	.25
	n. Pane of 4, 2 schillings stamps	1.00	

262		MNHVF	UseVF
2s	multicolored *(158,000 printed)*	.50	.25
	n. Pane of 4, 2 schillings stamps	1.00	
	n1. Full booklet of 6 panes	3.50	
	FDC *(Dec. 4, 1998) (any pane)*		—

1999. REGULAR ISSUE Adapted as a stamp by Robert Stein, U.S. from a detail from *Volcanic Landscape* by Peter Pongratz, Austria, which is on display at the Vienna International Centre. *Offset by Joh. Enschedé and Sons, Netherlands. Perforated 13.*

263 *Volcanic Landscape by Peter Pongratz*

263		MNHVF	UseVF
8s	multicolored *(660,000 printed)*	1.00	.70
	FDC *(Feb. 5, 1999)*		1.75
	Inscription block of 4	5.00	

Commemorative Issues

1999. WORLD HERITAGE - AUSTRALIA ISSUE The fifth in the U.N. World Heritage Sites Series. Designed by Passmore Design of Melbourne, Australia. Uluru-Kata Tjuta National Park (4.50s) is home to reptile species in numbers unparallelled anywhere. The Tasmanian Wilderness (6.50s) contains Australia's last great wild river system, its deepest lake and its most spectacular, ancient mountains. *Offset by The House of Questa, U.K. Perforated 13.*

264		MNHVF	UseVF
4.50s	multicolored *(540,000 printed)*	.75	.60
	FDC *(March 19, 1999)*		1.00
	Inscription block of 4	3.00	

265		MNHVF	UseVF
6.50s	multicolored *(540,000 printed)*	.90	.70
	FDC *(March 19, 1999)*		1.50
	Inscription block of 4	3.50	

1999. WORLD HERITAGE AUSTRALIA BOOKLET The six designs in the U.N. Heritage Site issue are re-valued in a 172x92mm Prestige booklet of 24 stamps, a block of 4 stamps in each design. *Perforated 13.*

266 *Tasmania;* 267 *Uluru-Kata Tjuta;* 268 *Wet Tropics;* 269 *Kakadu;* 270 *Great Barrier Reef;* 271 *Willandra Lakes*

266		MNHVF	UseVF
1s	multicolored *(29,000 printed)*	.50	.25
	FDC *(March 19, 1999)*		1.00

267		MNHVF	UseVF
2s	multicolored *(29,000 printed)*	.50	.25
	FDC *(March 19, 1999)*		1.00

268		MNHVF	UseVF
1s	multicolored *(29,000 printed)*	.50	.25
	FDC *(March 19, 1999)*		1.00

269		MNHVF	UseVF
2s	multicolored *(29,000 printed)*	.50	.25
	FDC *(March 19, 1999)*		1.00

270		MNHVF	UseVF
1s	multicolored *(29,000 printed)*	.50	.25
	FDC *(March 19, 1999)*		1.00

271		MNHVF	UseVF
2s	multicolored *(116,000 printed)*	.50	.25
	FDC *(March 19, 1999)*		1.00
	n. Booklet of 24 stamps, 6 panes	3.50	

> Please read the introduction to this catalog carefully. It contains much valuable information for all stamp collectors, and also makes the catalog easier for you to use.

1999. ENDANGERED SPECIES ISSUE Seventh in a series to highlight the need for protection of endangered species throughout the world. Designed by Jefery Terreson, United States. *Printed by Joh. Enschedé and Sons, Netherlands. Perforated 12 1/2x13 3/4.*

272 Orangutan;
273 Dalmatian
Pelican; 274
Yellow Anaconda;
275 Caracal

272		MNHVF	UseVF
7s	multicolored *(552,000 printed)*	1.00	.25
	FDC *(April 22, 1999)*		1.50

273		MNHVF	UseVF
7s	multicolored *(552,000 printed)*	1.00	.25
	FDC *(April 22, 1999)*		1.50

274		MNHVF	UseVF
7s	multicolored *(552,000 printed)*	1.00	.25
	FDC *(April 22, 1999)*		1.50

275		MNHVF	UseVF
7s	multicolored *(552,000 printed)*	1.00	.25
	FDC *(April 22, 1999)*		1.50
	Inscription block of 4	4.00	

1999. UNISPACE III ISSUE A series of satellites aids in weather fore-casting, ocean research, climate mapping, navigation and disaster relief management. Designed by *Gravure by Helio Courvoisier, Switzerland. Rouletted.*

276 Planet surface,
distant satellite; 277
Close-up satellite

276		MNHVF	UseVF
3.50s	multicolored *(1,200,000 printed)*	.50	.25
	FDC *(July 7, 1999)*		1.00

277		MNHVF	UseVF
3.50s	multicolored *(1,200,000 printed)*	.50	.25
	FDC *(July 7, 1999)*		1.00

1999. UNISPACE III SOUVENIR SHEET The full design of the se-tenant Nos. 276-277 are combined on a 90x75mm souvenir sheet and given a higher denomination. *Perforated 11 3/4.*

278
Surface, 2
satellites
side by side

278		MNHVF	UseVF
13s	multicolored *(350,000 printed)*	2.00	1.00
	FDC *(July 7, 1999)*		2.00
	Perforated in SS	2.00	
	Overprinted for Philexfrance	2.00	

1999. UNIVERSAL POSTAL UNION 1874-1999 ISSUE Postal patrons in distinctive dress and means of carrying mail around the globe signify the impact of the Universal Postal Union over the last 125 years. Designed by Mark Hess, U.S. *Gravure by Helio Courvoisier, Switzerland. Perforated 11 1/2x11 3/4.*

279 Denomination
upper left; 280
Denomination upper
right; 281 Denomination
lower left; 282
Denomination lower
right

279		MNHVF	UseVF
6.50s	multicolored *(417,000 printed)*	.75	.25
	FDC *(Aug. 23, 1999)*		1.00

280		MNHVF	UseVF
6.50s	multicolored *(417,000 printed)*	.75	.25
	FDC *(Aug. 23, 1999)*		1.00

281		MNHVF	UseVF
6.50s	multicolored *(417,000 printed)*	.75	.25
	FDC *(Aug. 23, 1999)*		1.00

282		MNHVF	UseVF
6.50s	multicolored *(417,000 printed)*	.75	.25
	FDC *(Aug. 23, 1999)*		1.00
	Inscription block of 4	3.00	
	FDC *(Aug. 23, 1999) (block)*		3.00

1999. IN MEMORIAM ISSUE U.N. flags at half-staff honored those who have died in U.N. service for the cause of peace. Designed by Robert Stein, U.S. *Offset by Walsall Security Printers, Ltd., U.K. Sheet stamp perforated 14 1/2, souvenir sheet perforated 14.*

283 Flags fly
at half staff
outside the
Vienna
International
Centre to
honor those
who have died
in U.N. service
for the cause
of peace; 284
SS with flags
at half staff

283		MNHVF	UseVF
6.50s	multicolored *(530,000 printed)*	.75	.25
	FDC *(Sept. 21, 1999)*		1.00
	Inscription block of 4	3.00	

284		MNHVF	UseVF
14s	multicolored *(338,000 printed)*	2.00	1.00
	FDC *(Sept. 21, 1999)*		2.00
	Single stamp	2.00	

1999. EDUCATION - KEYSTONE TO THE 21ST CENTURY ISSUE Designed by Romero Britto, Brazil. *Offset by Osterreichische Staatsdruckerei. Perforated 13 3/4x13 1/2.*

285 A boy and girl leap gleefully over an open book; 286 A crowd of people read books happily

285		MNHVF	UseVF
7s	**multicolored** *(490,000 printed)*	.75	.25
	FDC *(Nov. 11, 1999)*		1.00
	Inscription block of 4	3.00	

286		MNHVF	UseVF
13s	**multicolored** *(490,000 printed)*	1.50	.50
	FDC *(Nov. 11, 1999)*		1.50
	Inscription block of 4	6.00	

Commemorative Issues

2000. INTERNATIONAL YEAR OF THANKSGIVING ISSUE Glory Window in the Chapel of Thanksgiving at Thanks-Giving Square in Dallas, Texas, designed by Gabrielle Loire of Chartres, France, for the Thanks-Giving Foundation. Stamps designed by Rorie Katz, U.S. *Offset by Cartor Security Printing, France, perforated 13.*

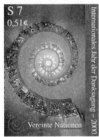

287 Glory Window in the Chapel of Thanksgiving, *Dallas, Texas*

287		MNHVF	UseVF
7s	**multicolored** *(510,000 printed)*	.75	.20
	FDC *(Jan. 1, 2000)*		1.50
	Inscription block of 4	3.00	

2000. ENDANGERED SPECIES ISSUE The eighth set in the Endangered Species series. Designed by Lori Anzalone, U.S. *Printed by Joh. Enschéde and Sons, Netherlands, perforated 12 1/2 x 13 3/4, (2,192,000 stamps, 137,000 panes printed).*

288 Leopard; 289 White or European Spoonbill; 290 Chilean Huemal; 291 Killer Whale

288		MNHVF	UseVF
7s	**multicolored**	.75	.20

289		MNHVF	UseVF
7s	**multicolored**	.75	.20

290		MNHVF	UseVF
7s	**multicolored**	.75	.20

291		MNHVF	UseVF
7s	**multicolored**	.75	.20
	FDC *(April 6, 2000)*		1.50
	Inscription block of 4	3.00	

2000. OUR WORLD ISSUE A celebration of the new millennium, the stamps depict paintings submitted to a worldwide competition on the theme, "My Country in the Year 2000." Paintings adapted as stamps by Robert Stein, U.S. *Offset by Cartor Security Printing, France, perforated 13.*

292 Tomorrow's Dream, *by Voltaire Perez, Philippines (1998)*

292		MNHVF	UseVF
7s	**multicolored**	.75	.20
	FDC *(May 30, 2000)*		1.50
	Inscription block of 4	3.00	

293 Remembrance, *by Dimitris Nalbandis, Greece (1998)*

293		MNHVF	UseVF
8s	**multicolored**	1.00	.50
	FDC *(May 30, 2000)*		2.50
	Inscription block of 4	4.00	

2000. 55TH ANNIVERSARY OF THE UNITED NATIONS Photographs documented the construction of the United Nations Headquarters complex in New York City. The first occupation took place in 1950. Designed by Rorie Katz, U.S., based on U.N. photographs. *Offset by Cartor Security Printing, France, perforated 13.*

294 *The completed Secretariat Building looms over the steel framework of the dome of the General Assembly Hall in a 1951 photo*

294		MNHVF	UseVF
7s	**multicolored** *(440,000 printed)*	.75	.20
	FDC *(July 7, 2000)*		1.50
	Inscription block of 4	3.00	

295 *In 1949, U.N. Secretary-General Trgve Lie helps to unfurl a U.N. flag that was part of a "topping-out" ceremony for the 39-story Secretariat Building*

295y *Mini-sheet of two stamps against a photo of workers cheering as a U.N. flag is unfurled atop the framework of the Secretariat Building*

295		MNHVF	UseVF
16s	multicolored *(440,000 printed)*	1.75	1.00.
	FDC *(July 7, 2000)*		2.50
	y. Sheetlet of 2	1.75	1.00
	y1. Se-tenant pair #294-295	1.75	1.00

2000. THE U.N. IN THE 21ST CENTURY ISSUE Intended to show the work of the United Nations in promoting respect for human rights, protection of the environment, economic development and reduction of poverty and disease. Designed by Wilson McLean, United Kingdom. *Offset by Government Printing Office, Austria, perforated 14, (330,000 panes printed).*

296a-f *The United Nations in the 21st century, couple at left*

296		MNHVF	UseVF
3.50s	multicolored	.50	.20
	a. Farm machinery	.50	.20
	b. Men and youngsters	.50	.20
	c. Field workers	.50	.20
	d. Soldiers and mine detector	.50	.20
	e. Medical researcher	.50	.20
	f. Man in wheelchair	.50	.20
	FDC *(Sept. 15, 2000)*		1.50
	Sheetlet of 6	3.00	1.50

2000. WORLD HERITAGE - SPAIN ISSUE The sixth U.N. stamp issued to illustrate World Heritage sites and the fourth in a series of stamps and booklets to focus on sites in one geographical area. World Heritage sites have been designated to indicate places whose importance reach beyond geographical and political boundaries. Designed by Robert Stein, U.S. *Offset by The House of Questa, United Kingdom, perforated 14.*

297 *The Roman aqueduct of Segovia, whose 128 pillars were built without mortar, channeled water from the River Frio, about 11 miles away;* 298 *Creations of Antonio Gaudi y Cornet (1852-1926) in Barcelona represent an eclectic and personal architectural style*

297		MNHVF	UseVF
4.50s	multicolored	.50	.20
	FDC *(Oct. 6, 2000)*		1.50
	Inscription block of 4	2.00	

298		MNHVF	UseVF
6.50s	multicolored	.75	.50
	FDC *(Oct. 6, 2000)*		2.50
	Inscription block of 4	3.00	

2000. WORLD HERITAGE - SPAIN PRESTIGE BOOKLET ISSUE *Offset by The House of Questa, United Kingdom, perforated 14.*

299-304 *World Heritage - Spain Prestige Booklet*

299		MNHVF	UseVF
1s	multicolored, Grenda	.50	.20

300		MNHVF	UseVF
1s	multicolored, Cuenca	.50	.20

301		MNHVF	UseVF
1s	multicolored, Segovia	.50	.20

302		MNHVF	UseVF
2s	multicolored, Merida	.50	.20

303		MNHVF	UseVF
2s	**multicolored,** Toledo	.50	.20

304		MNHVF	UseVF
2s	**multicolored,** Barcelona	.50	.20
	FDC *(Oct. 6, 2000)*		2.50
	n. Booklet of 6	4.40	

2000. RESPECT FOR REFUGEES ISSUE Called attention to the U.N. High Commissioner for Refugees, which noted its 50th anniversary in 2000. *Offset by Joh. Enschéde and Sons, Netherlands, perforated 12 3/4 x 13 1/4.*

305 *A youngster carries a book in a group of refugees*

305		MNHVF	UseVF
7s	**multicolored** *(530,000 printed)*	.75	.20
	FDC *(Nov. 9, 2000)*		1.50
	Inscription block of 4	3.00	

306 *the mini-sheet stamp image is taken from the far-left portion of a larger group of refugees*

306		MNHVF	UseVF
25s	**multicolored** *(273,000 printed)*	3.00	1.00
	FDC *(Nov. 9, 2000)*		3.00
	y. Sheetlet of 1	3.00	

Postal Cards

1982. POSTAL CARD ISSUE Designed by Rolf Christianson, Finland (3s), M.A. Munnawar, Pakistan (5s). *Gravure by Helio Courvoisier, Switzerland.*

PC1 *Olive branch*

PC1		MNHVF	UseVF
3s	**multicolored, cream** *(500,000 printed)*	1.00	.65
	FDC *(April 28, 1982)*		2.00

PC2 *Bird, olive branch and globe*

PC2		MNHVF	UseVF
5s	**multicolored** *(500,000 printed)*	.90	.65
	FDC *(April 28, 1982)*		2.00

1985. EMBLEM OF THE UNITED NATIONS ISSUE Abstract design by George Hamori, Australia. *Offset by Joh. Enschedé and Sons, Netherlands.*

PC3 *Abstract and U.N. emblem*

PC3		MNHVF	UseVF
4s	**multicolored** *(350,000 printed)*	2.00	.20
	FDC *(May 10, 1985)*		6.00

1992. SURCHARGED BIRD AND OLIVE BRANCH ISSUE PC4 revalued 5s (PC2) with 1s overprint in black at left. Designed by M.A. Munnawar, Pakistan. *Gravure by Helio Courvoisier, Switzerland.*

PC4 *Bird, olive branch and surcharge*

PC4		MNHVF	UseVF
5s + 1s	**multicolored** *(71,700 printed)*	17.50	.55
	FDC *(Jan. 1, 1992)*		13.50

1992. VIENNA INTERNATIONAL CENTRE ISSUE Adaptation of 1.50s Definitive of 1990. Designed by Kurt Regschek, Austria. *Offset by Mercury-Walch, Australia.*

PC5 *Vienna International Centre*

PC5		MNHVF	UseVF
6s	**multicolored** *(445,000 printed)*	2.35	.60
	FDC *(Sept. 4, 1992)*		11.00

1993. INTERNATIONAL CENTRE ISSUE Adaptation of 22¢ Peoples of the World Definitive of 1985, designed by Fritz Henry Oerter, Germany (PC6). Photo of Vienna International Centre by Florian Hausman, Austria (PC7). *Offset by Leigh Mardon, Australia.*

PC6 Peoples of the World

PC6		MNHVF	UseVF
5s	**multicolored** *(450,000 printed)*	9.00	.45
	FDC *(May 7, 1993)*		12.00

PC7 *Vienna International Centre*

PC7		MNHVF	UseVF
6s	**multicolored** *(450,000 printed)*	4.00	.50
	FDC *(May 7, 1993)*		7.50

1994. PEOPLES OF THE WORLD REVALUED ISSUE PC6 revalued with surcharge, adaptation of Vienna No. 1, Tree of doves, at left.

PC8 *Peoples of the World plus Tree of doves*

PC8		MNHVF	UseVF
5s + 50g	**multicolored** *(350,000 printed)*	3.00	.50
	FDC *(Jan. 1, 1994)*		9.00

1997. INTERNATIONAL CENTRE REVALUED ISSUE PC5 revalued with surcharge, adaptation of 50g Vienna No. 167, Tree of doves, at left on (PC9). PC7 revalued with surcharge, adaptation of 1s Vienna No. 203, U.N. flag, at left on (PC10). *Offset by Mercury-Walch, Australia (PC9), offset by Leigh Mardon, Australia (PC10).*

PC9 *Vienna International Centre plus Tree of doves*

PC9		MNHVF	UseVF
6s + 50g	**multicolored**	2.50	.50
	FDC *(July 1, 1997)*		9.00

PC10 *International Centre plus U.N. flag*

PC10		MNHVF	UseVF
6s + 1s	**multicolored**	2.50	.50
	FDC *(July 1, 1997)*		9.00

1998. VIENNA INTERNATIONAL CENTRE ISSUE Designed by Robert Stein, U.S. from photo by Günter Leidenfrost, Austria. *Offset by Mercury-Walch, Australia.*

PC11 *Vienna International Centre*

PC11		MNHVF	UseVF
6.50s	**multicolored** *(137,000 printed)*	1.00	.50
	FDC *(May 20, 1998)*		1.50

1999. SCHÖNBRUNN PALACE ISSUE Priority Postal Card featured the Gloriette of Schönbrunn Palace, World Heritage Site in Vienna. *Offset by Government Printing Office, Austria.*

PC12 *The Gloriette of Schönbrunn Palace*

PC12		MNHVF	UseVF
7s	**multicolored** *(136,000 printed)*	1.10	.55
	FDC *(Feb. 5, 1999)*		1.50

Postal Card

2000. HUMAN RIGHTS POSTAL CARD ISSUE A postal card for the WIPA stamp exhibition in Vienna, Austria, featured as its indicia a reproduction of the 1983 7s United Nations stamp for the 35th anniversary of the Universal Declaration of Human Rights (UNV38), two figures in a boat. The front of the card featured a reproduction of the 14s stamp for the Social Summit (UNV179), issued in 1995. The card was a tribute to Friedensreich Hundertwasser, Austria, the designer of the stamps, who died Feb. 19, 2000.

PC13 *Universal Declaration of Human Rights (two figures in a boat)*

PC13		MNHVF	UseVF
7s	**multicolored** FDC *(June 2, 2000)*	1.20	.70
	FDC *(May 30, 2000)*		2.00

Postal Stationery

1982. CONTEMPORARY DOVE ISSUE Designed by Ingrid Ousland, Norway. *Offset by Joh. Enschedé and Sons, Netherlands.*

E1 *Fanciful dove facing right*

E1		**MNHVF**	**UseVF**
9s	**multicolored, light green,** entire *(650,000 printed)*	2.50	1.25
	FDC *(April 28, 1982)*		4.50

1986. CONTEMPORARY DOVE REVALUED ISSUE revalued 9s (E1) with 2s overprint black to left of stamp. Designed by Ingrid Ousland, Norway. *Offset by Joh. Enschedé and Sons, Netherlands.*

E2 *Fanciful dove and overprint*

E2		**MNHVF**	**UseVF**
9s + 2s	**multicolored, light green** entire *(131,190 printed)*	40.00	5.00
	FDC *(Feb. 3, 1986)*		25.00

1987. BIRDS IN FLIGHT ISSUE Designed by Mieczyslaw Wasilewski, Poland. *Offset by Mercury-Walch, Australia.*

E3 *Flock of white birds*

E3		**MNHVF**	**UseVF**
11s	**bright blue** entire *(414,000 printed)*	2.75	1.25
	FDC *(Jan. 30, 1987)*		7.00

1992. BIRDS IN FLIGHT REVALUED ISSUE revalued 11s (E3) with 1s overprint in black to left of stamp. Designed by Mieczyslaw Wasilewski, Poland. *Offset by Mercury-Walch, Australia.*

E4 *Flock of white birds and overprint*

E4		**MNHVF**	**UseVF**
11s + 1s	**bright blue,** entire *(80,000 printed)*	40.00	1.60
	FDC *(Jan. 1, 1992)*		22.50

1992. VIENNA INTERNATIONAL CENTRE ISSUE Designed by Rocco J. Callari. *Offset by Mercury-Walch, Australia.*

E5 *Vienna International Centre, aerial view*

E5		**MNHVF**	**UseVF**
12s	**multicolored** *(200,000 printed)*	5.00	1.15
	FDC *(Sept. 4, 1992)*		22.50

1995. REGULAR ISSUE Designed by Hannes Margreiter, Austria. *Offset by Mercury-Walch, Australia.*

E6 *Vienna International Centre;* E7 *Landscape*

E6		**MNHVF**	**UseVF**
6s	**multicolored** *(128,000 printed)*	1.25	1.00
	FDC *(Feb. 3, 1995)*		2.50
E7		**MNHVF**	**UseVF**
7s	**multicolored** *(128,000 printed)*	1.40	1.10
	FDC *(Feb. 3, 1995)*		2.50

1998. RIVER SCENE ISSUE Designed by Robert Stein, U.S. from photo by Georg Popp, Austria. *Printed by Mercury-Walch, Australia.*

E8 *River scene*

E8		**MNHVF**	**UseVF**
13s	**multicolored** *(87,000 printed)*	2.00	1.25
	FDC *(March 13, 1998)*		3.00

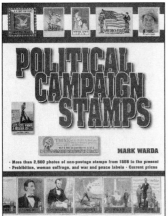

NEW RELEASES FROM THE HOBBY LEADER

2001 Krause-Minkus Catalog of U.S. Stamps

Edited by Maurice D. Wozniak
You'll find over 8,000 stamps listed plus many new varieties in this up-to-date edition, which features more price listings and photos that the previous edition. New stamps issued during 2000 are featured, and U.S. and territories listings are more complete than ever. Individual sections include airmail, special delivery, postage due, parcel post, revenue, Confederate states, U.S. Possessions issues, encased postage, postal stationery and seldom-seen Test Stamps.

Softcover • 8-1/2 x 11
672 pages • 5,600+ b&w photos
SCM04 • $24.95
Available 11/00

2001 Krause-Minkus Stamps & Prices

A Mini-Catalog of United States Stamps
Edited by Maurice D. Wozniak
This new guide features more than 4,000 U.S. postage issues, priced used and unused in the most collectible formats. All regular and commemorative U.S. Postal issues are covered and numerous photos and keys make stamp identification fast and easy. It is inexpensive, easy to carry and reference when at shows, and features extra space for cross-referencing with other catalog systems.

Softcover • 6 x 9
200 pages
STP1 • $14.95

Krause-Minkus Standard Catalog™ of Israel Stamps

Edited by Maurice D. Wozniak
Key information on every Israeli postage stamp - regular, commemorative and air-mail - issue is available in this one convenient source. More than 1,500 stamps are listed and priced for used and unused stamps in the most collectible grades. Crisp, clean black and white photos of all stamps are available to aid in identification. Stamps are listed in easy-to-follow chronological order, with an accompanying table of tabs for specialty collectors.

Softcover • 6 x 9
104 pages
ISR1 • $14.95

Krause-Minkus Standard Catalog™ of Australia Stamps

Edited by Maurice D. Wozniak
Find information on every postage stamp from Australia and its territories - regular, commemorative and airmail - since 1902 in this volume. Features more than 1,900 stamps in used and unused prices in the most collectible grades. Crisp black and white photos aid in stamp identification, and stamps are listed in easy-to-follow chronological order. Handy, small size format makes it easy to carry and reference at shows.

Softcover • 6 x 9
104 pages
AUS1 • $14.95

The 1999 Comprehensive Catalogue of United States Stamp Booklets

Postage and Airmail Booklets
by Robert Furman
Find everything you need to know about booklet panes, unexploded booklets and unfolded panes in this exciting book. Featuring the Minkus numbering system and all the varieties from the first issues of 1900 to the latest releases, this book will benefit both the expert and novice.

Softcover • 6 x 9
192 pages • 300+ b&w photos
USBK2 • $17.95

All About Stamps

An Illustrated Encyclopedia of Philatelic Terms
by Wayne L. Youngblood
What's a cinderella stamp? You'll find the answers to many stamp collecting questions in All About Stamps, An Illustrated Dictionary of Philatelic Terms. Whether you're an advanced or beginning collector, you'll appreciate quick, clean definitions for almost every English philatelic term. Extremely well illustrated with hundreds of crisp, clear photos, this handy reference gives you the essence of the hobby without the clutter of country identifiers and confusing, outdated text.

Softcover • 6 x 9
192 pages • 300+ b&w photos
ABS • $14.95

FREE MINKUS-SCOTT CROSS REFERENCE

Krause - Minkus
STANDARD CATALOG OF
CANADIAN
& UNITED NATIONS STAMPS

Includes Canadian Provincials and UN Offices in Geneva and Vienna

2ND EDITION

- Complete and Updated, Including Recent Issues
- Every Canadian and U.N. Issue - Over 6000 Prices!
- Commemorative, Regular, Airmail Issues and More
- Includes Postal Card and Stationery Listings
- Background History On Many Issues
- Over 2000 Highly Defined Black & White Photos

Dear Readers:

As a purchaser of the Krause-Minkus Standard Catalog of Canadian & United Nations Stamps, you are entitled to receive a cross-reference booklet FREE. This booklet contains both Minkus to Scott and Scott to Minkus catalog number cross-references in an easy-to-use format.

Please complete this card and return it for your FREE cross-reference booklet.

Krause Publications
700 E. State St., Iola, WI 54990-0001